Oxford Engineering Science Series

Editors: L. C. WOODS, W. H. WITTRICK, A. L. CULLEN

Metal fatigue

N. E. FROST
K. J. MARSH
L. P. POOK

CLARENDON PRESS · OXFORD
1974

Oxford University Press, Ely House, London W. I

GLASGOW   NEW YORK   TORONTO   MELBOURNE   WELLINGTON
CAPE TOWN   IBADAN   NAIROBI   DAR ES SALAAM   LUSAKA   ADDIS ABABA
DELHI   BOMBAY   CALCUTTA   MADRAS   KARACHI   LAHORE   DACCA
KUALA LUMPUR   SINGAPORE   HONG KONG   TOKYO

ISBN 0 19 856114 8

ⓒ OXFORD UNIVERSITY PRESS 1974

PRINTED IN NORTHERN IRELAND
AT THE UNIVERSITIES PRESS
BELFAST

Preface

We offer little excuse for writing this book; it is intended to be a definitive monograph on fatigue and attempts to bring together all facets of the fatigue of metals, components, and structures, presenting a unified perspective of the subject. Some of the reasons for embarking on the book and for the form it has taken are mentioned in Chapter 1. We are, however, fully conscious of the fact that its presence on or absence from the shelves of the technical library of a firm will not be reflected in the number of fatigue failures that the firm's products suffer in ensuing years; nor will a final-year engineering student fail to get a 'first' because this book was not on his recommended reading list. The most that we hope for is that it may clear up some misconceptions about the subject which are still commonplace. As must ultimately be the reason why anyone devotes part of his life to some activity (apart from monetary gain), we wrote the book because we wanted to, and derived pleasure from so doing.

Acknowledgement

This book is published with the permission of the Director of the National Engineering Laboratory of the Department of Trade and Industry. The authors acknowledge gratefully the assistance, in a variety of ways, of many of their colleagues at NEL.

East Kilbride
June 1973

N. E. F.
K. J. M.
L. P. P.

Contents

ILLUSTRATIONS

The following list of figures appear as separate plate sections.

1 Introduction

MATERIALS, whether they be metallic or non-metallic, are of no practical use to mankind until they are turned into working components or structures. One link in the process chain by which this happens is called engineering design.

A major problem facing the designer is the selection of the right materials from which to manufacture a particular design of component or structure; the material properties must ensure that it carries out the duties for which it was designed without breaking within a guaranteed life and yet enable it to be sold at a price which the customer is prepared to pay. To enable him to do this, the designer needs to know the loads to which his component or structure will be subjected in service, the environment in which it will work, the working life expected, and what it will cost to make. This information now sets boundaries on the range of materials from which to select those to use for his specific design. To finalize the choice of materials, he needs to know how they behave under various loadings in various environments (that is, the material properties), and then, knowing these properties, he must be able to correlate them with the load-carrying capacity of his proposed component or structure. The subjects of stress analysis and fracture mechanics have been developed exclusively for this purpose.

However, a number of indeterminate factors arise: the loading to be experienced by the component or structure in service is often known only imprecisely, manufacturing and fabrication techniques may induce residual stresses whose magnitudes are unknown at the design stage, the actual geometry in some local region may deviate from that stipulated on the drawing so that the original stress analysis may be in error, or the properties of the material used in manufacture may be different from those assumed by the designer. Thus, experience in both choice of material and allowable working stresses for any common grouping of various types of components and structures is all-important in achieving a successful end-product.

Traditional design was based on the concept of a factor of safety (to supposedly cover all unknown and imprecisely known factors), the tensile strength of the material, and a nominal stress analysis procedure. This, of course, was the only approach possible when little was known of material properties, fracture mechanisms, detailed stress analysis, and service loadings. The factor of safety used was generally a matter of personal intuition and past experience. In many instances, this procedure worked extremely well. For example, limiting the allowable design stress to 80 MN m^{-2} permitted the manufacture and successful operation of a vast number of mild steel components and structures, using only elementary stress procedures and without the need to evoke sophisticated stress analysis, elaborate testing procedures, or a detailed knowledge of fracture mechanisms.

A designer is continually endeavouring to achieve more economical designs. To attain this he must increase his allowable design stress; metallurgists have responded nobly with increases in tensile strengths of all classes of materials. However, designers soon discovered that factors of safety appropriate to a particular type of mild steel component or structure when applied to the new stronger steels (or other materials) did not necessarily lead to a satisfactory service performance. Success in traditional design was due largely to the avoidance of past errors and to the use of familiar materials in familiar situations.

Early in the history of engineering design, the need to know the different methods by which a material or component may fail was recognized. Failure was inevitably associated with fracture or excessive deformation; thus failure under static tensile, compressive, or shear loads became widely known. Early design also aimed at making a component or structure that would last for ever.

However, with the development of the steam engine and mechanical transport and the more extensive use of mechanical devices, failures of moving parts that carried a repeatedly applied load were beginning to become a common occurrence. Failures were found to occur at low nominal stresses but in situations where the load was repeatedly changing and were usually located at a change in section in the component or structure. That these failures were starting to worry engineers over a hundred years ago is illustrated by the fact that in 1830 Albert [1] repeatedly proof-loaded welded mine hoist chains, continuing some tests up to 10^5 cycles. Between 1850 and 1865, both Hodgkinson [2] and Fairbairn [3] carried out repeated bending tests on beams, Fairbairn using a mechanism actuated by a water-wheel to apply repeatedly a load to the centre of a 6·7 m long wrought iron built-up girder. The beam broke statically under a central load of 120 kN, but Fairbairn found repeated loads of only 30 kN would eventually cause failure.

Materials fracturing under repeated loadings were found to exhibit no gross deformation and gave the appearance of having suddenly snapped. As early as 1840 Rankine [4] noted the characteristic brittle appearance of material broken under a repeated loading. Because these failures occurred in a part that had functioned satisfactorily for a certain time, the general opinion developed that the material had tired of carrying the load or that the continual re-application of a load had in some way exhausted the ability of the material to carry load. Thus the word 'fatigue' was coined to describe such failures, and the name has survived to this day. With the increasing demand for more efficient and economic components and structures (for example, higher operating speeds and minimum weight design), the number of failures by fatigue has continued to increase until today it is by far the commonest cause of failure of load-carrying metallic parts operating at or close to room temperature.

The reasons for the failure of materials under the continued application of a stress which if applied once would not cause failure have engaged the engineer and metallurgist for a long time. Accounts of this early work have been given by Gough [5], Moore and Kommers [6], and Mann [7]; it is of interest to note that it is now over a hundred years since Wöhler [8] published the results of his classical experiments on fatigue. He constructed various types of fatigue testing machines and carried out the first fatigue tests on metallic specimens in which strict attention was paid to the magnitude of the applied loads. He concluded from tests on iron and steel specimens that the range of applied stress rather than the maximum tensile stress in the loading cycle determined the life of a specimen, and that a limiting lower stress range existed below which a specimen did not break no matter how many times the stress cycle was applied. Since Wöhler's work, the fatigue properties of different materials tested under various conditions of loading and environment have been studied intensively. In addition, fatigue tests have been carried out on both components and structures, often subjecting them to loading cycles comparable with those to which it is expected they will be subjected in service. However, despite the fact that most engineers and designers are aware of fatigue and that a vast body of experimental data has been accumulated, many important breakdowns of plant and machinery still occur today. All too often, plant or equipment whose over-all functional demands have been adequately met will break down in service because of the fatigue failure of a detail apparently not immediately concerned with the functional requirements of the complete unit. Thus, lack of attention to some aspect of detail design is a major factor responsible for fatigue failures. There is nothing as effective as a failure in service for making an engineering designer concerned about detail design. When a failure in service does occur, whether it be of a dramatic or spectacular nature such as the Comet aircraft or the Queen Elizabeth II turbine blade or at a more humble level such as a vehicle stub-axle, there is usually no lack of expert opinion as to why it happened. Some reasons for failure appear so obvious after failure has occurred that it is difficult to appreciate why it was not so before the event happened [9]. Factors contributing to this state of affairs are: exact information for a particular set of circumstances is not always available and a designer must estimate fatigue performance from whatever data is to hand; only rarely do the fatigue properties of a material bear any general relationship to component performance in service; precise service loadings are unknown either through ignorance or accidental overloading or because the service requirements have been altered after the part has been manufactured.

A further factor is that traditional design assumed a material to be a flawless continuum. However, we know today that rational design and material assessment needs an understanding of the cracked continuum. Many materials, components, and structures either contain flaws or defects inherently, as part of the manufacturing procedure, or develop them at some stage of their life. It is shown throughout this book that an understanding of how a cracked body behaves under loading is essential to an understanding of any fatigue problem.

Because much of the information on fatigue from both laboratory tests and service behaviour was obtained and interpreted before the study of cracked-material behaviour was established, there was no underlying central theme to correlate the data. Thus isolated sets of data became almost fatigue folklore, and their relationship to other sets of data was not obvious.

The purpose of this book is to attempt to bring together all facets of the fatigue of materials, components, and structures into one rational picture. Readers having only a passing acquaintance with the subject of strength of materials should refer to Appendixes 1–7, which describe some elementary concepts concerning laboratory fatigue testing, stress concentrations, and material stress–strain relationships, before proceeding to Chapter 2.

The advanced reader may feel, at first sight, that only the chapters on microcrack initiation (Chapter 2) and macrocrack propagation (Chapter 5) contribute greatly to the understanding of the fatigue problem as a whole and, indeed, in some senses this is true. The whole essence of metal fatigue lies there: all else follows from this. There would be much to be said for grouping these two chapters together, all the others being subsidiary. However, after due thought, it has been decided to retain the conventional order of plain fatigue strength, notched fatigue strength, in order to trace the historical development of the understanding of metal fatigue and to lead up to the vital concepts of the cyclic stress necessary to cause a crack to grow and the macrocrack propagation characteristics of metals. Following the description of the mechanism of fatigue crack initiation in Chapter 2, therefore, Chapter 3 presents and interprets a comprehensive and detailed collection of data on factors affecting the plain fatigue strength of a material. Chapter 4 presents data on the effect of stress concentrations or notches and, in the interpretation of these, leads on to the stress necessary for macrocrack growth. Chapter 5 then deals with theories and interpretation of fatigue crack propagation, presenting data thereon. Finally, Chapter 6 covers certain specific aspects of fatigue which warrant a more detailed treatment, interpreting them in the light of the understanding of the processes of microcrack initiation and macrocrack propagation.

In any book on metal fatigue, the question of units, particularly for stress, presents problems. British fatigue data are often in tonf in^{-2} units, data from aircraft engineering are commonly in 10^3 lbf in^{-2} units (usually referred to as k.s.i.) as is the practice in the U.S.A., fracture mechanics units both in Britain and the U.S.A. are almost invariably k.s.i. (in)$^{\frac{1}{2}}$ and, of course, there are Continental practical units such as kgf mm^{-2}. For reasons of consistency, therefore, all such practical units have been abandoned and S.I. units used throughout. Although this may present some inconvenience to those not yet accustomed to thinking in S.I. units, it is thought that this disadvantage is far outweighed by the benefits of a logical and consistent unit system which must surely become the accepted system of the future.

Conversions for commonly used units are:

Stress

1 tonf in^{-2} = 15·4443 MN m^{-2}; 1 MN m^{-2} = 0·064 749 tonf in^{-2}
10^3 lbf in^{-2} = 6·8948 MN m^{-2}; 1 MN m^{-2} = 0·145 038 × 10^3 lbf in^{-2}
1 kgf mm^{-2} = 9·8067 MN m^{-2}; 1 MN m^{-2} = 0·101 972 kgf mm^{-2}.

Force

1 tonf = 9·9640 kN; 1 kN = 0·100361 tonf
10^3 lbf = 4·4482 kN; 1 kN = 0·224809 × 10^3 lbf
10^3 kgf = 9·8067 kN; 1 kN = 0.101 972 × 10^3 kgf.

Stress intensity factor

10^3 lbf in$^{-\frac{3}{2}}$ = 1·0988 MN m$^{-\frac{3}{2}}$; 1 MN m$^{-\frac{3}{2}}$ = 0·91005 × 10^3 lbf in$^{-\frac{3}{2}}$.

References

1. ALBERT, W. A. J. *Arch. Miner. Geognosie Berg. Hüttenkunde*, **10,** 215 (1838).
2. HODGKINSON, E. A. H.M.S.O. Command paper No. 1123 (1849).
3. FAIRBAIRN, W. *Phil. Trans. R. Soc.* **154,** 311 (1864).
4. RANKINE, W. J. M. *Proc. Instn civ. Engrs* **2,** 105 (1843).
5. GOUGH, H. J. *The fatigue of metals.* Scott, Greenwood, and Son, London (1924).
6. MOORE, H. F. and KOMMERS, J. B. *The fatigue of metals.* McGraw-Hill, New York (1927).
7. MANN, J. Y. *J. Aust. Inst. Metals.* **3,** 222 (1958).
8. WÖHLER, A. *Z. Bauw.* **8,** 642 (1858); **10,** 583 (1860); **13,** 233 (1863); **16,** 67 (1866); **20,** 74 (1870); *Engineering* **11,** 199 (1871).
9. FIELD, J. E. and SCOTT, D. The diagnosis of service failures. *Institution of Mechanical Engineers Conference on safety and failure of Components, University of Sussex* (1969).

2 | Crack initiation

2.1. Introduction

THE onset of damage in a cyclically stressed ductile metal is generally associated with a free surface, and this chapter is concerned only with metals in which fatigue cracks are initiated at a free surface; other materials in which sub-surface cracking occurs are mentioned in later chapters.

Arguments that damage in a polycrystalline ductile metal is associated with grains having a free surface rather than those within the body of the metal are:

1. Surface grains are in intimate contact with the atmosphere; thus, if environment is a factor in the damage process, they are obviously the more susceptible.
2. A surface grain is the only part of a polycrystal not wholly supported by adjoining grains. Because the slip systems in neighbouring grains of a polycrystal are not related to each other, a grain having a free surface will be able to deform plastically more easily than a grain in the body of metal which is surrounded by other grains.
3. It has been shown that if a fatigue test is stopped after some fraction (say, 20 per cent) of the expected life of the specimen, a thin layer of metal removed from the test-section, and the test continued at the same stress level, the total life of the specimen is longer than the expected life of the original specimen [1]. If a surface layer is removed at frequent intervals throughout a test, the expected life may be exceeded may times; in fact, provided that the stress amplitude is maintained constant and the frequency of removal and depth of removed layer are sufficient, the life will be limited only by the initial cross-sectional area of the specimen.
4. The fatigue strength of small specimens cut from the interior of the test-section of a larger specimen broken in reversed direct stress (that is, cut from material which has been subjected to a stress level greater than the plain fatigue limit) is not inferior to that of the virgin material [2].
5. If the surface of a specimen is hardened, either metallurgically or by surface working, the fatigue strength of the specimen as a whole may be increased. Similarly, any procedure which softens the surface decreases the fatigue strength of the specimen.

6. Metallurgical examination of broken fatigue specimens of nominally homogeneous metallic specimens which have been subjected to a uniform stress distribution over their cross-section does not reveal cracks in the body of the specimen. In certain circumstances, however, cracks may form in the interior of a specimen at inclusions or flaws or beneath hardened surface layers.

The onset of damage and cracking is thus associated with the surface grains, only those grains in the body of a specimen through which a crack, formed in a surface grain, passes as it grows across the specimen being damaged. This means that it is a relatively simple matter to observe directly the progressive development of cracking during a fatigue test. In general, only one crack penetrates into the metal to any considerable depth, but many additional cracks may be visible to the naked eye on the surface of soft metals (for example, copper, mild steel), especially when tested at stress levels giving failure after a relative short endurance (say, less than 10^5 cycles). On the other hand, no cracks, apart from the one leading to complete failure, may be visible to the naked eye on the surface of specimens of hard metallic alloys such as high strength steels and aluminium alloys.

2.2. Surface examination

The surfaces of suitably prepared specimens can be studied by metallo-graphic techniques during the course of a test [3]. These techniques consist essentially of preparing the specimen surface metallurgically and either examining the surface directly through an optical microscope or preparing surface replicas for examination in an electron microscope.

In general, slip lines formed under static loading appear, under low and moderate magnifications, as sharp, straight lines and are distributed evenly over each grain. Under high magnification, the individual lines appear as bands of parallel lines of various heights. The slip lines produced under cyclic stressing form in bands, which do not necessarily extend right across a grain, new slip lines forming beside old ones as a test proceeds, the inter-vening regions between the bands being apparently free from slip [4]. The appearance of slip markings on the surface of a specimen during a fatigue test is shown on Fig. 2.1.

Slip-line development on the surface of a fatigue specimen has been studied by many workers since the turn of the century. As early as 1903, Ewing and Humphrey [5] tested specimens of Swedish iron in rotating bending at stress levels above their fatigue limit, a test being stopped at frequent intervals and the specimen surface polished and etched. They observed few slip lines initially, but as a test proceeded, new slip lines formed close to existing ones, producing bands of slip. Although these bands grew wider and more dense, there were areas between the bands where no slip was observed. Fatigue cracks formed eventually in the broadened bands, but it was not possible to define precisely when this happened. Numerous slip bands were found to contain cracks at the end of a test, especially when a specimen had a long life.

Successive workers using other ductile polycrystals and more sophisticated metallographic techniques have added more detail which, in general, has confirmed the sequence of events described by Ewing and Humphrey. For example, some fifty years later, Thompson, Wadsworth, and Louat [6] tested annealed electropolished, polycrystalline high-purity copper specimens in reversed direct stress (zero mean load), a specimen being removed from the fatigue machine periodically and examined metallurgically. Slip bands appeared early in a test and became more numerous as the test progressed. Electropolishing removed the roughness associated with a slip band, and most of them became invisible. A few, however, became accentuated and were termed 'persistent slip bands'; fatigue cracks grew eventually from these bands. If the electropolishing was continued until the persistent bands were removed, it was found that, on retesting, the slip bands reformed and again became persistent. In many cases the pattern of the new bands reproduced in some detail that which had been removed, implying that slip was still active on the same planes. No new markings were ever uncovered during the electropolishing, showing that the origin of cracking was associated with the free surface. Persistent slip bands were observed in some tests after only 5 per cent of the total life, but they did not in general extend far down into the metal; for example, none were found to be more than 30 μm deep after 25 per cent of the life. Photographs illustrating the development of persistent slip bands during a test are shown in Fig. 2.1. All persistent slip bands more than one grain long were found to open under an applied static tensile load. Similar observations were made on polycrystalline nickel specimens, the main difference from the copper observations being the absence of slip bands other than those directly associated with cracks.

As well as leading to the formation of crevices or intrusions, intensive slip can give rise to the complementary process of extrusion. This was first reported by Forsyth [7, 8], who studied the surface characteristics of many pure metals and alloys, at various temperatures, using specimens about 0·6 mm thick, tested in reversed plane bending at relatively large strain amplitudes. He found that, whereas cyclic deformation in annealed aluminium consisted of coarse slip situated in bands with fine slip markings spread widely across the grains between the coarse bands, cracks appearing first in these coarse bands, in an age-hardened $4\frac{1}{2}\%$ Cu–aluminium alloy the coarse slip bands were absent; instead a fine dispersion of slip-line markings was observed after cyclic stressing. Some of these became accentuated and clearly defined on the surface, cracks appearing from irregular markings associated with the accentuated slip lines. These irregular markings were found, under higher magnification, to be ribbon extrusions, not thicker than 0·1 μm and about 10 μm long. A photograph and schematic sketch of these extrusions are shown in Fig. 2.2.

The extrusion process seemed to start suddenly and then stop after a small number (usually less than 100) of loading cycles. The extruded ribbons left crevices in the surface which sometimes developed into cracks, although cracks sometimes developed without the formation of a ribbon. The amount of extrusion was reduced by decreasing the test temperature, and at $-196\,°C$ slip bands, similar to those formed on pure aluminium, appeared. Extrusions similar to those occurring in the $4\frac{1}{2}\%$ Cu–aluminium alloy were also found to occur in a 10% Zn–aluminium alloy; moreover, in this alloy these still occurred at $-196\,°C$. At elevated temperatures, the extrusions from the $4\frac{1}{2}\%$ Cu-aluminium alloy became thicker and more irregular and, on re-polishing and etching to remove them, not only were cracks observed in slip bands but they etched differently from the rest of the grain. It was argued that this implied over-ageing was more rapid in the slip band than in the sur-rounding material and that extrusion and cracking occurred in the softer over-aged material.

Subsequently many workers have observed both intrusions and extrusions occurring at slip bands in polycrystalline ductile metals (for example, low-carbon steel [9] and alloy steels [10]), over a wide range of temperatures. To study extrusion formation in more detail, Forsyth [7] tested transparent single and polycrystal silver chloride specimens and found that profuse slip and extrusion phenomena occurred. He observed that extrusions did not create internal voids; instead, complementary surface crevices or intrusions, of about the same size as extrusions, formed. Cottrell and Hull [11] also found from reversed direct stress fatigue tests on copper that both extrusions and intrusions occurred in comparable abundance and with similar dimensions along slip bands and that this was so at temperatures down to $-250\,°C$. Examples of extrusions and intrusions formed along slip bands in specimens tested at $-183\,°C$ are shown in Fig. 2.3. The authors stated that cracks could clearly originate from intrusions.

Further work [12] showed that extrusions and intrusions could form in slip bands even when the temperature of the specimen was lowered to that of liquid helium, intrusions being detected on some specimens after only 1 per cent of their life. This suggested that their formation was by purely mechanical movement of atoms and was not dependent on diffusion processes. Intrusions have also been shown to act as crack nuclei on specimens subjected to a wholly compressive loading cycle [10].

Because cracking in ductile polycrystals is transcrystalline, the behaviour of single crystals must follow the same general pattern. Indeed, as grain-boundary effects can play no part in single-crystal behaviour, then even in those metals in which intergranular cracking occurs in the polycrystalline state, this cannot be the mode of failure of single crystals.

Gough [13] subjected aluminium, copper, silver (face-centred cubic), iron (body-centred cubic), antimony, bismuth (face-centred rhombohedral), and zinc (close-packed hexagonal) single crystals to cyclic torsional stresses (zero mean load) and found that, for all metals but antimony and bismuth, the operative slip plane and slip direction in each part of the crystal were determined, as under static loading, by the maximum resolved shear stress component at that point. Cracks were associated with regions of maximum resolved shear stress and areas of previous heaviest slip. In addition to slip bands, a large number of mechanical twins formed in zinc, cracks developing along basal planes or along the edge of twins. No slip bands appeared in antimony and bismuth crystals; the former failed by cleavage, whereas the latter twinned profusely, cracks forming parallel to the twin planes. Some cracks which formed in the antimony crystals did not appear to grow after quite long endurances. When a static tensile or compressive end-load was applied in addition to the cyclic torsional stress, the range of resolved shear stress was again responsible for the initiation of cracks in regions of heaviest slip. However, although the static stress had no effect on crack initiation, it did cause an increase or a decrease in the rate at which cracks grew, depending on whether it was tensile or compressive.

Persistent slip bands formed on high-purity copper single crystals have been found to contain nearly equal quantities of both intrusions and extrusions [14]. The mechanism of failure of high-purity zinc single crystals tested in reversed direct stress was the development of a crystallographic notch by repeated reversed slip on parallel planes, followed by intense slip and crack growth at the stress concentration [15]. Few cracks were detected on the surface during a test, implying that, in zinc, once a critical surface notch was formed, a crack grew rapidly from it, leading to catastrophic fracture by cleavage. Fig. 2.4 shows examples of the progressive outcrop of slip leading to changes in surface contour occurring in the sides of a large pit (whose sides were initially straight) etched in an aluminium single crystal of square cross-section, which was subjected to cyclic torsional strains [16].

Torsional fatigue tests have been carried out on aluminium specimens composed of two or more grains. Slip-band formation was as in the single aluminium crystals, but the bands sometimes did not extend right across a grain. The fatigue strength of the polycrystals was not significantly different from that of the single crystals and no signs of grain-boundary cracking were found [13].

Slip-band cracking can occur in ductile metal polycrystals, which does not necessarily lead to complete failure of the test-piece. For example, [17, 18] 0·09% C steel strip specimens tested in reversed plane bending, cyclically stressed 33 per cent above the fatigue limit, showed slip lines formed in a few grains after 1 per cent of the life, the lines growing longer and broader as a test continued until they formed bands. Slip markings, however, did not form in all grains. No slip lines appeared after 15×10^6 cycles on specimens stressed 20 per cent lower than the fatigue limit, but they did appear in a few individual grains in specimens stressed just below the fatigue limit. In general, slip markings did not lead in every case to the formation of a microcrack, but microcracks did appear primarily in those grains having distinct slip markings. Subsequent electropolishing caused those slip bands which contained either flat micro-fissures or none at all to disappear, only those slip bands interspersed with deeper microcracks remaining visible.

Electron microscopy examination of specimens stressed above the fatigue limit showed that slip bands were interspersed with sub-microscopic fissures and crevice-like grooves (Fig. 2.5(a)), and indeed sub-microscopic fissures were present in a small number of slip bands on specimens stressed below the fatigue limit (Fig. 2.5(b)). Similar microcracks (from $10 \, \mu m$ to $100 \, \mu m$ deep) have been found in slip bands on various carbon steels tested at stress levels either equal to or just less than their fatigue limits [19].

Although slip-band cracking has been widely observed in many ductile metals tested at room temperature and stress levels not too far removed from the fatigue limit, altering the conditions of test or adding certain alloying constituents can lead to grain-boundary cracking.

Raising the temperature has been used by many workers to change the mode of cracking from transcrystalline to intercrystalline. For example, reversed direct stress tests on 4 mm diameter magnesium specimens were carried out at both room temperature and 250 °C [20]. It was found that at room temperature, all cracks were transcrystalline, being initiated in either slip bands or twin boundaries. On the other hand, at 250 °C all cracks were intergranular; it was suggested that this was a consequence of grain-boundary sliding. At sub-zero and room temperatures cracks in pure aluminium developed in persistent slip bands [21, 22], but at elevated temperatures they were initiated mainly at grain boundaries. Both slip-band and grain-boundary cracking were found to occur after less than 5 per cent of the expected life. Grain-boundary cracking occurred generally in those boundaries lying close to the maximum shear stress direction and also in those boundaries separating grains which had a large difference in orientation, so that slip from one grain could not be transmitted to the neighbouring one.

If a ductile metal is alloyed so that the boundaries are weak relative to the grains, cracks will occur in the boundaries at a stress level lower than that required to cause slip-band cracking within a grain. For example, weakening the grain boundaries of a pure iron containing 0·1 per cent phosphorus by quenching from 700 °C resulted in all fatigue cracks being intercrystalline [23]. A study [24] of the surface characteristics resulting from cyclic stressing a series of aged zinc–magnesium–aluminium alloys having compositions ranging from 10 % Zn, 1 % Mg to $3\frac{1}{2}$ % Zn, 6 % Mg, showed that fatigue was essentially a grain-boundary phenomenon in alloys having a high zinc–magnesium ratio and the main crack was always intercrystalline. The deformation in alloys having a lower zinc–magnesium ratio occurred within the grains, being concentrated in slip bands; fatigue cracking was transcrystalline and associated with these preferred slip bands. The fatigue process in alloys having the lowest zinc–magnesium ratio was accompanied by little or no evidence of deformation, and these alloys had the highest fatigue strengths. The alloys in which intense slip bands were observed showed a lack of stability of the precipitate in these localized regions and were found frequently to contain cavities, to a depth of 2μm, whose formation appeared to precede the development of a crack. Twin boundaries can also be the sites of cracking, and it has been suggested, from evidence obtained from reversed plane bending tests on 1·5 mm thick copper strip specimens containing annealing twins [25], that a prerequisite for cracking at twin boundaries was that slip must occur on planes parallel to the twin boundary. Thus, cracks formed at twin boundaries simply because they were parallel to potential slip planes and contained stress raisers in the form of non-coherent steps, which gave rise to secondary slip, and it could be argued that a portion of a grain boundary which was so oriented would also serve equally as a site for cracking.

Increasing the stress level so that a test-piece has a shorter life can change the mode of cracking. Rotating bending tests [26] on high-purity copper showed that persistent slip bands formed only on those specimens tested at low stress amplitudes giving failure after long endurances; they were virtually absent from specimens tested at high stress amplitudes, giving failure after short endurances. It was also found that whereas all cracks were transcrystalline in specimens tested at ± 100 MN m^{-2}, they were intercrystalline in those tested at ± 170 MN m^{-2}. The S/N curve obtained from rotating bending tests on annealed copper specimens has been reported as being made up of two separate curves with a junction at about ± 150 MN m^{-2} [27]. Metallographic examination showed that cracks were formed in slip bands on those specimens tested below ± 150 MN m^{-2}, whereas they were formed from L- or Z-shaped nuclei in specimens tested at stress levels above this.

With the stronger, more complex alloys, it is often difficult to see progressive surface markings because the surface plastic strains leading to cracking become extremely localized. For example, slip bands were only prominent on high-stress low-life specimens of the age-hardening $5\frac{1}{2}$ % Zn–aluminium alloy (DTD683); they could not be observed on specimens tested at stress levels giving lives of 10^7 cycles or longer [28]. Reversed plane bending tests on specimens of high-purity aluminium having up to 4 per cent magnesium added showed that, although both pure aluminium and the alloys went through the same stages of slipping and cracking, the alloying had pronounced effect on details of deformation [29]. Different areas of the surface of a pure aluminium

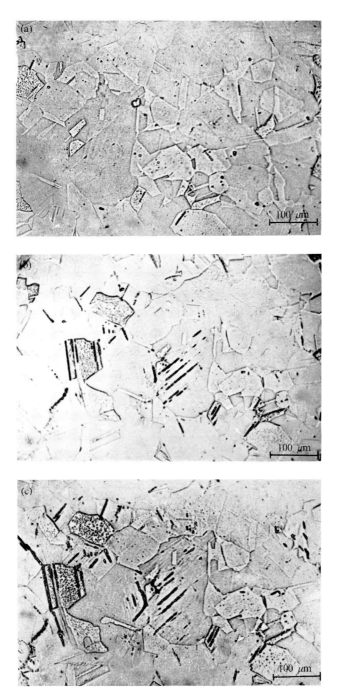

FIG. 2.1. Development of persistent slip bands in copper. (a) Polished after $7\frac{1}{2}$ per cent of the life. (b) Polished after 42 per cent of the life; almost same field as (a). (c) Polished after 77 per cent of the life; same field as (b). (Taken from Thompson, Wadsworth, and Louat [6].)

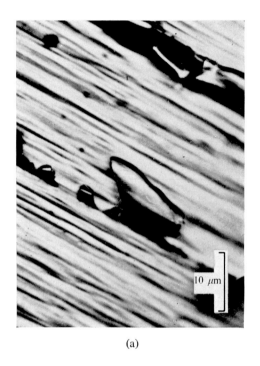

(a)

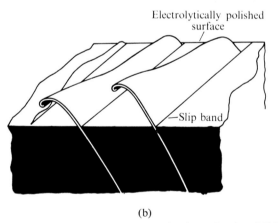

(b)

FIG. 2.2. Slip-band extrusion. (a) Slip-band extrusion in age-hardened $4\frac{1}{2}\%$ Cu–aluminium alloy. (b) Diagrammatic sketch of slip-band extrusion (Taken from Forsyth [8].)

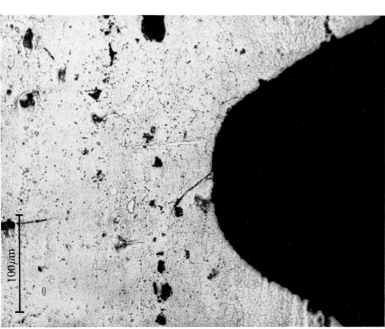

FIG. 4.11. Cracks found in $4\frac{1}{2}\%$ Cu–aluminium alloy rotating bending specimen having a circumferential vee-notch 1·3 mm deep, root radius 0·05 mm. Unbroken after $51·93 \times 10^{6}$ cycles at ± 39 MN m^{-2}.

100μm

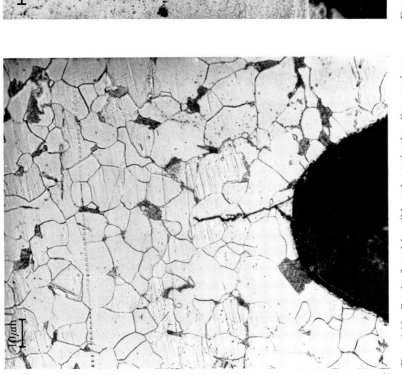

FIG. 4.10. Cracks found in mild steel rotating bending specimen having a circumferential vee-notch 1·3 mm deep, root radius 0·07 mm. Unbroken after $23·83 \times 10^{6}$ cycles at ± 39 MN m^{-2}.

10μm

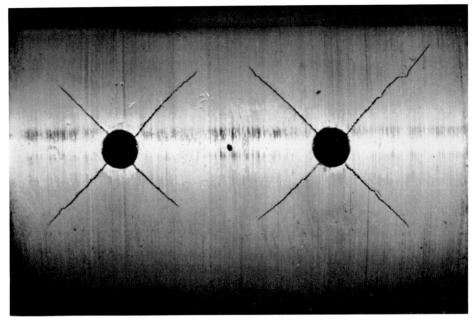

FIG. 4.19. Fatigue cracks growing from holes in a shaft subjected to cyclic torsional stresses.

FIG. 4.23. Fracture surface of mild steel specimen tested in brine.

specimen behaved similarly and extensive deformation and surface crack-ing took place prior to complete fracture. On the other hand, the changes in surface features of the alloys were highly localized, certain areas showing extensive change while adjoining areas appeared unaffected. In addition, as the amount of slip deformation was decreased, a smaller percentage of the slip bands which formed reached the cracking stage and fewer of the cracks which developed left the confines of the parent grain. Thus, although the alloying additions increased the static strength, they made fatigue an in-creasingly localized phenomenon, and it was this localized weakness rather than over-all strength which determined the fatigue strength. Forsyth [30] found that the stronger aluminium alloys exhibited few coarse slip bands during fatigue, and it was not easy to identify any form of damage preceding the formation of a crack, apart from a short slip band. He argued that, because resolved shear stresses were responsible for the formation of surface cracks whose rate of growth was slow until they began to develop under the normal tensile stress component of the loading cycle, alternating torsion would seem the best form of cyclic loading to reveal precracking damage of these alloys.

In these strong, complex alloys, inclusions and intermetallics can be sources of cracking. For example, examination of the surfaces of fatigue specimens cut from 0.2% and 0.4% C steel bar and forgings, either parallel or trans-verse to the direction of working, showed that in all transverse specimens, microcracks were observed at the edges of inclusions but in the longitudinal specimens, microcracks appeared mainly in slip bands, only very rarely forming at inclusions [31]. Similarly, Grosskreutz and Shaw [32] found that, although microcracks formed in slip bands on soft 1% Si–aluminium alloy specimens, they appeared to nucleate at constituent particle inclusions in the high-strength solution-treated and aged $4\frac{1}{2}\%$ Cu–aluminium alloy.

Because of work-hardening, slip under cyclic conditions does not occur in a reversible manner on the same planes. In other words, if the application of a given tensile load results in slip occurring on a series of planes, slip in the reversed direction will occur on a different series of planes when the load is removed and a numerically equal load applied in compression. For example the behaviour of slip lines on the surface of both cold-worked and annealed high-purity aluminium single crystals subjected to alternate tensile and com-pressive loads has been studied [33], the magnitude of the applied loads being such that the strain during any half-cycle was less than a few tenths of a per cent. It was found that there was no obvious relationship between the slip lines formed during tension and those formed during the subsequent com-pression loading. A slip line was unaffected, in general, by a reversal of load up to a value of twice the initial load. This would seem to imply that fatigue cracking is due to the geometric surface effects caused by extrusions and intrusions and not due to some internal damage process along a particular slip plane. (For example, it has been argued, from the results of torsional fatigue tests on copper and brass specimens, that although striking changes in surface contour occurred where a slip zone emerged, it was the weakening of internal slip zones that was the primary cause of failure, the free surface playing only a secondary role [34]).

There is experimental evidence showing that the ease with which slip can be transferred to neighbouring planes aids the process of producing a notch-like surface [35, 36]. McEvily and Machlin [37] investigated the role of cross-slip by testing LiF, NaCl, AgCl, and KRS-5 (44 mole % TiBr and 56 mole % TiI) crystals in reversed bending. The latter two crystals exhibit easy cross-slip at room temperature, whereas the former two do not. In no case did fatigue failure occur with the LiF and NaCl crystals at stress levels up to at least ten times the static yield stress applied for at least 10^7 cycles. On the other hand, all the AgCl and KRS-5 crystals failed in fatigue, mostly at stress levels below twice the yield stress applied for less than 10^6 cycles. Others [38, 39] have found from tests on copper and aluminium single crystals that fatigue cracks formed in active slip bands, slip-band cracking being considered the result of active slip in the presence of a free surface and cross-slip being important in establishing the conditions necessary to create a surface notch. A thick and unbroken anodic film was found to inhibit the formation of cracks, presumably because it prevented surface notches forming; any break in the anodic film became a source of failure.

Environment might be expected to have an effect on surface cracking. It has been found that persistent slip bands formed on copper fatigue-tested in nitrogen in about the same time as in air, but that the cracks associated with them took much longer to spread across the test-piece [6]. This was confirmed by Wadsworth and Hutchings [40], who tested strip polycrystalline copper, aluminium, and gold specimens in reversed bending in both air and a vacuum (10^{-5} mm Hg). They found that the ratio of life in air to life in a vacuum, at a given surface strain, was about 1:20 for copper, 1:5 for aluminium, and 1:1 for gold. However, persistent slip bands and associated small cracks, a few micrometres deep, formed after about the same number of cycles, irrespective of whether a specimen was tested in air or a vacuum. The authors concluded, therefore, that the atmosphere had little effect on the initiation of surface cracks but that it did cause an increase in their rate of development in copper and aluminium specimens. Further tests on a high-purity iron containing 0·5% carbon showed that its fatigue limit in vacuum was about 20 per cent greater than that in air and that the life in vacuum, at a given surface strain greater than that at the *in vacuo* fatigue limit, was about ten times longer than in air. Small cracks formed in slip bands and appeared to be present in slip bands formed on specimens tested either in air or in a vacuum at cyclic strain amplitudes less than the respective fatigue limits. Moreover, although microcracks were present in specimens tested in a vacuum at a strain level just below the *in vacuo* fatigue limit, these cracks did not propagate when the test was continued subsequently in air at the same strain level.

Crack initiation at grain boundaries may be accentuated if normal atmospheric conditions give rise to stress–corrosion effects. For example, in beta-brass specimens, the slip markings produced were found [41] to show little tendency to form in bands and specimens tested at ± 70 MN m^{-2} exhibited a few grain-boundary cracks even though they were unbroken after 3×10^8 cycles. It was considered that the marked elastic anisotropy of beta-brass resulted in severe stress concentrations at grain boundaries which, at a free surface, caused intercrystalline cracking, perhaps aided by grain boundary stress corrosion to which beta-brass is susceptible. The minimum cyclic stress required for subsequent transcrystalline crack propagation was sensitive to environment and, when greater than that needed for intercrystalline cracking, led to the occurrence of non-propagating cracks.

To study in finer detail the changes in material structure both at and below a cyclically stressed surface, slices have been cut from specimens, electrolytically thinned, and examined by electron microscopy. Optical microscopy has revealed the breakdown of parent grains into sub-grains by cyclic stressing [7, 21, 22]. For example, Forsyth [7] found that a feature associated with fine slip was the breakdown of the original grains into a sub-structure which became more widespread and marked the higher the strain amplitude. The sub-grains had sharply defined boundaries and were usually between 1 μm and 10 μm diameter, those near the coarse slip bands generally being the smallest. Generally similar results were found on a $\frac{1}{2}$ per cent Ag–aluminium alloy, a Mn–aluminium alloy, Armco-iron, and copper. A region of sub-grains always formed ahead of a growing crack; they also formed at liquid nitrogen temperature. The use of the electron microscope enables these features to be studied in greater detail. For example, Grosskreutz [42] studied reversed direct stress and reversed plane bending polycrystalline aluminium and copper specimens, examining the surface of specimens by back-reflection X-ray techniques and thin foils cut from specimens by electron transmission microscopy. Provided that the strain range was sufficiently high, sub-grains formed within the parent grains. The first evidence of dislocation generation and accumulation into sub-grain boundaries was obtained after the first 0·1 per cent of the expected life, the density of dislocations in the boundaries reaching a saturation level after about 1 per cent of the expected life. Further structural changes then occurred only in the vicinity of a surface crack. There appeared to be no distinctive behaviour of the dislocation network as a whole which would nucleate a crack, although sub-grain formation was the dominant structural change. Instead, metallurgical observation of the surface confirmed that cracks formed in persistent slip bands, which tapered sections showed were notch-like fissures. The sub-grain structure in some aluminium specimens was observed to form at strain amplitudes down to ± 0.0005. The dislocations which made up the sub-boundaries were heavily jogged, scalloped, and tangled, the density of dislocations within the boundaries seeming to increase as a test proceeded.

Aluminium (99·98%) single crystals of square cross-section which had been subjected to large cyclic torsional strains at a frequency of 0·03 Hz have been examined using thin-film electron microscopy [16]. Thin foils were cut from the specimens so that they intersected the operative slip planes at various known angles. Fig. 2.6 shows the (110) face of a [$\bar{1}$12] torsion axis crystal in which a same plane pair slip system was operative. The crystal is divided into large sub-grains by dislocations on boundary planes perpendicular to the active slip plane and up to 10 μm apart. Dislocation tangles tending to run parallel to the trace of the operative slip plane occur within a sub-grain. Boundaries parallel to the trace of the active slip plane form easily in all crystals, even when, as in the case of single and cross-slip systems, no low-angle boundary on this plane is favoured by the operative slip systems. In these cases, the dense dislocation arrays on the active slip plane have a characteristic wavy trace when viewed edge-on. Fig. 2.7 shows the effect on the ($\bar{2}\bar{1}$1) face of a [001] axis crystal in which a single slip system on a plane normal to the foil is active. Typical dislocation clusters within a sub-grain are also visible. The main sub-grain boundaries are formed at an early stage in a test and persist throughout the life. Their formation is associated, therefore, with the bulk work-hardening of the crystal in the early stages of a test, whereas the non-work-hardening range extending over the major part of the test life appears to involve the movement of dislocations within the sub-grains. There is no evidence that the sub-grain boundaries are the sites of cracking. For example, [9] thin foils cut from both the body and surface (that is, within a distance of 10 μm from the surface) of reversed direct stress low-carbon steel specimens, on examination by electron transmission microscopy showed that the dislocation arrangement in the surface layer differed from that inside the specimen. The stress level had little influence on the surface-layer dislocation arrangement, which consisted of zones of very high dislocation density separated by zones of very low dislocation density. Persistent slip appeared to form in the high dislocation density zones. Inside the specimen, the dislocations formed a cell structure at high stress levels, but at lower stress levels (giving lives of about 10^6 cycles) they arranged themselves into bands about 1–2 μm long. Hirsch and others [43] studied the distribution and density of dislocations in both statically and cyclically loaded metals by means of electron transmission microscopy techniques. In cold-worked polycrystalline silver pulled in static tension to strains of up to 30 per cent, the dislocations were arranged in dense networks forming the boundaries of an otherwise relatively dislocation-free cell structure, the cell structure becoming more pronounced with increasing deformation. Copper, nickel, gold, and stainless steel polycrystalline fatigue specimens were tested in either reversed direct stress or reversed plane bending at stress levels giving lives of from 3×10^5 cycles to 2×10^6 cycles. Examination of thin foils cut from specimens tested to various percentages of their expected lives showed that the dislocations were concentrated in local regions, a few micrometres in extent (density 10^{14}–10^{15} per m^2) separated by regions of similar width but with a lower dislocation density (10^{12} per m^2). There appeared to be no correlation between surface slip bands and dislocation density below the surface, that is, regions corresponding to surface slip bands contained areas of both high and low dislocation density. At high magnification, many of the dislocations in the densely packed regions resolved clearly as loops. Wilson and Forsyth [44] carried out reversed plane bending tests on pure aluminium and $\frac{1}{2}\%$ Ag–aluminium alloy foil specimens. After testing, a foil was thinned electrolytically and examined by electron transmission microscopy. They found that the structure developed at room temperature consisted of dislocation arrays essentially similar to the arrays produced by polygonization in a metal statically strained at elevated temperature. All conditions of sub-boundaries were observed, from irregularly massed concentrations to perfectly formed arrays. The sub-boundaries, which contained certain zones having a very high density of defects, formed early in a test, becoming more widespread and well defined as a test proceeded. Feltner [45] found that the predominant characteristic of the defect structure revealed by electron transmission microscopy studies of fatigued metals was the presence of an excessively large number of dislocation loops, which aggregated into walls to form a cellular arrangement, the average cell size being about 4 μm. He considered that the cyclic hardening of annealed metals during the early stage of a fatigue test was a consequence of this dislocation network build-up.

2.3. Changes in bulk properties

In addition to the surface observations described, many workers have studied the changes in mechanical properties and metallurgical structure that occur in a cyclically loaded specimen. The measurements taken generally record a change in strain range response to a given stress range (often detected by a change in the shape of the hysteresis loop generated), a hardening or softening of the material, a change in temperature, enhanced diffusion characteristics, or a change in X-ray diffraction pattern; results are grouped loosely under various headings for ease of reading, even though, apart from diffusion and strain-ageing effects, all responses result from either a cyclic hardening or softening of the specimen as a whole.

2.3.1. Hysteresis loop and damping measurements

The change in shape of the hysteresis loop generated during the course of a reversed direct stress fatigue test can be measured by having extensometers attached directly to the specimen. In general, soft metals exhibit initially a wide hysteresis loop which narrows rapidly as a test proceeds, usually within the first 5 per cent of expected life. Provided the stress level is less than the fatigue limit, the loop now maintains a constant width. If the stress level is above the fatigue limit, the loop width increases gradually, its width increasing very rapidly just prior to fracture. This final increase is associated with the growth of cracks. The initially wide loop and its subsequent narrowing is absent in the case of hard metals [46, 47]; the initial narrowing of the wide hysteresis loop obtained with soft metals and alloys is a consequence of cyclic work-hardening. Some metals (for example, mild steel) exhibit continually a hysteresis loop of finite width even when subjected to a stress level below the fatigue limit.

Wadsworth [48, 49] has reported that the rate of hardening of copper single crystals subjected to a constant plastic strain amplitude was much less than in a unidirectional test. The peak stress in each half-cycle needed to maintain the plastic strain amplitude increased slowly as a test progressed and reached a maximum value after a few hundred cycles. After the first few cycles, the hysteresis loops generated each cycle were of similar shape, the stress at all points increasing similarly as the specimen hardened.

From a study of the damping characteristics of many metals and alloys, there appears to be a critical alternating stress for a given material, below which the damping characteristics remain constant irrespective of endurance [50]. At higher alternating stresses, the damping characteristics vary from material to material, some showing a steady increase in damping, others an increase followed by either a levelling-off or a decrease. By investigating the damping characteristics of various aluminium alloys in a resonance torsional fatigue machine in which a specimen was subjected initially to a small cyclic shear stress amplitude which was increased progressively, it was found [51] that the hysteresis loss was small and of a constant value for a solution-treated and aged $4\frac{1}{2}$ % Cu–aluminium alloy until the surface shear strains approached $\pm 3 \times 10^{-3}$; thereafter, it increased at a rate roughly proportional to the eighth power of the strain. The corresponding critical surface shear strains for the same alloy in either the solution-treated or annealed condition were $\pm 1 \cdot 3 \times 10^{-3}$ and $\pm 2 \times 10^{-4}$, respectively. These values bore no relationship to the fatigue strengths of the alloy in the corresponding condition. A different damping behaviour was noted with a strain-hardening Mg–aluminium alloy. Here the hysteresis losses either increased continuously or reached values which remained constant until complete failure occurred.

2.3.2. Changes in mechanical properties, stiffness, hardness, etc.

Depending on stress range, a soft material may work-harden, whereas a hard material may work-soften during a fatigue test. For example, steel, copper, nickel, and aluminium specimens were subjected to reversed direct stresses greater than their respective fatigue limits, a test being stopped after a certain endurance and static compression stress–strain curves and hardness values determined [52]. It was found that, although annealed metals hardened, cold-drawn metals showed a more or less pronounced softening. Similar conclusions have been drawn for other metals [53, 54].

The changes in hardness usually occupy only a relatively small percentage of the total life, cyclic hardening of a soft material requiring a smaller number of cycles to reach a stable hardness than cyclic softening of a hard material. For a given material the hardness usually attains the same value, irrespective of whether it was originally in the annealed or hardened condition. For example, tests on both cold-worked (95 HV) and annealed (38 HV) copper rotating bending specimens at ± 100 MN m^{-2} or ± 170 MN m^{-2} showed that at each stress the cold-worked specimens had longer lives than the annealed ones. From hardness measurements, taken at intervals throughout a test, it was found that both the cold-worked and annealed specimens eventually attained a hardness of about 75 HV. At either stress level, the number of cycles from the point where the hardness first attained a value of 75 HV until fracture occurred was the same for both the cold-worked and annealed metals [55]. Thus the difference in total life could be attributed to the relatively large number of cycles required to soften the cold-worked copper compared to the small number of cycles required to harden the annealed copper. The work-hardening of annealed copper by cyclic stress is sensibly independent of stress amplitude and reaches its stable value after a few thousand cycles [38, 56].

Tests other than hardness and stress–strain determinations which have been carried out on cycled material include impact and creep tests. For example, Holden [57] subjected 25 mm diameter 0·09 % C steel specimens, heat-treated to produce differing grain sizes, to reversed direct stresses whose amplitude was initially just below the fatigue limit but which was increased by small increments at regular intervals, so that, by the time it eventually broke, a specimen had been subjected to a large number of stress cycles whose magnitude was not far removed from the fatigue limit. It was found from room-temperature tensile tests on specimens cut longitudinally from the broken fatigue specimens that, for all grain sizes, cyclic stressing eliminated the yield point but increased the limit of proportionality by about 40 per cent. The brittle–ductile transition temperature determined from the impact specimens cut from the broken fatigue specimens was much higher than that of the unfatigued steel.

Creep tests on cyclically hardened copper have shown it has a higher creep resistance at 300 °C than specimens hardened to the same level by the application of a static load [56]. It has also been found that superimposing a cyclic stress on the static stress applied in a creep test on a polycrystalline specimen of either iron, copper, zinc, or lead produces an increase in creep rate which decreases to a steady value, generally greater than that in a comparable static creep test. However, when the cyclic stress is removed, the creep rate decreases to a value even lower than that in a comparable static creep test [58]. To a first approximation, the creep characteristics caused by the superposition of a cyclic load will depend on whether the cyclic stress work-hardens or work-softens the material. For example, if the material under test is in the cold worked condition, creep may occur in the presence of a cyclic load, whereas it would not occur in its absence. Packer and Wood [59] applied both a static axial load and an alternating torsional load to a cylindrical high-purity cold-drawn copper specimen. The axial creep deformation was measured for various static tensile and alternating torsional loads, it being found that, in general, the axial creep which occurred was primarily a consequence of the softening of the metal by the alternating torsional loads.

2.3.3. Changes in physical properties

These tests have consisted of either measuring the change in temperature, density or electromagnetic properties of a specimen subjected to cyclic loading.

Temperature measurements taken at the centre and ends of a reversed direct stress specimen have shown that the rate of heat dissipation from annealed metals is large initially but decreases rapidly and becomes roughly constant as a test continues. No further change occurs, provided that the stress level is below the fatigue limit of the metal but, if above, the rate of heat generation increases after the first initial drop. This steady increase continues until just before fracture when a very rapid increase occurs. The large initial rate of heat dissipation is absent in hard metals [60].

Density determinations on annealed commercially-pure aluminium poly-crystalline specimens before and after subjecting them to reversed direct strain amplitudes of up to ± 0.1 for 80 per cent of their expected life have been carried out to see if they would provide evidence of the formation of voids in the metal during the test. However, the density variations before and after testing were insignificant [61]. Measurement of the magnetic and electrical properties of a fatigue specimen have been made during the course of a test. Such changes as have been detected have been at stress levels in excess of the fatigue limit and are usually ascribed to changes in hardness occurring in the test [62].

2.3.4. Strain-ageing effects: coaxing, rest-periods, intermittent heat-treatments

The fatigue strength of some metals can be increased by prior testing at a lower cyclic stress. For example, if a specimen of such a metal is tested for, say, 10^7 cycles, at a cyclic stress level just less than its fatigue limit, its life on retesting at a cyclic stress level greater than the fatigue limit will be longer than that of a virgin specimen of the same metal tested at the latter stress level.

In addition, if, after 10^7 cycles at the initial stress level, the stress amplitude is increased by a very small amount, the test allowed to continue for a further 10^7 cycles, the stress amplitude again increased by a very small amount, and this sequence continued, the maximum cyclic stress level which will just not cause the specimen to break will exceed the fatigue limit of the virgin metal. These testing procedures are referred to as coaxing; if they increase the fatigue strength of a material, the material is said to have the ability to be coaxed.

In an extensive study of the coaxing behaviour of a selection of materials (ingot iron, in both the unstrained and strain-aged condition, 2 carbon steels, an aluminium alloy, and a 70/30 brass), having differences in their ability to be strengthened by strain-ageing and in their capacity to work-harden, Sinclair [63] found that, whereas the fatigue strengths of the unstrained ingot iron and the 2 carbon steels were increased considerably by coaxing, those of the other materials showed no improvement. He concluded, therefore, that only those materials having the ability to strain-age were capable of being coaxed. Appreciable increases in the fatigue strength of strain-ageing materials can be realized by coaxing. For example, Gough [64] found by testing a mild steel (fatigue limit ±252 MN m^{-2}) specimen initially at ±247 MN m^{-2} for 15×10^6 cycles, the stress level then being increased in increments of ±3 MN m^{-2} every 15×10^6 cycles, that the specimen did not break until the stress level has reached a value of ±325 MN m^{-2}. The fatigue limit of grey cast iron specimens subjected to such coaxing procedures has been reported [65] to be increased by 30 per cent.

A comparison of the shapes of the S/N curves exhibited by various metals and alloys suggests that only those having the ability to strain-age during a fatigue test possess a definite fatigue limit. In addition, fatigue tests on a strain-ageing material have shown that removing the elements responsible for strain-ageing from the specimen surface results in the definite fatigue limit exhibited by the virgin material becoming much less pronounced. For example, it was found that, although a 0·1% C steel had a definite fatigue limit when tested in the as-received condition, partial removal of carbon and nitrogen from the specimen surface resulted in a lowering of the fatigue limit, the knee of the S/N curve becoming less definite and occurring at a considerably longer life [66]. It was argued that complete removal of the carbon and nitrogen would have suppressed the fatigue limit completely. On the other hand, Ferro and Montalenti [67] found that iron single crystal, polycrystalline Armco-iron, and low-carbon steel specimens, carefully purified from carbon and nitrogen by long annealing at 1480 °C in hydrogen, did exhibit a fatigue limit, when tested in rotating bending. They concluded that the definite fatigue limit exhibited by pure iron was an intrinsic characteristic of the iron structure, and it was therefore unnecessary to postulate strain-ageing as the origin of both the definite fatigue limit and the sharp knee exhibited by the mild steel S/N curve. Kettunen [68], however, found that carefully cooled 99·999% pure iron exhibited no definite yield point and gave a smooth S/N curve with no fatigue limit or knee. He argued that the carbon and nitrogen content of a conventionally cooled iron must be kept below 0·0001–0·0002 per cent to prevent strain-ageing and the fact that Ferro and Montalenti's iron S/N curve exhibited a definite fatigue limit was due to the purity of their iron being insufficient to prevent strain-ageing from occurring.

Strain-ageing, being a diffusion process, must be temperature dependent and it has been found that the lives of low-carbon steel specimens tested at temperatures up to 370 °C are, for a given stress amplitude, longest when tested at 230 °C [69]. The occurrence of the maximum life peak at 230 °C was associated with strain-ageing occurring during a test because, when similar tests were carried out on specimens decarburized prior to testing, this maximum life peak disappeared.

As an alternative to removing carbon and nitrogen to prevent strain-ageing in steel, the strain-ageing capacity can be exhausted by prior coaxing at a cyclic stress just below the fatigue limit. Subsequent fatigue testing of such a steel showed that both the knee and the fatigue limit exhibited by the virgin metal were eliminated [70]. The percentage by which the fatigue limit could be increased by coaxing was about the same as that by which the tensile strength could be increased by repeated strain-ageing in an interrupted tensile test. However, it has been shown that the sharpness of the knee in the S/N curve of a soft steel depends on grain size. Fatigue tests on low-carbon steel specimens having various grain sizes and differing carbon and nitrogen contents showed that, irrespective of interstitial content, those specimens having a fine grain size exhibited an S/N curve having a much sharper knee than that given by specimens having a coarser grain size. Thus, although there was no doubt that strain-ageing increased the fatigue strength of mild steel, the sharpness of the knee in the S/N curve appeared to be controlled by grain size, being sharper the smaller the grain size [71].

Interrupting a fatigue test on a strain-ageing material at intervals and allowing a specimen to rest may result in an increase in life. Rest-periods, however, have little if any effect on the lives of other metals or of strain-ageing metals whose ability to strain-age has been exhausted. For example, improvement in the lives of those soft iron and carbon steel fatigue specimens that had been allowed to rest at intervals during a test has been reported [72]. On the other hand, no improvement due to intermittent rest periods in the lives of alloy steel specimens tested at 300 °C and 400 °C has been found [73].

Fatigue tests have also been interrupted at regular intervals and the specimen given some type of annealing heat-treatment in an attempt to determine at what percentage of the specimen life damage occurs which cannot be removed by reannealing. If the fatigue damage could be removed, the life of the specimen would be increased; if not, the life would be as for a virgin specimen. For example, brass specimens re-annealed at intervals of either 20 or 50 per cent of the expected life had lives not significantly different from the lives of untreated specimens tested at comparable stress levels [74]. Similar tests on aluminium [75], a 0·15% C steel [76], and gold [77] also showed that re-annealing at various intervals throughout a test had no significant effect on the life to failure.

2.3.5. Diffusion and surface emission studies

Cyclic stressing may enhance diffusion processes in some metals, allowing them to occur at lower temperatures and in shorter times than if subjected to static stresses of comparable magnitude (strain-ageing in mild steel is a common example). It has been argued [78] that enhanced diffusion rates, when they occur, are not a result of local high temperatures near active slip planes, because analysis shows that local temperature increases near active slip bands can reach only moderate values and, in addition, the duration of the temperature increase is too short to enhance diffusion processes appreciably; they would seem to be associated with dislocations, vacancies, and interstitials rather than local heating [3].

Internal oxidation, by cyclic stressing, in an 0·05% Si–copper alloy has been reported [79]. The gauge length of a specimen stressed at ± 43 MN m^{-2} for 220 hours (50 Hz) at 325 °C became permeated with silica-rich regions, indicating that oxygen and silicon had been able to combine in significant quantities, whereas a specimen subjected to a static stress of 43 MN m^{-2} for 220 hours at 325 °C showed no comparable effect. On the other hand, it has been reported that such internal oxidation occurs only at grain boundaries [80]; no evidence of internal oxidation within grains was found with both 0·05% Si and 0·26% Si–copper alloys subjected to cyclic stresses of ± 29 MN m^{-2} and ± 65 MN m^{-2} at 325 °C and 450 °C for 100 hours (50 Hz), and it was concluded that enhancement of internal oxidation only took place under cyclic stressing in those regions where there was already a supply of oxygen, that is, in grain boundaries having a free surface. There is no evidence that cyclic stressing enhances gross diffusion of one metal into another. For example, the diffusion of zinc into aluminium has been studied using 5 mm thick aluminium plates having an 8 μm thick layer of radioactive zinc deposited on the surface [81]. The plates were tested in both reversed direct stress and plane bending at temperatures between 300°C and 375°C at cyclic stresses causing failure in about 30 hours. A comparison of the depths to which the zinc diffused into either a fatigued plate or an unstressed plate held at the same temperature for a similar time showed there was little effect due to cyclic stressing.

Precipitates, which are normally produced only at elevated temperatures, have been observed in metals subjected to cyclic stresses at room temperature.

Bands of precipitates in both surface and interior grains have been reported in commercial age-hardening aluminium specimens when subjected to cyclic torsion stress [51]. The precipitation of iron carbide on the slip lines produced by prior static loading has been reported in cold stretched Armco-iron subjected to cyclic stressing [17]. However, to produce the precipitates, it was necessary to progressively increase the cyclic stress from a low value to a value well above the fatigue limit so as to ensure that a large number of stress reversals were applied. No precipitation occurred if the Armco-iron was not prestretched prior to fatigue testing. Cyclic stressing of a supersaturated solid solution of Alpha-iron also resulted in numerous carbide precipitates becoming visible in slip bands, despite the fact that the temperature of the metal during the fatigue test did not increase above room temperature [82].

Gas bubbles have been reported [83] to be emitted from the surface of a fatigue specimen, numerous bubbles forming under transparent tape applied to the surface of flat strip aluminium alloy and carbon steel reversed plane bending specimens, during the course of a test. The bubbles were found to be hydrogen and were generated before any surface cracks could be detected by metallographic techniques. The number generated could be decreased and sometimes eliminated by keeping the specimen and tape in a dry box for several days and then testing the specimen as soon as it was taped and removed from the box. No bubbles were produced if the stress level was less than that which led eventually to surface cracks forming; neither could they be produced by loading a specimen statically. No bubbles were observed, irrespective of stress level, on copper, brass, cadmium, nickel, stainless steel, tin, titanium, and zinc specimens. Hydrogen evolution has also been observed along active slip bands in specimens of a $5\frac{1}{2}\%$ Zn–aluminium alloy when tested in reversed torsion in a 3% salt spray [84].

2.3.6. X-ray diffraction studies

Changes in bulk properties of a cyclically loaded specimen have been detected by X-ray diffraction techniques. Here a monochromatic beam of X-rays is directed at a small area of the specimen and the diffracted beam detected on a photographic film. Undistorted annealed crystals produce a series of sharp spots; these become diffuse arcs when the crystal is distorted.

X-ray diffraction patterns from both statically and cyclically loaded metal specimens have shown that in both cases failure is characterized by a progressive breakdown of the original grains into sub-grains or crystallites about 10^{-3}–10^{-4} mm in size and of random orientation. This structural change appears abruptly in a statically loaded specimen when the yield stress is reached, and becomes progressively more marked as the fracture stress is approached. The same progression of structural change occurs with increasing number of stress cycles in specimens of 0·1 % C normalized mild steel [85], malleable iron [86], 70/30 brass [87], copper, aluminium, and brass [88] stressed above their fatigue limit, but no change occurs in specimens stressed below the fatigue limit, even when tested for up to 10^7 cycles, other than that which might have occurred during the first loading cycle.

Fragmentation of the grains (as detected by blurring of the X-ray reflection) in a fatigue specimen increases during the initial work-hardening stage being dependent on stress amplitude, but ceases after the initial work-hardening period is completed [88, 89]. Subsequent high-temperature annealing does not appear to remove the sub-grain structure [89].

Because the sub-grain formation is associated with the initial work-hardening part of the life [85], the application of a mean stress, particularly in the case of annealed metals, can make a marked change in the diffraction pattern [90]. The frequency of the stress application has been reported as having an effect [87]; for example, the blurring of the X-ray diffraction patterns obtained from an annealed 70/30 brass was less marked when the stress was applied at 34 Hz than when applied very slowly. This can only be associated with the different stress–strain relationships occurring at the two frequencies.

The half-breadth value of X-ray diffraction interference lines has been taken as a measure of the change in structure of a metal [91]. From X-ray patterns taken at various stages during rotating bending tests on annealed, cold-worked or heat-treated carbon steels, aluminium alloys, and copper alloys, the half-breadth value was found to increase rapidly during the early stage of all tests on annealed materials. It then increased gradually, reaching a limiting value for stress levels below the fatigue limit or continuing to increase when a specimen was stressed above its fatigue limit, until just before fracture when it increased noticeably. The pattern of behaviour is analogous to the change in shape of the hysteresis loop and it would seem that the X-ray patterns are merely reflecting the changing stress–strain response of the metal during the test. It was pointed out many years ago that it is difficult to accept that both static and fatigue fractures are a consequence of a fragmented structure since the use of severe deformations to obtain cold-worked materials results in a fragmented structure yet increases the nominal strength [85]. In the case of cold-worked steel fatigue specimens, no change in structure can be detected from specimens tested at stress levels less than their fatigue limit. However, when tested at higher stress levels, they give initially a diffraction picture consisting of a continuous ring, a progressive drop in the intensity of the ring occurring as a test proceeds. However, no further radial diffusion, indicating further breakup of the crystallites, occurs.

2.4. Discussion of surface crack initiation

Early theories of fatigue generally fall into two categories; those based on repeated slip leading to some form of damage along a preferred slip plane and hence eventually to a crack (for example, the attrition theory of Ewing and Humphrey [5]) and those based on the repeated work-hardening of a soft element, surrounded by an elastic matrix (or of a grain surrounded by grains having different elastic limits and strain-hardening characteristics), the work-hardened element (or grain) either reaching a stable state not leading to fracture or work-hardening until it reaches its fracture stress (for example, Afanasev [92], Dehlinger [93], and Orowan [94]). Even as late as 1965, theories (for example, Yoshikawa [95]) based on a critical amount of plastic strain being accumulated were being postulated.

It is worth emphasizing at the outset that

(1) fatigue failure is a consequence of the initiation of a crack and the subsequent growth of this crack;
(2) in homogeneous metals, cracks initiate at a free surface and no damage is done to metal away from this surface by the cyclic stressing;
(3) the initiation of a slip-band crack is only possible in ductile metals;
(4) other materials may exhibit fatigue characteristics but this is due to the propagation of a crack from some initial defect or flaw.

In ductile metals, cyclic stressing can be thought of as a very sensitive technique for detecting the onset of plastic deformation or slip in a particular surface grain. It is not necessary for the bulk of the grains in a piece of metal to deform plastically for it to fail by fatigue; continuing cyclic plastic deformation in one localized surface region is sufficient. It is this fact, that fatigue failure is a consequence of an extremely localized surface occurrence, that distinguishes it from other modes of mechanical failure.

The experimental data given in this chapter (together with some additional data given in § 6.1) show that the general features of fatigue failure do not vary with stress level [96] and are the same in all homogeneous ductile metals. The exceptional case of failure after a very few cycles is not strictly fatigue failure and is discussed in § 6.1 [97]; the case of initiation of failure at sub-surface defects is discussed in later chapters.

The general and basic features of fatigue failure are the initiation of surface microcracks and their subsequent extension across and penetration into the body of the metal. The increased life resulting from the removal of a surface layer at frequent intervals throughout a test, irrespective of whether the life is many millions or only a few thousand cycles [98] demonstrates that crack initiation is confined to the surface grains. The direction of development of surface microcracks is initially that of the operative slip planes. It remains so until a microcrack is of such a size that the amount it opens and closes, under resolved cyclic stresses acting normal to the crack faces, is sufficient to affect a large enough volume of material along its edge for it to grow as if in a continuum. The growth process is now associated with the magnitude of the tensile strain range in the volume of material just ahead of the crack edge (which depends on the amount that the crack is opened and closed during the loading cycle). The direction of crack growth is now that which allows the maximum crack opening and closing during the fatigue cycle. Ideally, this is approximately perpendicular to the nominal maximum cyclic tensile stress (see § 5.2) and is independent of any crystalline slip plane, although in the early stages the crack may follow a crystallographic plane close to the ideal direction. The crack can now be termed a macrocrack; its growth rate is much faster than that of the initial microcrack, and it now spreads rapidly through the metal. The growth behaviour of macrocracks is discussed in Chapter 5; the conditions governing the size at which a microcrack changes to a macrocrack (the former is sometimes referred to as a Stage I crack and the latter a Stage II crack [99]) are discussed in Chapter 4. The brittle appearance of a fatigue fracture follows from the fact that, during the macrocrack growth stage, the cyclic plastic strain occurring at any instant (at stress levels less than those causing general yielding) is confined to the small volume of material just ahead of the crack front.

Because the initiation and development of surface microcracks are associated with localized surface regions of cyclic plastic strain, the fatigue strength of a metal or alloy will be increased by any metallurgical hardening process which increases, or decreased by any process which decreases, the cyclic stress level necessary to maintain this cyclic plastic strain. For this reason, the initiation and development of microcracks by to-and-fro slip along crystallographic planes will be influenced by local differences in microstructure (the more complex the microstructure, the more pronounced the effect) and the time taken, at a given nominal stress level, for a microcrack to reach the macrocrack stage may therefore vary in different specimens of nominally similar material. However, having reached the macrocrack stage, local changes in microstructure generally have little effect on the growth rate (see Chapters 4 and 5), and thus the scatter in lives of nominally identical specimens subjected to the same nominal stress level is associated with the effect of microstructure on the initiation and rate of development of microcracks.

The fact that the initiation and development of microcracks are a consequence of cyclic plastic strain means that whether or not they form is dependent on the magnitude of the resolved maximum cyclic shear stresses in the loading cycle. Thus, the addition of a mean stress does not have a marked effect on the cyclic shear stress necessary to initiate a microcrack, and therefore they are able to form under a wholly compressive loading cycle [10]. A compressive mean stress, however, tends to prevent a microcrack opening and so retards its development to the macrocrack stage. Of course, if the loading cycle is such that the crack faces are never opened, cracks can only keep developing as microcracks (provided the cyclic stress level is sufficiently high); they cannot grow as macrocracks. The introduction of surface compressive stresses of sufficient magnitude and depth therefore increases the fatigue strength of a specimen as a whole. On the other hand, a tensile mean stress tends to open a microcrack and so enhances its development to the macro-crack stage.

Although the general process of fatigue failure is the same for different metals and stress levels, the metallographic work described shows that the appearance and location of surface cracking depends on the metal, stress level, and temperature. At room temperature and stress levels not too far removed from the fatigue strength at long endurances, microcracks originate, in most ductile pure metals and simple alloys, from persistently active slip bands, which are spaced irregularly over the surface grains. Bands of slip form because it is more difficult for slip to occur on a plane on which slip has already occurred than on a neighbouring plane on which slip has not occurred previously. The fact that slip lines develop under cyclic stressing indicates that slip occurring during the reverse half-cycle is not a reversal of that occurring in the forward half, otherwise the surface would remain smooth and no slip would be visible [100]. This transfer of slip to neighbour-ing planes results in surface steps being created in a slip band, so giving a notch-like surface profile. The ease with which slip can transfer to different planes will determine the stress range necessary to maintain continuing to and fro slip within a band. The surface roughening produced by slip occur-ring on neighbouring planes becomes more intense with increasing numbers of stress cycles and leads eventually to the formation of surface fissures or intrusions which can be considered as microcracks.

The presence of a normal tensile stress across a slip plane for part of the loading cycle during a uniaxial fatigue test and its absence in a torsion fatigue test, will, for the same maximum resolved shear stress amplitude, enable a microcrack to reach the macrocrack stage more quickly in the former type of test. This accounts both for the more intense slip-plane damage found in cyclic torsion tests and for the fact that slip markings are more easily observed on either strong or brittle metals [15, 30] when subjected to cyclic torsional stresses rather than uniaxial cyclic stresses. Surface cracks large enough to open up under a static tensile load have been detected after only a few per cent of the expected life, usually in soft metals, because of the difficulty in stopping a conventional fatigue test on a hard or brittle metal specimen so as to observe a sizable crack before it has caused complete fracture.

Because slip-band intrusions (microcracks) have been found to occur at liquid helium temperatures, it has been argued that their formation is by a purely mechanical movement of atoms. Wood [101] suggested that slip caused pronounced changes in local surface contours and the formation of surface microcracks was primarily a simple geometric consequence of to-and-fro slip movements within broad slip bands (see Fig. 2.8). Cottrell and Hull [11] proposed a model for forming extrusions and intrusions on the

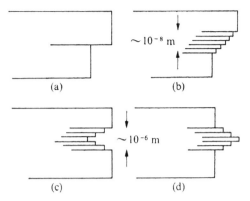

FIG. 2.8. Formation of surface cracks by slip. Static slip forms unidirectional step. (a) Optical microscope. (b) Electron microscope. Fatigue slip by to-and-fro movements in slip band may form notch (c) or peak (d). (Taken from Wood [101].)

surface based purely on the mechanical movement of atoms by supposing that two intersecting slip bands (Fig. 2.9) operated sequentially during both the tension and compression halves of the stress cycle.

Other dislocation models leading to surface cracking have been proposed (for example, Fujita [102], and Mott [103]) and these are summarized by Kennedy [104]. They essentially lead to a geometric cause of damage or to

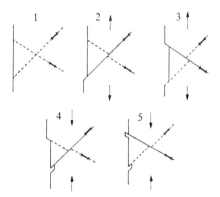

FIG. 2.9. Cottrell and Hull's model for producing extrusions and intrusions (Taken from Cottrell and Hull [11].)

damage on the slip plane itself [3, 105]. Damage on the slip plane itself entails slip occurring on the same plane and progressively unbonding atoms each cycle. If this were so, it might be expected that environment may affect crack initiation. For example, a film of oxide or absorbed gas may form on the exposed slip step and be drawn down the plane in successive cycles, thus forming a surface microcrack. However, as slip-band cracking can occur under high vacuum conditions, oxidation of freshly created surfaces does not seem essential to the cracking process. Nevertheless, with some metals, chemical reaction of the fresh surfaces exposed by slip with oxygen and moisture seems to occur in the slipping regions, the reaction with moisture leading in some cases to the emission of hydrogen. Excluding the atmosphere from the crack tip certainly decreases the rate at which macrocracks spread in some metals, presumably by either enabling some rebonding of freshly created surfaces at the crack tip or by eliminating any chemical attack by the atmosphere on the highly strained material at the crack tip. The effect of environment on both crack initiation and propagation is discussed in later chapters.

The evidence would suggest that the major role played by slip is to cause a geometric change to the surface profile rather than to cause damage leading to a crack along the slip plane itself. Assuming this geometric consequence of slip, May [106] considered that the disturbance of a surface by to-and-fro slip movements in slip bands might be due to dislocations making return journeys along paths which were shifted in a random fashion with respect to previous paths, the shifts being comparable to the width of the slip bands. Such a random distribution of slip would roughen the surface, leading to a redistribution of stress, so that in later cycles slip would tend to be concentrated in the valleys already formed. Subsequent surface movement would make some valleys less deep but others would become deeper and in these more slip would be concentrated. To see whether such a model led to cracks forming after a reasonable time, he assumed that after t cycles, the fraction f of the valleys of width w which had depths between z and $z+\mathrm{d}z$ was

$$f = F \exp\left[-\{\sqrt{(z+w)} - \sqrt{w}\}^2/b\varepsilon t\right],$$

where F was a slowly varying function of z, w, and t. The slip vector b and the plastic strain range ε in the slip band were assumed constant for a given test. He then assumed that at some large value of z (say Z) a valley was deep enough to be considered a crack. Thus $Z/b\varepsilon$ was regarded as a time constant T, controlling the rate at which valleys attained the depth Z. When cracks reached this depth, their subsequent growth rate was considered to be rapid so that T could be regarded as the life of the specimen. May assumed that a valley of depth ten times its width was a true crack (a macrocrack), that is $Z = 10w$, which for $w = 10^{-3}$ mm, $b = 5 \times 10^{-6}$ mm, and $\varepsilon = 10^{-3}$ gave a value for T ($= Z/b\varepsilon$) of 2×10^6 cycles; from this he concluded that his model could predict lives of the right order.

Unlike polycrystalline specimens in which there are always some surface grains having active slip planes favourably oriented with respect to the maximum resolved cyclic shear stresses, the appearance of surface markings on single crystals depends on the relative orientation of the maximum resolved shear stresses and operative slip planes. It has been pointed out that, in the case of single crystals of square cross-sections subjected to cyclic torsional loading, if a crystal has its operative slip vector lying parallel to a face then, because the shear stresses are a maximum in the middle of each face of a specimen and reduce to zero at the corners, at no position on the crystal is there a slip movement with a component out of the surface and thus surface cracking due to slip outcrop will be least effective [16].

Although slip-band cracking appears to occur in many ductile pure metals and simple alloys tested at room temperature and stress levels not too far removed from the fatigue strength at long endurances, the metallographic work shows that other metals may exhibit grain-boundary cracking and, indeed, that at stress levels or strain amplitudes leading to fracture after short endurances, cracking may occur in the grain boundaries [26, 28, 96] of those metals which exhibit slip band cracking at lower stress levels. Drastic changes in surface deformation result in grain-boundary cracking, presumably because the inability of grain boundaries to accommodate large cyclic deformations occurring in neighbouring grains creates severe strain gradients at the boundaries, so providing an additional shearing mechanism giving rise to surface crevices [98]. Because different grains have different elastic and plastic properties, the severity of strain incompatibility across a grain boundary depends on the number of slip bands that can be activated in neighbouring grains so as to relieve the incompatibility at a common grain boundary. Thus, whether or not grain-boundary cracking occurs at room temperature depends on whether the induced cyclic plastic strains can be accommodated by repeated slip in the grains, hence relieving the incompatibility across a grain boundary, or whether the incompatibility sets up such severe strain gradients that cracking occurs here before the slip mechanisms can operate in the grains. It follows, therefore, that grain-boundary cracking will occur whenever the boundaries are weakened relative to the grains. This can be brought about either by alloying or by raising the temperature so that the grain boundaries become glissile, and grains slide over each other. Cracking will also occur at grain boundaries if these are preferentially attacked by the atmosphere. It has been suggested that twin and grain boundaries can serve as sites for cracking if they are parallel to potential slip planes and contain stress raisers associated with non-coherent steps that give rise to secondary slip [25].

Stress and strain concentrations around inclusions or intermetallics in highly alloyed metals, having a complex microstructure inhibiting slip, can result in cracks forming at the inclusion–matrix boundary before the stress level necessary to cause cyclic slip in a surface grain is reached. This can occur either by initiating a crack as at an internal notch (see Chapter 4), or by the strain inhomogeneity causing the inclusion–matrix interface or the inclusion itself to fracture, depending on the strength of this interface. Inclusion-dependent cracking is the most likely reason why the fatigue limit of specimens cut transverse to the working direction of, for example, a rolled steel bar is often less than that of those cut parallel to the working direction (see § 3.1).

It would seem, therefore, that surface cracking can occur in any of three ways, namely, as a continuation of surface roughening in broad slip bands, as a result of severe strain incompatibilities across grain boundaries, or because of the presence of inclusions or inhomogeneities in the surface. The type of cracking that occurs will depend on material, stress level, and environment. If the grain boundaries or inclusion–matrix interfaces can sustain the imposed strain incompatibilities across them without cracking, microcracks will develop from slip bands.

The fatigue strength of many metals (for example, steels, brass, and magnesium alloys [107, 108]) increases with decreasing grain size, although results have been reported on other metals (zinc [109] and niobium [110]) whose fatigue strength was insensitive to grain size. Generally a material's resistance to plastic deformation (yield stress and hardness) increases as the grain size decreases, and thus the cyclic stress to cause continuing slip might also be expected to increase in qualitatively the same way. Whether or not this is so, for a particular material, the grain size may also affect the cyclic stress necessary for a microcrack to develop beyond the grain in which it formed. If this were the case, then the fatigue strength would decrease with increasing grain size, because with a small grain size, a microcrack may not be able to penetrate to a sufficient depth for it to grow as a macrocrack before encountering a grain boundary, whereas it may be able to do so in a larger grain. If the metal is such that microcracks change into macrocracks at smaller sizes, any change in grain size above this has no effect on the subsequent fatigue strength (§ 4.11).

It is worth emphasizing that, if a specimen is so loaded that it eventually breaks, changes in surface topography occur from the first stress cycle applied, and in this sense it is irrelevant to divide the life into the number of cycles to initiate a crack and the number of cycles to propagate it across the specimen. Rather it is more correct to consider the number of cycles spent in developing a microcrack to the macrocrack stage and the number of cycles spent in propagating the macrocrack.

Both electron microscopy and X-ray observations show that a sub-structure may form within the original grains of a metal, especially when subjected to large cyclic strain amplitudes, the dislocations in metals of high stacking-fault energy (for example, aluminium) forming well-defined sub-grains several micrometres across, whereas in metals of lower stacking-fault energy (for example, copper) regions of high and low density alternate on a micrometre scale [16]. Although there is some evidence that surface cracks may outline sub-grain boundaries, the high dislocation density boundary regions are not necessarily the source of cracking; they certainly do not promote cracking in the metal remote from a free surface. Indeed, the internal fatigue structure does not suggest any fracture mechanism, for it has been demonstrated that if in a cyclically strained metal the sub-structure is maintained, a small additional mean stress will cause unidirectional flow even though a static stress equal to the peak stress in the loading cycle does not, that is, the structure is not approaching a ductility limit. In view of this apparently harmless internal structure, it is unfortunate that cyclically plastically straining a ductile metal leads to slip outcrop at a free surface which can cause a deepening groove and ultimately a crack. Thus, the price that the engineer must pay for using ductile metals and alloys which can be easily machined, worked, and fabricated and also resist brittle fracture is that, when they are subjected to a cyclic loading, he must restrict his working stresses to values considerably less than those necessary to cause static failure. It is only in ductile metals that surface cracks are initiated by cyclic stressing alone; although certain non-metallic materials may fail under cyclic stressing, they generally do so by the growth of an inherent defect or flaw which is of sufficient size to grow directly as a macrocrack. As crack initiation is a consequence of surface topography, the stress to initiate a crack is not solely dependent on material but also depends on the initial surface topography; this is discussed in § 3.3.

Depending on stress amplitude, the bulk properties (as detected, for example, by hysteresis loop measurement or X-ray diffraction measurements) of a metal may change during cyclic stressing; annealed metals work-harden, cold-worked metals work-soften. The metal usually achieves a stable condition after a relatively small number of stress cycles and, although changes in specimen hardness alter its strain response to a given stress, they do not affect the basic processes involved in the initiation and development of a microcrack. In any case, these are too localized to be detected by changes in bulk properties. The fact that machining a layer off the surface of a specimen increases its life implies that the accumulated work done, determined, say, from hysteresis loop measurements, need bear no relationship to the specimen life. In addition, specimens of some metals may have longer lives to failure (at a given stress level) when tested in a vacuum rather than in air, yet the shape of the hysteresis loop is not affected by the environment.

Internal diffusion processes may be enhanced by cyclic stressing and may occur at lower temperatures and in shorter times than under comparable static conditions. The fact that mild steel strain-ages during a fatigue test is a common example. However, unless there are peculiar test conditions (for example, those giving rise to excessively high temperatures during the testing procedure) cyclic stressing does not lead to embrittlement of the metal (see § 4.3.10, where evidence is presented showing that unless cracks are already present, cyclic stressing has no effect on the subsequent notched impact resistance of steel). On the other hand, enhanced diffusion can result in local over-ageing occurring in the precipitation and age-hardening high static strength aluminium alloys, the locally softened regions giving rise to the relatively low fatigue strength/tensile strength ratios of these alloys [111]. The magnesium–aluminium alloys have a higher fatigue strength/ tensile strength ratio than the high-strength copper and zinc age-hardening aluminium alloys, because in the former precipitation occurs sluggishly and good strain-ageing is achieved, whereas in the latter alloys precipitation occurs readily and presumably there is little strain-ageing in the fully hardened material [112]. Additional precipitation caused by cyclic stressing thus leads to over-ageing and the creation of locally softened regions more easily in the latter than former alloys. However, the fact that cracks may be initiated at brittle second-phase particles in the stronger alloys may also be responsible for their relatively low fatigue strength/tensile strength ratios.

The experimental data suggest that only those metals and alloys which strain-age have their fatigue strength increased by coaxing procedures and rest periods, and exhibit S/N curves having sharp knees and definite fatigue limits. There is also evidence that microcracks are present in slip bands in strain-ageing metals at stress levels corresponding to or just below their fatigue limit. This implies that before a microcrack has reached the necessary size for it to be able to grow as a macrocrack, strain-ageing, by locally increasing the flow stress, inhibits the to-and-fro slip processes responsible for its development. Their fatigue limit thus corresponds to the maximum cyclic stress that will just not cause the microcrack to continue developing rather than that necessary to just initiate continuing to-and-fro cyclic slip. These arguments are supported by the fact that, although strain-ageing increases the fatigue limit of mild steel, the sharpness of the knee of the S/N curve is dependent on grain size, the smaller the grain size the sharper the knee [71]. Thus, microcracks formed in small grains will not have reached the necessary size to grow as macrocracks before they reach the grain boundaries. If their development is held up by the grain boundary (because operative slip planes are at different orientations in adjacent grains), the fatigue limit, that is the stress level necessary to force the crack to pass the grain boundary is greater the smaller the grain size. If the grains are large, microcracks can reach the macrocrack stage before they reach the boundaries; the boundaries do not now retard the growth of a macrocrack, and the knee in the S/N curve becomes less definite. The fact that the stress level at the fatigue limit of a strain-ageing material, such as mild steel, is greater than that required to cause continuing plastic deformation of the bulk of the material explains why it exhibits a hysteresis loop at and just below the fatigue limit stress.

Although non-strain-ageing materials do not exhibit an S/N curve having a sharp knee and a definite fatigue limit, the slopes of their S/N curves usually become very shallow at about 10^8 cycles, and provided the specimen surface is not attacked chemically by the atmosphere, the curve must ultimately become asymptotic to the maximum stress level that will just not cause continuous to-and-fro slip. If the atmosphere does attack the surface, then the fatigue strength decreases continuously with increasing endurance (see § 3.9).

References

1. SIEBEL, E. and STAHL, G. *Arch. EisenhüttWes.* **15**, 519 (1942).
   LISSNER, O. *Colloquium on fatigue*, p. 148. Springer–Verlag, Berlin (1955).
   MOLLER, H. and HEMPEL, M. *Arch. EisenhüttWes.* **25**, 39 (1954).
   THOMPSON, N., WADWSORTH, N. J., and LOUAT, N. *Phil. Mag.* **1**, 113 (1956).
   FOSTER, B. K. *Aircr. Engng* **29**, 211 (1957).
   HARRIES, D. R. and SMITH, G. C. *J. Inst. Metals* **88**, 182 (1959–60).
   YOUNG, J. M. and GREENOUGH, A. P. *J. Inst. Metals* **89**, 241 (1960–1).
2. SMITH, G. C. *Coil Spring J.* **44**, 18 (1956).
   FROST, N. E. *Metallurgia* **57**, 279 (1958).
   HARRIES, D. R. and SMITH, G. C. *J. Inst. Metals* **88**, 182 (1959–60).
   MODLEN, G. F. and SMITH, G. C. *J. Iron Steel Inst.* **194**, 459 (1960).
3. THOMPSON, N. and WADSWORTH, N. J. *Phil. Mag. Suppl.* **7**, 72 (1958).
4. CRAIG, W. J. *Proc. Am. Soc. Test. Mater* **52**, 877 (1952).
5. EWING, J. A. and HUMPHREY, J. C. W. *Phil. Trans.* A200, 241 (1903).
6. THOMPSON, N. *International conference on fatigue, Institution of Mechanical Engineers*, p. 527 (1956), *Fracture*, p. 354. Technology Press, Wiley, New York (1959).
   THOMPSON, N. and WADSWORTH, N. J. *Br. J. App. Phys. Suppl.* **6**, 51 (1957); *Phil. Mag. Suppl.* **7**, 72 (1958).
   THOMPSON, N., WADSWORTH, N. J., and LOUAT, N. *Phil. Mag.* **1**, 113 (1956).
7. FORSYTH, P. J. E. *J. Inst. Metals* **80**, 181 (1951–2); **82**, 449 (1953–4); *Nature, Lond.* **171**, 172 (1953); *Phil. Mag.* **2**, 437 (1957); *Proc. R. Soc.* A242, 198 (1957).
   FORSYTH, P. J. E. and STUBBINGTON, C. A. *Nature, Lond.* **175**, 767 (1955); *J. Inst. Metals* **83**, 173 (1954–5); **83**, 395 (1954–5); **85**, 339 (1956–7).
   STUBBINGTON, C. A. and FORSYTH, P. J. E., *J. Inst. Metals* **86**, 90 (1957–8).
8. FORSYTH, P. J. E. *International conference on fatigue, Institution of Mechanical Engineers*, p. 535 (1956).
9. KLESNIL, M. and LUKÁŠ, P. *J. Iron Steel Inst.* **203**, 1043 (1965).
10. CINA, B. *J. Iron Steel Inst.* **194**, 324 (1960).
11. COTTRELL, A. H. and HULL, D. *Proc. R. Soc.* A242, 211 (1957).
12. HULL, D. *J. Inst. Metals* **86**, 425 (1957–8).
13. GOUGH, H. J. *Proc. Am. Soc. Test. Mater.* **33**, 3 (1933).
14. LAUFER, E. E. and ROBERTS, W. N. *Phil. Mag.* **14**, 65 (1966).
15. BROOM, T. *Phil. Mag.* **8**, 1847 (1963).
16. HOLDEN, J. *Acta metall.* **11**, 691 (1963).
17. HEMPEL, M. *Fatigue in aircraft structures*, p. 83. Academic Press, New York (1956); *Fracture*, p. 376. Technology Press, Wiley, New York (1959).
18. HEMPEL, M. *International conference on fatigue, Institution of Mechanical Engineers*, p. 543 (1956).

19. WATANABE, J. and KUMADA, Y. *Trans. Soc. mech. Engrs., Japan* **37,** 67 (1961).
20. MAY, M. J. and HONEYCOMBE, R. W. K. *J. Inst. Metals* **92,** 41 (1963–4).
21. HARRIES, D. R. Ph.D. Thesis, University of Cambridge (1955).
22. HARRIES, D. R. and SMITH, G. C. *Colloquium on fatigue*, p. 89. Springer–Verlag, Berlin (1956).
23. TIPLER, H. R. and FORREST, P. G. *International conference on fatigue, Institution of Mechanical Engineers*, p. 510 (1956).
24. POLMEAR, I. J. and BAINBRIDGE, I. F. Aero. Res. Lab., Dept. of Supply. Australia, Rep. No. ARL/MET 31 (1958); *Phil. Mag.* **4,** 1293 (1959).
25. BOETTNER, R. C., McEVILY, A. J., and LIU, Y. C. *Phil. Mag.* **10,** 95 (1964).
26. KEMSLEY, D. S. *J. Inst. Metals* **85,** 417 (1956–7); **85,** 420 (1956–7); *Nature, Lond.* **178,** 653 (1956); *Phil. Mag.* **2,** 1103 (1957).
27. PORTER, J. and LEVY, J. C. *J. Inst. Metals* **89,** 86 (1960–1).
28. POLMEAR, I. J., BAINBRIDGE, I. F., and GLANVILL, D. W. *J. Aust. Inst. Metals* **7,** 222 (1962).
29. HUNTER, M. S. and FRICKE, W. G. *Proc. Am. Soc. Test. Mater.* **55,** 942 (1955); **54,** 717 (1954).
30. FORSYTH, P. J. E. Min. of Supply, R.A.E. Tech. Note Met. 310 (1959); STUBBINGTON, C. A. and FORSYTH, P. J. E. Min. of Aviation R.A.E. Tech. Rep. No. 65025 (1965).
31. WATANABE, J. and KUMADA, Y. *Trans. Soc. mech. Engrs. Japan* **37,** 67 (1961).
32. GROSSKREUTZ, J. C. and SHAW, G. C. Midwest Research Institute, Tech. Rep. AFML-TR65-127 (1965).
33. CHARSLEY, P. and THOMPSON, N. *Phil. Mag.* **8,** 77 (1963).
34. WOOD, W. A. *J. Inst. Metals* **91,** 225 (1962–3); *Acta metall.* **11,** 643 (1963). WOOD, W. A., COUSLAND, S. M., and SARGANT, K. R. *J. Inst. Metals* **91,** 304 (1962–3); **91,** 391 (1962–3).
35. RUDOLPH, G., HAASEN, P., MORDIKE, B. L., and NEUMANN, P. *International conference on fracture, Sendai, Japan*, Vol. 2, B1-1 (1965).
36. McEVILY, A. J. and JOHNSON, T. L. *International conference on fracture, Sendai, Japan*, Vol. 2, B1-23 (1965).
37. McEVILY, A. J. and MACHLIN, E. S. *Fracture*, p. 450. Technology Press, Wiley, New York (1959).
38. EBNER, M. L. and BACKOFEN, W. A. *Trans. metall. Soc. A.I.M.E.* **215,** 510 (1959). BACKOFEN, W. A. *Fracture*, p. 435. Technology Press, Wiley, New York (1959).
39. ALDEN, T. H. and BACKOFEN, W. A. *J. Metals, N.Y.* **12,** 748 (1960).
40. WADSWORTH, N. J. and HUTCHINGS, J. *Phil. Mag.* **3,** 1154 (1958). WADSWORTH, N. J. *Phil. Mag.* **6,** 397 (1961).
41. WILLIAMS, H. D. and SMITH, G. C. *Phil. Mag.* **13,** 835 (1966).
42. GROSSKREUTZ, J. C. Wright Air Development Division, Tech. Rep. 60–313 (1960); *J. appl. Phys.* **34,** 372 (1963).
43. BAILEY, J. E. and HIRSCH, P. B. *Phil. Mag.* **5,** 485 (1960). SEGALL, R. L., PARTRIDGE, P. G., and HIRSCH, P. G. *Phil. Mag.* **6,** 1493 (1961).

44. WILSON, R. N. and FORSYTH, P. J. E., Min of Aviation R.A.E. Tech. Note Met. 311 (1959); *J. Inst. Metals*, **87**, 336 (1958-9).
45. FELTNER, C. C. *Phil. Mag.* **8**, 2121 (1963).
46. FORREST, P. G. *Engineering* **174**, 801 (1952); *International conference on fatigue, Institition of Mechanical Engineers*, p. 171 (1956).
    FORREST, P. G. and TAPSELL, H. J. *Proc. Instn mech. Engrs* **168**, 763 (1954).
47. ROBERTS, E. and HONEYCOMBE, R. W. K. *J. Inst. Metals* **91**, 134 (1962-3).
48. WADSWORTH, N. J. Ph.D. Thesis, University of Bristol (1955).
    THOMPSON, N. and WADSWORTH, N. J. *Phil. Mag. Suppl.* **7**, 72 (1958).
49. WADSWORTH, N. J. *Acta metall.* **11**, 663 (1963).
50. LAZAN, B. J. *International conference on fatigue, Institution of Mechanical Engineers*, p. 90 (1956).
    LAZAN, B. J. and WU, T. *Proc. Am. Soc. Test. Mater.* **51**, 649 (1951).
51. HANSTOCK, R. F. *J. Inst. Metals* **74**, 469 (1948); **83**, 11 (1954-5); *Proc. phys. Soc.* **59**, 279 (1947); *International conference on fatigue, Institution of Mechanical Engineers*, p. 425 (1956); *Fatigue in aircraft structures*, p. 62. Academic Press, New York (1956).
    HANSTOCK, R. F. and MURRAY, A. J. *J. Inst. Metals* **72**, 97 (1946).
52. POLAKOWSKI, N. H. and PALCHOUDHIERI, A., *Proc. Am. Soc. Test. Mater.* **54**, 701 (1954).
53. PARDUE, T. E., MELCHER, J. L. and GOOD, W. B. *Proc. Soc. exp. Stress Analysis* **1**, 27 (1950).
54. DUGDALE, D. S. *J. Mech. Phys. Solids* **7**, 135 (1959).
55. KEMSLEY, D. S. *J. Inst. Metals* **87**, 10 (1959).
56. SIEDE, A. and METCALFE, A. G. *Trans. metall. Soc. A.I.M.E.* **215**, 947 (1959).
57. HOLDEN, J. *Acta metall.* **7**, 380 (1959).
58. MELEKA, A. H. *Iron Steel, Lond.* **34**, 619 (1961).
    MELEKA, A. H. and EVERSHED, A. V. *J. Inst. Metals* **88**, 411 (1959-60).
59. PACKER, M. E. and WOOD, W. A. *J. Inst. Metals* **92**, 413 (1963-4).
60. HAIGH, B. P. *Trans. Faraday Soc.* **24**, 125 (1928).
61. TAVERNELLI, J. F. and COFFIN, L. F. *Proc. Am. Soc. Test. Mater.* **59**, 952 (1959).
62. CAVANAGH, P. E. *Proc. Am. Soc. Test. Mater.* **47**, 639 (1947).
63. SINCLAIR, G. M. *Proc. Am. Soc. Test. Mater.* **52**, 743 (1952).
64. GOUGH, H. J. *The fatigue of metals*. Scott, Greenwood, and Son, London (1924).
65. KOMMERS, J. B. *Proc. Am. Soc. Test. Mater.* **30**, 368 (1930).
66. LIPSITT, H. A. and HORNE, G. T. *Proc. Am. Soc. Test. Mater.* **57**, 587 (1957).
67. FERRO, A. and MONTALENTI, G. *Phil. Mag.* **8**, 105 (1963).
68. KETTUNEN, P. *Phil. Mag.* **9**, 713 (1964).
69. LEVY, J. C. and SINCLAIR, G. M. *Proc. Am. Soc. Test. Mater.* **55**, 866 (1955).
70. LEVY, J. C. and KANITKAR, S. L. *J. Iron Steel Inst.* **195**, 296 (1961).
71. YOSHIKAWA, A. and SUGENTO, T. *Trans. metall. Soc. A.I.M.E.* **233**, 1314 (1965).
72. KUZMANOVIC, B. O. and WILLEMS, N. *Eng. Fracture Mech.* **4**, 687 (1972).
73. BOLLENRATH, F. and CORNELIUS, H. *Z. Metallk.* **34**, 151 (1942).

74. SINCLAIR, G. M. and DOLAN, T. J. *Proceedings of the 1st U.S. National Congress of applied mechanics, American Society of Mechanical Engineers*, p. 647 (1951).
75. HARRIES, D. R. and SMITH, G. C. *J. Inst. Metals* **88**, 182 (1959–60).
76. MODLEN, G. F. and SMITH, G. C. *J. Iron Steel Inst.* **194**, 459 (1960).
77. YOUNG, J. M. and GREENOUGH, A. P. *J. Inst. Metals* **89**, 241 (1960–1).
78. WADSWORTH, N. J. Min. of Supply, R.A.E. Tech. Note Met. 251 (1956). ESHELBY, J. D. and PRATT, P. L. *Acta metall.* **4**, 560 (1956).
79. HOLDEN, J. *The fatigue of metals*, p. 3. Institute of Metallurgists (1955).
80. KILPATRICK, J. A. and MARTIN, J. W. *Metallurgia* **70**, 21 (1964).
81. PEARSON, S., BOARD, A. J., and WHEELER, C. *Phil. Mag.* **6**, 979 (1961).
82. KLESNIL, M. and RYS, P. *Hutn. Listy* **16**, 565 (1961).
83. HOLSHOUSER, W. L. and BENNETT, J. A. *Proc. Am. Soc. Test. Mater.* **62**, 683 (1962).
84. STUBBINGTON, C. A. and FORSYTH, P. J. E. *J. Inst. Metals* **90**, 347 (1961–2).
85. GOUGH, H. J. and WOOD, W. A. *Proc. R. Soc.* **154**, 510 (1936); **165**, 358 (1938).
86. SPENCER, R. G. *Phys. Rev.* **55**, 991 (1939).
87. WOOD, W. A. and THORPE, P. L. *Proc. R. Soc.* **174**, 310 (1940).
88. WOOD, W. A. and SEGALL, R. L. *Proc. R. Soc.* A**242**, 180 (1957).
89. GROSSKREUTZ, J. C. and ROLLINS, F. R. Wright Air Development Centre, Tech. Rep. 59–192 (1959).
90. DAVIES, R. B. *Nature, Lond.* **174**, 980 (1954).
91. TAIRA, S. and HONDA, K. *International conference on fracture, Sendai, Japan*, D1-55 (1965).
92. AFANASEV, N. N. *J. tech. Phys. U.S.S.R.* **10**, 1553 (1940).
93. DEHLINGER, V. *Z. Phys.* **115**, 625 (1940).
94. OROWAN, E. *Proc. R. Soc.* A**171**, 79 (1939).
95. YOSHIKAWA, A. Letter to *Nature, Lond.* (1965).
96. LAIRD, C. and SMITH, G. C. *Phil. Mag.* **7**, 847 (1962); **8**, 1945 (1963).
97. BENHAM, P. P. and FORD, H. *J. mech. Engng Sci.* **3**, 119 (1961).
98. RAYMOND, M. H. and COFFIN, L. F. *Trans. Am. Soc. mech. Engrs., J. bas. engng* **85**, 548 (1963).
99. FORSYTH, P. J. E. *Crack propagation Symposium, Cranfield*, p. 76 (1961).
100. KEMSLEY, D. S. and PATERSON, M. S. *Acta metall.* **8**, 453 (1960).
101. WOOD, W. A. *Phil. Mag.* **3**, 692 (1958); *Fracture*, p. 412. Technology Press, Wiley, New York (1959).
102. FUJITA, F. E. *Scient. Rep. Res. Inst. Tohoku Univ.* **6**, 565 (1954).
103. MOTT, N. F. *Acta metall.* **6**, 195 (1958).
104. KENNEDY, A. J. *Processes of creep and fatigue in metals*. Oliver and Boyd, Edinburgh (1962).
105. SHANLEY, F. R. *Colloquium on fatigue*, p. 251. Springer-Verlag, Berlin (1955).
106. MAY, A. N. *Nature, Lond.* **185**, 303 (1960).
107. VITOVEC, F. H. Wright Air Development Centre, Tech. Note 58-539 (1958).
108. YOKOBORI, T. *Proceedings of the 2nd Japanese Congress on testing materials*, p. 10 (1959).

109. FEGREDO, D. M. and GREENOUGH, G. B. *J. Inst. Metals* **87,** 1 (1958–9).
110. ENRIETTO, J. F. and SINCLAIR, G. M. Department of Theoretical and Applied Mechanics, University of Illinois T & AM Report No. 567 (1959).
111. FORM, G. W. *Trans. Am. Soc. Metals* **52,** 514 (1960).
112. BROOM, T., MOLINEUX, J. H., and WHITTAKER, V. N. *J. Inst. Metals* **84,** 357 (1955–6).
    BROOM, T., MAZZA, J. A., and WHITTAKER, V. N. *J. Inst. Metals* **86,** 17 (1957–8).

3 | Fatigue strength of plain specimens

3.1. Introduction

IF EITHER the plain fatigue limit or the plain fatigue strength at a given endurance of a material has been determined from a batch of specimens tested at zero mean load, in air, at room temperature, using a particular testing technique, it is of practical importance to know how this value is affected by, for example, the surface finish of the specimens, a superimposed mean load, temperature, environment, a combined stress loading, or the presence of a notch or discontinuity. It would be of considerable convenience, of course, if the effect of any of these variables could be estimated without the necessity of having to carry out further experimental work. In addition, a knowledge of the effect of a combination of two or more of these variables may be required. In general, this information is unlikely to be available and consequently must be assessed from a careful consideration of the variables acting separately.

The values of the plain fatigue limits or strengths at long endurances (that is, at endurances at which the slope of the S/N curve becomes very shallow) of various metals and alloys are discussed in § 3.2; following sections then discuss in some detail how these values are affected by the surface finish of the specimen, different testing methods, the application of a mean stress, a combined stress loading, the speed of testing, temperature, and environment. The effect of introducing a discontinuity or notch into a specimen is discussed in Chapter 4.

3.2. The fatigue limit, or fatigue strength at long endurances

Comprehensive collections of the fatigue strengths of many metals and alloys have been assembled [1–4], the fatigue strengths of many high-strength steels [5], non-ferrous metals and alloys [6], and other materials [7], being specifically documented. Typical values of the fatigue limits (or strengths at long endurances) of a few metals and alloys, as might be obtained from mechanically polished specimens cut in a direction parallel to the working direction (for wrought materials) and tested at zero mean load, are given in Table 3.1.

Because the fatigue strengths given in Table 3.1 are estimated from S/N curves derived from a series of test results exhibiting a certain amount of scatter (which will increase if specimens are cut from different batches of nominally similar material) and the life of a specimen at a given stress level may depend on the method of manufacture and testing, the reliability of a quoted value for the fatigue strength of a material (as opposed to that of a

TABLE 3.1

Material	Tensile strength (MN m^{-2}	Fatigue limit or strength (MN m^{-2})†
Annealed gold	115	± 46 (10^8)
Annealed copper	216	± 62 (10^8)
Cold-worked copper	310	± 93 (10^8)
Annealed brass	325	± 100 (10^8)
Cold-worked brass	620	± 140 (10^8)
Phosphor bronze	540	± 230 (10^8)
Aluminium bronze	770	± 340 (5×10^7)
Annealed nickel	495	± 170 (10^8)
Cold-worked nickel	830	± 280 (10^8)
Magnesium	216	± 70 (10^8)
Aluminium	108	± 46 (10^8)
$4\frac{1}{2}$% Cu–aluminium alloy	465	± 147 (10^8)
$5\frac{1}{2}$% Zn–aluminium alloy	540	± 170 (10^8)
Flake graphite cast iron	310	± 130
Malleable cast iron	385	± 185
Armco-iron	294	± 185
Mild steel	465	± 230
Nickel–chromium alloy steel	1000	± 510
High tensile steel	1700	± 695 (10^8)
Titanium	570	± 340 (10^7)
Lead	—	± 3 (10^7)
1% Sn–lead alloy	—	± 9 (10^7)

† Figures in parentheses are the endurances at which the fatigue strengths were estimated.

batch of similar specimens of the same material tested under the same conditions) cannot be considered better than ± 5 per cent, and may often be much worse. A further point to be taken into account when considering the fatigue strength of wrought materials is that the fatigue strength of specimens cut transverse to the working direction may be somewhat less than that of specimens cut parallel to the working direction; some data are given in § 3.6.

In general, the S/N curve for a steel having a tensile strength less than 1100 MN m^{-2} exhibits a definite fatigue limit, the value of which increases as the tensile strength increases, irrespective of whether the increased tensile strength results from alloying, heat-treatment, or cold-work, provided that neither the severity of the heat-treatment nor the degree of cold-work is such as to cause cracking. For example, the effect of microstructure on the fatigue limits of various carbon and alloy steels has been studied by using different quenching techniques to obtain various amounts of martensite in the structure [8]. Although the fatigue limit of a steel having a structure containing a high percentage of martensite appeared to depend on the percentage of martensite present, when this was less than 85 per cent, the fatigue limits of steels of a given hardness and tensile strength, irrespective of their microstructure, were not significantly different.

Cast steels, heat-treated to give a fine homogeneous structure, have fatigue limits when determined using polished specimens not greatly inferior to those of wrought steels of the same hardness. In addition, the fatigue limit of a cast homogeneous steel is independent of the direction from which the specimens are cut from the initial block of material. However, the presence of casting defects can cause a pronounced drop in fatigue strength; these can be present either as micro-shrinkage cavities or as inclusions, the former being the more common. Reversed direct stress fatigue tests on cast steel (0.2% C, 0.5% Si, 0.7% Mn, tensile strength 450 MN m^{-2}) specimens containing defects of various sizes showed that the fatigue limit decreased as the defect size increased [9]. For example, specimens containing defects between 0·2 mm and 0·5 mm mean diameter had a fatigue limit of ± 185 MN m^{-2} compared to a value of ± 140 MN m^{-2} for specimens containing defects between 3 mm and 8 mm mean diameter.

The fatigue limits of steels having tensile strengths greater than about 1250 MN m^{-2} do not continue to increase with increasing tensile strength as do those of the softer steels. Indeed, increasing the tensile strength of conventionally melted steels much above 1250 MN m^{-2} results in little, if any, increase in fatigue limit [5]. This is because cracks in these steels are initiated at either surface or sub-surface inclusions and the cyclic stress necessary to initiate a crack no longer needs to increase in proportion to the hardness of steel, as is the case with the softer steels in which surface microcracks are initiated as a result of continuing cyclic slip in a surface grain. For example, the origins of fatigue cracks in various alloy steels, having tensile strengths between 930 MN m^{-2} and 2100 MN m^{-2} were found to be small silicate inclusions located at or close to the surface [10]. The fatigue limit of a steel of a given tensile strength decreased with increasing inclusion size, for example, inclusions of up to 0·06 mm mean diameter had no effect on the fatigue limits of steels having tensile strengths of 930 MN m^{-2}, but inclusions down to a mean diameter of 0·006 mm initiated fatigue cracks in steels having tensile strengths of 2100 MN m^{-2}. Other investigators have shown that the fatigue limits of high-tensile steels depend on the size [11] and shape [12] of non-metallic inclusions. A linear relationship has been proposed [11] for steels having tensile strengths in excess of 1300 MN m^{-2} between fatigue limit and the product of tensile strength and reduction in area, the higher this product the higher the fatigue limit. Because the reduction in area of these steels is controlled by the number and shape of non-deformable inclusions (that is, the scarcer and smaller the inclusions, the greater the reduction in area), the proposed relationship follows from the fact that the greater the reduction in area of a steel of a given tensile strength, the smaller are the inclusions it contains and, provided fatigue cracks originate at inclusions, the higher its fatigue limit. It must be noted, of course, that, if fatigue cracks are not initiated at inclusions, the fatigue limit of a steel will not depend on its static ductility but will be proportional to its hardness or tensile strength.

If inclusions in the original steel billet are elongated during forming of subsequent bars, they will present a larger flaw area on a transverse cross-section than on a longitudinal one, and this may give rise to a significant difference between the fatigue limits of specimens cut from the bars in the transverse and longitudinal directions. Rotating bending fatigue tests on En25 steel specimens [13], cut either longitudinally or transversely from the initial worked blank and heat-treated to give tensile strengths between 930 MN m^{-2} and 2000 MN m^{-2}, showed that the fatigue limits of the longitudinal specimens increased from ± 510 MN m^{-2} to ± 770 MN m^{-2} as the tensile strength increased from 930 MN m^{-2} to 2000 MN m^{-2}, whereas those of the transverse specimens remained at about ± 460 MN m^{-2} irrespective of tensile strength. That inclusions in transverse specimens were more severe than in longitudinal specimens was reflected in the corresponding static reduction in areas; values obtained from the former specimens were only about one half those obtained from the latter specimens. It would seem therefore, that although inclusions were of little importance in determining the fatigue limits of longitudinal specimens, their projected shapes on transverse sections were of sufficient severity to determine the onset of cracking, this occurring at a stress level less than that necessary to cause slip-band cracking in the matrix.

Improved manufacturing processes, such as vacuum melting, which result in a reduction in inclusion size would be expected to increase the fatigue strength of a high-strength steel. This, and the effect of transverse flaws, are illustrated by repeated bending tests on SAE 4340 (0·4% C, 1·7% Ni, 1·0% Cr) steels [14] prepared either by the normal commercial method or by vacuum melting, specimens being cut from the rolled bars both parallel and transverse to the rolling direction. The results in Table 3.2 show that vacuum melting not only increases the fatigue limits of both longitudinally and transversely cut specimens but considerably reduces directionality effects. The fatigue strength (10^8 cycles) of a conventionally melted ball bearing steel (SAE 52100, 1% C, 1½% Cr, tensile strength 2200 MN m^{-2}) was found to be increased from ± 725 MN m^{-2} to ± 800 MN m^{-2} by vacuum melting [15]. In addition to cracks being initiated by inclusions, it has been suggested that, in very high strength steels, localized high stresses resulting from an austenite–martensite reaction might nucleate sub-microscopic cracks. Tests on 18 high-tensile low-alloy steels [16] showed that the fatigue strength (10^5 cycles)/tensile strength ratio of steels of the same alloy content decreased with increasing carbon content, sub-surface nucleation of cracks becoming prevalent in steels having the highest fatigue strengths. The origin of a sub-surface failure is at the centre of a small whitish circular area, clearly visible on the fracture face, similar in appearance to that shown on Fig. 6.18 and discussed further in § 6.4.3.

TABLE 3.2

	Fatigue limit ($MN\ m^{-2}$) (Maximum stress in loading cycle)	
	Commercial steel	Vacuum melted steel
Longitudinal specimens	800–880	960
Transverse specimens	460–540	830

When cracks are initiated at inclusions, the fatigue limit of the material does not depend on the hardness, but rather on the nature, shape, size, and location of inherent inhomogeneities (see § 2.4). Identical flaws or inclusions are more damaging when situated at the surface rather than in the interior of the material. Thin penny-shaped voids lying normal to the loading direction are more damaging than spherical-shaped inclusions having similar stress–strain characteristics to those of the matrix. For example, whereas finely-distributed small rounded lead particles have no effect on the fatigue limit of mild steel [17], grey cast iron has a fatigue limit markedly less than mild steel. This is because failure occurs from flaws in the form of plate-like graphite flakes; since these are numerous and randomly distributed, a flaw having an edge in the free surface is the normal source of failure. The highest fatigue strength is obtained when the graphite occurs in spherical or nodular form.

It is shown in Chapter 4 that the minimum cyclic stress required to just cause a crack to grow depends on crack size, but for a crack of a given size and orientation relative to the loading direction the stress has roughly the same value for all steels, irrespective of their tensile strengths. Thus, if crack-like flaws are present in a material, a limiting-sized flaw (measured normal to the loading direction) exists for a steel of a given tensile strength, which is unable to grow at cyclic stresses less than those required to initiate and develop surface microcracks. The minimum cyclic stress required to cause a flaw of greater than critical size to grow then determines the subsequent fatigue limit of the steel. When testing a large number of specimens cut from an ingot of a nickel–chromium alloy steel (BS 970, En24) heat-treated to a tensile strength of 1300 $MN\ m^{-2}$ [18], no direct association was found between inclusion content and fatigue strength, presumably because all inclusions were smaller than the limiting size for the stress levels involved; the steel would have needed to be heat-treated to a higher tensile strength before cracks grew from inclusions in preference to surface microcracks being developed by continuing cyclic slip.

Wrought aluminium alloys can be divided into two groups, low- and medium-strength alloys, whose strength primarily depends on alloying constituents in solution, and the high-strength alloys whose strength is developed by precipitation, that is, the age-hardening alloys. The former alloys, such as the magnesium–aluminium alloys may exhibit a definite fatigue limit. They also have better fatigue strengths in relation to their tensile strengths than the age-hardening alloys (for example, the $4\frac{1}{2}\%$ Cu, BS L65 and $5\frac{1}{2}\%$ Zn, DTD 683 alloys) which exhibit S/N curves similar to that shown on Fig. A6.3. As mentioned in Chapter 2, the relatively low fatigue strength/tensile strength ratio of these age-hardening alloys is probably associated with the fact that cyclic stressing enhances over-ageing during a fatigue test, the resulting locally softened regions permitting crack initiation at stress levels which are low relative to the bulk static properties. The fatigue strength of a non-age-hardening alloy may be increased by cold-work, but cold-work has little effect on the fatigue strength of the high-strength age-hardening alloys; indeed, it may result in a slight decrease. It is not improbable that in the highest-strength aluminium alloys the size, distribution, and location of intermetallic particles may affect the fatigue strength in a similar manner to the way that inclusions play a part in determining the fatigue limit of the high-strength steels. An exceptionally high fatigue strength (at 10^8 cycles) has been reported [19] for an extruded zinc–magnesium–aluminium alloy of the DTD 683 type, that is, about ± 230 MN m^{-2} compared to the usual value of about ± 160 MN m^{-2}. It is not known whether this high value resulted from all the intermetallics being very small or from very high surface compressive residual stresses being induced in the material surface during extrusion, thus retarding the development of surface microcracks. Cast aluminium alloys tend to have fatigue strengths, when determined from polished specimens, somewhat lower than wrought alloys of the same tensile strength [4].

The fatigue strengths of most other metals, (lead, copper, nickel, magnesium, titanium, etc.) are increased by alloying, the fatigue strength increasing as the tensile strength increases, although the rate of increase varies with metal and alloy. Cold-working also tends to increase the fatigue strength of most metals and alloys, but the effect usually becomes less pronounced the greater the endurance at which the fatigue strength is estimated. In general, cold-working increases the tensile strength more than the fatigue strength so that the fatigue strength/tensile strength ratio tends to decrease with increasing cold-work. It has been found that the S/N curves of niobium, tantalum, molybdenum, tungsten, and cobalt all exhibit a definite fatigue limit prior to 10^7 cycles [20], in general the fatigue limits of the body-centred cubic metals being a higher fraction of their tensile strengths than those of the face-centred metals.

Many attempts have been made to estimate the fatigue limit or strength at long endurances of a metal from its static mechanical properties, the relationships evolved (usually for steels) ranging from a simple fraction of either the tensile strength or yield stress to complex relationships involving, for example, functions of the tensile strength, yield stress, and ductility. However, none of the suggested relationships [2, 21] can be considered to be true for all metals and alloys and, indeed, over a wide range of materials are no more reliable than simply taking the fatigue limit as some fraction of the tensile strength. A compilation of many wrought steels [22] having tensile strengths from 310 MN m^{-2} to 2000 MN m^{-2} showed that the fatigue limit $(\pm\sigma_a)$/tensile strength (σ_t) ratio lay between 0·4 and 0·54, having an average value of 0·46. Other investigators have suggested average values of 0·48 [23] and 0·46, but dependent on the microstructure [2]. For practical purposes, therefore, there is little error in assuming for steels having tensile strengths up to about 1250 MN m^{-2} that $\sigma_a = \sigma_t/2$. Although the fatigue limits or strengths at long endurances of other materials cannot be predicted with as much confidence from their tensile strengths as for the wrought steels, the ratio σ_a/σ_t offers a useful first guide to the fatigue strength of a material. Typical values of this ratio β are given in Table 3.3.

TABLE 3.3

Material		β†	References
Wrought steels having tensile strengths up to 1250 MN m^{-2}		0·5	
Wrought carbon steels,	ferritic	0·6	
	pearlitic	0·4	
	martensitic	0·25	2
	sorbitic	0·55	
Wrought alloy steels,	austenitic	0·4	
	martensitic	0·35	
	sorbitic	0·55	
Cast carbon steels		0·4–0·45	4, 24
Cast alloy steels		0·4–0·5	
Flake, nodular, or malleable cast iron		0·4	4, 23, 25
Wrought copper alloys	annealed	0·35–0·45 (10^8)	1, 4
	cold-worked	0·25–0·35 (10^8)	
Wrought nickel base alloys		0·35–0·45 (10^8)	4
Wrought titanium alloys		0·4–0·55 (10^7)	4, 26
Wrought aluminium alloys		0·35–0·4 (10^8)	
Cast aluminium alloys		0·25–0·35 (10^8)	4, 23, 27
Wrought magnesium alloys		0·25–0·4 (10^8)	
Cast magnesium alloys		0·2–0·3 (10^8)	

† Figures in parentheses are endurances at which fatigue strength is estimated.

It has been suggested [23] that the values of β for wrought aluminium alloys vary with their tensile strengths and the endurance at which the fatigue strength is estimated, a more accurate value being given by

$$\beta = \frac{1+0\cdot0031n^4/(1+0\cdot0065\sigma_t)}{1+0\cdot0031n^4},$$

where σ_t is the tensile strength in MN m^{-2} and n is the logarithm of the endurance at which the ratio is required. For $n = 8$ and $\sigma_t = 480$ MN m^{-2}, β has a value of about 0·3. On the other hand, numerous rotating bending fatigue tests [27] on specimens of wrought high-strength copper– and zinc–aluminium alloys cut from rolled plate, extrusions, and forgings showed that differences between the materials in their various conditions were masked by scatter.

A different approach [28] is to relate the fatigue limit to the true stress/true strain properties. It is claimed that the equation

$$\sigma_a = (1\cdot0139)^{1/n}(\sigma_{1\cdot0})^{0\cdot911},$$

where $\pm\sigma_a$ is the rotating bending fatigue limit, $\sigma_{1\cdot0}$ is the true stress at unit true strain, and n is the strain-hardening coefficient, that is, the slope of the logarithmic true stress/true strain curve, gives a very good correlation with data from 25 steels. Aluminium alloys, however, fit a different equation, namely,

$$\sigma_a = (1\cdot0075)^{1/n}(\sigma_{1\cdot0})^{0\cdot843},$$

where $\pm\sigma_a$ is now the fatigue strength at 5×10^8 cycles.

In addition to predicting the σ_a/σ_t ratio, many investigators have attempted to express the shape of the S/N curve in mathematical form. Any such prediction must be treated with caution as the shape of the finite life portion of the S/N curve may depend on material, type of loading, and specimen shape and size. Some suggested equations are given below, where $\pm\sigma$ is the stress range (zero mean load), $\pm\sigma_a$ is the fatigue-limit stress range, σ_t is the tensile strength, and N is the endurance. Other symbols are constants which are assessed from comparison with experimental data; $\pm$ signs are omitted for convenience.

Stromeyer [29] $\qquad\qquad \sigma = \sigma_a + C\left(\dfrac{10^6}{N}\right)^{\frac{1}{4}}$

Yoshikawa [30] $\qquad\qquad N(\sigma^m - \sigma_a^m) = C$

Weibull [31] $\qquad\qquad\quad N = K(\sigma - \sigma_a)^m$

Heywood [23] $\qquad\qquad \sigma = \sigma_t\left(\dfrac{1+0\cdot0038n^4}{1+0\cdot008n^4}\right)$ for steels

$$\sigma = \sigma_t\left(1 + \frac{0\cdot0031n^4}{1+0\cdot0065\sigma_t}\right)\Big/(1+0\cdot0031n^4) , \text{ for aluminium alloys}$$

where $n = \log N$ and σ_t is in MN m^{-2}.

A further equation, in terms of strain range rather than stress range [32] is

$$\varepsilon = \frac{3 \cdot 5}{E} \sigma_t N^{-0 \cdot 12} + D^{0 \cdot 6} N^{-0 \cdot 6},$$

where $\pm \varepsilon$ is the applied strain range, E is Young's modulus, and

$$D = \ln \left(\frac{1}{1 - \text{reduction in area}} \right).$$

Additional data on the relationship between the life and the applied strain range, either expressed as the total strain range or the plastic component of the strain range, are given in § 6.1.

3.3. Effect of surface finish

Because the initiation of microcracks is associated, in general, with a free surface, the fatigue strength of a material, particularly at long endurances, determined by testing a given batch of similar specimens, depends on the roughness and condition of the specimen surfaces created by the particular techniques used in their preparation. This section contains some experimental data relating to the effect of the different surface finishes and conditions produced on components and specimens by various manufacturing techniques (for example, grinding, turning, forging, and extrusion) on their subsequent fatigue strength. The effects of additional surface treatments, such as electroplating, shot-peening, and surface-hardening, are discussed in § 6.4.

There are three reasons why the manufacturing techniques used to prepare the specimen surface may affect fatigue strength: (1) notch-like surface irregularities may have been created; (2) the condition of the material at the surface may have been changed, for example, it may have been hardened by cold-work or softened by decarburization; (3) residual stresses may have been introduced into the surface layers.

An estimate of the magnitude of the surface irregularities created by a particular machining process can be obtained from a profile record of the specimen surface, although these records do not necessarily afford an accurate record of the surface profile as the probe used to make the record cannot explore a groove narrower than itself. The roughness is often expressed by a single figure representing the centre-line average (CLA) roughness over that length of surface traversed by the probe; the higher the figure, the rougher the surface. A mechanically fine-turned or ground finish may have a CLA value of 0·125 μm, a rough ground or turned finish 0·75–1·25 μm. Rough estimates [33] of the stress concentration factors (see Chapter 4) due to the surface irregularities created by rough-grinding, fine-grinding, and honing are 2·1, 1·5, and 1·2 respectively. However, specimens having a honed finish may not necessarily have a higher fatigue strength than those of the same material which have been rough-turned, because the latter process may have work-hardened the surface and induced high compressive residual stresses into the surface layers, whereas the former method may not have done so. Thus, it is necessary, when preparing batches of specimens for determining the intrinsic fatigue strength of a material, not only to ensure that the surfaces are as smooth as can be achieved consistently but that the surface layers are not hardened and have not had residual stresses induced into them. The former is usually achieved by fine longitudinally polishing, the latter by either stress-relieving in vacuum or electropolishing the finally mechanically polished specimens.

Some relevant experimental data are given below.

3.3.1. Method of machining

Steels. Some rotating bending test results are summarized in Table 3.4.

TABLE 3.4

Surface condition	Reference	Fatigue limit ($MN\ m^{-2}$)	
		0·49% C steel	Armco-iron
Rough-turned		±282	±154
Fine-turned		±294	±167
Circumferentially ground	34	±316	—
Longitudinally polished 00 emery		±340	±185
Longitudinally polished 00 emery and rouge		±352	—
		0·4% C steel tensile strength 570 MN m^{-2}	0·6% C steel tensile strength 620 MN m^{-2}
Ground, 30 wheel (coarse)		±232	±244
Ground, 46 wheel (medium)		±258	±253
Ground, 120 wheel (fine)	35	±268	±260
Polished, 0 emery		±272	±286
Buffed with red lead		±276	±280
Polished, 0000 emery		±280	±286

In general, it has been found that there is little difference between the rotating bending fatigue limits of fine-ground (CLA $\approx$ 0·125 μm) and mechanically polished (CLA $\approx$ 0·06 μm) specimens of various carbon and low-alloy steels [36, 37]. Coarse-grinding (CLA $\approx$ 0·75 μm) gives an average reduction in fatigue limit from 10 per cent [36, 38] to 25 per cent [37], and rough-turning a reduction of about 10 per cent [38].

Aluminium alloys. Coarse-turning or grinding appears to reduce the fatigue strength at long endurances by about 10–20 per cent below that of fine polished specimens, although there is conflicting evidence as to which method of polishing is most effective. Table 3.5 gives some experimental data in terms of the ratio of fatigue strength to tensile strength of various aluminium alloys.

TABLE 3.5

Surface finish	Reference	Fatigue strength (10^8 cycles) / Tensile strength
		24 ST ($4\frac{1}{2}\%$ Cu) aluminium alloy, tensile strength 460 MN m^{-2}
Circumferentially coarse-turned		0·28
Circumferentially diamond-turned		0·34
Longitudinally ground		
46NV silicon carbide wheel		0·28
60M silicon carbide wheel		0·34
60NBE aluminium oxide wheel	39	0·29
120-5NX cotton-bonded wheel		0·30
Longitudinally hand-polished 220 grit		0·34
400 grit		0·34
Circumferentially hand-polished 220 grit		0·37

Surface finish	Surface roughness (μm)	Reference	Fatigue strength (10^7 cycles) / Tensile strength	
			DTD 683, tensile strength 550 MN m^{-2}	BS 6L1 tensile strength 350–510 MN m^{-2}
Rough-machined	2·5		0·29	0·31
Fine-machined	1·6		0·29	0·31
Circumferentially polished	0·23	40	0·31	0·33
Longitudinally polished	0·14		0·33	0·35

3.3.2. Effect of electropolishing

Several investigators [41–3] have shown that electropolished steel specimens have a lower fatigue limit than mechanically polished specimens, the reduction in strength varying from a few per cent up to 25 per cent; Table 3.6 gives some experimental data. The higher fatigue limit of the mechanically polished specimens is due to the cold-worked surface layer produced by polishing; X-ray diffraction and stress-relieving experiments have shown this is removed by electropolishing [42]. Titanium alloy specimens [44] and $4\frac{1}{2}\%$ Cu–aluminium alloy specimens [43] also show the same effect, the latter markedly, due to surface pitting produced during electropolishing.

TABLE 3.6

Type of steel	Type of test	Specimen diameter (mm)	Reference	Fatigue limit (MN m^{-2})	
				Mechanically polished	Electro-polished
0·37% C	Reversed direct stress	16		±234	±213
	Plane bending	8		±270	±238
		16		±268	±244
		24	41	±266	±227
	Rotating bending	2		±280	±229
		4		±270	±220
		8		±256	±207
		16		±241	±202
		32		±220	±216
13% Cr				±540	±450
20% Cr				±295	±230
25/20 Cr Ni				±295	±230
Mn Cr Ni	Rotating bending		42	±370	±280
18/8 Cr Ni				±295	±260
3% Ni				±450	±380

3.3.3. Effect of stress-relieving

Stress-relieving has a similar effect to that of electropolishing in that it reduces the beneficial effects of cold-working produced during turning or mechanical polishing; this is evident in the results, given in Table 3.7, of rotating bending fatigue tests on a 0·6% C steel [45].

Moreover, it would be expected that the effects of different surface finishes noted at room temperature would not occur in tests carried out at a sufficiently elevated temperature, since beneficial compressive residual stresses from cold-working would then be stress-relieved. This was found to be so [46] in tests on as-turned, ground, and polished specimens of a low-alloy steel. Differences in the fatigue limits of the cold-worked, turned, and polished specimens and that of the almost stress-free ground-finish specimens observed at

TABLE 3.7

Surface finish	Fatigue limit (MN m^{-2})
As-turned	±415
Turned and electropolished	±385
Turned, ground, and mechanically polished	±525
Turned, ground, mechanically polished, and electropolished	±435
Turned, ground, mechanically polished, and stress-relieved	±450
Turned, ground, mechanically polished, stress-relieved, and electropolished	±465

room temperature did not occur at 540 °C, although the fatigue strength of a polished specimen was higher at short endurances. At 730 °C there was no significant difference in fatigue strengths at all endurances between the different batches of specimens. That these effects were due to stress-relieving was shown by additional tests on specimens stress-relieved prior to testing, a change of surface roughness from 0.125 μm to 2 μm having no marked effect on either the room or elevated temperature fatigue strength.

3.3.4. Effect of forged surfaces

In general, the fatigue limit of specimens having an as-forged surface is markedly less than that of polished specimens. Table 3.8 gives some data for

TABLE 3.8

Material	Tensile strength (MN m^{-2})	Reference	Rotating bending fatigue limit (MN m^{-2})	
			Mechanically polished	As-forged
Mild steel	465	47	$\pm$230	$\pm$170
Alloy steel	930		$\pm$465	$\pm$230
Alloy steel	1550		$\pm$770	$\pm$140
SAE 4140 (0·43% C, 0·9% Cr)	970	48	$\pm$465	$\pm$310

steels. Similar effects have been found [49, 50] with extruded aluminium alloys. Unmachined $4\frac{1}{2}$% Cu–aluminium alloy bars, 25 mm diameter and 1·5 m long, tested in reversed bending as free–free beams [44] had a fatigue strength (10^7 cycles) of $\pm$120 MN m^{-2} compared to a value of $\pm$185 MN m^{-2} obtained from polished specimens cut from the bars. By machining 0·6 mm off the surface of an extruded bar, the fatigue strength was increased to $\pm$160 MN m^{-2}, while surface-rolling an extruded bar increased its fatigue strength to that of the polished specimens.

3.3.5 Discussion

In Chapter 4, it is shown that, in general, the fatigue limit of a specimen containing a surface notch decreases as both the depth and sharpness of the notch increases. It is also shown that a sharp surface notch may cause a greater reduction in the fatigue limit of one material than another; for example, a surface scratch of a given size causes a greater reduction in the fatigue limit of a high-strength steel than in that of a mild steel. Estimates of the depth which a surface scratch or flaw must achieve before significantly affecting the fatigue limit of a material are also given in that chapter. However, the experimental data given in this section show that an improvement in the surface finish of a batch of specimens does not necessarily result in an improvement in fatigue limit. This is because changes in surface hardness and the introduction of residual surface stresses caused by the finishing process employed can override geometric effects. Because the initiation of a surface microcrack depends on some minimum cyclic surface shear stress being exceeded, processes either hardening or softening the surface either raise or lower this value, but it is not markedly dependent on the value of any superimposed residual or static stress. However, a residual or static stress does affect the development of a microcrack to the macrocrack stage, compressive residual stresses tending to prevent the crack opening and so delaying the onset of the macrocrack stage and tensile residual stresses tending to open the crack, thus enhancing the onset of the macrocrack stage. This implies that the depth to which residual stresses extend below the surface is important because, if this is very small, a microcrack would pass through the affected layer before reaching the macrocrack stage, and the residual stresses would consequently have little effect on the subsequent fatigue strength. However, if compressive residual stresses extend to a sufficient depth, a microcrack would need to penetrate this depth before being able to open and grow as a macrocrack, and hence both the life at a given stress level and the fatigue strength at a given endurance would be increased. Thus, processes inducing compressive residual stresses of sufficient depth and hardening the surface layers are beneficial, whereas those inducing tensile residual stresses and softening the surface layers are detrimental. Fatigue limits estimated from tests on mechanically polished specimens tend to be higher than those estimated from tests on either specimens vacuum stress-relieved or electropolished after polishing or having a fine-ground finish (although fine-grinding may give results only slightly inferior), implying that mechanical polishing hardens the surface and induces compressive residual stresses into the surface. Work-hardening and the introduction of residual compressive stresses depend on the surface layers being deformed plastically by the finishing process employed; thus, the beneficial effects obtained by mechanical polishing decrease as material hardness increases, and the geometric effects of surface roughness will tend to predominate. In addition, the beneficial effects of mechanical polishing on the softer materials are less evident when the tests are carried out in reversed direct stress than in rotating bending (see § 3.4).

The reduction in fatigue strength caused by an as-forged or as-cast surface depends on the severity of the surface roughness, the degree of surface softening (due to decarburization in the case of steels), and oxidation of grain boundaries, and is, in general, greater for stronger materials. For example, the ratio of the fatigue limit of an as-forged steel surface to that of a mechanically polished one may vary from about 0·2 for a steel having a tensile strength of 1500 MN m^{-2} to about 0·7 for a steel having a tensile strength of 600 MN m^{-2}. This arises because a cyclic stress high enough to initiate and

5

develop a surface microcrack in the softened decarburized surface layer to the macrocrack stage allows the macrocrack to grow into the harder steel below the surface at this same stress level irrespective of the tensile strength of the steel, for as discussed in Chapters 4 and 5, macro-crack growth characteristics are essentially the same in all steels. Extruded surfaces are rougher than polished surfaces and so, in general tend to give lower fatigue strengths. However, the process may work-harden and induce compressive residual stresses of sufficient magnitude into the surface layers, so that the detrimental effects of the surface roughness are minimized.

Thus, in assessing the effect of surface preparation, not only is it necessary to consider surface geometry but also whether the surface layers have been work-hardened or have had residual compressive stresses induced in them. The latter two factors tend to outweigh the former in soft materials, the former becoming more important the stronger and harder the material. The effects of residual stresses and hard and soft layers are discussed further in §§ 6.3 and 6.4.

3.4. Different testing methods and size effects

There are three common methods of applying a stress cycle varying from a maximum nominal tensile stress to a numerically equal nominal compressive stress (that is, a zero mean stress loading cycle), namely, reversed direct stress, reversed plane bending, and rotating bending. However, it has long been known that the fatigue strength of a material estimated from batches of specimens tested by each of these methods may be different for each testing method. For example, over forty years ago, a survey of literature available at that time [34] suggested that the ratio of the fatigue limit in reversed direct stress to that in rotating bending was between 0·7 and 1·0. It was also realized at that time that the experimental difficulties of obtaining perfect alignment in a reversed direct stress test could be a major cause for this discrepancy. Indeed, in 1925, reversed direct stress and rotating bending fatigue tests on various steels and non-ferrous alloys [51] were carried out, in which great care was taken in aligning the specimens in the former tests; both testing methods then gave similar fatigue limits. However, it is often found that, even when the same testing method is used, the fatigue limit obtained tends to decrease with increasing specimen diameter, causing a size-effect. Data illustrating the effect of different testing methods and size-effects are given below.

Reversed direct stress tests [52] on mechanically polished mild and nickel–chromium steel specimens, ranging in diameter from 4·8 mm to 33 mm, showed that the fatigue limit of each material was independent of specimen diameter. Table 3.9 summarizes various data obtained from rotating bending tests on batches of specimens of different diameters cut from nominally similar material, the specimens being mechanically polished.

T A B L E 3.9

Material	Reference	Fatigue limit (MN m^{-2}) Specimen diameter (mm)												
		1·3	3·2	5	6·3	10	12·5	19	20	25	38	45	50	100
0·44% C, 0·6% Mn steel	53	±240			±246		±230			±216			±218	
0·42% C, 0·6% Mn steel		±232			±220		±226			±230				
0·6% C steel		±330					±340							
0·45% C steel		±218					±221						±224	
0·19% C steel		±179			±191					±168				
0·18% C, 0·64% Mn steel	54			±220		±226			±216					±200
0·4% C, 0·55% Mn steel				±293		±288			±275					±260
0·35% C, 0·9% Mn, 1% Ni steel				±352		±338			±334					±318
0·3% C, 1·1% Cr SAE X4130 steel	55		±520		±475		±450	±450			±440			
0·2% C, SAE 1020 steel	55		±240		±220		±193			±200			±200	
0·2% C SAE 1020 steel, stress-relieved	56		±270		±280					±250			±240	
0·35% C SAE 1035 steel	55		±200		±200		±193			±193		±193		
0·4% C, 1·8% Ni 0·74% Cr steel	57		±260		±260		±240			±240		±240		
0·46% C, 3·3% Ni, SAE 2345 steel	56		±570		±560		±540			±510		±510		
0·46% C, 0·7% Mn, 0·12% Mo steel	58		±480		±460		±460	±440			±460			
SAE X4340 steel	59				±550					±500			±500	
5½% Zn–aluminium alloy (10^{7} cycles)	60		±150		±165		±150			±165		±175		

The results show that, in general, the fatigue limits of the steels decrease as the specimen diameter increases, the decrease seeming to be less when specimens are stress-relieved prior to testing. On the other hand, the fatigue strength (10^7 cycles) of the high-strength aluminium alloy appears to be independent of specimen diameter.

Although the results in Table 3.9 imply that the fatigue limit of a 50 mm diameter specimen is little, if any, lower than that of a 25 mm diameter specimen, the fatigue limit of specimens of larger diameter may be markedly less. For example, the rotating bending fatigue limits [61] of 0·45% C steel specimens of 7·5 mm, 38 mm, and 150 mm diameter (the former being longitudinally polished, the latter two sizes being left in the fine-turned condition) were ± 226 MN m^{-2}, ± 193 MN m^{-2}, and ± 120 MN m^{-2}, respectively. Rotating bending tests [62] on 12·5 mm and 230 mm diameter alloy steel (2·8% Ni, 0·35% Cr, 0·25% C, 0·35% Mo, tensile strength 725 MN m^{-2}) specimens having ground test-sections gave an estimated fatigue limit of about ± 260 MN m^{-2} for the 230 mm diameter shafts compared to that of ± 390 MN m^{-2} for the 12·5 mm diameter specimens.

Table 3.10 summarizes data which compares the rotating bending and reversed direct stress fatigue limits of mechanically polished specimens of the same material.

T ABLE 3.10

Material	Reference	Fatigue limit or strength (MN m^{-2})		Ratio of direct stress to rotating bending fatigue strengths
		Rotating bending	Reversed direct stress	
Various wrought irons, carbon steels, and rail steels (0·6–0·8% C)	63			0·75–1·0 average 0·86
11 aluminium alloys	64			0·95–1·0
2% Zn, 0·65% Zr magnesium alloy (10^8 cycles)	65	± 100	± 90	0·90
Nickel–chromium–molybdenum alloy steel (tensile strength 870 MN m^{-2})	66	± 460	± 460	1·0
0·24% C steel, 400 °C (10^8 cycles)	67	± 280	± 260	0·93
RR58 aluminium alloy 200 °C (5×10^7 cycles)		± 54	± 43	0·79
0·17% steel		± 262	± 216	0·82

The fatigue limits of some materials, estimated from mechanically polished specimens, may be reduced by electropolishing or stress-relieving *in vacuo*. Thus, because this reduction varies with method of testing, the ratio of the fatigue limit in reversed direct stress to that in rotating bending varies with the type of surface finish.

Table 3.11 summarizes some data obtained using three different testing methods. The fatigue limits of mechanically-polished rotating bending specimens decrease with increasing diameter; for large diameters they approach that of the mechanically-polished reversed direct stress specimens. The average value of the fatigue limits of the mechanically-polished, reversed direct stress specimens falls between those of the mechanically-polished and electropolished rotating bending specimens. Plane bending fatigue limits are higher than the corresponding rotating bending values. Electropolishing reduces the rotating bending fatigue limit of the two stainless steels but has no effect on that in reversed direct stress.

Rotating bending and reversed direct stress tests were carried out [69] on normalized mild steel specimens whose surfaces were either mechanically polished, mechanically polished and stress-relieved *in vacuo*, or surface-rolled. In addition, rotating bending tests were carried out on mechanically polished specimens cut from mild steel blanks cold-worked to the same hardness as that of the surface of either the mechanically polished or cold-rolled specimens. Table 3.12 gives the results. Hardening the surface is seen to increase the fatigue limit in rotating bending more than in reversed direct stress; the rotating bending fatigue limit of through-hardened specimens is greater than that of corresponding surface-hardened specimens.

In addition to plane and rotating bending tests on specimens of circular cross-section, plane bending tests have been carried out on specimens of other cross-sections. Table 3.13 gives some results.

An attempt [67] to correlate rotating bending and reversed direct stress fatigue strengths has been made on the basis that the maximum fibre stress in rotating bending is calculated from the applied bending moment, assuming ideal elasticity, whereas when the maximum fibre stress is greater than the dynamic elastic limit, the true surface stress will be less than the calculated elastic value. Dynamic stress-strain curves were derived from hysteresis loop measurements taken at a series of different stress levels in reversed direct stress tests on three materials at temperatures and testing speeds corresponding to those at which rotating bending tests were carried out. Assuming a linear strain distribution across a specimen, the relationship between nominal elastic surface stress and true surface stress in a bending test, for different maximum surface strain values can be obtained for each material and temperature. Replacing the nominal stress value in a rotating bending test by the corresponding true surface stress gave a rotating bending S/N curve coinciding with that (for lives greater than 10^5 cycles) obtained in

TABLE 3.11

Material	Reference	Specimen diameter (mm)	Fatigue limit (MN m^{-2})					
			Reversed direct stress		Rotating bending		Plane bending	
			Mechanically polished	Electro-polished	Mechanically polished	Electro-polished	Mechanically polished	Electro-polished
0·37% C steel heat-treated to fine-grain size	41	2	—	—	±280	±238	—	—
		4	±236	—	±270	±221	—	—
		8	±246	—	±256	±207	±272	±240
		16	±232	±213	±242	±202	±268	±246
		23	—	—	—	—	±267	±225
		32	±224	—	±219	±218	—	—
		56	—	—	±225	—	—	—
13% Cr stainless steel (25×10^6 cycles)	68		±415	±415	±540	±450	—	—
20% Cr stainless steel (25×10^6 cycles)	68		±200	±200	±290	±230	—	—

TABLE 3.12

Specimen condition	Fatigue limit (MN m^{-2})	
	Rotating bending	Reversed direct stress
Mechanically polished and stress-relieved *in vacuo*	±190	±178
Mechanically polished	±225	±185
Surface-rolled	±240	±190
Through-hardened to same hardness as surface of mechanically polished specimens	±240	—
Through-hardened to same hardness as surface of surface-rolled specimens	±295	—

TABLE 3.13

Material	Reference	Specimen cross-section	Fatigue strength (MN m^{-2})
$4\frac{1}{2}\%$ Cu–Aluminium alloy (10^7 cycles)	70	Circular, 25 mm diameter	±173
		Square, 25 mm sides	±137
		Square, 25 mm sides, corners removed to give 3 mm radius	±150
		Diamond, 25 mm sides	±160
		Diamond, 25 mm sides, corners removed to give 3 mm radius	±173
$5\frac{1}{2}\%$ Zn–Aluminium alloy (10^8 cycles)	71	Square	±145
		Circular	±200
		Circular rotating bending	±173
0.24% C steel (fatigue limit)	72	Circular, 7 mm diameter	±260
		Diamond, 1 mm sides, sharp corners	±285

reversed direct stress: results for 0.17% C steel at air temperature and 34 Hz are shown on Fig. 3.1.

Although good correlation was obtained by the above analysis, it has been argued [32] that the derivation is strictly applicable only to plane bending, and S/N curves obtained from plane bending tests on cylindrical steel and aluminium alloy specimens, when plotted in terms of true surface stress, agreed well with corresponding reversed direct stress S/N curves. Whereas, in a plane bending test, the stress at the two extremities of a horizontal strip element of cross-section is the same, this is not so in the case of rotating bending, because here the strain at one extremity of the element is increasing to its maximum value while that at the other extremity is decreasing, depending on the direction of rotation. This is shown by the fact that the deflection of the end of a rotating bending specimen is vertical only if the specimen material is perfectly elastic [73]. When a specimen exhibits a hysteresis loop, the neutral axes of stress and strain are no longer coincident, and a lateral deflection occurs. This lateral deflection depends on the direction of rotation and is proportional to the width of the hysteresis loop; the vertical deflection depends on the rigidity of the specimen. Indeed, measurements of the lateral and vertical

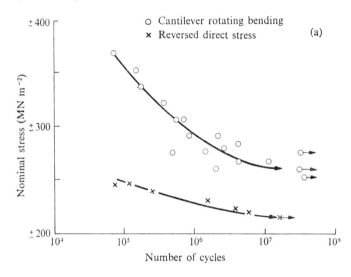

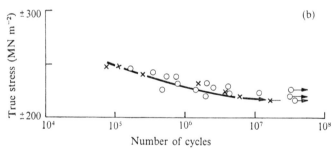

FIG. 3.1. Comparison of reversed direct stress and rotating bending S/N curves for 0·17% C steel. (a) On a nominal-stress basis. (b) On a true-stress basis. (Taken from Forrest and Tapsell [67].)

deflections of the end of rotating bending specimens have been taken during the course of a test to indicate the changes that may occur in the shape of the hysteresis loop [74]. Thus the corresponding stresses at the extremities of the horizontal strip must be determined from the appropriate loading and un-loading portions of the hysteresis loop and not from an averaged dynamic stress–strain curve. It may well be that the plane bending fatigue limit of cylindrical specimens is higher than that in rotating bending because the true surface stress in the former test is lower than that in the latter test for the same specimen diameter and nominal elastic surface stress. Similarly, the different plane bending fatigue strength of specimens of square or diamond cross-section can probably be explained by stress-distribution effects.

Differences between different test methods can also be explained qualitatively by considering the behaviour of individual grains. For example, the higher fatigue limits obtained when circular cross-section specimens are tested in plane bending rather than in rotating bending could arise because, despite the fact that the stress gradients through a vertical diameter are the same in both tests, the surface grains adjacent to the most severely stressed grain are subjected to different stress histories. In the former case, the adjacent grains are never subjected to the maximum stress, whereas, in the latter case, all the grains are subjected in turn to the maximum stress as the specimen rotates. Thus, it may be more difficult in the former case for a microcrack to develop beyond the boundaries of the grain in which it is initiated.

Data on the plane bending fatigue strength of specimens having either square- or diamond-shaped cross-sections show that the presence of a sharp corner can cause a decrease in fatigue limit. This may follow from the fact that a grain situated at a sharp corner has less support from neighbouring grains than a normal surface grain, and it may be easier, therefore, both for slip to occur and for a microcrack to develop in the former than in the latter case. However, work-hardening and residual stress patterns may also be different in an isolated corner grain; presumably the steel specimens of diamond cross-section having sharp corners, described earlier, had a higher fatigue limit than that of circular specimens owing to beneficial work-hardening and residual stress effects.

3.4.1. Discussion

Various arguments can be advanced to explain why the fatigue strength depends on testing method and especially in bending tests why it depends on specimen diameter; these are based on either the effect of stress gradients or the amount of surface subjected to the maximum fatigue stress.

In a uniaxially cyclically loaded plain bar of homogeneous material, the proportion of the total life spent in initiating and developing a surface microcrack to the macrocrack stage is large compared to that spent in growing a macrocrack across a specimen (§ 4.11). Thus, over the usual range of laboratory specimen sizes, difference in cross-section that a macrocrack has to traverse makes little difference to the total number of cycles to failure. Size-effects in plain specimens tested in air at room temperature must therefore be associated with the initiation and development of microcracks, although, as discussed in §§ 3.9 and 4.3, differences in specimen cross-section that a macrocrack has to traverse can lead to size-effects in both plain specimens tested in a corrosive environment and in specimens containing sharp notches.

The experimental data described show that size-effects are more pronounced in bending than in direct stress tests, the fatigue limit of the former specimens decreasing as the specimen diameter increases and that the fatigue limit obtained in bending tests is higher than that obtained on specimens of the same diameter tested in direct stress. The change in fatigue limit with size and the difference in fatigue limits obtained in bending and direct stress appear to be most marked in specimens having a worked finish, such as that created by mechanical polishing or surface-rolling. There are four factors which might contribute to these effects:

1. The maximum stress on any cross-section in a bending test occurs theoretically at either a line or a point on the surface. If it is necessary for a finite region of the material to be subjected to cyclic stresses greater than some minimum value before a surface microcrack can be initiated and developed to the macrocrack stage, then the presence of a stress gradient across a specimen would imply that the fatigue limit is not dependent solely on a particular critical surface stress value.
2. The surface stress in a bending fatigue test is conventionally calculated from elastic theory. If the specimen exhibits a hysteresis loop at the fatigue limit, then the true surface stress will be less than that calculated from the applied bending moment, assuming the specimen is wholly elastic.
3. If the specimen surface is hardened or has residual stresses induced into it during the manufacturing processes or if the material has not been uniformly worked or heat-treated during manufacture, then it can no longer be considered homogeneous.
4. Depending on the method of stressing, only part of a specimen surface may be subjected to the maximum cyclic stresses: for example, a line across a plate tested in cantilever plane bending, a line around the circumference of a waisted cantilever rotating bending specimen, and the whole of the test-section of a cylindrical reversed direct stress or four-point loading constant bending moment rotating bending specimen. Differences in the amount of surface area subjected to the maximum cyclic stresses may invoke probability effects concerned with the chance of a local soft region being subjected to the maximum stresses, although for the usual type of laboratory specimen these may not be significant. For example, the variation in alternating stress required to initiate a microcrack in one localized region in preference to another may be small in relation to the load sensitivity of the fatigue machine.

Arguments concerned with (1) have been developed mainly in an attempt to explain the behaviour of notched fatigue specimens, and they are discussed in Chapter 4. Although the presence of a stress gradient makes it more difficult for a microcrack to initiate and develop to the macrocrack stage in a bending test than in a reversed direct stress test at the same surface stress level, unless the stress gradient across a bending specimen is particularly severe, its effect would not be expected to be of major importance in determining the fatigue limit in rotating bending. For example, if a microcrack must penetrate 0·1 mm in from the surface of a 10 mm diameter specimen before growing as a macrocrack, the stress at a point 0·1 mm in from the surface is only 2 per cent less than the surface stress.

Redistribution of stress arguments (2) assume that the specimen is homogeneous and that the material exhibits a hysteresis loop at the fatigue limit stress level. However, stress redistribution arguments do not predict a size-effect and the fact that specimens of different diameters give different rotating bending fatigue limits implies that other factors are involved. The experimental data show that size-effects are small for rotating bending specimens made of a material which exhibits a hysteresis loop of negligible width at the fatigue limit (for example, alloy steels and the stronger aluminium alloys) and whose surface layers have not been work-hardened during machining and polishing. In addition, these fatigue limits agree reasonably well with those obtained in reversed direct stress.

Arguments concerned with inhomogeneity (3) appear most successful in explaining size-effects. Consider a material which exhibits a hysteresis loop at the fatigue limit and whose fatigue limit increases with cold-work; the data show that the rotating bending fatigue limit, determined from specimens whose surfaces have been cold-worked and have had residual compressive stresses induced in them during manufacture, increases with decreasing specimen diameter more markedly than specimens which have not been cold-worked. The difference between the rotating bending and reversed direct stress fatigue limits (for a given specimen diameter) of these specimens is also much greater than those which have not been cold-worked and, indeed, of those specimens of the former material in which the hardened surface, even that due to mechanical polishing, has been removed by stress-relieving or electropolishing. This arises because, although the cyclic stress required to initiate and develop a microcrack in a hardened surface layer will be higher than that necessary in the unhardened material, it does not always follow that the fatigue limit of the specimen as a whole will be increased. Consider a specimen having a surface layer hardened by cold-work and tested in reversed direct stress. When the applied stress level exceeds the fatigue limit of the core material, this will deform plastically each cycle. Because the strain in the hardened layer must equal that in the core at the common interface and because the dynamic elastic limit of the layer material is higher than that of the core, it follows that the true stress in the hardened layer will be higher than that in the core. Thus the applied cyclic stress may not have to exceed the core fatigue limit appreciably before the true stress in the surface layer is sufficient to cause a microcrack to form and to relax any residual compressive stresses which may have retarded its development.

In the case of a rotating-bending specimen having a hardened layer thin compared to its diameter, the deflection for a given bending moment will not be greatly different from that of a specimen made wholly of the core material. Therefore, although there will be some increase in fatigue limit above that of a stress-relieved specimen (in addition to the surface being harder, residual compressive stresses will be present in a cold-worked layer which will tend both to extend the microcrack stage and then retard the growth of a macrocrack), the fatigue limit will be less than that of a specimen through-hardened to the same surface hardness. However, as the ratio of the layer thickness to specimen diameter increases, the more nearly the fatigue limit approaches that of a through-hardened specimen. Thus, as mechanical polishing hardens roughly the same depth of surface material and induces the same pattern of compressive residual stresses irrespective of specimen diameter, the rotating bending fatigue limit of mechanically polished specimens would be expected to increase with decreasing specimen diameter. Removal of the hardened layer reduces the size-effect in rotating bending and makes the fatigue limit approach that for reversed direct stress, any difference now being accountable for by stress-redistribution effects.

Similar arguments apply to specimens which do not have a mechanically produced hardened surface layer but in which the surface layers are stronger than the core because of changes in metallurgical structure over the cross-section produced by fabrication and heat-treatment. Thus, the drastic decrease in rotating bending fatigue limit found with specimens of large diameter is probably due to the fact that the material in the core has not been worked as much as that at the outside nor has the same refinement in metallurigcal structure been produced by subsequent heat-treatment. The core material, therefore, will have a lower dynamic yield stress and hence will result in a lower fatigue strength than would be expected from the surface hardness. This is supported by the fact that large specimens may become warm even when tested at nominal cyclic stresses lower than the expected reversed direct stress fatigue limit estimated from the surface hardness.

The arguments given concerning the effect of a hardened layer apply only when a microcrack is initiated in a surface grain. The origin of failure in a specimen having an extremely hard surface layer, such as that produced by carburizing, is often situated just below the hardened layer. This type of failure is discussed in § 6.4.3, and the effect of surface compressive residual stresses on the fatigue strength in § 6.3.

Summarizing, size-effects and differences between bending and reversed direct stress fatigue limits occur in homogeneous materials if the fatigue limit is above the dynamic elastic limit. The results can be correlated simply by calculating the true surface stress in the rotating bending tests. However, if the surface is cold-worked (the mechanical-polishing techniques commonly used in the preparation of fatigue specimens cold-work the surface of softer materials) a greater size-effect occurs and greater differences between rotating bending and reversed direct stress fatigue limits occur than with homogeneous specimens. This arises because of the division of the load between the hardened layer and core material; it also explains why large diameter specimens may have low fatigue limits if the core material is not in the same condition as the surface layers.

3.5. Effect of a mean stress

The direct stress machines described in Appendix 5 enable either a compressive or tensile mean stress to be applied to a specimen in addition to a given alternating stress. Fig. 3.2 shows the stress cycle $\sigma_m \pm \sigma$, where σ_m

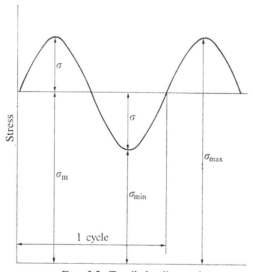

FIG. 3.2. Tensile loading cycle.

is considered positive; it follows that

$$\sigma_{max} = \sigma_m + \sigma$$
$$\sigma_{min} = \sigma_m - \sigma.$$

The ratio $\sigma_{min}/\sigma_{max}$ is called the stress ratio and is commonly denoted by R; for example, $R = -1$ represents a test at zero mean stress.

Test programmes designed to study the effect of a mean stress generally involve establishing S/N curves for a series of values of mean stresses, so that a diagram can be plotted showing the relationship between the fatigue limit at a particular mean stress and the corresponding value of the mean stress. In order to avoid the necessity of carrying out comprehensive series of tests at different mean stresses, on different materials, attempts have been made to formulate relationships linking the pertinent variables, so enabling the fatigue limit of a material (or strength at a given endurance) under a given mean stress to be predicted from the fatigue limit at zero mean stress. The most common requirement for practical design purposes is the fatigue limit under a tensile mean stress. It is interesting to note that the two relationships generally accepted as representing the experimental data, one due to Goodman [75] and the other to Gerber [76], were both formulated before the turn of the century. Gerber found that Wohler's tensile mean stress data (references to this have been given in Chapter 1) conformed to a parabola, having

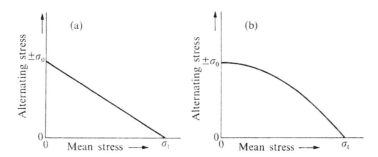

FIG. 3.3. Modified Goodman (a) and Gerber (b) diagrams.

as end-points the fatigue limit at zero mean stress and the tensile strength of the material. Goodman assumed that the safe repeated tension loading cycle was zero to half the tensile strength of the material σ_t, that is, $\sigma_t/4 \pm \sigma_t/4$, the safe stress decreasing linearly to zero at σ_t and increasing linearly to the zero mean stress condition; this gives a zero mean stress fatigue limit of $\pm \sigma_t/3$. This relationship was subsequently modified (and is now called the modified Goodman relationship) so that the fatigue limit decreased linearly with increasing tensile mean stress from its experimentally determined zero mean stress value to zero at σ_t, the tensile strength of the material. Both relationships are illustrated on Fig. 3.3; they can be expressed in the form

$$\pm \sigma = \pm \sigma_0 \left\{ 1 - \left(\frac{\sigma_m}{\sigma_t} \right)^n \right\},$$

where $\pm \sigma$ is the fatigue limit (or strength at a given endurance) when a tensile mean stress σ_m is present, $\pm \sigma_0$ is the fatigue limit (or strength at the same endurance) at zero mean stress, σ_t is the tensile strength, $n = 1$ is the modified Goodman relationship, and $n = 2$ is the Gerber relationship.

If the above equation is written in the form (omitting $\pm$ signs)

$$\frac{\sigma}{\sigma_0} = 1 - \left(\frac{\sigma_m}{\sigma_t} \right)^n,$$

the diagram of Fig. 3.3 can be replotted using the non-dimensional variables σ/σ_0 and σ_m/σ_t, as shown on Fig. 3.4. This figure is often referred to as the R–M diagram because it shows the relationship between the safe range of stress R and the mean stress M. If a line is drawn on Fig. 3.4 joining the points A and B, where A and B are the yield or 0·1 per cent proof stress of the material divided by σ_0 and σ_t respectively, then points to the right of AB represent tests in which the maximum tensile stress in the cycle is sufficient to cause gross yielding. To ensure that neither yielding nor fatigue failure occurs,

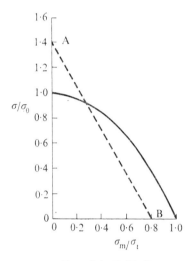

FIG. 3.4. R–M diagram.

a diagram of similar form to the modified Goodman diagram has been proposed in which the criterion of failure at zero alternating stress is taken as the yield or 0·1 per cent proof stress instead of the tensile strength; the straight line joining this point to $\pm\sigma_0$ is often referred as the Soderberg line. In all these diagrams loading conditions inside the curve or straight line are supposedly safe, those outside lead to failure.

Some of the early experimental work implied that the fatigue limit of a material decreased when the mean stress was compressive and Gerber may have proposed his parabolic relationship in order to allow for this decrease when the mean stress was negative. However, subsequent data show that this is not so and, provided the specimen does not yield or buckle, the fatigue limit tends to increase above the zero mean stress value with increasing compressive stress. Provided σ_t is always taken as the tensile strength, the Goodman relationship, of course, predicts such an increase.

Heywood [23] derived an empirical relationship from analysis of available data which can be written in the form

$$\frac{\sigma}{\sigma_t} = \left(1 - \frac{\sigma_m}{\sigma_t}\right)\left\{\frac{\sigma_0}{\sigma_t} + \gamma\left(1 - \frac{\sigma_0}{\sigma_t}\right)\right\},$$

where

$$\gamma = \left(\frac{\sigma_m}{3\sigma_t}\right)\left(2 + \frac{\sigma_m}{\sigma_t}\right) \quad \text{for steels}$$

and

$$\gamma = \left(\frac{\sigma_m}{\sigma_t}\right)\left\{1 + \left(\frac{n\sigma_t}{2200}\right)^4\right\}^{-1} \quad \text{for aluminium alloys.}$$

n is the logarithm of the life at which the fatigue strength is estimated and all stresses are in MN m^{-2}; γ can be considered as the curvature factor of a line on the σ/σ_0 versus σ_m/σ_t diagram, the expression reducing to the modified Goodman relationship when $\gamma = 0$.

Some experimental data relating to the effect of a mean stress on the uni-axial (reversed direct stress) fatigue limit are given below; data concerned with the effect of a mean shear stress on the torsional fatigue limit of a material are given in the next section.

Data obtained on wrought ductile metallic alloys (steels, aluminium alloys, brasses, etc.) subjected to tensile mean stresses tend to lie between the modified Goodman and Gerber lines. Many examples of this behaviour have been given [77]; a survey of the literature [4] showed that 90 per cent of the data lay above the Goodman line, falling mainly between the Goodman and Gerber lines. However, some of the low- and medium-strength aluminium alloys give values lying below the Goodman line. These alloys exhibit a high zero mean stress fatigue limit to tensile strength ratio but a low yield stress to tensile strength ratio and, even at low mean stresses, the maximum stress in the loading cycle may cause yielding and hence a marked mean stress effect. A study of the effect of a tensile mean stress on the fatigue strength of 11 different aluminium alloys [64] showed that the results for all but the soft magnesium–aluminium alloys lay between the Goodman and Gerber lines; those for these latter alloys lay somewhat below the Goodman line. An indication of the degree of correlation between some experimentally deter-mined fatigue limits taken from the literature and the corresponding values predicted by both the modified Goodman and Gerber relationships may be obtained from the results given in Table 3.14.

Results for a $4\frac{1}{2}\%$ Cu–aluminium alloy which conform closely to the Gerber parabola are plotted on Fig. 3.5; those for a magnesium alloy which conform to the modified Goodman line are shown on Fig. 3.6, while the results of a $5\frac{1}{2}\%$ Zn–aluminium alloy which fall between the Goodman and Gerber lines are shown on Fig. 3.5.

In general, the experimental values listed in Table 3.14 lie between the values predicted by the Gerber and modified Goodman relationships. Those

TABLE 3.14

Material	Tensile strength $(MN\ m^{-2})$	Reference	Tensile mean stress $(MN\ m^{-2})$	Fatigue strength $(MN\ m^{-2})$		
				Calculated		Experimental
				Modified Goodman	Gerber	
Mild steel	410	78	0	±190	±190	fatigue limit ±190
			43	±160	±185	±182
			91	±148	±179	±168
			148	±122	±165	±159
			250	±74	±120	±153
			310	±46	±82	±105
Nickel–chromium alloy steel	865	66	0	±480	±480	fatigue limit ±480
			155	±394	±465	±448
			310	±310	±418	±418
			465	±224	±340	±356
SAE 4130 steel	800	79	0	±338	±338	fatigue limit ±338
			70	±310	±334	±338
			140	±283	±328	±330
			210	±252	±317	±317
24S-T3 aluminium alloy	510	79	0	±152	±152	10^7 cycles ±152
			70	±131	±148	±131
			140	±110	±142	±124
			210	±90	±128	±110
75S-T6 aluminium alloy	570	79	0	±207	±207	10^7 cycles ±207
			70	±184	±204	±173
			140	±159	±193	±145
			210	±131	±179	±131
2014-T6 aluminium alloy	480	80	0	±104	±104	5×10^8 cycles ±104
			70	±90	±100	±104
			140	±76	±97	±104
			210	±59	±87	±97
			280	±45	±70	±90
			350	±31	±53	±76
2024-T4 aluminium alloy	465	80	0	±118	±118	5×10^8 cycles ±118
			70	±100	±114	±118
			140	±84	±107	±110
			210	±65	±93	±104
			280	±48	±76	±83
			350	±31	±56	±62

TABLE 3.14 (*contd.*)

Material	Tensile strength (MN m^{-2})	Reference	Tensile mean stress (MN m^{-2})	Fatigue strength (MN m^{-2})		
				Calculated		Experimental
				Modified Goodman	Gerber	
6061-T6						5 × 10^8 cycles
aluminium	310	80	0	±84	±84	±84
alloy			70	±65	±79	±76
			140	±45	±65	±70
			210	±28	±45	±56
7075-T6						5 × 10^8 cycles
aluminium	570	80	0	±137	±137	±137
alloy			70	±120	±134	±131
			140	±107	±131	±117
			210	±86	±120	±104
			280	±70	±107	±97
			350	±56	±86	±83
			420	±39	±65	±70
24S-T4						5 × 10^7 cycles
aluminium	465	81	0	±173	±173	±173
alloy			70	±145	±165	±151
			140	±120	±159	±123
			240	±83	±128	±87
			420	±20	±39	±53
75S-T6						5 × 10^7 cycles
aluminium	570	81	0	±193	±193	±193
alloy			70	±173	±190	±159
			140	±140	±179	±138
			240	±110	±159	±120
			420	±53	±90	±93
14S-T6						5 × 10^7 cycles
aluminium	480	81	0	±165	±165	±165
alloy			70	±142	±162	±138
			140	±117	±151	±124
			240	±83	±124	±97
			420	±25	±42	±70
2½% Zn, 0·65% Zr magnesium alloy	260	65	0	±90	±90	5 × 10^7 cycles ±90
			28	±79	±90	±83
			56	±70	±87	±70
			90	±59	±79	±48
5·6% Zn 0·66% Zr magnesium alloy	355	81	0	±151	±151	5 × 10^7 cycles ±151
			35	±137	±151	±131
			70	±120	±145	±120
			140	±93	±128	±90
			210	±62	±100	±62
			280	±34	±59	±34

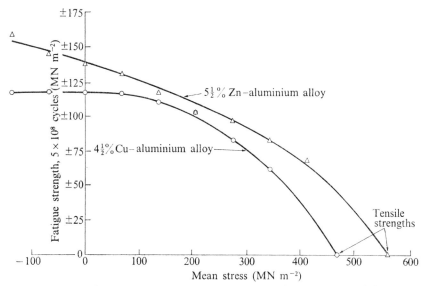

FIG. 3.5. Effect of mean stress on the fatigue strength of 2 wrought aluminium alloys. (Taken from Howell and Miller [80].)

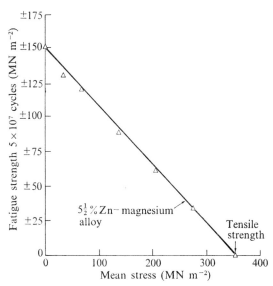

FIG. 3.6. Effect of tensile mean stress on the fatigue strength of a wrought magnesium alloy. (Taken from Lazan and Blatherwick [81].)

for the magnesium alloys and some of the aluminium alloys can lie close to the values predicted by the modified Goodman relationship and, indeed, may occasionally fall below them, particularly if the fatigue strength is estimated at a life less than 10^8 cycles. The Soderberg relationship would seem to give a safe prediction for all the metals included in the Table.

TABLE 3.15

Material	Reference	Compressive mean stress (MN m^{-2})	Fatigue strength (MN m^{-2})
2014-Te			10^8 cycles
aluminium alloy		0	±103
		−70	±103
		−140	±103
2024-T4			
aluminium alloy		0	±118
		−70	±118
		−140	±118
6061-T6			
aluminium alloy	80	0	±83
		−70	±90
		−140	±97
7075-T6			
aluminium alloy		0	±140
		−70	±145
		−140	±160
Nickel–chromium			fatigue limit
alloy steel	66	0	±480
		−155	±510
		−310	±510
			fatigue limit
0·4% C steel	82	0	±390
		−173	±410

Provided a specimen does not yield or buckle under the maximum compressive stress in the loading cycle, the fatigue limit does not decrease below the zero mean stress value when a compressive mean stress is superimposed. The data on Fig. 3.5 show that, in one case, the fatigue strength remains constant with increasing compressive mean stress, whereas in the other case, it increases. Data on steels and aluminium alloys have been given [4] which imply that the fatigue limit increases linearly with increasing compressive mean stress, the value of the fatigue limit at a compressive mean stress equal to the yield stress of the material being about 1·4 times that at zero mean stress. Some data illustrating the variation of fatigue strength with compressive mean stress are given in Table 3.15.

In all cases, it is seen that the fatigue limit either increases above or remains equal to the zero mean stress value. This conclusion has also been drawn [64] from tests on 11 different aluminium alloys; the results for two of the alloys tested are shown in Fig. 3.7. Specimens subjected to a wholly

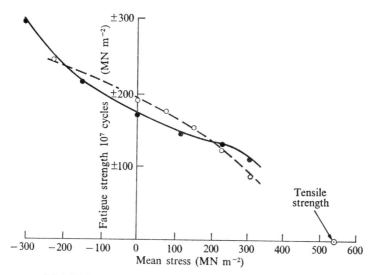

○ BS 1476. HE 15W(4·2% Cu, 0·8% Mn, 540 MN m⁻² tensile strength, 390 MN m⁻² 0·1% proof stress)
● BS 1476. HE 15WP (4·5% Cu, 0·8% Mn, 540 MN m⁻² tensile strength, 490 MN m⁻² 0·1% proof stress)

FIG. 3.7. Effect of a compressive mean stress on the fatigue strength of 2 aluminium alloys. (Taken from Woodward *et al* [64].)

compressive loading cycle exhibited numerous surface cracks, pieces of material often flaking away from the surface.

It has been reported that a more accurate prediction of the effect of a tensile mean stress can be obtained by using true stress instead of nominal stress and the fracture stress of the material instead of the tensile strength. Experimental points from various steels and aluminium alloys tested at various tensile mean stresses [83, 68] fall around a straight line on a true stress/modified Goodman diagram.

A material whose fatigue limit depends on whether or not cracks can grow directly from inherent flaws responds more markedly to mean stress (either tensile or compressive) than a material whose fatigue limit depends on whether or not the applied cyclic stress is sufficient to initiate and develop surface microcracks. Cast iron is an example of the former material, and it is found [4] that a tensile mean stress reduces and a compressive mean stress increases its fatigue limit by a greater extent than that predicted by the modified Goodman relationship. The ratio of the fatigue limit of cast iron in repeated compression to that in repeated tension averages about 3·3 compared to an average value of about 1·5 for malleable cast irons and wrought steels. This is further illustrated by the following fatigue limits for grey cast iron [23]:

> pulsating tension   0 to 100 MN m^{-2}
> zero mean stress ± 73 MN m^{-2}
> pulsating compression 0 to -450 MN m^{-2}.

3.5.1. Discussion

The above experimental data suggest that, except for soft metals which deform appreciably under the applied loads, the fatigue limits of wrought ductile metals and alloys fall between the values predicted by the modified Goodman and Gerber relationships, the former giving the safer prediction. There is a tendency for the data to lie closer to the modified Goodman line at low mean stresses and to the Gerber line at high mean stresses. This may well be the reason why it has been reported that the data can be more accurately represented by the modified true-stress Goodman line, because this line lies above the conventional Goodman and Gerber lines at mean stresses which are a large fraction of the tensile strength. Materials which exhibit a definite fatigue limit give results somewhat closer to the Gerber line than to the Goodman line; materials which do not exhibit an S/N curve having a sharp knee, such as high-strength aluminium alloys, give results falling around the modified Goodman line when the fatigue strength is estimated at relatively low endurances (about 10^7 cycles) but tend to approach the Gerber line when the fatigue strength is estimated at relatively long endurances (greater than 10^8 cycles). For all these materials, the Soderberg line gives a safe prediction, but in many cases it would be excessively safe.

There is no recent evidence to suggest that compressive mean stresses reduce the zero mean stress fatigue limit, the data suggesting that the fatigue limit either remains constant or increases, approximately linearly, above the zero mean stress value as the compressive mean stress increases in magnitude, provided that buckling or gross yielding does not occur.

Because the initiation of a surface microcrack in a wrought ductile metal depends on the resolved cyclic shear stresses necessary to cause continuing cyclic slip exceeding some minimum value, the effect of a mean stress on its fatigue limit depends on the extent to which this minimum value is either increased or reduced by the resolved static stresses acting both along and normal to the operative slip planes. The data imply that, for metals exhibiting a sharp knee and definite fatigue limit, this effect is small until the maximum stress in the cycle is above the yield stress; for other materials there is a gradual decrease with increasing static tensile stress and perhaps a slight increase with increasing compressive mean stress.

Provided that the maximum shear stress in the cycle does not exceed the yield stress, a mean shear stress has no effect on the torsional fatigue limit of a homogeneous ductile material (§ 3.6). This implies that, if the yield stress is not exceeded, a mean stress can have only a small effect on the cyclic shear stress necessary to initiate continuing cyclic slip. However, a mean stress has a marked effect both on the cyclic stress necessary to develop a microcrack to the macrocrack stage and on the subsequent growth of the macrocrack, because a static mean tensile stress across a crack tends to keep it open, whereas a compressive mean stress keeps it closed. Thus, in the former case the length, for a given cyclic stress, to which a microcrack must develop before being able to grow as a macrocrack is decreased and the life under a given cyclic stress reduced whereas, in the latter case, the microcrack stage is prolonged and the fatigue strength or life under a given cyclic stress increased. Indeed, if the compressive mean stress in the loading cycle is such that the loading is wholly compressive, the macrocrack stage can never be reached. Thus, provided the cyclic stress is sufficiently high, many surface microcracks will develop, and because they are unable to grow as macrocracks they will eventually tend to run into each other, with the possible consequence of intervening pieces of material being released from the surface.

The marked effect of a mean stress on a material such as cast iron, in which macrocracks can grow directly from inherent flaws, follows from the more marked effect a mean stress has on the growth of a macrocrack than on the initiation of a surface microcrack. Indeed, it can be argued that, if the fatigue limit of a material decreases markedly with increasing tensile mean stress and the specimen has not yielded, the material must contain inherent flaws of such a shape and size that macrocracks can grow from them directly. It follows that the fatigue limit of such a material increases markedly if a compressive mean stress is applied.

The fact that the decrease in fatigue strength of the high-strength aluminium alloys is more closely in accord with the Goodman relationship when the fatigue strengths are estimated at relatively low endurances, whereas it is more closely in accord with the Gerber relationship when the fatigue strengths are estimated at long endurances, suggests that, in the former case, the fatigue strength at a given life is controlled by the cyclic stress required to develop a microcrack to the macrocrack stage whereas, in the latter case, the fatigue strength at very long endurances is controlled by the cyclic stress necessary to initiate a surface microcrack.

3.6. Effect of combined stresses and anisotropy

So far, discussion has been restricted to the fatigue limit (or strength at long endurances) of specimens subjected to a uniaxial cyclic loading. In many practical applications, components are subjected to more general loading cycles, for example, combined bending and torsional loads. The combined cyclic loadings usually applied to laboratory specimens are either in-phase bending and torsion or in-phase biaxial tension.

In general, attempts to predict the fatigue limit (or strength at long endurances) at zero mean stress, under a combined stress loading, from the corresponding uniaxial fatigue limit or strength have been based on the usually accepted criteria for predicting the onset of plastic deformation under a static combined stress loading, the limiting static stresses merely being replaced by the corresponding limiting cyclic stress amplitudes. Only biaxial stress systems need be considered in the case of those materials in which cracks are initiated at a free surface and the three failure criteria most commonly used (that is, maximum principal stress, maximum shear stress, and the maximum shear-strain energy or von Mises) may consequently be expressed by the formulae:

maximum principal stress

$$\sigma_e = \frac{\sigma_x + \sigma_y}{2} + \tfrac{1}{2}\{(\sigma_x - \sigma_y)^2 + 4\tau_{xy}^2\}^{\frac{1}{2}},$$

maximum shear stress

$$\sigma_e = \{(\sigma_x - \sigma_y)^2 + 4\tau_{xy}^2\}^{\frac{1}{2}},$$

von Mises

$$\sigma_e = (\sigma_x^2 - \sigma_x\sigma_y + \sigma_y^2 + 3\tau_{xy}^2)^{\frac{1}{2}},$$

where σ_e is the equivalent principal stress, σ_x and σ_y are normal stresses, and τ_{xy} is the shear stress. For a cylindrical bar subjected to combined bending and torsional loads, the formulae for surface stresses become:

maximum principal stress

$$\sigma_e = \tfrac{1}{2}\{\sigma + (\sigma^2 + 4\tau^2)^{\frac{1}{2}}\},$$

maximum shear stress

$$\sigma_e = (\sigma^2 + 4\tau^2)^{\frac{1}{2}},$$

von Mises

$$\sigma_e = (\sigma^2 + 3\tau^2)^{\frac{1}{2}},$$

where σ is the maximum surface bending stress and τ is the maximum surface shear stress. Verification of whether or not fatigue data obtained on a particular material conform to any of these criteria may be obtained from the value of the ratio of its torsional fatigue limit to uniaxial fatigue limit (the above criteria require this ratio to equal 1, 0·5, and 0·577 respectively) and by determining the fatigue limits of specimens subjected to various combined stress loadings. Convenient methods of carrying out these latter tests are either to apply in-phase bending and torsional stresses to cylindrical specimens or to subject thin-walled tubes to in-phase pulsating internal pressure and axial cyclic loading.

Average values of the ratio of the fatigue limit in torsion to that in rotating bending have been quoted as in Table 3.16.

The value of the ratio obtained from tests on the stronger wrought aluminium alloys which do not exhibit a distinct fatigue limit depends on the endurance at which the torsional and bending fatigue strengths are estimated [4]. Average values of 0·64 and 0·56 have been obtained when the fatigue strengths are estimated at 10^7 cycles and 5×10^8 cycles respectively.

TABLE 3.16

Materials	Reference	Ratio of fatigue limit in torsion to that in rotating bending
19 carbon steels		0·55
14 alloy steels	34	0·58
5 non-ferrous alloys		0·52
Over-all average		0·55
49 wrought metallic alloys	22	0·56
14 wrought alloys	2	0·575

It would appear, therefore, that for those metals in which failure is initiated at a free surface, the ratio of the fatigue limit (or strength at very long endurances) in torsion to that in uniaxial loading has an average value not far removed from that predicted by the von Mises criterion, the value for a particular material depending on the endurance at which the fatigue strength is estimated and on metallurgical structure.

Most data relating to combined stresses have been obtained for combined bending and torsional stresses. Gough [84] used a machine designed to apply either an alternating bending or an alternating torsion loading or a loading consisting of any in-phase combination of the two, to obtain data for numerous ferrous alloys. The fatigue limit (zero mean stress) of each material was obtained under alternating bending, alternating torsion, and five different combinations of alternating in-phase bending and torsional stresses, using 7·6 mm diameter plain specimens. None of the usual theories of failure under combined stresses were found to represent all the results; instead, it was suggested that for the wrought steels tested (these covered a range of tensile strengths from 400 MN m^{-2} to 1850 MN m^{-2}) the experimental results for each steel could be represented by an ellipse quadrant having as end points the fatigue limits in pure torsion and pure bending. Three typical sets of results are shown on Fig. 3.8.

The equation of the ellipse quadrant is (omitting $\pm$ signs)

$$\frac{\sigma_b^2}{\sigma_{0b}^2} + \frac{\sigma_q^2}{\sigma_{0q}^2} = 1,$$

where $\pm\sigma_{ob}$ and $\pm\sigma_{oq}$ are the fatigue limits in pure bending and torsion respectively and $\pm\sigma_b$ and $\pm\sigma_q$ are the stress ranges due to bending and torsion respectively at the fatigue limit under a combined stress loading. It is equivalent to the maximum shear stress criterion if $\sigma_{ob}/\sigma_{oq} = 2$ and to the von Mises criterion if $\sigma_{ob}/\sigma_{oq} = \sqrt{3}$. Although it was considered that the

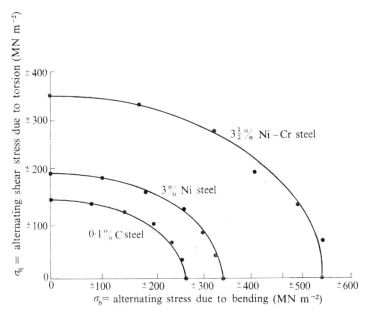

FIG. 3.8. Fatigue limits of 3 steels under combined bending and torsional alternating stresses. (Taken from Gough et al. [84].)

σ_{ob}/σ_{oq} ratio obtained for the various steels did not agree exactly with either of these two criteria, consideration of all the data for any one steel shows that, in general, they are not far removed from that predicted by the von Mises criterion [85]. Some data are replotted, using σ_b^2 and σ_q^2 axes, on Fig. 3.9. The full line represents the von Mises criterion; the dotted line is the best straight line through the points. On the other hand, experimental data obtained from cylindrical $4\frac{1}{2}\%$ Cu–aluminium alloy specimens subjected to in-phase combined bending and torsion [86] correlated best with the maximum shear stress criterion.

Quoted [2, 4, 22, 34] values of the torsion/uniaxial ratio for various cast irons usually lie between 0·9 and 1·0, thus appearing to conform more closely to the maximum principal stress rather than to the von Mises criterion. Fatigue failure of cast iron is associated, however, with the presence of inherent flaws. Some tests carried out [84] on both cast iron plain specimens and wrought steel notched specimens gave results that could not be represented by an ellipse quadrant. Instead the fatigue limits lay around an ellipse

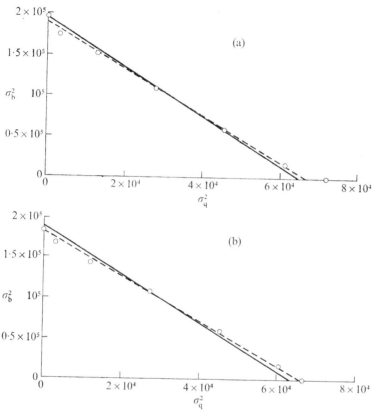

FIG. 3.9. σ_b^2 versus σ_q^2 diagrams. (a) 3–3½% Ni steel (tensile strength 700–770 MN m⁻²) (b) Chromium–Vanadium steel (tensile strength 700–770 MN m⁻²). (Taken from Frost [85].)

arc having the equation

$$\frac{\sigma_q^2}{\sigma_{0q}^2}+\frac{\sigma_b^2}{\sigma_{0b}^2}\left(\frac{\sigma_{0b}}{\sigma_{0q}}-1\right)+\frac{\sigma_b}{\sigma_{0b}}\left(2-\frac{\sigma_{0b}}{\sigma_{0q}}\right)=1.$$

A set of results obtained from plain 'Silal' cast iron specimens and vee-notched wrought steel specimens are shown on Fig. 3.10.

A specimen containing a notch subjected to uniaxial loading has a biaxial stress system set up in the material at the notch root. Tests on chromium–vanadium and 0·14% C steel specimens, notched to create a known biaxial stress system on the surface of the notch root [87], gave fatigue limits in good agreement with the von Mises criterion. Failure from notches and material containing inherent flaws, such as cast iron, are dealt with in Chapter 4.

Several workers have subjected thin-walled tubes to an in-phase pulsating internal oil pressure and a fluctuating axial load. This results in each element of the tube wall being subjected to in-phase fluctuating biaxial tensile stresses.

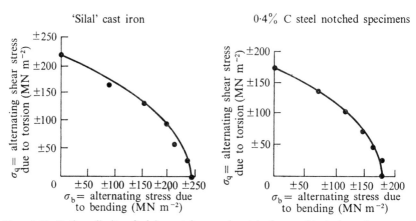

FIG. 3.10. Fatigue limits of plain cast iron and notched wrought steel specimens under combined bending and torsional alternating stresses. (Taken from Gough, *et al.* [84].)

However, the experimental techniques are somewhat complicated, and the speed of load application is relatively low compared to a conventional fatigue test. Tubes of $4\frac{1}{2}\%$ Cu–aluminium alloy subjected to four different longitudinal to hoop stress ratios [88] showed that none of the combined stress criteria mentioned previously correlated the test results. However, this was considered not altogether surprising because the uniaxial fatigue strength of the tube material in the circumferential direction was only 60 per cent of that in the longitudinal direction. From similar tests on $4\frac{1}{2}\%$ Cu–aluminium alloy tubes [89], it was concluded that the usual combined stress theories of failure were inadequate unless they could be modified to allow for the fact that the fatigue strength in the longitudinal direction was higher than that in the circumferential direction. By making an allowance for this effect, it was shown that the results correlated best with the von Mises criterion. Tests on $0\cdot2\%$ C steel tubes showed [90] that although the results exhibited a certain degree of scatter, they correlated best with the von Mises criterion. However, tests on $0\cdot1\%$ C steel tubes, subjected to various hoop to longitudinal stress ratios [91], suggested that the results did not permit a theory of failure appreciably different from the maximum principal stress criterion. The failure of internally pressured cylinders is further discussed in § 6.5.

It has been argued that correlation of data with criteria of failure is complicated if the material is not isotropic with respect to its fatigue properties. The role of anisotropy (if indeed it is important) is difficult to evaluate in combined stress fatigue tests as a specimen may be machined so that the grain flow or direction of working is parallel either to the greatest principal stress or to the greatest principal shear stress. In combined bending and torsion tests the grain flow is usually parallel to the bending stress and hence makes various angles to the principal stresses and shear stresses. As mentioned earlier, the presence of inclusions in high-strength steels could lead to the fatigue properties in the transverse direction being inferior to those in the longitudinal direction. There is also experimental evidence that, even in those metals and alloys in which fatigue failure is initiated by cyclic slip in surface grains, the fatigue strength of specimens cut from the stock material transverse to the working direction is inferior to that of specimens cut parallel to the working direction. Some typical data are given below.

Rotating bending tests on specimens cut either longitudinally or transversely from 22 mm diameter rolled bars of 11 different steels [85] showed that, in general, the fatigue limit of the latter was about 10 per cent less than that of the former. Similar tests [24] showed that the fatigue limits of specimens cut transversely from various wrought steel bars could be as much as 13 per cent lower than that of specimens cut in the longitudinal direction. The ratio of transverse to longitudinal fatigue limits of specimens cut from SAE 4340 (0·4% C) steel forgings [92] was found to be about 0·7 to 0·8. Collected data [93] on about 40 different steels ranging in plain fatigue limit from ±150 MN m^{-2} to ±650 MN m^{-2} showed that the fatigue limit of transverse specimens could be 5–25 per cent less than that of corresponding longitudinal specimens. However, little difference was found [94] between the fatigue strengths of specimens cut either transverse or parallel to the direction of working from wrought bars or plates of the stronger age-hardened aluminium alloys.

Rotating bending and torsion fatigue tests on specimens of two wrought aluminium alloys and a 0·4% C steel [95], cut either longitudinally, diagonally or transversely from bar material, in all cases gave the highest rotating bending fatigue limit for the longitudinally cut specimens. The diagonally cut specimens gave the next highest, and the transversely cut specimens the lowest fatigue limit. There was little difference between the torsional fatigue limits of any of the three groups of specimens of each material. Little difference was again found between the torsional fatigue limits of specimens cut either longitudinally or transversely from an alloy steel (En25) rolled bar [96].

The data, therefore, show that there can be a difference between the fatigue limits of specimens cut either longitudinally or transversely from bar material especially when tested under uniaxial loading conditions, but that this difference tends to disappear when tests are carried out in cyclic torsion. Several investigators have attempted to take anisotropy and other factors into account when interpreting combined stress data.

It has been shown that, by assuming the ratio of the static shear stress to cause slip in a single crystal to the corresponding static tensile stress is 0·5, the ratio of the shear to tension stress necessary to cause all the grains to slip in a randomly oriented aggregate in the form of a thin-walled tube, assuming that all grains are equally stressed, subjected to either static torsion or tension is very nearly equal to 0·577 [97, 98]. However, it can be argued that, unlike static yield conditions, fatigue cracking originates in one grain and is not dependent on slip occurring in all the grains in a specimen [99]. It would need slip to occur in at least 25 per cent of the grains which were subjected to the maximum cyclic stresses in order to account for the apparent agreement of the experimental data with the von Mises criterion. It was concluded that, if indeed slip in only one grain was necessary to initiate a surface microcrack, then the fact that the ratio of the experimental torsional to uniaxial fatigue limits of ductile metals generally exceeded a half could not be accounted for by slip relations. The anisotropy of the specimen material and the normal stress component acting on the operative shear plane were suggested to be contributing factors which might need consideration.

The magnitude and sign of the normal stress occurring on the maximum shear stress planes would be expected to influence the initiation and development of surface microcracks [100, 101], and since a normal stress is present on the planes of maximum shear stress in bending but is absent in torsion, it might be expected to produce differences in the ratio of the fatigue limit in bending to that in torsion. To allow for the influence of the normal stress and also for anisotropy of the material, it was suggested that the maximum shear stress criterion, for example, could be modified as follows.

Let $\pm\sigma_{ob}$ and $\pm\sigma_{oq}$ = fatigue limits in pure bending and torsion respectively,

$\pm\sigma_{b}$ and $\pm\sigma_{q}$ = stress ranges due to bending and torsion at the fatigue limit of the combined stress loading,

then, writing $\sigma_{ob} = 2K\sigma_{oq}$ (omitting $\pm$ signs), where K is a correction factor to allow for the state of stress and anisotropy, the maximum shear stress criterion $\sigma_{b}^{2}+4\sigma_{q}^{2} = \sigma_{ob}^{2}$ can be written as

$$\sigma_{b}^{2}+4(K\sigma_{q})^{2} = \sigma_{ob}^{2}$$

which, on substituting for K, gives

$$\frac{\sigma_{b}^{2}}{\sigma_{ob}^{2}}+\frac{\sigma_{q}^{2}}{\sigma_{oq}^{2}} = 1.$$

This equation was referred to as the modified maximum shear stress theory; it is identical to the Gough ellipse quadrant. However, because the von Mises criterion can be similarly modified and K can only be determined from experimental data, no light is thrown on which of the two criteria is indeed correct in the first place. It was also shown that the maximum principal strain criterion of failure could be similarly modified to give a relationship identical to the Gough ellipse arc.

The effect of a mean stress on uniaxial fatigue strength has been discussed in § 3.5. There are less data available on the effect of superimposing a static

TABLE 3.17

Superimposed static stress $(MN\ m^{-2})$	Fatigue limit $(MN\ m^{-2})$
Bending+torsion	Bending+torsion
0+ 0	±585+ 0
265+ 0	±550+ 0
530+ 0	±530+ 0
0+ 0	0+±370
0+170	0+±340
0+340	0+±345
0+170	±550+ 0
0+340	±540+ 0
265+ 0	0+±310
530+ 0	0+±285

shear stress on the torsional fatigue limit and even less on the effect of superimposing either or both static bending and torsion loads on the fatigue limit under combined bending and torsion. What data are available suggest that, provided the maximum shear stress in the loading cycle does not exceed that causing gross yielding, the fatigue limit in pure torsion decreases only slightly with an increasing static shear stress. For example, torsional fatigue tests on alloy steels [96, 102] showed that the addition of a torsional mean stress caused only a moderate decrease in the torsional fatigue limit, provided that a specimen did not yield, the torsional fatigue limit of En25 being found to decrease [96] approximately linearly from ± 280 MN m^{-2} at zero mean stress to ± 235 MN m^{-2} when a mean shear stress of 250 MN m^{-2} was applied. A review of available literature on steels, aluminium alloys, and copper alloys [103] also concluded that a mean torsion stress had little effect on the torsional fatigue limit until the specimen yielded. The effect of superimposed bending and torsional mean stresses on the combined stress fatigue limits of a 1000 MN m^{-2} tensile strength alloy steel has been studied [84]. The results, given in Table 3.17, show that the torsional fatigue limit was decreased by the application of a static bending stress to a greater extent than the bending fatigue limit was decreased by the application of a static torsion stress. However, even when considerable static bending and torsion stresses were applied, the combined stress fatigue limits could still be represented by an ellipse quadrant, the effect of the static stresses being merely to reduce the major and minor axes of the ellipse. In fact, it was concluded that, whatever the applied system of static stresses, having determined experimentally the stress ranges at the fatigue limits in pure bending and pure torsion, the stress range at the fatigue limit of any combination of bending and torsional cyclic stresses could be obtained from the ellipse quadrant.

Sines [104] suggested that the experimental data could be summarized as follows:

(1) the combined stress fatigue limits of wrought metallic alloys were in good agreement with the von Mises criterion;
(2) the uniaxial fatigue limit was decreased by a tensile mean stress and increased by a compressive mean stress, the change in fatigue limit, for practical purposes, being linearly dependent on the mean stress provided the material did not yield;
(3) both the torsional and uniaxial fatigue limits were unaffected by a static torsion mean stress, provided the material did not yield;
(4) the torsional fatigue limit was affected by a mean tensile or compressive mean stress as in (2);

and thus expressed the relationship between the static and permissible cyclic stresses as

$$\tfrac{1}{3}\{(P_1-P_2)^2+(P_2-P_3)^2+(P_3-P_1)^2\}^{\frac{1}{2}} \leqslant A-\alpha(S_x+S_y+S_z)$$

where $P_{1,2,3}$ are the principal cyclic stresses, $S_{x,y,z}$ are the orthogonal static stresses, and A and α are material constants. He suggested that the constants could be evaluated from uniaxial tests carried out at zero mean stress and with a zero to tension loading cycle.

If $\pm\sigma_1$ is the fatigue limit at zero mean stress, then

$$S_x, S_y, S_z, P_2, P_3 = 0; \quad P_1 = \pm\sigma_1,$$

therefore

$$A = \frac{\sqrt{2}}{3}\sigma_1.$$

If $\sigma_2\pm\sigma_2$ is the fatigue limit under a zero to tensile stress loading cycle, then

$$P_2, P_3, S_y, S_z, = 0; \quad S_x = \sigma_2; \quad P_1 = \pm\sigma_2,$$

therefore

$$A-\alpha\sigma_2 = \frac{\sqrt{2}}{3}\sigma_2,$$

from which

$$\alpha = \frac{\sqrt{2}}{3}\left(\frac{\sigma_1}{\sigma_2}-1\right).$$

Somewhat similar analyses have been given elsewhere [105–7].

3.6.1. Discussion

It would seem that, for ductile metals and alloys in which microcracks are initiated and develop in surface grains, the criterion of failure under an in-phase combined stress loading is some function of the resolved cyclic maximum shear stresses, the von Mises criterion being sufficiently accurate for practical purposes. In the case of in-phase combined bending and torsion, the results are well represented by an ellipse quadrant having as end-points the fatigue limits in pure bending and pure torsion. Little work has been done on the effect of out-of-phase combined stress loadings, but it is difficult to visualize their effect being more dangerous than when the corresponding loadings are applied in-phase. Combined bending and torsion fatigue tests in which there were various phase differences between the bending and torsion loading [108] confirmed that in no case was the fatigue strength less than the corresponding in-phase case. The fact that the ratio of the fatigue limit in torsion to that in uniaxial loading is nearer 0·57 than 0·5 is probably due to the fact that there is a normal stress across the operative slip planes in the latter tests but not in the former. Thus, although the criterion for the onset of surface slip in a surface grain may indeed be that of maximum shear stress (as indeed it is for the onset of static slip in a single crystal), the progressive development of a microcrack, as discussed in § 3.5.1, will be easier when a normal stress acts across its faces than when it is absent, and thus the uniaxial fatigue limit is less than twice the torsional fatigue limit. The fact that this ratio approximates to that predicted by the von Mises criterion therefore may be coincidental; indeed, it has been argued [109] that, although the strain energy or von Mises criterion is useful as a design formula, there is no evidence that fluctuating strain energy is a cause of fatigue cracking. In tests on materials not possessing a definite fatigue limit, the ratio of torsional to bending fatigue strengths increases progressively above the von Mises predicted value of 0·57 as the endurance at which the fatigue strengths are estimated decreases. This is presumably because it is easier for a crack having a normal cyclic stress acting across its faces to grow than one which does not, thus making the bending fatigue strength (at a given endurance) increase less rapidly with decreasing endurance than the corresponding torsional fatigue strength. This fact may also account for the more marked effect, on both the uniaxial and torsional fatigue limit, of a uniaxial rather than a torsional mean stress, because the latter does not induce a normal stress component across the operative slip planes.

7

The effect of anisotropy does not appear to be important in interpreting combined bending and torsion fatigue tests, presumably because the fatigue limit in torsion is not significantly dependent on the direction from which specimens are cut from the stock material. On the other hand, tests on thin-walled tubes subjected to in-phase pulsating internal pressure and longitudinal fluctuating uniaxial loads appear to give rather erratic results, usually ascribed to anisotropy, because the circumferential fatigue limit is markedly less than that in the longitudinal direction. However, it is shown in § 6.5 that the presence of a fluctuating oil pressure can have a marked effect on the fatigue limit of a cylinder, and since the circumferential fatigue limits of the thin-walled tubes mentioned in this section were determined in the presence of pulsating pressurized oil, whereas the longitudinal fatigue limits were not, it is probable that the presence of the pressurized oil in contact with the cyclically stressed material had some effect on the fatigue strength in addition to that of anisotropy.

In fracture-mechanics terms (§ 5.2.3) a crack usually grows in Mode I, that is, perpendicular to the direction of loading in a uniaxially loaded fatigue specimen. Fatigue cracks in torsional fatigue specimens, in general, may follow one of three directions. This arises because, in a cylindrical bar subjected to a torque, the planes of maximum shear stress along which microcracks develop are transverse and parallel to the bar axis, whereas the planes of maximum principal stress along which Mode I cracks grow are at 45° to the bar axis. Soft ductile metals generally give torsional fatigue fracture faces which are transverse to the bar axis, although some specimens exhibit longitudinal cracking especially at high strain amplitudes, whereas the fracture faces of specimens of harder metals follow a helicoidal path around the circumference. It would seem therefore that when a surface microcrack has developed to a certain size under a pure torsional cyclic load, it can either continue growing as a microcrack on a transverse or longitudinal plane or, if it deviates from these planes for some reason, the cyclic normal stress now acting across it will enable it to grow eventually as a macrocrack in Mode I on a plane at 45° to the bar axis; this results in a helicoidal fracture face. However, the crack front of a microcrack intersects a 45° plane at only one point, so that this change of direction is not easily achieved. Obstacles to the progress of a microcrack in the form of intermetallics, inclusions, flaws, etc., which will cause it to deviate from a transverse plane so enabling it to grow as a macrocrack following the principal tensile stress direction, are much more likely to be present in the harder and more complex alloys than in the softer pure metals and simple alloys. It is interesting to note that of 10 wrought ductile steels tested in torsional fatigue [84], 7 gave a helicoidal fracture face. Materials containing numerous inherent flaws should exhibit such a fracture under cyclic torsional stresses. An example is cast iron which contains a random distribution of flaws in the form of graphite flakes;

both cast irons tested [84] in pure torsion exhibited helicoidal fracture faces. (See also § 4.6.2.)

3.7. Effect of frequency of stress application

It is obviously time-saving to carry out fatigue tests at the highest possible speed attainable by the particular fatigue machine being used. However, for some materials, a limitation on the testing speed is imposed by the fact that, depending on material and stress level, exceeding a certain testing speed results in the temperature of the specimen increasing markedly above air temperature. This happens if the material is subjected to a cyclic stress suffic- ient for it to exhibit a hysteresis loop of finite width, because now the work done in deforming the specimen plastically each cycle is converted to heat in the specimen, and the specimen temperature increases until the rate of heat generated in the specimen is equal to the rate at which the specimen can dissi- pate the heat to the surrounding atmosphere. For example, a mild steel specimen, tested in reversed direct stress at a stress level somewhat higher than its plain fatigue limit, may reach 'blue heat' at quite moderate testing speeds. The heat generated depends on the volume of highly stressed material in the specimen, whereas the heat dissipated depends mainly on its surface area. Thus, for a given cyclic stress, speed, and specimen diameter, specimens tested in reversed direct stress tend to become hotter than those tested in rotating bending, while, for a given cyclic stress and method of testing, the specimen temperature increases as its diameter increases.

If the test conditions are such that the specimen surface is corroded or oxidized, or if internal diffusion processes or changes in the metallurgical structure of the material occur as a consequence of either testing in a corrosive environment or increasing the specimen temperature, then because these effects are time dependent, they can result in the fatigue strength, at a given number of cycles, varying with testing speed. Speed effects in corrosive environments and at elevated temperatures are discussed in §§ 3.9 and 3.8 respectively.

A determination of the repeated tensile stress fatigue strengths (10^6 cycles) of 3 carbon and 5 alloy steels at 5·8 Hz and 133 Hz [110] showed that the ratio of the fatigue strengths at the higher to lower testing speeds was about 1·05–1·07 for the 3 carbon steels but was only 1·03 or less for the alloy steels and aluminium alloys. Rotating bending tests [111] at 29 Hz, 58 Hz, and 177 Hz on 4 ferritic steels, annealed and cold-worked austenitic steel, Inconel, and forged and cast aluminium alloys showed that there was no significant difference in the fatigue limits of a given material at any of the three testing speeds. The rotating bending fatigue strength (10^7 cycles) of a $4\frac{1}{2}\%$ Cu–aluminium alloy [112] was found not to change significantly with testing speed for speeds up to 200 Hz. However, the endurance of a specimen tested at a stress level giving failure in less than 10^7 cycles appeared to increase with increasing testing speed. Again, the fatigue strength (10^7 cycles) of an 0.2% C steel [113] was not significantly different at testing speeds between 13 Hz and 250 Hz. However, the fatigue strength (10^7 cycles) of a chromium–molybedenum–vanadium steel did appear to increase slightly with increasing testing speed. The results of rotating bending tests [114] on various materials at speeds of 25 Hz, 167 Hz, and 500 Hz are shown in Table 3.18. In general, there is little difference between the fatigue limits at the first two testing speeds, but the fatigue limit at 500 Hz is in all cases greater than that at 25 Hz.

TABLE 3.18

	Fatigue limit (MN m^{-2})		
	25 Hz	167 Hz	500 Hz
SAE 1020 steel	±215	±215	±230
Stainless steel	±415	±435	±480
SAE 4140 steel	±675	±680	±700
Rail steel	±345	±345	±350
Grey cast iron	±70	±70	±77
Alloy cast iron	±180	±180	±200
Brass†	±140	±165	±185
Aluminium alloy†	±105	±105	±120

† Fatigue strength at 5×10^7 cycles.

At testing speeds greater than 200 Hz the fatigue limit generally increases with increasing testing speed, although there is some data which suggests that, when some critical frequency is exceeded, the fatigue limit decreases. Using an electromagnetic wire-bending machine [115], the fatigue limit at 1000 Hz was found to be greater than that at 50 Hz by 9 per cent for copper, 8 per cent for Armco-iron, and 6 per cent for mild steel. Exciting small beam specimens by an air blast causing vibration in the free–free mode at frequencies up to 17 kHz [116] showed that the fatigue limits of copper, 0.1% C steel, and aluminium increased gradually as the frequency increased up to the maximum value. However, although the fatigue limits of Armco-iron and an 0.8% C steel increased initially as the frequency increased, they reached a maximum value at a frequency of about 10 kHz, and then decreased as the frequency was increased further. Similar tests [117] using an air jet showed that the fatigue strengths (10^8 cycles) of 8 different steels increased with frequency up to frequencies between 1 kHz and 2 kHz (the maximum fatigue strength being about 10 per cent greater than that at 120 Hz), but then decreased as the frequency was increased further. On the other hand, other similar tests on steel beams [118] vibrated in the free–free mode by an air jet showed that, although the fatigue limit of a given steel changed little as the frequency was increased from 50 Hz to 500 Hz, it increased continually as the frequency was increased from 500 Hz to 1800 Hz, being about 40 per cent greater at 1800 Hz than at 50 Hz. Two carbon steels were tested [119] at frequencies up to 100 kHz using a ferrite magnetostrictive vibrator, the specimens being cooled with treated water at 5 °C. The results, given in Table 3.19, show that the fatigue limits of both steels increase with increasing frequency, there being no evidence of a critical frequency beyond which the fatigue limit decreases with further increase in frequency.

Tests on aluminium alloy (2 % Cu, 1 % Mg) beams, vibrated in the first free–free mode [120], showed that the fatigue strength increased as the

TABLE 3.19

Frequency (Hz)	Fatigue limit (MN m^{-2})	
	0·08 % C steel	0·2 % C steel
40	±205	—
200	±220	±235
550	±230	±245
13 000	±275	±285
50 000	±325	±325
100 000	±370	±350

frequency increased up to a maximum value of 3·8 kHz. For example, the fatigue strength (10^7 cycles) increased from ±140 MN m^{-2} at 24 Hz up to ±160 MN m^{-2} at 3·8 kHz. Tests on the 4½ % Cu– and 5½ % Zn–aluminium alloys [121, 122] showed that their fatigue strengths increased progressively as the testing speed increased from 10 Hz to 1000 Hz [122] and that lives at 20 kHz were between 10 and 100 times longer than in corresponding tests at 200 Hz [121]. At 20 kHz, the temperature rise of a specimen tested at the highest stress level was only about 1 °C [121]. It was argued [122] that the speed effect arose because tests in air on these materials were, in fact, corrosion fatigue tests and because chemical attack of the specimen surface by the atmosphere was time dependent, the life at a given stress would not depend solely on the number of stress cycles.

To summarize, the data show that, over the frequency range 1–200 Hz, the fatigue limit or strength at long endurances of a material which does not heat up or whose surface is not chemically attacked during a test remains constant for practial purposes, although there is, in fact a slight increase with increasing testing speed. At higher testing speeds, the fatigue limit continues to increase with testing speed up to frequencies of about 2 kHz, but beyond this frequency the experimental data are not in accord, there being evidence for and against a peak frequency beyond which the fatigue strength decreases with increasing frequency.

Provided a specimen was inert and remained wholly elastic, a speed effect would not become apparent until the frequency exceeded that corresponding to the time taken for an elastic stress wave to propagate through the specimen. However, most metals are not inert and do not remain wholly elastic when tested at stress levels equal to and greater than the plain fatigue limit. Thus a speed effect at room temperature can arise from two causes; first, the atmosphere can attack the surface and so cause damage which is dependent on time rather than on the number of applied stress cycles and, secondly, the cyclic stress necessary to cause continuing plastic deformation may increase with increasing rate of stress application (that is, the width of the hysteresis loop at a given stress level decreases with increasing testing speed) because there is less time available in each cycle during which plastic strain can occur. This latter effect would be expected to be more evident in softer rather than harder materials. An additional factor which may arise in the case of the high-strength precipitation and age-hardened aluminium alloys is that the over-ageing processes, which lead to the production of local soft spots and thus to the relatively low fatigue strength/tensile strength ratio of these alloys, have less time to occur in each cycle the faster the testing speed, and so too could give rise to a speed effect. Presumably in those alloys in which a speed effect is due to a narrowing of the hysteresis loop, the S/N curves obtained at different testing speeds could be correlated if the results were expressed in terms of either the total or plastic strain amplitude induced by the applied cyclic stress amplitude instead of the stress amplitude. It is difficult to see how any of the factors suggested can explain the occurrence of a peak frequency above which the fatigue strength tends to decrease with further increase in frequency. The possibility of secondary stresses being induced by the testing equipment and the difficulty of measuring accurately the true stresses imposed on the specimen at these very high frequencies are factors which cannot be overlooked until further experimental work has clarified this inconsistency.

Although there is little or no information on the effect of waveforms other than sinusoidal on the fatigue limit of a material, the fact that there is no significant speed effect (at room temperature) over the range of about 1–200 Hz implies that over this speed range at least, variations in waveforms are unlikely to have any significant effect on the fatigue limit although they could well have an effect on the lives of specimens tested at higher stress levels.

3.8. Effect of temperature

In some practical applications, components are required to operate at temperatures either above or below room temperature, the former being the more common requirement. This is reflected in the fact that there are much more experimental data available on the fatigue strength of materials at temperatures above room temperature than at temperatures below it. A further reason for this may be that the fatigue strength of a material increases as the temperature decreases, for example, the ratio of the fatigue limit at liquid air temperature to that at room temperature is in the range 1·5–2·5 for most metallic alloys [4], softer materials generally giving higher values of this ratio than harder materials. Thus, a design based on room-temperature fatigue data will be safe for use at lower temperatures, although, of course, any increased susceptibility to brittle fracture under the applied loadings must be taken into account. Materials for use at elevated temperatures, in addition to possessing adequate static and fatigue properties, must be resistant to corrosive attack by the atmosphere at the operating temperature. Special alloys possessing these properties have been developed for components such as the blades and discs in a gas-turbine engine. At elevated temperatures, factors which have no significant effect at room (and lower) temperatures become important, for example, metallurgical changes in microstructure due to prolonged soaking at the operative temperature and chemical attack of the specimen surface by the atmosphere. Because these effects become more pronounced the longer the specimen is kept at the elevated temperature, surface damage may occur which is not solely dependent on the amplitude of the stress cycle and the number of times it is applied.

3.8.1. Low-temperature fatigue

Data illustrating the increase in the fatigue strength of some common alloys with decreasing temperature are given in Table 3.20; there are other collections of data [123] in the literature.

Forrest [4] has tabulated the average values of the ratio of the fatigue strengths (10^6 cycles) of several groups of metallic alloys at $-40\,°C$, $-78\,°C$, and $-188\,°C$ to the corresponding values at room temperature; they are shown in Table 3.21.

The high-strength age-hardening aluminium alloys have relatively low

T ABLE 3.20

Material	Refer-ence	20 °C	−40 °C	−78 °C	−188 °C	−253 °C	−269 °C
		\multicolumn{6}{c}{Fatigue strength (MN m⁻²)}					

Material	Reference	20 °C	−40 °C	−78 °C	−188 °C	−253 °C	−269 °C
Copper‡	124	±100	—	—	±145	±240	±260
Brass‖	125	±175	±185	—	—	—	—
Cast iron‖	125	±60	±75	—	—	—	—
Mild steel†	126	±185	—	±255	±570	—	—
Carbon steel†	2	±230	—	±290	±625	—	—
Nickel–chromium alloy steel†	2	±540	—	±580	±765	—	—
Duralumin‖	125	±115	±145	—	—	—	—
Aluminium alloys§ 2014-T6		±100	—	—	±170	±310	—
2020-T6	127	±125	—	—	±155	±280	—
7075-T6		±85	—	—	±140	±240	—

† Fatigue limit. ‡ Fatigue strength, 10^6 cycles. § Fatigue strength, 10^7 cycles. ‖ Fatigue strength, 5×10^7 cycles.

TABLE 3.21

Alloys	Ratio $\dfrac{\text{fatigue strength }(10^6\text{ cycles}) \text{ at given temperature}}{\text{fatigue strength }(10^6\text{ cycles}) \text{ at room temperature}}$		
	$-40\,°C$	$-78\,°C$	$-188\,°C$
Carbon steels	1·2	1·3	2·6
Alloy steels	1·05	1·1	1·6
Stainless steels	1·15	1·2	1·5
Aluminium alloys	1·15	1·2	1·7
Titanium alloys	—	1·1	1·4

room-temperature fatigue strengths because of over-ageing due to cyclic stressing. It has been argued that they exhibit a more marked increase in fatigue strength with decreasing temperature than the non-age-hardening magnesium–aluminium alloys because of the progressive retardation of over-ageing with decreasing temperature [128]. For example, the tensile and fatigue (10^7 cycles) strengths of the age-hardening $4\frac{1}{4}\%$ Cu–aluminium alloy [121] increase from room temperature values of 570 MN m^{-2} and ±125 MN m^{-2} to 800 MN m^{-2} and ±275 MN m^{-2} at $-253\,°C$, respectively, that is, the ratio of fatigue strength to tensile strength increases from 0·22 to 0·34.

The fatigue strengths (10^6 cycles) of polycrystalline specimens of copper, silver, gold, aluminium, magnesium, zinc, cadmium, and iron at 20 °C, $-183\,°C$, $-253\,°C$, and $-268\cdot8\,°C$ have been determined [124]. Except for zinc and iron, which exhibited brittle fracture at sub-zero temperatures, the fatigue strengths increased considerably as the temperature was reduced. The tensile strengths of these metals also increased with decreasing temperature, there being a marked correlation between the corresponding increases in fatigue and tensile strengths. Additional tests on copper and cadmium at $-271\cdot3\,°C$ showed that, within the limits of experimental error, there was no further increase in either the tensile or fatigue strength compared to that at $-268\cdot8\,°C$, implying that a limiting value of both these properties existed in the region of this temperature.

There is no reason to suppose that the effect of either a mean stress or a combined stress loading on the fatigue strength at low temperature does not conform to the room-temperature pattern of behaviour. Indeed, what data are available on the effect of a tensile mean stress on the low-temperature fatigue strength suggest that the results lie between the appropriate Goodman and Gerber lines.

3.8.2. Elevated-temperature fatigue

Factors which are unimportant at room temperature may play an important part in determining the fatigue strength of a material at elevated temperatures; these include testing speed, the shape of the cyclic loading waveform (usually altered by holding the specimen at the maximum stress in the cycle for a certain length of time), and atmospheric attack of the surface. In addition, if a mean stress is present in the loading cycle, a specimen may creep appreciably, and mechanisms responsible for creep fracture may play a part in both the initiation of a surface crack and in providing easy fracture paths for it to follow through the body of the specimen. The ratio of the test temperature to the melting point of the material has a bearing on whether fatigue or creep mechanisms are the prime cause of crack initiation for a

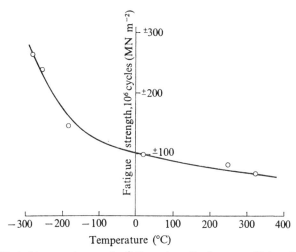

FIG. 3.11. Effect of temperature on the fatigue strength of copper. (Taken from Allen and Forrest [128].)

given set of loading conditions, creep mechanisms becoming of greater importance the higher this ratio. Because the fatigue strength at elevated temperatures can depend on the factors mentioned, the fatigue strengths quoted in this section are strictly true only for the particular testing conditions employed and should be considered merely as indicating a trend in general behaviour.

The fatigue strengths (10^6 cycles) of copper at different temperatures between $-269\ ^\circ$C and 325 $^\circ$C, plotted on Fig. 3.11, illustrate the influence of temperature on the fatigue strength of a pure metal or simple alloy whose structure remains stable over the entire temperature range. However, this simple type of behaviour does not occur if either internal diffusion processes are enhanced or metallurgical structural changes take place at the higher temperatures. Thus, the fatigue strength (and the tensile strength) of a strain-ageing material varies in a more complex manner with increasing temperature than is illustrated in Fig. 3.11. For example, the tensile strength of mild steel reaches a peak value at about 250 $^\circ$C, before beginning to decrease with further increase in temperature; the fatigue limit, although decreasing initially as the temperature is increased up to about 100 °C, also increases to a peak value at about 250–350 °C (the precise value depends on testing speed), before beginning to decrease with further increase in temperature. The lives of 0·15% C steel specimens were found to be appreciably greater at a given stress level at 200–260 °C than at room temperature [129] and it was argued

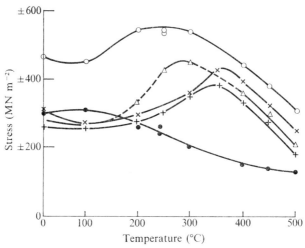

○ Tensile strength

● Yield stress, or 0·1 per cent proof stress

× Bending fatigue strength (500 000 cycles) at 33 Hz

+ Bending fatigue strength (10^8 cycles) at 33 Hz

△ Bending fatigue strength (500 000 cycles) at 0·17 Hz

FIG. 3.12. Effect of temperature on the tensile strength and rotating bending fatigue strength of a 0·17% C steel. (Taken from Allen and Forrest [128].)

from strain ageing considerations that increasing testing speed would increase the temperature at which this maximum strength occurred. Fig. 3.12 shows results on a 0·17%C mild steel. The rotating bending fatigue strength determined at 0·17 Hz is seen to decrease below the room temperature value as the temperature is increased to 100 °C, and then reaches a peak value at about 250 °C. At 33 Hz the results follow the same pattern except that the peak value occurs at 350 °C. Below 200 °C, the S/N curves exhibit a definite fatigue limit, but above 250 °C they are smooth curves.

Table 3.22 gives some results [2] on various steels showing that their fatigue limits at 100 °C are less than those at room temprature but then, except for the high-strength nickel-chromium steel, reach a peak value higher than the room temperature value at about 300–400 °C.

TABLE 3.22

| Material | Rotating bending fatigue strength, 10^7 cycles (MN m^{-2}) | | | | | |
	20 °C	100 °C	200 °C	300 °C	400 °C	500 °C
Grey cast iron† (3·2% C, 1·1% Si)	±90	±90	±90	±105	±110	±95
Nickel–chromium alloy steel (4·6% Ni, 1·6% Cr)	±535	±500	—	±485	±420	—
0·35% C steel	±298	—	±310	±330	—	±275
0·6% C steel	±370	±355	±395	±505	±425	±185
Low-alloy steel (0·14% C, 0·5% Mo)	±315	—	—	±400	±370	±275

† Additional data on cast iron are given in Reference [126].

Further results [2] showing how the fatigue strengths of steels do decrease at temperatures up to 100 °C are given in Table 3.23. These results are of interest practically because many engine components may operate (for example, in hot oil) at these moderately elevated temperatures.

Aluminium alloys retain reasonable fatigue strengths at temperatures up to 100–150 °C, but these decrease rapidly at higher temperatures. This is

TABLE 3.23

| Steel | Fatigue strength, 10^8 cycles (MN m^{-2}) | | |
	20 °C	70 °C	100° C
0·6% C, 0·7% Mn	±430	±370	—
0·24% C, 3·9% Ni, 1·0% Cr	±490	±430	—
0·2% C, 4·7% Ni, 1·4% Cr, 0·6% Mo	±570	—	±450

illustrated by the results in Table 3.24 obtained [130] from plane bending fatigue tests. It has been argued [4] that because the high strength age-hardening aluminium alloys depend for their strength on precipitation-hardening, a marked drop in their fatigue strengths occurs when the operating temperature is higher than that at which over-ageing occurs. Thus those alloys which

TABLE 3.24

| Aluminium alloy | Fatigue strength 12×10^7 cycles (MN m^{-2}) | | | | |
	20 °C	150 °C	200 °C	250° C	300 °C
DTD 683 (5½% Zn)	±170	±115	±60	—	—
BS L65 (4½% Cu)	±130	±80	±57	±39	±39
DTD 324 (12% Si)	±127	±85	±60	±39	±29
BS L64 (4¼% Cu)	±125	±90	±62	±54	±39

best resist over-ageing at the operating temperature will have the best fatigue (and creep) strengths. Magnesium alloys behave in a similar manner, a marked reduction in fatigue strength occurring at operating temperatures which result in over-ageing.

Alloy steels retain appreciable fatigue strengths up to about 600 °C, the fatigue strengths of quenched and tempered steels decreasing markedly when

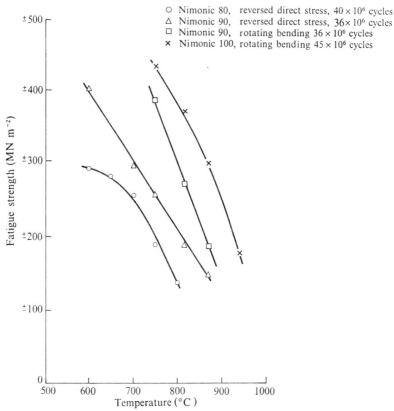

FIG. 3.13. Effect of temperature on fatigue strength of nimonic alloys. (Taken from Betteridge [131].)

the operating temperature approaches the tempering temperature. The fatigue strengths of titanium alloys are comparable to those of alloy steels for temperatures up to 500 °C. Above 600 °C, austenitic steels have superior fatigue properties to plain carbon and low-alloy steels. For operating temperatures above 750 °C, ferrous alloys are replaced by nickel or cobalt base alloys. The nickel base Nimonic series of alloys were developed especially and are indeed widely used for such highly stressed components as gas-turbine blades; some typical fatigue strengths are given on Fig. 3.13. Nimonic

75, 80, 80A are essentially 20% Cr–nickel base alloys with titanium added, Nimonic 90 and 95 are 20% Cr, 18% Co, 3% Ti–nickel base alloys, while Nimonic 100 is an 11% Cr, 20% Co, 5% Al, 5% Mo, $1\frac{1}{2}$% Ti–nickel base alloy.

Because the S/N curves of materials at elevated temperatures continue to decrease with increasing endurance, it is often necessary to continue tests up to 10^8 cycles and beyond to obtain an estimate of the safe stress level for a particular application. The fatigue strengths at 10^8 cycles of 4 high-strength alloys [132] obtained in plane bending on round specimens vibrated at 120 Hz are given in Table 3.25.

TABLE 3.25

	Fatigue strength 10^8 cycles $(MN\,m^{-2})$	
Material	650 °C	815 °C
Rolled Vitallium	±435	±300
Cast Vitallium	±300	±280
Inconel X	±450	±275
Nimonic 80	±385	±185

The metallurgical development of high-temperature alloys has been directed, in general, to the problem of obtaining high static tensile and creep properties over the required range of operating temperatures. However, data for a variety of materials have been given [128] which, in general, indicate that the higher the creep strength exhibited by a material at a given temperature, the higher its fatigue strength. The condition of a material giving the optimum creep strength, however, may not be the condition for the optimum fatigue strength, and alternative heat-treatments might be desirable for service conditions where dynamic stresses are dominant. Fracture under static loading is usually transcrystalline at low temperatures and intercrystalline at high temperatures, the temperature at which the change occurs not being defined precisely and depending on stress level. Failure under cyclic stresses also follows a similar pattern [128], but the temperature at which the change from transcrystalline to intercrystalline fracture occurs is higher than for comparable static stresses.

Many materials may have poor fatigue strengths at elevated temperatures, not so much because they are softened at the operating temperature but because their surface is either oxidized or attacked chemically by the atmosphere (§ 3.9). Protective surface treatments therefore may allow some materials, which otherwise would not be acceptable on account of their poor oxidation resistance, to be used at elevated temperatures. For example, the improvement in high-temperature fatigue strength of 4 low-alloy steels [133] which had been treated by either a chromium diffusion process, being hot-dipped in aluminium, or having a sprayed aluminium coating diffused into the surface was such as to extend their use up to 650 °C. Oxidation-resistant coatings were found [134] to increase the fatigue strength of molybdenum at temperatures up to 980 °C. Special testing techniques are required if it is necessary to protect the specimen surface from oxidation at the test temperature. Although there is little difficulty in finding suitable protective paints or coatings [135] for temperatures up to 200 °C, these are usually unsuitable for temperatures above 400 °C. One suggestion is to encase the specimen (in this case, rotating bending) in a flexible capsule consisting of a section of stainless steel bellows welded in an argon atmosphere to the ends of the specimen and then filled with argon. Using this technique, it was found that the fatigue strength (5×10^8 cycles) of uranium at 300 °C was ± 120 MN m^{-2}.

The fatigue properties in air and vacuum (2×10^{-6} mm Hg) of nickel, stainless steel, and Inconel X at 820 °C have been compared [136]. All three materials exhibited longer lives in vacuum than in air at stress levels giving short endurances, but at stress levels causing fracture at long endurances, the life in air approached that *in vacuo* and in some cases exceeded it. It was suggested that the reason for the life in air exceeding that in a vacuum at long endurances was because, in air, fatigue cracks filled with oxides which could transmit load across a crack so reducing its opening at a given stress level. This only occurred at low stress levels because an appreciable length of time was required for the oxides to form.

Some reasons were mentioned previously why the fatigue strength at elevated temperature is more dependent on testing speed than at room temperature (§ 3.7). An additional reason is that the longer the time taken for the stress to change from zero to its peak value in the cycle, the more time there is for plastic deformation to occur during each cycle. A dependence on testing speed implies that the fatigue strength will be dependent on waveform. For example, if the loading cycle is such that the maximum tensile stress is held constant for a period of time, the fatigue strength would be expected to decrease the longer the holding time. Rotating bending tests at 300 °C and 500 °C on a 0·2% C and a chromium–vanadium alloy steel [113] showed that fatigue strengths (10^7 cycles) obtained at different testing speeds between 13 Hz and 250 Hz reached a peak value at about 125 Hz but tended to decrease at higher frequencies. Similar tests [137] on 2 carbon steels and a 13% Cr alloy steel at temperatures of 450–600 °C and testing speeds of from 2·8 Hz to 25 Hz showed that, although at high stress amplitudes the specimen life was independent of testing speed, the life at a stress amplitude giving a long endurance increased as the testing speed increased. Both reversed direct stress and rotating bending tests on a 0·17% C steel at 450 °C and testing speeds of 0·17 Hz, 2 Hz, and 33 Hz showed [67] that the fatigue strength at a given endurance increased as the testing speed increased. It was found however that, on replotting the data obtained at the three different testing speeds, on stress–log(time) axes instead of the conventional stress–log(number of cycles) axes, the experimental points for each type of stressing tended to lie around a single curve. Subsequently it was found [138] that, at a given stress level, the cyclic plastic strain in a reversed direct stress test (obtained from hysteresis loop width measurements) decreased as the testing speed increased. Plotting the value of the cyclic plastic strain amplitude against

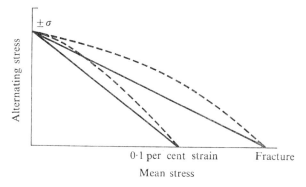

FIG 3.14. Alternating stress versus mean stress diagram for a specific time.

endurance on logarithmic axes resulted in the reversed direct stress data for the three testing speeds falling around the same line.

Because of their low melting points, the behaviour of lead alloys at room temperature is similar to that of other metallic alloys at elevated temperatures, and it is found that the fatigue strength of lead and lead alloys at room temperature increases as the testing speed increases[139].

The presence of a mean stress in the loading cycle, if the temperature is sufficiently high, may cause the specimen to extend continuously with time. Thus, a component subjected to both mean and alternating stresses must be designed to prevent the occurrence of both fatigue and creep failure (designated either by creep rupture or by some maximum permissible creep strain). A diagram (see Fig. 3.14) relating the alternating and tensile mean stresses (§ 3.5) can be drawn [140] to give design information at a specified life, say for example, 1000 hours. The value of the fatigue strength $\pm\sigma$ at 1000 hours is obtained at a testing speed corresponding to the frequency of stress application in service; the end-point on the mean stress axis depends on whether the required failure criterion is either creep rupture or that the creep strain must not exceed a stipulated value, say, 0·1 per cent strain in 1000 hours. Any combination of mean tensile and alternating stresses within the area bounded by a straight line or some curve such as an ellipse quadrant or parabola joining the two end-points give a supposedly safe design for the stipulated period of time. For rupture in a given time, the results of combined creep and fatigue tests on the Nimonic 80A and 90 alloys at 800 °C and 900 °C fall around an ellipse on this type of diagram [141]. Fig. 3.14 can be replotted in non-dimensional form by having, as ordinate and abscissa alternating stress/fatigue strength at zero mean stress and tensile mean

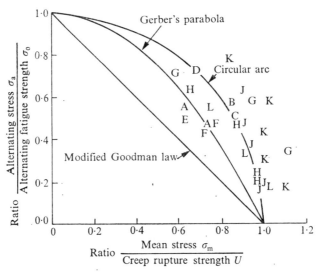

All results are based on an endurance of 300 hours

A	REX 78	600 °C	G	Ni 80A	700 °C
B	REX 78	650 °C	H	Ni 80A	750 °C
C	REX 78	700 °C	J	N 155	649 °C
D	Ni 80	600 °C	K	N 155	732 °C
E	Ni 80	650 °C	L	N 155	815 °C
F	Ni 80	700 °C			

FIG. 3.15. Non-dimensional alternating stress versus mean stress diagram for high temperature alloys. (Taken from Allen and Forrest [128].)

stress/rupture stress (or stress for a given strain) in a given time, respectively. The experimental data for several high-temperature alloys (see Fig. 3.15) have been found to lie generally on the safe side of a parabola joining the two end-points, the straight line relationship being excessively safe [128]. Collections of combined fatigue and creep data on various alloys plotted on similar diagrams to those shown on Figs. 3.14 and 3.15 have been given elsewhere [142–5]. The effect of creep relaxation on high-strain fatigue at 600 °C has been investigated [146] using a $2\frac{1}{4}\%$ Cr, 1% Mo steel, showing marked reductions in cycles to failure at longer hold times.

The ratio of the repeated tension to zero mean load fatigue strengths at long endurances does not appear to be highly temperature dependent within the working temperature range for a particular material. This is illustrated by the results obtained on a 0·4% C steel [147], shown in Table 3.26.

Although it is generally found that the addition of a tensile mean stress reduces the fatigue life at a given alternating stress level, the addition of an alternating stress, especially when its magnitude is small compared to the mean stress, does not always result in an increased creep strain. This can result in the curve drawn through experimental data plotted on an alternating-stress versus mean-stress diagram (as Fig. 3.14) bulging out at low alternating stresses to the right of the abscissa end-point. Forrest [4] suggests

TABLE 3.26

Temperature (°C)	Fatigue strength 15×10^6 cycles (MN m^{-2})		Ratio $\dfrac{\text{maximum tension}}{\text{zero mean stress}}$
	Zero mean stress	Repeated tension, 0–maximum tension	
Room	±480	0–800	1·7
320	±440	0–660	1·5
430	±415	0–565	1·4
560	±270	0–450	1·7

that this might arise for two reasons. First, the alternating stresses may accelerate microstructural changes in an alloy at elevated temperature which result in an increase in hardness, and, secondly, transcrystalline cyclic slip may relieve grain-boundary stress concentrations and thus inhibit grain-boundary cracking. The creep behaviour of materials when an alternating stress is superimposed on the static mean stress has been reviewed elsewhere [148].

3.8.3. Thermal fatigue

Thermal fatigue usually refers to the cracking of a piece of material which is not subjected to external loads but which is subjected to varying temperature conditions. Thermal stresses can arise in a piece of material if either free expansion or contraction is prevented or if it is heated or cooled in such a way that a thermal stress gradient exists across it. These thermal stresses are seldom large enough, in practice, to cause static failure, but repeated applications may lead to fatigue failure [4]. Thermal fatigue tests can be divided into two groups: (1) those in which the essential feature of the apparatus is that it imposes longitudinal constraint on the specimen so that thermal stresses are induced by the heating and cooling cycle and (2) those in which an unrestrained piece of material, usually in the form of a small disc thicker

8

at the centre than at the edges is alternately heated and cooled rapidly so that severe thermal gradients are set up across a diameter, giving rise to high cyclic stresses and strains around the periphery.

The thermal fatigue characteristics of several nickel base alloys were investigated [149] by subjecting small discs of material to alternate rapid heating and cooling. A succession of heating shocks were found to be generally more damaging than a succession of cooling shocks between the same temperature limits; the duration of the shock and the upper temperature of the heating cycle were the dominant factors. Cracks were initiated at the surface and were intercrystalline in origin and propagation; it was suggested that surface oxidation, which was intergranular, may have played a part in the cracking process. Discs [150], 40 mm diameter, 7 mm thick at the centre and tapered to an edge at the periphery, of wrought nickel–chromium base high-temperature alloys, were subjected to alternate 2-min immersion periods in a furnace at a temperature of between 750 °C and 1050 °C and, in water, at 20 °C; the number of cycles to the first appearance of a crack was noted. No evidence of a relationship between fatigue life and the static rupture strength or ductility of the different alloys was found. Except for some transcrystalline cracking below 800 °C, cracks were almost always intercrystalline, and it was suggested that oxide penetration facilitated cracking. Thermal fatigue tests have been carried out on solid cylindrical specimens of Nimonic 80A [151] in which the thermal expansion of the bar was restrained by a clamping frame of known stiffness. Temperature–reaction-force hysteresis loop measurement showed that, for a series of different temperature cycles giving lives less than 3×10^4 cycles, the experimental points fell around the same curve when plotted on a plastic strain range–life diagram. Several reviews of thermal fatigue have been written [152–4]. Although thermal fatigue tests such as those described are useful for particular applications (for example, the tapered disc tests are representative of the conditions at the leading edge of a turbine blade), it is difficult to apply the results to predict the results of other problems, because the behaviour is influenced markedly by the operating conditions. Forrest [4, 155], however, suggested that some guidance could be obtained by considering individually the factors determining the resistance to thermal fatigue. He considered the more important of these were the coefficient of thermal expansion α, the thermal conductivity K, and the resistance of the material to an alternating strain $\pm\varepsilon$. When thermal strains are a result of a material being constrained, the thermal conductivity K will be of no consequence; on the other hand, when thermal strains are a consequence of thermal gradients resulting from rapid heating or cooling, a high conductivity may reduce the temperature gradients and hence the thermal strains, provided, of course, that the rate of heating is not so high that the outside edges of the specimen reach their maximum temperature before any significant temperature change can occur in the body of the material. Thus, depending on operating conditions, either of the parameters ε/α or $K\varepsilon/\alpha$ can be used as an indication of thermal fatigue resistance, but there is little direct experimental evidence of the life–alternating-strain relationship under varying temperature conditions. Slow-speed constant deflection reversed bending tests [156], however, suggested that the resistance to alternating strain when the temperature was fluctuated in phase with the applied strain cycle was about the same as when the temperature was held constant at its maximum value.

3.8.4. Discussion

It is seen that the general pattern of the variation of fatigue strengths of ductile metals with temperature is similar to that of their static tensile strengths. As discussed in Chapter 2, cracking at elevated temperatures may originate at grain boundaries rather than in slip bands; certainly, fractures tend to become predominantly intercrystalline as the temperature is raised, especially when a tensile mean stress is present. This is not unexpected, for creep fractures generally occur as a result of grain-boundary sliding with the consequent nucleation and development of grain-boundary voids and fissures. Thus, a combined cyclic and tensile mean stress is able to initiate and develop surface cracks at a lower stress level than either could independently; certainly a cyclic stress causes a crack formed at a grain boundary by a tensile mean stress to spread more easily than it could if the static tensile stress was applied independently. For example [157], by assuming that intercrystalline cracks formed early in a high-temperature fatigue test and the total life was occupied wholly by crack propagation, high-temperature S/N curves can be made to correlate with corresponding room-temperature curves, that is, the main difference in life at a given stress level is due to the number of cycles spent in initiating a crack at room temperature. Similarly, tests on an 11% Cr steel [158] at 20 °C and 750 °C showed that, for a given value of P, although the life of a specimen at 20 °C subjected to the loading cycle $\pm P$ was shorter than that subjected to the loading cycle 0–P, there was little difference between the lives of corresponding specimens tested at 750 °C. This implies that, at high temperatures, intercrystalline cracks form just as quickly under the loading cycle 0–P as under $\pm P$. For, if a macrocrack forms early in a test, the life of a specimen depends merely on the tensile stress range, because no strain concentration occurs when the crack faces are pressed together, and a crack grows just as quickly under the loading cycle 0–P as under the loading cycle $\pm P$.

In addition to the increasing ease of grain-boundary cracking with increasing temperature, the general softening of a material as the temperature increases will result in the minimum cyclic stress necessary to cause continuing cyclic slip decreasing and will cause the fatigue strength to decrease at temperatures at which grain boundary cracking does not occur. Corrosive attack by the atmosphere will also increase in severity as the temperature rises and will lead to a decrease in fatigue strength. Both grain-boundary cracking due to the application of a mean tensile stress and corrosive attack are time dependent and hence lead to the fatigue strength at high temperatures becoming frequency dependent. A frequency dependence implies a waveform dependence, because the slower the speed of load application the longer the time per cycle for deformation to occur. Wave-forms having a flat peak (that is, cycles containing hold times) will cause a decrease in fatigue strength because the higher the ratio of the root mean square stress value to peak stress, the greater the opportunity for either corrosive attack or grain boundary cracking to occur. For example, a change from transcrystalline to intercrystalline cracking was observed [159] in an austenitic steel subjected to a strain range of ± 1.5 per cent at 600 °C when tensile dwell periods greater than about 10 minutes were introduced into the loading cycle. Also, if intercrystalline cracking occurs in the body of the material, easy fracture paths are provided for a macrocrack to follow, again resulting in a lower fatigue strength.

The fact that the fatigue limit of a strain-ageing material decreases as the temperature is raised initially, and then rises to a peak value before finally decreasing with increasing temperature, results from a balance between general softening with increasing temperature and the inhibition by strain-ageing (which, depending on diffusion processes, is enhanced as the temperature increases) of the slip processes leading to the development of a surface microcrack. This effect will presumably only occur with materials and test conditions such that grain boundary cracking plays no significant part below the peak temperature.

The modified Gerber- or Goodman-type diagrams (§ 3.5), with end-points corresponding to the tensile mean stress necessary to cause either creep rupture or a certain creep strain in a given time and the zero mean load fatigue strength at an endurance corresponding to this time, obtained at a frequency of stressing the same as that occurring in the practical situation of interest, seem to allow a safe prediction for any combination of mean and alternating stress; the Goodman straight line obviously gives the safer prediction.

If the applied cyclic stress induces metallurgical changes which tend to harden the material, a small alternating stress superimposed on a tensile mean stress may cause a decrease in creep rate, even though the super-imposing of the tensile mean stress reduces the fatigue strength (at a given endurance) of the material. A good high-temperature fatigue strength would be expected from a material able to retain a high resistance to cyclic slip within a grain, to sliding at grain boundaries, and to attack from the atmosphere. Because high creep resistance materials possess these properties, they usually have correspondingly good high-temperature fatigue strengths.

3.9. Effect of environment

Fatigue tests are normally carried out with the specimen surface in intimate contact with the surrounding atmosphere. That any chemical reaction between the cyclically stressed specimen surface and the atmosphere plays a part in determining the fatigue strength of some materials is apparent from data described later, which show that preventing the atmosphere from reaching the specimen surface may result in an increase in fatigue strength. It follows, therefore, that the in-air fatigue strength of some materials may depend on the humidity content of the atmosphere and indeed the experimental data show that the in-air fatigue strength of some of the aluminium alloys is less when the humidity is high than when it is low. The usually pronounced scatter of experimental results exhibited by the high-strength aluminium alloys may be partially a consequence of varying humidity, because it tends to be reduced when specimens are tested with their surfaces smeared with grease or mineral oil; this also tends to increase their fatigue strength at long endurances [2].

Tests carried out specifically in environments which chemically attack a material to such an extent that surface cracks develop and propagate at stress levels lower than those in air (that is, the fatigue strength is reduced by the environment) are called corrosion fatigue tests. Because the corrosion fatigue strength decreases continuously with increasing endurance, it is necessary to quote the fatigue strength at a particular endurance. Also, because corrosive attack is time dependent, the fatigue strength at a given endurance depends on testing speed. Several reviews of the effect of environment on fatigue strength are available [160–3]. The corrosion fatigue strengths of a series of metallic materials follow generally the same pattern as their ability to resist the corrosive attack of the environment, that is, materials which have a high resistance to chemical attack from a particular corrosive environment exhibit higher corrosion fatigue strengths in that environment than those materials having a lower corrosion resistance.

Examples of the types of S/N curves obtained by testing plain specimens of various metallic materials in reversed direct stress at 37 Hz in either air or in a brine spray [164, 165] are shown on Fig. 3.16.

In a corrosion fatigue test, the combined effects of cyclic stressing and corrosive attack enable a microcrack to develop at lower stresses than in an in-air test. Fatigue-crack growth rates, however, are relatively unaffected by environment (§ 5.9.4), depending on stress level and crack length, as in air. Hence, the lower the stress level at which a microcrack can form and develop to the macrocrack stage, the more slowly will it grow as a macrocrack across the specimen. This means that a much greater proportion of the total life is occupied by macrocrack growth [166]. This has two consequences. First, many surface cracks will have the opportunity to form and develop to significant depths before one reaches such a size that it causes complete failure

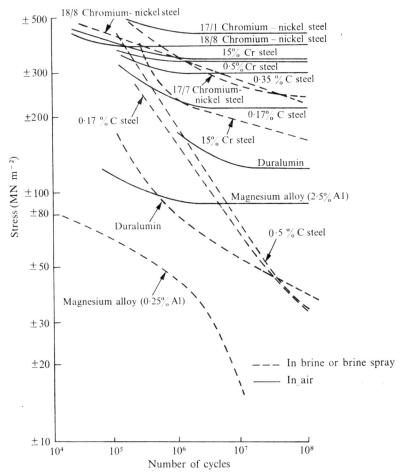

FIG. 3.16. S/N curves in air and in brine spray. (Taken from Gough and Sopwith [164].)

of the specimen; this results in a serrated fracture face (caused by surface cracks intersecting each other) which is characteristic of corrosion fatigue failures. Secondly, the fatigue strength at a given life may increase with increasing specimen size, because the larger the specimen size the greater the number of cycles required for a crack to traverse its cross-section. For example, the fatigue strengths given in Table 3.27 were obtained [167] using

TABLE 3.27

Specimen diameter (mm)	In-air fatigue limit (MN m⁻²)	Corrosion fatigue strength, 6 × 10⁷ cycles (MN m⁻²)
10	±210	±50
130	±195	±115

0·22% C steel rotating bending specimens either 10 mm or 130 mm diameter, tested in a dripping 3% salt solution. It is seen that, although the in-air fatigue strengths are similar, the corrosion fatigue strength (6×10^7 cycles) of the larger specimens is double that of the smaller ones.

Another consequence of the longer macrocrack growth stage is that, in general, the results of such tests show less scatter than those of conventional in-air tests. In air, scatter in life is associated more with the effect of local variations in microstructure on the development of a surface microcrack than with the growth of a macrocrack; since microcrack development occupies the major part of the life of a plain specimen (§ 4.11), variations in the number of cycles to develop a microcrack to the macrocrack stage have a marked effect on the over-all life. However, in a corrosion fatigue test, microcrack development occupies a much smaller percentage of the total life and, in addition, the presence of a corrosive environment enables a microcrack to develop to the macrocrack stage with much less dependence on the microstructure than in an in-air test.

3.9.1. Mechanism of corrosion fatigue

The shape, size, and distribution of the pits that form on both corrosion and corrosion-fatigue steel specimens when sprayed with either water or salt solution have been studied [168]. Corrosion pits tend to be roughly hemispherical at first, but then change to a saucer-like form and spread irregularly over the surface. Sharp root-like projections form at the bottom of the rounded pits, especially those in carbon steels sprayed with salt solution. Cyclic stressing accelerates the corrosion pitting and causes transverse extension of the pits by the development of crevices or fissures. Corrosion-fatigue cracks are usually transcrystalline, although intercrystalline cracking can occur in metals whose grain boundaries are attacked preferentially by the environment. The surface cracks found in components which have failed in service, or in specimens which have been subjected to corrosion for a considerable length of time, are wider at the surface than normal fatigue cracks as a result of the continual corrosive attack, but they taper below the surface to give the usual fine in-air fatigue crack appearance. This implies that when the leading edge of the crack is well removed from the surface, the effect of the corrosive environment is much reduced, and macrocrack growth is not so profoundly affected by a corrosive environment as the initiation and development of surface microcracks. The effect of environment on the propagation of macrocracks is discussed in Chapters 4 and 5.

The effect of a corrosive medium on fatigue strength is most severe when it is applied while the specimen is being cyclically stressed and in such a manner that the atmosphere has free access to the specimen surface. The first point is clearly illustrated by numerous fatigue tests [169] carried out on various steel and aluminium alloy specimens, corroded prior to fatigue testing. It was found that their subsequent fatigue strengths were as would be expected if the corrosion pits on the surface acted simply as mechanical notches; the fatigue strengths were therefore considerably higher at long endurances than those of corresponding specimens having the corrosive media applied continuously throughout a test. The second point follows from the fact that the presence of oxygen is known to be important in many chemical corrosive processes, and hence the most destructive conditions with regard to fatigue strength are those in which the atmosphere has free access to the specimen surface. Thus, if the corrosive fluid is sprayed or dripped slowly on to the specimen surface, the subsequent fatigue strength is lower than if the specimen is immersed completely in the corrosive fluid. In fact, if a specimen is immersed completely in some corrosive environments, the plain fatigue limit may not be affected significantly by the environment. For example [2], the plain fatigue limit of a carbon steel when completely surrounded by a salt solution in an air-tight chamber was found to be only slightly lower than the in-air value. Again, the normal in-air fatigue limit of 1015 steel plain specimens was obtained when they were tested completely immersed in deaerated water or 3 % salt solution, whereas spraying with water or salt solution produced marked reductions in fatigue strength [170]. Similarly, the plain fatigue limit of mild steel was unaffected [171] by immersing specimens completely in tap water. An indication of the fatigue strengths that might be expected in dripping brine and tap water can be seen in Table 3.28 (§ 3.9.2).

Rotating bending tests in salt spray on both a high-purity and commercial-quality zinc–magnesium–aluminium alloy [172] suggested that corrosion fatigue was a transcrystalline phenomena similar in nature to fatigue in air. Transcrystalline cracks developed from corrosion pits formed within the grains of the high-purity alloy, whereas transcrystalline cracks were initiated from intergranular pits in the commercial alloy. Intercrystalline cracking, when it occurred under corrosion-fatigue conditions, was found to be due either to very high cyclic stresses causing grain-boundary creep or to small amounts of intercrystalline corrosion occurring after long endurances at low stress levels. The high-stress grain-boundary creep occurred equally under in-air fatigue conditions and was not accelerated appreciably by corrosion conditions. It has been argued that the formation of pits is not a requirement for corrosion fatigue [173]. However, whether or not cracks form at pits in a corrosive environment depends on the stress level. At stress levels above the in-air fatigue limit leading to failures in less than a million cycles, slip-band cracking occurs before pits have developed. At stresses well below the in-air fatigue limit, there can be no slip, and hence no slip-band cracking; pitting is therefore necessary to initiate cracks.

The mechanism of corrosion has been discussed elsewhere [162, 174]. It is considered that the corrosive attack of a specimen in a wet environment is an electrochemical process in which certain areas of the surface of the corroding specimen are anodic with respect to adjacent areas, the whole surface therefore consisting of a series of anodes and cathodes in which metal ions pass into solution at the anodes. This division of a surface into anodic and cathodic areas could arise in two ways. First, if the environment was non-uniform and one condition of the environment favoured either anode or cathode reaction, an anode or cathode would be so formed on those parts of the surface. Secondly, they might be due to inhomogeneities such as inclusions or foreign bodies embedded in the surface or even small areas of plastically deformed metal. In general, chemical reactivity of these areas would be different from the bulk of the material, and so a system of cells would be set up with these areas as one electrode and the rest of the surface as the other. Because the corrosion products are formed in solution, there is no possibility of the reaction being stifled, and as the attack is confined to the anodic regions, this will be severe if the anodic areas are smaller than the cathodic elements. In conditions where the cathodic reaction is reduction of dissolved oxygen [163], the supply of oxygen to the specimen surface appears to be the factor controlling the rate of corrosion. It is possible, however, for corrosion to occur in the absence of oxygen if the cathodic reaction in the environment is evolution of hydrogen. The critical corrosion rate below which the environment has no effect on the fatigue limit has been investigated [173] and for a 0·18% C steel in 3% brine solution is equivalent to an anodic current density of 0·02 A mm^{-2}.

3.9.2. Fatigue strength in water and brine

The corrosion fatigue strength (50×10^6 cycles) of some common metallic alloys [2, 163], when tested in either dripping fresh water or dripping salt water (a 3% salt solution is often used in the laboratory to simulate a marine environment), are given in Table 3.28. The values should be considered as

TABLE 3.28

Material	Fatigue strength 5×10^7 cycles (MN m^{-2})		
	Air	Fresh water	Salt water
Mild steel	±250	±140	±55
3½% Ni steel	±340	±155	±110
15% Cr steel	±385	±250	±140
0·5% C steel	±370	—	±40
18/8 austenitic steel	±385	±355	±250
4½% Cu–aluminium alloy	±145	±70	±55
Monel metal	±250	±185	±185
7½% Al–bronze	±230	±170	±155
8% Mg–aluminium alloy	±140	—	±30
Nickel	±340	±200	±160

showing only a general trend in behaviour, because slight variations in the composition of the corrosive fluid, the method of its application, the speed and method of testing, specimen size, and slight changes in temperature may have a pronounced effect on the fatigue strength. Also, unlike fatigue results obtained in air, care must be exercised in the application of such laboratory data to design problems, because components in service are often subjected to the corrosive environment for a much longer time than laboratory specimens.

Forrest [4] gives data showing that the fatigue strengths (20×10^6 cycles) in dripping fresh water of various carbon and low-alloy steels have values of

TABLE 3.29

Material	Tensile strength ($MN\ m^{-2}$)	Fatigue strength, 5×10^7 cycles ($MN\ m^{-2}$)			
		Rotating bending		Reversed direct stress	
		Air	Salt spray	Air	Salt spray
0·5% C steel	970	±385	±43	±340	±40
15% Cr steel	665	±380	±140	±340	±170
18/8 Chromium–nickel steel	1000	±365	±245	±385	±230
17/1 Chromium–nickel steel	850	±505	±190	±435	±240
4½% Cu–aluminium alloy	430	±145	±55	±125	±40

between $\pm 90\ MN\ m^{-2}$ and $\pm 140\ MN\ m^{-2}$ irrespective of their tensile strengths. Bronzes, in particular copper–beryllium alloys, have very good corrosion fatigue properties, and so has titanium. The corrosion-fatigue strength of commercially pure titanium in dripping brine was found to be at least as good as the in-air fatigue strength at the same endurance [175].

The effect of differing testing methods (§ 3.4) on corrosion-fatigue strength was investigated [164, 165] by subjecting specimens of various metallic alloys to either reversed direct stress or constant bending moment rotating bending stress while being sprayed with a 3% salt solution. The results, given in Table 3.29, show little difference between the fatigue strengths at 5×10^7 cycles obtained by either testing method. On the other hand, it has been reported [161] that the corrosion fatigue strength of a given material was greater in reversed direct stress than in cantilever rotating bending; in some cases, the life of a specimen tested in reversed direct stress was five times that of a specimen tested at the same stress level in rotating bending. It was argued that this was because all anodic areas on the test-section were subjected to the same cyclic stress in the former test but only a fraction of them were in the latter test. Consequently, the rate of corrosive damage would be slower in the former than in the latter test. The reasonable agreement found in the earlier investigation [164, 165] between the results of the two testing methods could well be because a larger surface area of a constant bending moment specimen at any instant, is subjected to high stress levels than is the case with a cantilever bending specimen.

Tests on various steels and light alloys [176] at tensile mean stresses, and on various steels [177] under both compressive and tensile mean stresses, show that the effect of a mean stress on the corrosion fatigue strength appears to follow the same pattern of behaviour as occurs in in-air tests on the same material [176] (§ 3.5). Temperature too does not have a more marked effect on the corrosion-fatigue strength than occurs in corresponding in-air tests (§ 3.8). This arises because, although the severity of the corrosive attack increases with temperature, the effect is usually limited by the fact that the solubility of air in the corrosive liquid decreases with increasing temperature [161]. Because corrosion processes are time dependent, the corrosion-fatigue strength (based on a life of a given number of cycles) tends to increase with testing speed. Several investigators [178, 179], for example, found that the corrosion fatigue strengths (at a given endurance) of various metallic alloys when tested in either a water or brine environment were reduced as the testing speed was reduced. The fatigue strength also depends on the form of the applied stress wave; for example, the fatigue strengths of steel and aluminium alloy specimens [180] tested in dripping brine were less, for a given peak stress, when the stress cycle had a trapezoidal form having a flat-topped peak than when of the usual sinusoidal form, the fatigue strength decreasing the longer the time the stress was maintained at its maximum value.

In addition to tests in water and brine environments, corrosion-fatigue tests have been carried out in other environments. A $3\frac{1}{2}\%$ Ni steel [181] was found to have a fatigue strength (5×10^7 cycles) of about ± 160 MN m^{-2} in a steam environment. Rotating bending fatigue tests on $0\cdot17\%$ C steel specimens at 550 °C in either air or town-gas showed [182] that the fatigue strength at long endurances was higher in gas than in air, but was lower in gas than in air at short endurances; it was considered that the decrease in fatigue strength in the gas environment at high stress levels was due to hydrogen embrittlement of the steel. The effect of hydrogen on the fatigue strengths of a 26% Ni, 15% Cr alloy steel, a 43% Co, 20% Ni, 20% Cr alloy and Inconel 700 (45% Ni, 29% Co, 15% Cr) was investigated [183] at temperatures of 650 °C and 815 °C, using tubular specimens. Either dried air or hydrogen was blown through the specimen while its external surface was exposed to normal air and a heat source. It was found that the life, at a given stress level, of any of the alloys was not significantly different irrespective of whether air or hydrogen was blown through the specimen.

3.9.3. *Effect of humidity*

A change in the humidity of the atmosphere may effect the fatigue strength of some materials. Rotating bending tests, carried out at 150 Hz on AISI 4340 (0·4% C, 0·8% Cr, 1·7% Ni) steel, a 4% Al–titanium alloy, 60/40 brass, and a 6% Al–magnesium alloy [184], in either a low (less than 3 per cent) or high (greater than 85 per cent) relative humidity, showed that the fatigue strengths (10^7 cycles) of all four materials were higher in low than in high humidities. However, the difference was never greater than 5 per cent. Some of the steel and magnesium alloy specimens were coated with dodecyl alcohol prior to testing; this had the effect of increasing the fatigue strength at both humidity levels but the fatigue strength of the coated specimens tested in a high humidity never exceeded that of uncoated specimens tested in a low humidity. A somewhat larger effect of humidity has been observed with aluminium alloys. The fatigue strength (2×10^6 cycles) of a 6061 aluminium alloy [185] was about 15 per cent higher when tested in a dry atmosphere (5–9 per cent relative humidity) than in a moist atmosphere (85–95 per cent relative humidity). Variations in fatigue strength caused by testing aluminium alloys in atmospheres of differing humidities were suggested [186] to be due to variations in the properties of the surface oxide films formed in these environments.

In contrast to conventional laboratory corrosion fatigue tests was a series of fatigue tests carried out in the open air [187]. Vibrating cantilever sheet specimens, having a 6 mm diameter hole in the test-section, were tested in a special machine designed to accommodate 100 specimens. The machine, operating at 8 Hz, applied a constant bending moment to each specimen as well as a cyclic bending moment. The mean moment was applied throughout but only 4000 cycles of the cyclic moment were applied in an 8-min period each working day. It rained on about 50 per cent of the days that the specimens were exposed, and there was a fairly heavy dew every morning. The air also contained a fair concentration of salt. Two aluminium alloys, $4\frac{1}{2}$% Cu (2024-T3) and $5\frac{1}{2}$% Zn (7075-T6), were tested in both the unclad and clad conditions, the results in Table 3.30 showing that, for the particular test

TABLE 3.30

Aluminium alloy	Condition	Nominal stress ($MN\ m^{-2}$)	Average number of cycles of alternating stress to failure	
			Indoor	Outdoor
2024–T3	Bare	83 ± 172	464 100	146 100
2024–T3	Clad	83 ± 104	590 600	550 900
7075–T6	Bare	83 ± 172	276 900	92 000
7075–T6	Clad	83 ± 100	430 300	282 600

conditions experienced, the outdoor environment caused a more drastic reduction in the lives of the unclad than the clad specimens.

3.9.4. Protective measures

As indicated by the results in Table 3.30, the corrosive fatigue strength of a material may be improved by superimposing some type of protective layer which is more resistant to the corrosive attack of the environment than the bare material, on to the material surface. However, purely mechanical protective coatings suffer from the disadvantage that they are ineffective once the coating becomes discontinuous. For example, although the rotating bending fatigue strengths of steel specimens tested in dripping brine [188] were increased by the application of various organic (vinyl resin, phenolic varnish, silicone resin) coatings, when the coating was scratched, the fatigue strength was reduced to that of the unprotected specimens. Because of the possibility that discontinuities are likely to either exist initially or develop in service, it is desirable to use a coating which is anodic to the base metal, so that it will afford electrochemical protection after mechanical protection has ceased. Galvanized [189, 190] and sheradized [190] coatings give very satisfactory protection on steel. Because both chromium and nickel plating on steel are cathodic coatings and have relatively low fatigue strengths compared to those of the medium- and high-strength steels, they become discontinuous once fatigue cracks form (so permitting access of the corrosive medium to the steel substrate), and hence have only a limited value in preventing corrosion fatigue [191]. On the other hand, zinc and cadmium platings on steel provide anodic coatings and thus lead to an improved corrosion-fatigue strength. For example, both electro-deposited zinc and cadmium give reasonable protection against salt spray [190]. Sprayed aluminium also improves the corrosion-fatigue strength of steel specimens. Nitriding suitable steels has been found to increase their corrosion-fatigue strength; for example, that of a nitriding steel (10^8 cycles) tested in dripping river water was increased from about ± 75 MN m^{-2} to ± 390 MN m^{-2} by nitriding [192]. Table 3.31 gives fatigue strengths obtained in air and in a stream of tap water on a quenched and

TABLE 3.31

Material	Fatigue strength, 10^8 cycles (MN m^{-2})	
	In air	In water
SAE 3140, 0·4% C steel	± 460	± 105
SAE 3140 steel, cadmium plated	—	± 115
SAE 3140 steel, zinc plated	—	± 195
SAE 3140 steel, cyanided	—	± 110
Nitrided SAE 6120 steel	± 725	± 585
Silicon-impregnated 0·1% C steel	± 155	± 155

tempered SAE 3140 steel [193] having either a thin electroplated cadmium or zinc coating (0·0025 mm thick) or after cyaniding (0·1 mm thick case), an SAE 6120 nitrided steel (0·5 mm thick case), and a 0·1 % C steel having a 0·5 mm thick silicon impregnated case.

The results given previously in Table 3.30 show that aluminium alloys can be protected and hence have their corrosion-fatigue strengths increased by cladding with pure aluminium, although, as discussed later in § 6.4.4, the soft cladding results in the plain fatigue strength in air being reduced. The corrosion-fatigue strength of the $4\frac{1}{2}$% Cu–aluminium alloy tested in salt spray was improved markedly by zinc plating, and to a lesser extent by aluminium spraying [194]. Coatings of organic resins and enamels can afford aluminium alloys a high degree of protection especially when they have been anodized previously (see § 6.4.2 for the effect of anodizing on the fatigue strength in air). Testing a 0·6% Mg, 1% Si–aluminium alloy in air, dripping tap water, and dripping brine [195] showed that the fatigue strengths (10^8 cycles) in tap water and brine were about one half and one quarter respectively of that in air. Anodizing increased appreciably the corrosion-fatigue strengths in both the water and brine environments, although the in-air fatigue strength was now somewhat lower than that of the unanodized material. Coating with a special alkyd paint gave extremely effective protection even under the severest corrosion conditions, the fatigue strength of painted specimens when tested in brine being slightly higher than that of the unpainted material in air. To obtain protection with paint, the suitably prepared metal surface should have an appropriate inhibitive priming coat (for example, zinc chromate for steels and aluminium alloys) prior to the application of suitable covering coats intended to confer mechanical strength to the whole covering and to exclude as far as possible the corrosive moisture and oxygen which are necessary for attack upon the metal itself [163]. The use of paint, pigmented with zinc dust, on steel can also result in a marked increase in its corrosion fatigue strength [161].

Dissolved corrosive inhibitors such as the chromates and dichromates may reduce, or perhaps even eliminate, the danger of corrosion fatigue from water or brine. The concentration of the dissolved inhibitor must be kept at a suitably high value, otherwise a dangerous intensified action may result [161, 162].

Experiments have been carried out in which an electric current was passed between a steel fatigue specimen and the surrounding corrosive fluid (potassium chloride solution) [162], the rate of production of iron compounds through corrosion with different current strengths, the number of cracks which form, and the specimen life being noted. By increasing the value of the cathodic current, the production of iron compounds diminished steadily until a value was reached (which depended on stress amplitude) at which their rate of production was very small. This retardation of corrosive effects by cathodic current, however, did not appear to be successful when the corrosive fluid was acid. The effect of variation of the pH of the corrosive fluid has been discussed elsewhere [173]. A study of the influence of cathodic protection on the corrosion fatigue strength of mild steel in brine [196] showed that by decreasing the electrode potential of the specimen to about $-1 \cdot 0$ V, the corrosion-fatigue strength in brine was increased to its in-air value.

3.9.5. *Exclusion of the atmosphere*

If a specimen is immersed completely in a liquid, thus preventing free access of the atmosphere, the fatigue strength may not be reduced even though the liquid is normally considered corrosive, for example, tap or salt water. Thus, the amount of air (presumably oxygen) that can

TABLE 3.32

Environment	Fatigue strength, 30×10^6 cycles ($MN\ m^{-2}$)	
	Copper	Brass
Normal atmosphere	± 68	± 114
10^{-3} mm Hg vacuum	± 76	± 142
Damp purified air	± 70	± 116
Dry purified air	± 76	± 124
Dry nitrogen	—	± 134
Damp nitrogen	± 76	± 124

reach the specimen surface is an important factor in determining the corrosion fatigue strength, and it has been found that, if tests are carried out in an evacuated chamber, so that the amount of oxygen, water vapour, etc. in contact with the specimen surface is less than in normal atmosphere conditions, the fatigue strength of some materials may be increased above their in-air values.

The ratio of the fatigue strength (30×10^6 cycles) in a vacuum of 10^{-3} mm Hg to that in air was found to be $1 \cdot 26$ for brass, $1 \cdot 13$ for copper, and $2 \cdot 24$ for lead, but was only slightly greater than unity for Armco-iron and mild steel [197]. From the results (given in Table 3.32) of additional tests on copper and brass in various environments, it was concluded that acid and alkaline impurities in the atmosphere played little or no part in the action which resulted in the reduced fatigue strength in air, but that oxygen and water vapour played a vital part.

Reversed plane bending tests on thin strip copper specimens in various air pressures between 1 atm and 7×10^{-6} mm Hg [198] showed that the relationship between the logarithm of the life and the logarithm of the air pressure was, for a given cyclic surface strain, linear over the range investigated, the ratio of life in air to that at the lowest air pressure being about 1:20. Specimens tested in atmospheres of argon, nitrogen, or carbon dioxide had lives compatible with the partial oxygen pressures in the gases. Water vapour was found to increase the effect of oxygen slightly but had no effect on its own. It also appeared to make no difference to the life of a specimen in a vacuum if a test was stopped, air admitted for a certain time, and then the test continued in a vacuum. Slip-band cracks formed in specimens tested *in vacuo* after about the same number of cycles as in an in-air test. Similar tests on aluminium and gold specimens gave ratios of life in air to that at the lowest air pressure of 1:5 and 1:1, respectively. With the aluminium specimens, slip-band and grain-boundary cracks were equally common, again forming after about the same life as in an in-air test. However, unlike the copper tests, the effect of water vapour alone on the life of an aluminium specimen was as detrimental as water and air. It was concluded that the increased life found with the copper and aluminium specimens tested in a vacuum was due to the fact that the rate of spreading of surface cracks to cause complete failure was increased by the presence of air. It was further suggested that, at the crack tip, air could assist crack propagation in two ways; it might attack the highly strained metal at the crack tip and so weaken it or alternatively, a chemisorbed layer formed on freshly exposed surfaces as soon as they separated could make the separation irreversible and prevent adhesion on the compressive half-cycle. Subsequently, the S/N curves shown on Fig. 3.17 were obtained [199, 200] by testing strip specimens of a high-purity iron containing 0.5% C in either air or in a vacuum of 7×10^{-6} mm Hg. The cyclic surface strain at the fatigue limit is seen to increase from the in-air value of $\pm 1.1 \times 10^{-3}$ for tests in a vacuum, the life *in vacuo* at a given strain level above the fatigue limit *in vacuo* being about ten times that in air. Slip-band cracks were present in specimens tested, either in air or vacuum, at strain levels equal to and just below their respective fatigue limits.

Reversed direct stress tests carried out [201] on the $4\frac{1}{2}\%$ Cu and $5\frac{1}{2}\%$ Zn high-strength aluminium alloys in either air, vacuum (2×10^{-6} mm Hg), or various gaseous environments showed that, of all the constituents of normal air, only water vapour significantly affected the fatigue life. For example, improvements in life of about eight times, compared to a life in air of 10^5 cycles, could be achieved in either a vacuum or a well-dried environment. Coating the specimen with butyl-rubber was found to give a similar improvement in life. It was suggested that water vapour apparently facilitated both the initiation and development of surface cracks, presumably by interaction with clean surfaces exposed by slip. Reversed plane bending tests on 99% purity aluminium strip [202] showed that the life at a given strain amplitude was only slightly increased by decreasing the air pressure to 10^{-2} mm Hg. However, a more marked increase in life (about seven times that in air) occurred as the pressure was reduced to 10^{-4} mm Hg; little, if any, further increase in life resulted from reducing the pressure to 7×10^{-9} mm Hg.

The life of lead single crystals was found to be increased by a factor of about five when the air pressure was reduced to below 2×10^{-2} mm Hg [203]. However, similar tests on polycrystalline lead specimens showed that when the air pressure was reduced below 2×10^{-2} mm Hg, the life at a given strain range was increased by a factor of about 30. This difference was attributed to

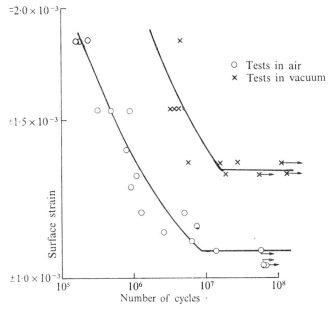

FIG. 3.17. S/N curves for 0·5 % C iron in air and a vacuum. (Taken from Wadsworth [200].)

the fact that intercrystalline cracking occurs easily in lead polycrystals in normal air (presumably due to corrosive attack of the grain boundaries by oxygen) but is suppressed when the oxygen pressure is reduced below 2×10^{-2} mm Hg.

The fact that, as mentioned earlier, completely immersing a specimen in a fluid may increase the fatigue strength implies that it is the prevention of the atmosphere (presumably oxygen and moisture) from reaching the surface rather than any reduced pressure effects that give rise to the improved fatigue strengths obtained in a vacuum. Indeed, quite marked improvements in fatigue strength can be obtained by immersing specimens completely in mineral oils. Cazaud [2] quotes some early results showing that the fatigue strength (10^7 cycles) of lead could be doubled by immersing the specimen

9

completely in oil. As with the tests in a vacuum mentioned above, this is presumably because of the suppression of intercrystalline corrosive attack leading to grain-boundary cracking in air.

Steels may have their plain fatigue limits increased by immersing in oil, but the effect is usually small. The rotating bending fatigue limit of SAE 4340 steel (0·4% C, 1·7% Ni, 0·8% Cr) was increased from ± 500 MN m^{-2} to ± 630 MN m^{-2} by coating the specimen surface with mineral oil [204]. Rotating bending tests on stress-relieved (1 hour, 650 °C, *in vacuo*) mild steel specimens of 7·6 mm diameter, either immersed completely in SAE

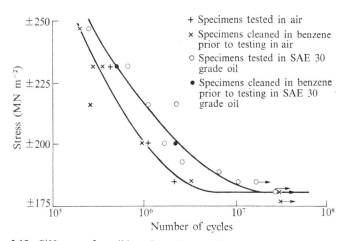

FIG. 3.18. *S/N* curves for mild steel rotating bending plain specimens tested in air and in SAE 30 grade oil. (Taken from Frost [171].)

mineral oil or in air [171], showed that, although the fatigue limit in oil was not significantly different from that in air, the lives at higher stress levels were greater in oil than in air, as can be seen in Fig. 3.18. This implies that it is the propagation of a crack across a specimen which is retarded by the absence of air rather than the initiation of a surface crack. Cleaning a specimen with benzene prior to testing had no effect on the life in either air or oil. As early as 1935, it was reported that the fatigue limit of steel wire could be increased by about 5 per cent by covering the wire in grease or heavy engine oil [205].

Tests on plain specimens of an 0·4% C steel, a magnesium alloy and a copper–beryllium alloy [206] showed that lives, at a given alternating stress, were increased by coating with certain polar organic compounds, but the full beneficial effect of the coatings was found only with compounds having a carbon chain of at least twelve. The coatings had no effect on the lives of titanium and high-strength aluminium alloy specimens, and resulted in only a slight improvement in the life of a 17/7 stainless steel. Organic solvents (benzene and xylene) had a deleterious effect on the fatigue life of those materials that were improved by the application of the oleophobic coatings. It was suggested that any improvement in life was due to a retardation of surface cracking, the coating presenting a barrier to water and oxygen molecules. It should be noted, however, that the stress levels applied, resulted in specimens having lives of less than a million cycles. Thus the results, in fact, imply that it is the development and growth of surface cracks not their initiation, which are retarded by the absence of air. Similarly, rotating bending tests [207] on plain specimens of En33 (3 % Ni) steel wholly immersed in various fluids (for example, medicinal white oil, silicone fluid, and mineral oil)

TABLE 3.33

Material	Condition	Environment	Fatigue strength, 10^7 cycles (MN m^{-2})
Copper	Annealed	Air	± 96
		Oil	± 94
		Water	± 103
Copper	Cold-drawn	Air	± 130
		Oil	± 132
		Water	± 133
70/30 brass	Annealed	Air	± 107
		Oil	± 106
		Water	± 113
70/30 brass	Cold-drawn	Air	± 93
		Oil	± 107
		Water	± 99
60/40 brass	Annealed	Air	± 180
		Oil	± 190
		Water	± 157

showed that the fatigue limit was little affected by the presence of a fluid, provided it was not corrosive, but that the life at a given stress level was greater than in-air. The fatigue strengths given in Table 3.33 were obtained [208] by testing plain copper and brass specimens immersed completely in either oil or water. It is seen that, in general, the fatigue strength of the immersed specimens is somewhat higher than that in air.

3.9.6. Discussion

Summarizing, the data show that, when an environment chemically attacks the surface of a fatigue specimen, pitting and surface roughness are produced, enabling surface cracks to form at cyclic stress levels less than those necessary in the absence of the environment; the surface cracks subsequently develop under the combined action of the cyclic stresses and any corrosive attack at their tips. Corrosive effects depend for their severity on free access of oxygen and moisture to the surface; the effects are small if this is not so. Therefore, corrosive action has a more pronounced effect on surface cracking than on the rate of subsequent growth of a crack into the body of material because, even if the corrosive fluid is able to reach the crack tip, it forms a barrier to the atmosphere, so nullifying to a great extent the corrosive attack. This is supported by data [209] showing that removal of the corrosive environment after a certain percentage of the expected life of a specimen does not significantly increase the over-all life, presumably because cracks had already formed and their subsequent rate of propagation was much the same in air as in the corrosive environment. Environments which reduce the fatigue limit of a plain specimen usually reduce the cyclic stress necessary to cause a crack of a given length to grow (§ 4.10) by a similar amount. Consequently, the length at which a microcrack starts to grow as a macrocrack (§ 4.11) will be about the same as in an in-air test. However, rates of macrocrack growth are relatively unaffected by corrosive environments, and as the stresses involved are lower, the rate of macrocrack growth will also be lower, so that the proportion of the total specimen life occupied by macrocrack growth is greater than for an in-air test.

If under severe corrosion conditions cracks form quickly even under low cyclic stresses, a large proportion of the life is occupied by macrocrack growth, and the corrosion fatigue strength will depend primarily on the crack propagation characteristics of the material. It is shown in Chapters 4 and 5 that the crack-propagation characteristics of plain carbon and low-alloy steels are essentially independent of their tensile strength. This implies that, under severe corrosive conditions, the corrosion-fatigue strengths of different steels will be approximately the same. Indeed, it has been shown [4] that carbon and low-alloy steels having tensile strengths between 300 MN m^{-2} and 1700 MN m^{-2} had corrosion-fatigue strengths in dripping water of about ± 90 MN m^{-2} to ± 140 MN m^{-2}. Thus, little advantage in corrosion-fatigue strength is gained by merely using stronger steels; improved fatigue strength requires a steel having improved surface corrosion resistance.

At low stress levels, the development of surface cracks is so slow that many are able to form and develop into the body of the specimen before one has grown far enough across the specimen cross-section to cause complete failure. This results in both the characteristic multi-cracking appearance of a corrosion-fatigue failure and a pronounced size-effect. Because corrosive attack is time dependent, the fatigue strength at a given endurance increases with increasing testing speed. The fatigue strength also depends on the shape of the loading cycle, decreasing, for a given peak stress, the flatter the form of the loading cycle or the longer the dwell time at the maximum stress in the cycle. Because the corrosion-fatigue strength of a material increases as the corrosion resistance of the material surface increases, any coating or process which minimizes or prevents the corrosive attack results in an increase in the corrosive-fatigue strength, coatings anodic to the base metal having the advantage that they afford electrochemical protection should the coating break down mechanically. Inducing high residual compressive stresses of sufficient depth into the surface layers (either by mechanical or metallurgical means) tends to increase the corrosion fatigue strength by preventing the growth of cracks formed at low stress levels.

The exclusion of oxygen and moisture from the surface of some metals results in an increase in fatigue strength, although the evidence suggests that this arises more from the retardation of the growth of surface cracks than from any increase in the cyclic stress necessary to initiate continuing surface slip and slip-band cracking. The effect of environment on the growth characteristics of macrocracks is discussed in Chapters 4 and 5. However, where the grain boundaries of a metal are attacked by the atmosphere with resultant intercrystalline cracking, removal of oxygen and moisture from the environment prevents this and so increases the cyclic stress necessary for crack initiation.

In some metals, for example, copper and steel, moisture does not play such an important role as oxygen. It is possible that, in these materials, oxygen is the dominant constituent which decides what fraction of the freshly created surfaces at the tip of a crack rebond and thus control the rate of crack propagation. With metals having an adherent oxide layer, such as aluminium, moisture appears to be the dominant constituent of normal air which affects the fatigue strength. For example, the fatigue strengths of aluminium alloys appear to be reduced in high-humidity environments. This may be associated with the effect which moisture has in determining the properties of the oxide film and both the stress level at which the oxide layer cracks and that at which the cracks pass into the base metal. The fact that the exclusion of the atmosphere reduces the growth rate of cracks means that surface slip-band marking and slip-band cracking have more time to occur in a vacuum than in air, and are therefore found to be more intense [210].

The precise roles that oxygen and moisture play in the initiation and propagation of fatigue cracks is not fullly understood at present; possible reasons both for the retardation of the development of a microcrack and the growth of macrocracks when the supply of oxygen and moisture is limited are (1) that some rebonding of the freshly created surfaces at the crack tip can occur (especially if the crack faces are pressed together for some part of the loading cycle) (2) that in the presence of air, the absorption of gas at the freshly exposed metal at the crack tip lowers the binding energy of the atoms, and (3) that the gas adsorbs on freshly created slip steps, so making microcrack development easier. However, because the prevention of free access of air to the specimen surface generally has a much more pronounced effect on crack propagation than on crack initiation, it is appropriate to leave further discussion to Chapters 4 and 5.

Care must always be exercised in applying laboratory corrosion-fatigue data to practical problems, particularly in those cases where the practical situation involves far longer exposure times (but not necessarily numbers of stress cycles) than are covered by the laboratory data. The longer the exposure time, the more likely is the problem to be dominated by corrosion aspects and successful service performance depends on correct material selection and appropriate surface protection.

References

1. GROVER, H. J., GORDON, S. A., and JACKSON, L. R. *Fatigue of metals and structures*. Bureau of Aeronautics, Dept. of U.S. Navy (1954).
2. CAZAUD, R. *Fatigue of metals*. Chapman and Hall, London (1953).
3. CUMMINGS, H. N. Wright Air Development Department Tech. Rep. 60/42 (1960).
4. FORREST, P. G. *Fatigue of metals*. Pergamon Press, Oxford (1962).
5. FRITH, P. H. *International Conference on fatigue, Institution of Mechinical Engineers*, p. 462 (1956).
6. MCKEOWN, J. *International Conference on fatigue, Institution of Mechanical Engineers*, p. 432 (1956).
7. GREENALL, C. H. and GOHN, G. R. *Proc. Am. Soc. Test. Mater.* **37**, 160 (1937) (Non-ferrous sheet materials).
   ANDERSON, A. R., SWAN, E. G., and PALMER, E. W. *Proc. Am. Soc. Test. Mater.* **46**, 678 (1946) (Copper alloys).
   GOHN, G. R. and ARNOLD, S. M. *Proc. Am. Soc. Test. Mater.* **46**, 741 (1946) (Copper–beryllium alloys).
   KENYON, J. N. *Proc. Am. Soc. Test. Mater.* **43**, 765 (1943) (Nickel alloy wires).
   BURGHOFF, H. L. and BLANK, A. I. *Proc. Am. Soc. Test. Mater.* **47**, 695 (1947); **43**, 774 (1943) (Copper alloys).
   GOETTSCH, P. E. Rock Island Arsenal Lab. Tech. Rep. No. 56-297A (1956) (Nodular cast irons).
   FOSTER, L. R. and STEIN, B. A. NASA Tech. Note D-1592 (1963) (Tungsten, molybdenum, niobium, and tantalum alloys).
   KELTON, E. H. *Proc. Am. Soc. Test. Mater.* **42**, 692 (1942) (Cast zinc alloys).
   ACHBACH, W. P. and WEINBERG, J. G. *Tabular summary of the notched and unnotched fatigue properties of titanium and titanium alloys*. Titanium Metallurgical Laboratory, Battelle Memorial Institute (1957) (Titanium alloys).
   ENRIETTO, J. F. and SINCLAIR, G. M. Department of Theoretical and Applied Mechanics., University of Illinois, T and AM Report No. 567 (1959) (Niobium alloys).
   LEWIS, W. C. *Proc. Am. Soc. Test. Mater.* **46**, 814 (1946) (Wood and glued joints).
8. BORIK, F., CHAPMAN, R. D., and JOMINY, W. E. *Trans. Am. Soc. Metals* **50**, 242 (1958).
9. DE KAZINCZY, F. *Jernkont. Annlr.* **150**, 493 (1966).
10. CUMMINGS, H. N., STULEN, F. B., and SCHULTE, W. C. *Proc. Am. Soc. Test. Mater.* **58**, 505 (1958).

11. DUCKWORTH, W. E. *Metallurgia* **69,** 53 (1964).
12. ATKINSON, M. *J. Iron Steel Inst.* **195,** 64 (1960).
13. BOYD, R. K. *Proc. Instn mech. Engrs* **179,** 733 (1965).
14. RANSOM, J. T. *Trans. Am. Soc. Metals* **46,** 1254 (1954).
15. SACHS, G., SELL, R., and WEISS, V. NASA Tech. Note D-239 (1960).
    SACHS, G., SELL, R., and BROWN, W. F. *Proc. Am. Soc. Test. Mater.* **59,** 635 (1959).
16. FRANKEL, H. E., BENNETT, J. A., and PENNINGTON, W. A. *Trans. Am. Soc. Metals* **52,** 257 (1960).
    FRANKEL, H. E., BENNETT, J. A., and CARMAN, C. M. *Proc. Am. Soc. Test. Mater.* **60,** 501 (1960).
17. EPREMIAN, E. and MEHL, R. F. NACA Tech. Note 2719 (1952).
18. INESON, E., CLAYTON-CAVE, J., and TAYLOR, R. J. *J. Iron Steel Inst.* **190** 277 (1958).
19. FINNEY, J. M. Dept. of Supply, Australia, Aero. Res. Lab. Struct. and Mats. Rep. 287 (1962).
20. FERRO, A., MAZZETTI, P., and MONTALENTI, G. *Phil. Mag.* **12,** 867 (1965).
21. VITOVEC, F. H. and LAZAN, B. J. Wright Air Development Centre, Rep. 53-122 (1953).
22. GOUGH, H. J. *The fatigue of metals.* Scott, Greenwood and Son, London (1924).
23. HEYWOOD, R. B. *Designing against fatigue.* Chapman and Hall, London (1962).
24. EVANS, E. B., EBERT, J., and BRIGGS, C. W. *Proc. Am. Soc. Test. Mater.* **56,** 979 (1956).
25. MORROGH, H. *Metal fatigue*, p. 220. Chapman and Hall, London (1959).
26. DEMMLER, A. W., SINNOTT, M. J., and THOMASSEN, L. *Proc. Am. Soc. Test. Mater.* **55,** 981 (1955).
    ROMUALDI, J. P. and D'APPOLONIA, E. *Proc. Am. Soc. Test. Mater.* **54,** 798 (1954).
27. TEMPLIN, R. L. *Fatigue and fracture of metals*, p. 31. Wiley, New York (1952); *Proc. Am. Soc. Test. Mater.* **54,** 641 (1954); **33,** 364 (1933).
28. ROWE, G. H. *J. Mater.* **1,** 689 (1966).
29. STROMEYER, C. E. *Proc. R. Soc.* **40,** 411 (1914).
30. YOSHIKAWA, A. *Acta metall.* **13,** 1025 (1965).
31. WEIBULL, W. *Fatigue testing and analysis of results.* Pergamon Press, Oxford (1961).
32. MANSON, S. S. William M. Murray Lecture, *Exp. Mech.* **5,** 193 (1965).
33. COX, H. L. Min. of Supply, R and M No. 2704, H.M.S.O. (1953).
34. MOORE H. F. and KOMMERS, J. B. *The fatigue of metals.* McGraw-Hill, New York (1927).
35. KAWAMOTO, M. and NISHIOKA, K. *Proceedings of the 4th Japan National Congress for applied mechanics* (1954).
36. CLEDWYN-DAVIES, D. N. *Proc. Instn. mech. Engrs.* **169,** 83 (1955).
37. TARASOV, L. P. and GROVER, H. J. *Proc. Am. Soc. Test. Mater.* **50,** 668 (1950).
    FLUCK, P. G. *Proc. Am. Soc. Test. Mater.* **51,** 584 (1951).

TARASOV, L. P., HYLER, W. S., and LETNER, H. R. *Proc. Am. Soc. Test. Mater.* **58,** 528 (1958).

38. VITOVEC, F. H. and BINDER, H. F. Wright Air Development Department, Tech. Rep. 56–289 (1956).
39. MANN, J. Y. Dept. of Supply, Australia, Aero. Res. Lab. Rep. SM 147 (1950).
40. GUNN, N. J. F. Min. of Supply, R.A.E. Tech. Note Met. 196 (1954).
41. MASSONET, C. *Proc. Am. Soc. Test. Mater.* **56,** 954 (1956).
42. CINA, B. *Metallurgia* **55,** 11 (1957).
43. OBERG, T. T. and WARD, E. J. Wright Air Development Department, Tech. Note, WCRT 53–117, (1953).
44. SINCLAIR, G. M., CORTEN, H. T., and DOLAN, T. J. *Trans. Am. Soc. Mech. Engrs.* **79,** 89 (1957).
45. HEMPEL, M. *Arch. Eisenhütt Wes.* **22,** 425 (1951).
46. FERGUSON, R. R. NACA Research Memo, E51, D17 (1951).
47. HANKINS, G. A., BECKER, M. L., and MILLS, H. R., *J. Iron Steel Inst.* **133,** 399 (1936).
48. MANN, J. Y., Dept. of Supply, Australia, Aero, Res. Lab., Struct. and Mats. Note 256 (1959).
49. GUNN, K. W. and WOODWARD, A. R. *Aeronaut. Q.* **13,** 271 (1962).
50. FISHER, W. A. P. and YEOMANS, H. Min. of Supply, R.A.E. Tech. Note, Struct. 162 (1955).
51. IRWIN, P. L. *Proc. Am. Soc. Test. Mater.* **25,** 53 (1925); **26,** 218 (1926).
52. PHILLIPS, C. E. and HEYWOOD, R. B. *Proc. Instn mech. Engrs* **165,** 113 (1951).
53. PETERSON, R. E. *Proc. Am. Soc. Test. Mater.* **29,** 381 (1929); *Trans. Am. Soc. Steel Treat.* **18,** 1041 (1930).
54. OUCHIDA, H. *Proceedings of the 2nd Japan Congress on testing materials, Kyoto*, p. 14. (1959).
55. MORKOVIN, D. and MOORE, H. F. *Proc. Am. Soc. Test. Mater.* **42,** 145 (1942); **44,** 137 (1944).
56. MOORE, H. F. and JORDAN, R. L. *Proceedings of the 5th International Congress on applied mechanics*, p. 188 (1939).
57. DOLAN, T. J. and HANLEY, B. C. University of Illinois, Engineering Experimental Station, Sixth Progress Report on an investigation of the behaviour of materials under repeated stress. (1948).
58. HORGER, O. J. and MAULBETSCH, J. L. *Trans. Am. Soc. Mech. Engrs, J. appl. Mechs.* **58,** A91 (1936).
59. GADD, C. W., ZMUDA, A., and OCHILTREE, N. A. *J. Soc. automot. Engrs,* **53,** 640 (1945).
60. HYLER, W. S., LEWIS, R. A., and GROVER, H. J. NACA, Tech. Note 3291 (1954).
61. HORGER, O. J. and NEIFERT, H. R. *Proc. Am. Soc. Test. Mater.* **39,** 723 (1939).
62. EATON, F. C. *Symposium on large fatigue testing machines, American Society for Testing Materials,* (1957).
63. FRANCE, R. D. *Proc. Am. Soc. Test. Mater.* **31,** 176 (1931).
64. WOODWARD, A. R., GUNN, K. W., FORREST, G. *International Conference on fatigue, Institution of Mechanical Engineers*, p. 158 (1956).
65. LOW, A. C. *J. R. aeronaut. Soc.* **59,** 629 (1955).

66. O'CONNER, H. C. and MORRISON, J. L. M. *International Conference on fatigue, Institution of Mechanical Engineers*, p. 102 (1956).
    WHITE, D. J., CROSSLAND, B., and MORRISON, J. L. M. *J. mech. Engng Sci.* **1**, 39 (1959).
67. FORREST, P. G. and TAPSELL, H. J. *Proc. Instn. mech. Engrs.* **168**, 763 (1954); *Engineering* **173**, 757 (1952).
68. CINA, B. *J. Iron Steel Inst.* **194**, 324 (1960).
69. FROST, N. E. and DENTON, K. *Metallurgia* **65**, 287 (1962).
70. CORTEN, H. T. and DOLAN, T. J. University of Illinois, Department of Theoretical and Applied Mechanics, Rep. No. 84 (1955).
71. OBERG, T. T. and ROONEY, R. J. *Proc. Am. Soc. Test. Mater.* **49**, 804 (1949).
    FULLER, F. B. and OBERG, T. T. *Proc. Am. Soc. Test. Mater.* **47**, 665 (1947)
72. RAGHAVAN, M. R. *Mater Res. Stand.* **4**, 290 (1964).
73. MASON, W. *Engineering* **115**, 698 (1923).
74. PARDUE, T. E., MELCHER, J. L., and GOOD, W. B. *Proc. Soc. exp. Stress Analysis* **7**, 27 (1950).
75. GOODMAN, J. *Mechanics applied to engineering*. Longman, Green, and Company, London (1899).
76. GERBER, W. *Z. bayer. Archit. Ing. Ver.* **6**, 101 (1874).
77. DOLAN, T. J. ASME Handbook, *Metals engineering Design*, p. 82. McGraw-Hill, New York (1953).
78. GOUGH, H. J. and WOOD, W. A. *Proc. Instn. mech. Engrs* **141**, 175 (1939).
79. GROVER, H. J. BISHOP, S. N. and JACKSON, L. R. NACA Tech. Note 2390 (1951).
    JACKSON, L. R. and GROVER, H. J. *Proc. Am. Soc. Test. Mater.* **46**, 783 (1946).
80. HOWELL, F. M. and MILLER, J. L. *Proc. Am. Soc. Test. Mater.* **55**, 955 (1955)
81. LAZAN, B. J. and BLATHERWICK, A. A. Wright Air Development Center Tech. Rep. No. 52–307 (1952); Rep. No. 53–181 (1953).
82. FINDLEY, W. N. *Am. Soc. Test. Mater.* **54**, 836 (1954).
83. GOUGH, H. J. and SOPWITH, D. G. *J. Iron Steel Inst.* **134**, 293 (1937).
84. GOUGH, H. J., POLLARD, H. V., and CLENSHAW, W. J. Aero. Research Council, R and M, 2522, H.M.S.O. (1951).
85. FROST, N. E. D.S.I.R., NEL Rep. AB Div. No. 17/56 (1956).
86. SAUER, J. A. *Proceedings of the 7th. International Congress for applied mechanics* **4**, 150 (1948).
87. SAWERT, W. Z. *Z. Ver. dt. Ing.* **87**, 609 (1943).
88. MARIN, J. and SHELSON, W. NACA Tech. Note 1889 (1949).
    MARIN, J. and HUGHES, W. P. NACA Tech. Note 2704 (1952).
89. BUNDY, R. W. and MARIN, J. *Proc. Am. Soc. Test. Mater.* **54**, 755 (1954).
90. MAJORS, H., MILLS, B. D., and MACGREGOR, C. W. *J. appl. Mechs.* **16**, 269 (1949).
91. MORIKAWA, G. K. and GRIFFIS, L. *Weld. J. Easton* **24**, 167s (1945).
92. RANSON, J. T. and MEHL, R. F. *Proc. Am. Soc. Test. Mater.* **52**, 779 (1952).
93. LOVE, R. J. Motor Industries Research Association Rep. No. 1950/9 (1950).
94. TEMPLIN, R. L., HOWELL, F. M., and HARTMAN, E. C. *Product Engng.* **21**, 126 (1950).

95. FINDLEY, W. N. and MATHUR, P. N. *Am. Soc. Test. Mater.* **55,** 924 (1955).
96. CHODOROWSKI, W. T. *International Conference on fatigue, Institution of Mechanical Engineers,* p. 122 (1956).
97. SACHS, G. *Z. Ver. dt. Ing.* **72,** 734 (1928).
98. COX, H. L. and SOPWITH, D. G. *Proc. phy. Soc.,* **49,** 134 (1937).
99. PETERSON, R. E. *Colloquium on fatigue,* p. 186. Springer-Verlag, Berlin (1956).
100. FINDLEY, W. N. and MATHUR, P. N. *Proc. Am. Soc. Test. Mater.* **55,** 924 (1955); *Proc. Soc. exp. Stress Analysis* **14,** 35 (1956).
101. FINDLEY, W. N., COLEMAN, J. J., and HANLEY, B. C. *International Conference on fatigue, Institution of Mechanical Engineers,* p. 150 (1956).
102. FINDLEY, W. N., MERGEN, F. C. and ROSENBERG, A. H. *Proc. Am. Soc. Test. Mater.* **53,** 768 (1953).
103. SMITH, J. O. University of Illinois, Engineering Experimental Station Bull. No. 334 (1942).
104. SINES, G. *Metal fatigue,* p. 145. McGraw-Hill, New York (1959); NACA Tech. Note 3495 (1955).
105. STULEN, F. B. and CUMMINGS, H. N. *Proc. Am. Soc. Test. Mater.* **54,** 822 (1954).
106. MARIN, J. *International Conference on fatigue, Institution of Mechanical Engineers,* p. 184 (1956).
107. FINDLEY, W. N., Brown University, Engng. Mats. Res. Lab. Tech. Rep. No. 6 (1958); *Trans. Am. Soc. Mech. Engnrs, J. Engng Ind.* **81,** 301 (1959).
108. NISHIHAKA, T. and KAWAMOTO, M. *Mem. Coll. Engng. Kyoto Univ.* **11,** 85 (1945).
109. FINDLEY, W. N., MATHUR, P. N., SZCZEPANSKI, E., and TEMEL, A. O. *Trans. Am. Soc. mech. Engrs. J. bas. Engng.* **83,** 10 (1961).
110. WYSS, T. *Bull. Am. Soc. Test. Mater.* No. 188, 31 (1953).
111. OBERG, T. T. and JOHNSON, J. B. *Proc. Am. Soc. Test. Mater.* **37,** 195 (1937).
112. MANN, J. Y. Dept. of Supply Australia, Aero. Res. Lab. Rep., SM 188 (1954).
113. KAWAMOTO, M., TANAKA, T., and OOKA, K. *Bull. J.S.M.E.* **6,** 8 (1963).
114. KROUSE, G. N. *Proc. Am. Soc. Test. Mater.* **34,** 156 (1934).
115. JENKIN, C. F. *Proc. R. Soc.* A**109,** 119 (1925).
116. JENKIN, C. F. and LEHMAN, G. D. *Proc. R. Soc.* A**125,** 83 (1929).
117. LOMAS, T. W., WARD, J. O., RAIT, J. R. and COLBECK, E. W. *International Conference on fatigue, Institution of Mechanical Engineers,* p. 375 (1956).
118. YAMANE, M. and SUDO, T. *Bull. J.S.M.E.* **5,** 625 (1962).
119. KIKUKAWA, M., OHJI, K., and OGURA, K. *Trans. Am. Soc. Mech. Engrs. J. bas. Engng.* **87,** 857 (1965).
120. WADE, A. R. and GROOTENHUIS, P. *International Conference on fatigue, Institution of Mechanical Engineers* p. 361 (1956). GROOTENHUIS, P. *Environ. Eng.* **1,** 10 (1962).
121. CLIFTON, T. E., HOCKENHULL, B. S., and SOLLARS, A. R., College of Aeronautics, Cranfield, Note No. 141 (1963).
122. HARRIS, W. J. *Aircr. Engng.* **31,** 352 (1959).
123. TEED, P. L. *The properties of metallic materials at low temperature.* Chapman and Hall, London (1950).

124. McCAMMON, R. D. and ROSENBERG, H. M. *Proc. R. Soc.* A**242**, 203 (1957).
125. BOONE, W. D. and WISHART, H. B. *Proc. Am. Soc. Test. Mater.* **35**, 147 (1935).
126. FORREST, P. G. *Metal fatigue.* Chapman and Hall, London, p. 158 (1959).
127. SCHWARTZBERG, F. R., KEYS, R. D., BROWN, M. J., and REIGHTLER, C. L. Martin–Marietta Corp., Rep. NASA-CR, 63–29 (1963).
128. ALLEN, N. P. and FORREST, P. G. *International Conference on fatigue, Institution of Mechanical Engineers*, p. 327 (1956).
129. LEVY, J. C. and SINCLAIR, G. M. University of Illinois, Department of Theoretical and Applied Mechanics, Tech. Note No. 39 (1954).
130. FRITH, P. H. *Properties of wrought and cast aluminium and magnesium alloys at room and elevated temperatures.* H.M.S.O. (1956); *Fatigue of metals*, p. 132. Institution of Metallurgists (1955).
   THORPE, P. L., TREMAIN, G. R., and RIDLEY, R. W. *J. Metals* **77**, 111 (1950).
131. BETTERIDGE, W. *The Nimonic alloys.* Edward Arnold, London (1959).
132. TOOLIN, P. R. and MOCHEL, N. L. *Proc. Am. Soc. Test. Mater.* **47**, 677 (1947).
133. MITCHELL, K. W., KING, H., and BRANDES, E. A. *Metallurgia* **61**, 15 (1960).
134. MITTENBERGS, A. A., WILLIAMS, D. N. JAFFES, R. I., and GROVER, H. J. Wright Air Development Corporation Tech. Rep. 60-427 (1960).
135. BOHN, J. R. and MURPHY, G. *Bull. Am. Soc. Test. Mater.* No. 57, 234 (1958).
136. DANEK, G. J., SMITH, H. H., and ACHTER, M. R. *Proc. Am. Soc. Test. Mater.* **61**, 775 (1961).
137. TAIRA, S. and KOTERAZAWA, R. *Bull. J.S.M.E.* **3**, 235 (1960).
138. FORREST, P. G. *J. Iron Steel Inst.* **200**, 452 (1962).
139. GOHN, G. R. and ELLIS, W. C. *Proc. Am. Soc. Test. Mater.* **51**, 721 (1951).
140. TAPSELL, H. J. *Symposium on high temperature steels and alloys for gas turbines, Iron and Steel Institute*, p. 169 (1952).
141. FORREST, P. G. and SMITH, P. A. *J. Inst. Metals* **92**, 61 (1963).
142. WEVER, F. *International Conference on fatigue, Institution of Mechanical Engineers*, p. 370 (1956).
143. LAZAN, B. J. and WESTBERG, E. *Proc. Am. Soc. Test. Mater.* **52**, 837 (1952).
144. DeMONEY, F. W. and LAZAN, B. J. *Proc. Am. Soc. Test. Mater.* **54**, 769 (1954).
145. TAIRA, S., KOTERAZAWA, R., and INOUE, M. *Bull. J.S.M.E.* **2**, 508 (1959).
   TAIRA, S., TANAKA, K., and KOTERAZAWA, R. *Proceedings of the 2nd Japanese Congress on testing materials*, Kyoto, p. 55 (1959).
   TAIRA, S. and KOTERAZAWA, R. *Bull. J.S.M.E.* **4**, 238 (1961). *Proceedings of the 4th Japanese Congress on testing materials*, p. 50 (1961).
146. EDMUNDS, H. G. and WHITE, D. J. *J. mech. Engng. Sci.* **8**, 310 (1966).
147. TRAPP, W. J. and SCHWARTZ, R. T. *Proc. Am. Soc. Test. Mater.* **53**, 825 (1953).
148. MELEKA, A. H. *Metall. Rev.* No. 64 (1962).
149. GLENNY, E. and TAYLOR, T. A. *J. Inst. Metals* **88**, 449 (1960).
150. FRANKLIN, A. W., HESLOP, J., and SMITH, R. A. *J. Inst. Metals* **92**, 313 (1964).
151. KREMPL, E. *International Conference on fracture*, Sendai, Japan, Vol. 3, D1-159 (1965).
152. KING, R. H. and SMITH, A. I. *International Conference on thermal and high strain fatigue, Institute of Metals*, p. 364 (1967).
153. YEN, T. C. *Bull. Weld. Res. Coun.* No. 72 (1961).

154. GLENNY, E. *Metall. Rev.* No. 61 (1961).
155. FORREST, P. G. D.S.I.R. N.P.L. Rep. M 2874, ML 5/1/01 (1961).
156. FORREST, P. G. and PENFOLD, A. B. *Engineering* **192**, 522 (1961).
157. MANSON, S. S. NASA Tech. Memo. TMX-52189 (1965).
158. TILLY, G. P. Min. of Aviation, N.G.T.E. Rep. No. R287 (1966); *Proc. Instn. mech. Engrs.* **180**, 1045 (1966).
159. PRICE, A. T. and ELDER, W. J. Central Electricity Research Laboratories, Lab. Note No. RD/L/N 9165 (1965).
160. GOUGH, H. J. *J. Inst. Metals* **49**, 17 (1932).
161. GOULD, A. J. *International Conference on fatigue, Institution of Mechanical Engineers*, p. 341 (1956).
162. EVANS, U. R. *Failure of metals by fatigue*, p. 84. Melbourne University Press (1947); *The corrosion and oxidation of metals*. Edward Arnold, London (1960).
163. GILBERT, P. T. *Metall. Rev.* **1**, 379 (1956).
164. GOUGH, H. J. and SOPWITH, D. G. *Engineering*, **136**, 75 (1933).
165. GOUGH, H. J. and SOPWITH, D. G. *J. Iron Steel Inst.* **127**, 301 (1933).
166. OKAMOTO, S. and KITAGAWA, H. *Proceedings of the 8th Japanese National Congress for applied mechanics*, p. 187 (1958).
167. HARA, S., HOSHINO, J., and ARAI, J. *Proceedings of the 10th Japanese National Congress for Applied mechanics*, p. 163 (1960).
168. MCADAM, D. J. and GEIL, G. W. *Proc. Am. Soc. Test. Mater.* **41**, 696 (1941).
169. MCADAM, D. J. *Trans. Am. Soc. Steel Treat.* **11**, 355 (1927).
      MCADAM, D. J. and CLYNE, R. W. *J. Res. nat. Bur. Stand.* **13**, 527 (1934).
170. DUQUETTE, D. J. and UHLIG, H. H. *Trans. Am. Soc. Metals* **61**, 450 (1968).
171. FROST, N. E. *Appl. Mater. Res.* **3**, 131 (1964).
172. STUBBINGTON, C. A. and FORSYTH, P. J. E. Min. of Supply, R.A.E. Tech. Note 289 (1958). *J. Inst. Metals* **90**, 347 (1962).
173. DUQUETTE, D. J. and UHLIG, H. H. *Trans. Am. Soc. Metals* **62**, 839 (1969).
174. WATERHOUSE, R. B. *Fatigue of metals*, p. 105. Institution of Metallurgists (1955).
175. INGLIS, N. P. *Metal Ind.* **90**, 185 (1957).
176. GOUGH, H. J. and SOPWITH, D. G. *J. Iron Steel Inst.* **135**, 293 (1937).
177. KITAGAWA, H. and MOROHASHI, T. *Proceedings of the 10th Japanese National Congress for applied mechanics*, p. 155 (1960).
178. MCADAM, D. J. *Proc. Am. Soc. Test. Mater.* **30**, 411 (1930).
179. ENDO, K. and MITAO, Y. *Bull. J.S.M.E.* **1**, 374 (1958).
180. ENDO, K. and KOMAI, K. *Mem. Coll. Engng. Kyoto Univ.* **27**, 415 (1965).
181. FULLER, T. S. *Trans. Am. Soc. Steel Treat.* **19**, 97 (1931).
182. ENDO, K. *Bull. J.S.M.E.* **3**, 41 (1960).
183. KLIMA, Y. *J. Japan Soc. Test. Mater.* **12**, 56 (1963).
184. SHIVES, T. R. and BENNETT, J. A. NASA Rep. CR-267 (1965).
185. BENNETT, J. A. *J. Res. natn. Bur. Stand.* **68C**, 91 (1964).
186. ECCLES, E. G. and THURSTON, R. C. A. Dept. of Mines and Tech. Surveys, Mines Branch, Canada, Metallurgy Div. Rep. PM-R-65-12 (1965).
187. LEYBOLD, H. A., HARDRATH, H. F., and MOORE, R. L. NACA Tech. Note 4331 (1958).

188. McMaster, R. C. *Proc. Am. Soc. Test. Mater.* **48,** 628 (1948).
189. Royez, A. and Pomey, J. *Revue Métall., Paris,* **56,** 122 (1959).
     Forsman, O. and Lundin, E. *Proceedings of the 1st World Metallurgists Congress, American Society of Metallurgists,* p. 606 (1951).
190. Gough, H. J. and Sopwith, D. G. *J. Iron Steel Inst.* **135,** 315 (1937).
191. Hammond, R. A. F. and Williams, C. *Metall. Rev.* **5,** 165 (1960).
192. Inglis, N. and Lake, G. F. *Trans. Faraday Soc.* **28,** 715 (1932).
193. Dolan, T. J. and Benninger, H. H. *Proc. Am. Soc. Test. Mater.* **40,** 568 (1940).
194. Gerard, I. J. and Sutton, H. *J. Inst. Metals* **56,** 29 (1935).
195. Inglis, N. P. and Larke, E. C. *J. Inst. Metals* **83,** 117 (1954).
196. Minami, Y. and Takada, H. *Proceedings of the 2nd Japanese Congress on testing materials, Kyoto,* p. 123 (1959).
197. Gough, H. J. and Sopwith, D. G. *J. Inst. Metals* **49,** 93 (1932); **56,** 55 (1935); **72,** 415 (1946).
198. Wadsworth, N. J. and Hutchings, J. *Phil. Mag.* **3,** 1154 (1958).
199. Wadsworth, N. J. *Internal stresses and fatigue in metals,* p. 382. Elsevier, Amsterdam (1959).
200. Wadsworth, N. J. *Phil. Mag.* **6,** 397 (1961).
201. Broom, T. and Nicholson, A. *J. Inst. Metals* **89,** 183 (1961).
202. Ham, J. L. National Research Corporation Rep. No. AF49(638), 1005 (1963).
203. Snowden, K. U. *Phil. Mag.* **10,** 435 (1964); *International Conference on fracture, Sendai, Japan,* Vol. 3, E 15 (1965).
204. Frankel, H. E. and Bennett, J. A. *Proc. Am. Soc. Test. Mater.* **55,** 891 (1955).
205. Goodacre, R. *Engineering* **139,** 457 (1935).
206. Frankel, H. E., Bennett, J. A., and Holshouser, W. L. *J. Res. natn. Bur. Stand.* **64,** 147 (1960).
207. Galvin, G. D. and Naylor, H. *Proc. Instn mech. Engrs.* **179,** 857 (1965).
208. Hukai, S. and Takeuchi, K. Sumitomo Light Metal Tech. Rep. Vol. 1, p. 88 (1960).
209. Evans, U. R. and Simnad, M. T. *Proc. R. Soc.* **188A,** 372 (1947).
210. Hudson, C. M. NASA Tech. Note, TN, D-2563 (1965).

Effect of stress concentrations and cracks on fatigue strength

4.1. Introduction

VERY few components or structural members are of uniform cross-section; most contain some form of change in cross-section resulting from a discontinuity such as, for example, a fillet, a hole, or an external groove or notch. For convenience, any of these discontinuities is generally referred to as a notch, irrespective of its geometric shape. Examination of components which have failed in service as a consequence of cyclic loadings, reveals that in many cases, the cause of failure has been the initiation of a fatigue crack at some point on the boundary of a notch. A crack forms here because the cyclic stresses at and near the notch boundary are higher than the nominal cyclic stresses remote from the notch.

An important difference between the behaviour of a statically-loaded notched member and a cyclically-loaded notched member of similar geometry and material may be illustrated by considering a cylindrical ductile metal bar containing a hole drilled transversely through a diameter. If subjected to a static tensile load, which gives rise to a nominal stress on the minimum cross-sectional area of, say, 80 per cent of the 0·1 per cent proof stress of the metal, the bar will not break, even though the metal in the highly stressed regions at and near the hole boundary will have deformed plastically. On the other hand, if the bar is subjected to a cyclic load such that the nominal stress range on the minimum cross-section is equal to 80 per cent of the plain fatigue limit of the metal, fatigue cracks will form at the hole boundary on the plane of minimum cross-sectional area because the local stress range here will be greater than the fatigue limit of the metal. Once formed in these highly stressed regions, cracks will propagate across the cross-section of the bar under the action of the nominal applied stress range and eventually cause complete fracture of the bar. Thus, in the former case, local stresses at the notch boundary higher than the yield stress merely cause plastic deformation but not necessarily catastrophic failure, whereas in the latter case, local stress ranges at the notch boundary greater than the plain fatigue limit initiate fatigue cracks which in many cases will continue growing under

the cyclic nominal stresses remote from the notch, until they cause catastrophic failure.

The need to provide data for the safe, yet economic, design of notched
components has led to fatigue tests being carried out on notched specimens.
Just as it is possible to estimate the plain fatigue limit (or strength at a given
endurance) of a batch of plain specimens of a given material, so it is possible
to determine the fatigue limit (or strength at a given endurance) of a batch of
nominally identical notched specimens. The ratio of the plain fatigue limit
to the corresponding notched fatigue limit is called the fatigue-strength

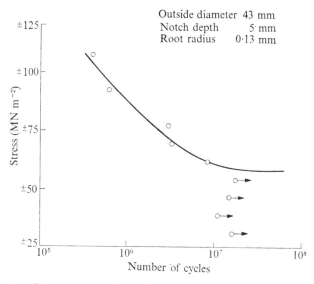

FIG. 4.1. *S/N* curve for notched mild steel specimens tested in reversed direct stress.

reduction factor, and is commonly denoted by K_f. The notch, of course,
may be of any shape, for example, a hole, a keyway, a fillet, or a circumferential groove, but generally the notch introduced into a laboratory specimen is either a hole or a circumferential vee-groove.

Fig. 4.1 shows an *S/N* curve obtained by testing in reversed direct stress
(zero mean load) a batch of mild steel cylindrical specimens, of 43 mm outside
diameter, having a circumferential 55° included-angle vee-groove 5 mm deep
and 0·13 mm root radius. Stresses are based on the minimum cross-sectional
area of a specimen; an arrow attached to a point indicates that the specimen
was unbroken at the end of the test. The notched fatigue limit estimated
from the experimental points on Fig. 4.1 is about ±58 MN m⁻²; it would
have a different value if a batch of specimens of the same material but containing a notch of a different geometry were tested. The notched fatigue

limit therefore, depends not only on the material but on the geometry of the notch.

The life of a broken notched specimen is the sum of the number of stress cycles required to initiate a surface crack in, and develop it through the highly stressed material at and around the notch root, and those required to propagate this crack across the remainder of the specimen cross-section which is subjected only to the applied nominal cyclic stresses. The ratio of the number of cycles spent in these two stages will vary with the material, notch geometry, specimen size, and stress level. Cracks may form quickly at the roots of sharp notches, even at low stress levels, and their propagation across the specimen may occupy the major part of the life. Indeed, if the notch is very sharp and the nominal stress range sufficiently small (or if the loading cycle is wholly compressive), cracks may form at the notch root which do not continue to grow across the specimen cross-section. Thus, the fact that a notched specimen is unbroken after testing does not necessarily imply that the material at the notch root is uncracked, a point that has often been overlooked in the interpretation of notched fatigue data. It follows, therefore, that the notched fatigue limit may be given by either the maximum cyclic stress which will just not initiate a crack at the notch root or that which will just not cause a crack to grow so as to cause complete failure. In many cases, these two fatigue limits are identical, but for some types of sharply notched specimens, they may well be different. Where confusion is likely to occur, that based on broken and unbroken specimens will be referred to as the conventional notched fatigue limit.

If a cylindrical specimen contains a circumferential sharp vee-notch, cracks can form at low nominal stresses, and the appearance of the fracture face shows that a crack forms all round the periphery of the notch root and grows uniformly across the cross-section, the final circularly-shaped static fracture area being the more central the higher the applied nominal stress level. On the other hand, if the notch root is blunt, a crack may form and develop from only one segment of the notch periphery, especially if the nominal stress level is near to the notched fatigue limit, the final static fracture area being located at the opposite side of specimen cross-section. At higher stress levels, cracks will again tend to form all round the notch root periphery, the final static failure area moving toward the centre of the specimen the higher the stress level.

It would seem obvious that if cracking is to be avoided at the root of a notch, the maximum local stress range at any point on the notch boundary should not exceed the fatigue limit of the specimen material. However, extensive laboratory fatigue data on notched test-pieces have been published which imply that local stress ranges greater than the plain fatigue limit of the specimen material can be tolerated without the specimen breaking, and much effort has gone into establishing relationships which supposedly enable designers to predict the nominal stress range that a notched component can withstand without breaking. The fact that notched specimens of some materials can withstand nominal cyclic stresses that are higher proportions of the plain fatigue limits of the materials than is the case with similarly notched specimens of other materials has led to the former materials being termed 'notch insensitive' and the latter 'notch sensitive'. It is important to emphasize at the outset that, unless a designer is fully conversant with the interpretation of notched fatigue data, this classification of materials may be misleading.

If it is required to compare the notched fatigue limit of a batch of notched specimens to the plain fatigue strength of the material, care must be exercised in machining the specimens to ensure that the material at the notch root is in as near as possible the same condition as that on the surface of a plain specimen, that is, work-hardening and induced residual stresses are kept to a minimum. Work-hardening and residual stresses, for some materials, can be minimized by stress-relieving the specimens after machining.

It is not unreasonable to expect that the value of the maximum stress range at the notch root, calculated from the elastic stress concentration factor, is an important factor in determining whether or not a crack forms at the root of a notch cut in a material whose plain fatigue limit is less than its yield or 0·1 per cent proof stress. In this chapter, the factors governing both the initiation of a crack at a notch and whether or not this crack grows to cause complete failure of a specimen are discussed. The rate at which a crack grows is discussed in Chapter 5.

4.2. Elastic stress distribution around a notch

The elastic stress distribution around a notch is dominated by the form of the notch, and the most important feature is the elevation of stresses in the vicinity of the notch root. If the maximum elastic boundary stress created by a given notch in a uniaxially longitudinally loaded specimen is known, the ratio of this maximum longitudinal elastic stress at the notch root σ_{max}, to the nominal elastic stress σ applied to the specimen, that is, σ_{max}/σ, is commonly denoted by K_t, where K_t is called the geometric elastic stress concentration factor. Similarly values of K_t can be obtained for notched specimens loaded in torsion, K_t now being the ratio of the maximum elastic shear stress at the notch root or boundary to the nominal shear stress applied to the specimen. Values of K_t for a wide variety of notch profiles due to either tension, bending or torsion loads are available [1–3], the data usually being presented in graphical form. Some data for the more common configurations encountered in practice are given in Appendix 7. The value of K_t depends on whether the nominal stress is based either on the area of the minimum cross-section of the specimen (that is, net area) or on the over-all cross-section of the specimen, ignoring the presence of the notch (that is, gross area). In practice, nominal stresses are usually based on net areas and consequently K_t is generally expressed in terms of net area stress.

Stress concentration factors provide a convenient single parameter description of the stress conditions at a notch root, but their utility is limited because they do not give information on the stress distribution around the notch. The localized nature of the high stress in the vicinity of a notch is

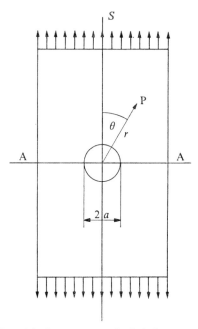

FIG. 4.2. Stresses around a hole in a sheet.

illustrated by the elastic stress distribution around a circular hole in a thin rectangular sheet whose boundaries are an infinite distance away from the centre of the hole. The stresses at the point P (Fig. 4.2) due to a longitudinal tensile stress distributed uniformly along two opposite edges of the sheet are given by [4],

$$\sigma_r = \frac{S}{2}\left(1-\frac{a^2}{r^2}\right)+\frac{S}{2}\left\{\left(1+\frac{3a^4}{r^4}-\frac{4a^2}{r^2}\right)\cos 2\theta\right\},$$

$$\sigma_\theta = \frac{S}{2}\left(1+\frac{a^2}{r^2}\right)-\frac{S}{2}\left(1+\frac{3a^4}{r^4}\right)\cos 2\theta,$$

$$\tau_{r\theta} = \frac{S}{2}\left(1-\frac{3a^4}{r^4}+\frac{2a^2}{r^2}\right)\sin 2\theta.$$

The longitudinal stress along the cross-section of the sheet through the diameter of the hole AA is obtained by putting $\theta = \pi/2$ in the second equation, that is,

$$\sigma_{\theta AA} = \frac{S}{2}\left(2+\frac{a^2}{r^2}+\frac{3a^4}{r^4}\right).$$

At the edge of the hole ($r = a$) on this section $\sigma_{\theta AA}$ has a maximum value of $3S$; this value approaches S rapidly as r increases.

In the case of a circumferentially notched cylindrical specimen subjected to tension or bending, the stress distribution is dominated by the notch root

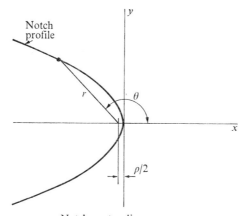

Notch profile

θ

r

$\rho/2$

Notch root radius $= \rho$

FIG. 4.3. Notch root nomenclature.

radius ρ. Provided that the notch depth is at least equal to ρ and the minimum specimen diameter is at least 10ρ then, in terms of the nomenclature of Figs. 4.2 and 4.3, $\sigma_{\theta AA}$ is given by [5]

$$\sigma_{\theta AA} = \frac{\sigma_{max}}{2\left(1+\frac{2r}{\rho}\right)^{1/2}}\left(1+\frac{1}{1+\frac{2r}{\rho}}\right),$$

where σ_{max} is the stress at the root of the notch. As $\rho \rightarrow 0$ the stress field approaches that for a crack, and can be conveniently expressed in terms of the opening mode stress intensity factor K_I (§ 5.2.1). Using the coordinate systems of Figs. 4.3 and 5.1, the stresses at a point near the notch root are given [6] by

$$\sigma_x = \frac{K_I}{(2\pi r)^{1/2}}\cos\frac{\theta}{2}\left(1-\sin\frac{\theta}{2}\sin\frac{3\theta}{2}\right)-\frac{K_I}{(2\pi r)^{1/2}}\frac{\rho}{2r}\cos\frac{3\theta}{2},$$

$$\sigma_y = \frac{K_I}{(2\pi r)^{1/2}}\cos\frac{\theta}{2}\left(1+\sin\frac{\theta}{2}\sin\frac{3\theta}{2}\right)+\frac{K_I}{(2\pi r)^{1/2}}\frac{\rho}{2r}\cos\frac{3\theta}{2},$$

$$\tau_{xy} = \frac{K_I}{(2\pi r)^{1/2}}\sin\frac{\theta}{2}\cos\frac{\theta}{2}\cos\frac{3\theta}{2}-\frac{K_I}{(2\pi r)^{1/2}}\frac{\rho}{2r}\sin\frac{3\theta}{2}.$$

These equations contain terms which vanish as $\rho \to 0$. The stress intensity factor K_{I} is related to the stress concentration factor K_t by the expression [7]

$$K_{\mathrm{I}} = \lim_{\rho \to 0} \tfrac{1}{2} K_t \sigma_{\mathrm{nom}} (\pi\rho)^{1/2},$$

where σ_{nom} is the nominal stress in the notched specimen.

The value of the elastic stress gradient at the root of a notch may be obtained by differentiating the appropriate stress distribution equation. Table 4.1 gives simple formulae [8] for obtaining an approximate estimate

TABLE 4.1

Type of notch	Type of loading	G
Hole in plate	longitudinal tension	$2 \cdot 3/\rho$
Fillet in bar	longitudinal tension	$2 \cdot 6/\rho$
Shallow groove in bar	longitudinal tension	$2 \cdot 5/\rho$
Deep groove in bar (depth $> \tfrac{1}{4}$ width or diameter of bar)	longitudinal tension	$1 \cdot 9/\rho$
Shallow groove in bar	bending	$2 \cdot 5/\rho$
Deep groove in bar	bending	$1 \cdot 9/\rho + 2/d$

of G due to a uniaxial loading, where G is the maximum longitudinal stress gradient at the notch root divided by the maximum longitudinal elastic stress, ρ is the notch root radius, and d is the diameter or depth of specimen.

4.3. Behaviour of notched laboratory specimens at zero mean load

4.3.1. Experimental data

There is a vast amount of zero mean load notched fatigue data scattered throughout the literature; Heywood [9] has collected and summarized much of what was available. This section presents some results selected from the literature, illustrating how the experimentally determined value of K_f relates to the K_t value appropriate to the notch and specimen geometry: in all cases, the notched fatigue limit used to determine K_f was taken as the maximum cyclic stress that would not cause a specimen to break completely, that is, that defined previously as the conventional notched fatigue limit. For materials which do not show a clearly defined fatigue limit, K_f is based on an endurance of at least 10^7 cycles. The data given below are typical of the behaviour of specimens cut from wrought ductile metals and alloys and, unless stated otherwise, have been obtained from specimens tested in the as-machined condition.

Many notched fatigue data have been obtained on relatively small cylindrical specimens (about 6–25 mm diameter) containing notches having K_t values between 1 and 4, on the grounds that many discontinuities in service give rise to stress concentration factors in this range; typical results are given in Tables 4.2–4.5.

T A B L E 4.2

Rotating bending fatigue data for circumferentially notched specimens [10]

	Specimen details				K_t	
Notch type	Outside diameter (mm)	Notch depth (mm)	Root radius (mm)	K_t	0·4% C steel	5½% Zn–aluminium alloy
60°vee	7·6	0.64	0·25	2·6	2·3	2·4
Semicircular	3·7	0·25	0·25	2·0	2·0	2·3
Semicircular	7·1	0·50	0·5	2·0	1·9	1·9
Semicircular	14·7	1·0	1·0	2·0	1·8	1·8
60°vee	10·2	2·2	0·25	2·9	2·4	—
60°vee	10·2	2·4	0·25	3·1	2·3	—
60°vee	10·2	2·4	0·64	2·1	2·1	—
60°vee	10·2	2·4	1·5	1·6	1·4	—

Some data have been obtained on sheet specimens containing either a central hole or two opposite edge-notches. Sheet specimens if sufficiently thin have an advantage in that the elastic stress distribution can be obtained directly from two-dimensional photo-elastic models. On the other hand, when tested in reversed direct stress, guide plates must be fitted to prevent buckling during the compression half of the loading cycle. Typical results are given in Tables 4.6 and 4.7.

T A B L E 4.3

Rotating bending fatigue data for circumferentially vee-notched specimens 10 mm outside diameter [11]

	Notch details			K_t		
Included angle (degrees)	Depth (mm)	Root radius (mm)	K_t	BS 6L1 4% Cu–aluminium alloy	DTD 683 5½% Zn–aluminium alloy	Z3Z magnesium alloy
20	1·0	0·25	2·9	1·9	2·0	2·7
30	1·0	0·25	2·9	2·5	1·7	2·6
45	1·0	0·25	2·9	2·1	1·8	2·5
60	1·0	0·25	2·9	2·1	2·0	2·5
80	1·0	0·25	2·9	2·1	1·9	2·5
100	1·0	0·25	2·9	2·0	1·7	2·1
60	0·5	0·25	2·9	1·9	1·9	2·7
60	1·0	0·25	2·9	2·1	2·0	2·5
60	1·5	0·25	2·9	2·3	1·9	2·9
60	2·0	0·25	2·7	2·6	1·7	3·3
60	2·5	0·25	2·6	3·1	2·4	3·9
60	1·0	0·25	2·9	2·1	2·0	2·5
60	1·0	0·5	2·3	2·0	1·7	2·1
60	1·0	0·89	1·9	1·5	1·4	1·9
60	1·0	1·0	1·9	1·6	1·1	1·6

TABLE 4.4

Rotating bending fatigue data for aluminium alloy specimens, 7·6 mm minimum diameter, containing circumferential fillets of various radii [12]

K_t	K_f		
	24S–T4 $4\frac{1}{2}\%$ Cu $1\frac{1}{2}\%$ Mg	61S–T6 1% Mg	75S–T6 $5\frac{1}{2}\%$ Zn $2\frac{1}{2}\%$ Mg
1·4	1·4	1·2	1·2
1·8	1·7	1·8	1·5

TABLE 4.5

Reversed direct stress fatigue data for aluminium and magnesium alloy circumferentially vee-notched specimens, 10 mm outside diameter, notch depth 0·64 mm or 1·27 mm [13]

Material	K_f		
	$K_t = 1·6$	$K_t = 2·4$	$K_t = 3·4$
Aluminium alloys			
14S–T6 $4\frac{1}{2}\%$ Cu, $\frac{1}{2}\%$ Mg ⎫	1·1	1·8	2·7
24S–T4 $4\frac{1}{2}\%$ Cu, $1\frac{1}{2}\%$ Mg ⎬ rolled	1·4	2·1	2·5
75S–T6 $5\frac{1}{2}\%$ Zn, $2\frac{1}{2}\%$ Mg ⎭	1·3	—	2·0
14S–T6 ⎫	—	—	2·9
24S–T4 ⎬ extruded	—	—	2·7
75S–T6 ⎭	—	—	2·8
Magnesium alloy $5\frac{1}{2}\%$ Zn	—	2·2	2·9

TABLE 4.6

Reversed direct stress fatigue data for tests on 64 mm wide sheet specimens 2 mm thick, containing two opposite parallel-sided edge-notches of various root radii [14]

Notch depth (mm)	K_t	K_f		
		24S–T3 aluminium alloy ($4\frac{1}{2}\%$ Cu, $1\frac{1}{2}\%$ Mg)	75S–T6 aluminium alloy ($5\frac{1}{2}\%$ Zn, $2\frac{1}{2}\%$ Mg)	SAE 4130 steel ($0·4\%$ C)
9·5	2	1·8	1·9	1·7
0·24	4	2·0	2·4	2·4
9·5	4	3·1	4·0	3·5
33	4	3·0	3·0	3·6
9·5	5	3·4	5·0	4·7

TABLE 4.7

Reversed direct stress fatigue data for 17/7 stainless steel sheet specimens 57 mm wide, 0·94 mm thick, containing either a central hole or two opposite parallel-sided edge-notches 4·5 mm deep [15]

Notch details	K_t	K_f
19 mm diameter central hole	2·3	2·1
1·45 mm root radius edge-notches	4·0	3·5
0·8 mm root radius edge-notches	5·0	4·6

TABLE 4.8

Rotating bending fatigue data for geometrically similar specimens containing circumferential semicircular grooves of radius 0·08 times the minimum diameter of a specimen, $K_t = 2$

Material	K_f					Reference
	Specimen diameter (mm)					
	3·2	6·4	12·7	24	44	
75S–T6, 5½% Zn aluminium alloy	1·8	2·2	2·2	1·7	1·6†	16
SAE 4340 steel	1·6	1·7	1·6	1·6	1·8	17
SAE 1020 steel	1·6	1·6	1·6	1·6	1·9	18
SAE 4130 steel	2·0	1·9	1·8	1·9	1·9	18
SAE 1035 steel, as-machined	1·4	1·5	1·8	1·8	1·8	18
SAE 1035 steel, stress-relieved	1·6	1·9	2·0	—	—	18

† Similar specimens with $K_t = 20$, gave $K_f = 1·8$

TABLE 4.9

Rotating bending fatigue data for geometrically similar specimens containing a circumferential hyperbolic groove, $K_t = 3·3$ [19]

Specimen diameter (mm)	K_f		
	0·18% C steel	0·37% C steel	Nickel–Molybdenum alloy steel
5	1·7	2·1	2·4
10	1·9	2·2	2·5
20	2·4	2·3	3·0
100	2·6	2·3	3·3

Tests have been carried out on geometrically similar notched specimens (that is, having the same K_t value) to see whether K_f varies with changing specimen size; some results are given in Tables 4.8–4.10.

Several workers have tested batches of cylindrical specimens containing a circumferential notch, different batches having notches of different root

TABLE 4.10

Reversed direct stress fatigue data for geometrically similar specimens containing a transverse hole of diameter one-sixth the outside diameter of the specimen, $K_t = 2 \cdot 8$ [20]

Diameter of transverse hole (mm)	K_f	
	Mild steel	Nickel–chromium alloy steel
5·5	2·2	2·8
4·0	2·0	2·8
2·4	1·7	2·4
1·4	1·6	2·3
0·8	1·8	2·6

TABLE 4.11

Reversed direct stress fatigue data for 43 mm outside diameter specimens containing circumferential 55° vee-notch 5 mm deep [20]

Notch root radius (mm)	K_t	K_f	
		Mild steel	Nickel–chromium alloy steel
5	2·0	2·2	—
0·63	4·4	3·8	5·0
0·05	14	3·8	8·2

TABLE 4·12

Rotating bending fatigue data for 12 mm outside diameter specimens containing a circumferential 60° vee-groove 1·9 mm deep [21]

Root radius (mm)	K_t	K_f (10^8 cycles)	
		75S–T6 aluminium alloy	24S–T6 aluminium alloy
12·7	1·1	1·1	—
2·7	1·4	1·5	1·4
1·6	1·6	1·6	—
0·8	2·0	2·0	1·7
0·005	18	2·8	2·1

radius but all being the same depth. An assessment of the 'notch sensitivity' of the material is often based on the manner in which K_f changes with increasing K_t the highest value of K_t tested generally being limited by the smallest root radius that it was possible to machine. Typical results are given in Tables 4.11–4.13.

TABLE 4.13

Rotating bending fatigue data for 12·7 mm outside diameter specimens containing circumferential vee-notches 1·9 mm deep

Root radius (mm)	K_t	K_f (10⁸ cycles)		
		Copper† [22]	4½% Cu–aluminium alloy [22]	5½% Zn–aluminium alloy [23]
2·0	1·5	1·2	1·4	1·5
0·46	2·4	1·4	2·1	1·7
0·15	3·8	1·4	2·7	1·7
0·08	5·5	1·4	3·2	1·7
0·013	10	1·5	1·7	1·7

† Vacuum annealed after machining.

Tests have been carried out on notched specimens heat-treated to produce differing grain sizes in order to see whether, for a given stress gradient at the notch root, K_f was a function of grain size. Some results are given in Tables 4.14 and 4.15.

It must be borne in mind when attempting to correlate notched fatigue data from different sources or, indeed, from the same source, that the processes used to machine the notches may have both work-hardened and induced compressive residual stresses into a region of material around the notch root. The notched fatigue limit of specimens in which the material at the notch root has been heavily work-hardened and contains high-compressive residual stresses may well be higher than that obtained on carefully machined and stress-relieved specimens of the same geometry and material. Indeed, the conventional notched fatigue limit of heavily machined notched mild steel (or any material which is easily work-hardened) specimens may be double that of carefully machined and vacuum stress-relieved specimens of the same

TABLE 4.14

Reversed direct stress fatigue data for 16 mm diameter 0·4% C steel specimens, heat-treated to produce three different grain sizes and containing circumferential hyperbolic notches [24]

Fine grain		Medium grain		Large grain	
K_t	K_f	K_t	K_f	K_t	K_f
1·8	1·7	1·8	1·4	1·8	1·5
2·3	1·9	2·3	1·7	2·3	1·7
3·0	2·0	—	—	—	—
4·6	2·7	3·9	2·6	3·9	2·5
7·1	2·6	7·1	2·1	7·1	2·2

TABLE 4.15

*Rotating bending fatigue data for 70/30 brass
specimens mechanically and thermally treated
to produce various grain sizes* [25]

Estimated grain size (mm)	Plain fatigue strength, 10^8 cycles (MN m^{-2})	K_f	
		$K_t = 1.8$	$K_t = 2.9$
0·047	±276	1·8	2·9
0·052	±207	1·4	2·5
0·075	±165	1·5	2·0
0·31	±152	—	1·8
0·66	±117	1·4	1·7
3·32	±83	1·2	1·3
7·75	±62	1·0	—

geometry: austenitic steels work-harden markedly and it has been found
[26] that the fatigue limit of notched specimens ($K_t = 2·6$) cut from annealed
austenitic stainless steel bar could even be higher than the plain fatigue limit
of the original annealed bar. Stress-relieving notched specimens after machining tends to make K_f approach more nearly to K_t (Table 4.8). However, it
is not always possible to fully stress-relieve notched specimens of some
materials, for example, the high-strength aluminium alloys, without markedly affecting the strength properties of the bulk material. Heavily machined
notched specimens may need to be tested to obtain data representative of the
behaviour of a component having a notch or discontinuity machined in a
similar manner, but it is obvious that the data are unsuitable for use in any
analysis involving the plain fatigue limit of the material and the K_t value of
the notch.

The experimental data given in Tables 4.2–4.15 may be summarized as
follows:

1. For low values of K_t, K_f may equal K_t, but in general is somewhat less.
2. For a series of geometrically similar specimens of different size but
   constant K_t, there is evidence both for and against a 'size-effect'.
3. Differing geometries producing the same K_t value may give differing
   K_f values.
4. For high values of K_t, K_f is often very much smaller than K_t.
5. For a given material and certain notch geometries, there appears to be
   a particular value of K_t at which K_f reaches a maximum value; higher
   values of K_t result in no further increase in K_f.
6. K_f appears to increase as grain-size decreases.

With the object of minimizing the need to test a large variety of notched
specimens of different materials, attempts have been made to formulate

relationships between K_t and K_f which supposedly enable the K_f value appropriate to a given specimen geometry and material to be predicted from the known K_t value. Some of these relationships are summarized below; in general, they apply only to the case of zero mean load.

4.3.2. K_f–K_t relationships

4.3.2.1. $K_f = K_t$. If the nominal stress at the fatigue limit of a batch of notched specimens, which remain wholly elastic, is $\pm\sigma_n$, the maximum longitudinal stress amplitude at the notch root is $\pm K_t\sigma_n$. By definition $\pm\sigma_n = \pm\sigma/K_f$ where $\pm\sigma$ is the plain fatigue limit of the material; thus K_f will equal K_t if a specimen remains wholly elastic and cracking and failure occur whenever the longitudinal stress amplitude at the notch root exceeds the plain fatigue limit.

4.3.2.2. Biaxial stress failure criterion. In § 4.3.2.1, cracking and failure were assumed to occur when the longitudinal stress amplitude at the notch root exceeded the plain fatigue limit. However, the material at the root of a notch may be subjected to a biaxial stress system even in a uniaxially loaded specimen. It was shown in § 3.6 that failure of a wrought ductile metal under a combined stress loading conformed closely to the von Mises criterion. Both a longitudinal stress, defined by K_t and a hoop stress of the same sign exist at the root of a circumferential vee-notch in a uniaxially-loaded cylindrical specimen. According to the von Mises criterion, the hoop stress will increase the longitudinal stress required to initiate failure; this is equivalent to a reduction of K_t. K_t^1 is defined as the value of K_t modified using the von Mises criterion to allow for a combined stress loading [3]; K_t^1 is always less than K_t, the greatest possible difference between them is about 13 per cent.

4.3.2.3. Effect of stress gradient. If the lower stressed grains remote from a notch root are regarded as giving support to the higher stressed grains at the notch root, by restricting their deformation, the steeper the stress gradient the greater the supporting effect. If, indeed, the severity of the stress gradient, as well as the value of the maximum stress range has an influence on the notched fatigue limit, it follows that the fatigue limits of batches of notched specimens all containing notches of the same K_t values but of different geometries will depend on the stress gradients at the notch roots, the steeper the stress gradient, the higher the notched fatigue limit.

It has been suggested [27] that the effect of the stress gradient could be allowed for by introducing a support coefficient n,

$$n = K_t \frac{\sigma_n}{\sigma} = \frac{K_t}{K_f},$$

which is a function of G, the non-dimensional stress gradient (Table 4.1), the relationship between n and G being obtained from experimental data.

4.3.2.4. Elementary structural unit. The theoretical elastic stress distribution around a notch implies that the maximum stress occurs only at a point or line on the notch surface. Real materials, unlike the ideal homogeneous material assumed in the theory of elasticity, cannot be sub-divided indefinitely without affecting their mechanical properties. Neuber suggested [28] that there may be an elementary structural unit of length A, measured inwards from the notch root on the plane of minimum cross-sectional area, over which the average cyclic stress must exceed the plain fatigue limit of the material before cracking can occur. Others have suggested a length h over which the stress must exceed the plain fatigue limit of the material. Either A or h is assumed to be constant for a given material.

Taking the effective stress at the root of a notch as equal to the average stress over the length A is equivalent [28] to replacing the notch root radius ρ by $A/2$, and the relationship between K_f and K_t can be written [29]:

$$K_f = 1 + \frac{K_t - 1}{1 + \{\pi/(\pi - w)\}(A/\rho)^{\frac{1}{2}}},$$

where ρ is the notch root radius and the factor $\pi/(\pi - w)$ corrects [28] for the effect of notch flank angle w. Analysis of a large number of zero mean load notched fatigue tests on various steels showed [29] that A was a function of tensile strength, varying from about 0·5 mm for a steel of tensile strength 350 MN m^{-2} to about 0·025 mm for a steel of tensile strength 1100 MN m^{-2}. For high strength $4\frac{1}{2}\%$ Cu– and $5\frac{1}{2}\%$ Zn–aluminium alloys, A was about 0·5 mm. Similar empirical relationships between A and tensile strength have been found [30] for wrought aluminium and titanium alloys. Another analysis [31] of notched steel data showed that the best correlation between K_f and K_t was obtained when A was formulated as a function of yield stress, and the flank-angle correction factor in the above equation was found to be unnecessary. Further tests in general do not confirm either relationship [15, 32]. It has been suggested [33] that the average cyclic shear stress over the length A calculated from the elastic shear-stress distribution must exceed the value of the cyclic shear stress at the plain fatigue of the material before cracking occurs; experimentally derived K_f values for mild steel, alloy steel, and aluminium alloy specimens corresponded to A values of 0·23 mm, 0·15 mm, and 0·13 mm, respectively. Attempts to correlate A with physical dimensions such as grain size [25, 34] have proved unsuccessful.

The concept of failure taking place when the stress at a distance h below the surface exceeds the plain fatigue limit was first used in an attempt to explain the decrease in rotating bending fatigue limit which sometimes occurs (§ 3.4) as the specimen diameter increases. It was found [35] from tests on 6 steels that the rotating bending fatigue limit could be predicted from the reversed direct stress fatigue limit by taking h as 0·2 mm. This figure was confirmed [17] for plain rotating bending alloy steel specimens of different diameters, but similar tests on notched specimens of the same steel could only be correlated by putting $h = 0.05$ mm. Other tests have given values of h of 0.1 mm for mild steel [36], 0.055 mm for 3 different carbon steels, and 0.08 mm for copper [37]. The value of 0.055 mm was confirmed for another carbon steel [38], but h was smaller for stronger alloys.

4.3.2.5. Inherent flaws. All materials contain inherent flaws of one type or another, such as inhomogeneity in stress distribution and local strength, variations in composition, anisotropic properties associated with orientation of individual grains, inclusions and cavities. These can be considered as numerous inherent flaws distributed at random within a material, each

TABLE 4.16

Material	a (mm)
Steel (tensile strength less than 700 MN m^{-2})	0·05
Steel (tensile strength more than 700 MN m^{-2})	0·015
Aluminium alloys†	0·05
Copper alloys	0·09
Magnesium alloys	0·04

† A somewhat lower value was obtained for the case of the high-strength aluminium alloys.

having a characteristic length a [1]. If there are many flaws in a specimen, the introduction of a mechanical notch of about the same size as a flaw will make little difference to the fatigue strength, and the resulting K_f value will be of the order of unity. If, however, the notch is large relative to the flaw size, then there will be a number of flaws wholly within the region of high stress around the notch root, and K_f will tend to approach K_t. Thus the inherent flaw concept can be used to predict a changing K_f for a given K_t; the larger the notch and the less steep the stress gradient it creates, the closer K_f approaches K_t.

The inherent flaw approach leads to equations of the type

$$K_f = K_t / \{1 + 2(a/\rho)^{\frac{1}{2}}\},$$

where $\rho =$ notch root radius. Empirically obtained [1] values of a are shown in Table 4.16. These do not appear to be related to any observable features of the material. Equivalent [39] and more elaborate [40] versions of the above equation have also been proposed.

4.3.2.6. Plasticity effects. If the plain fatigue limit of a material is higher than the dynamic elastic limit of the material, a specimen will exhibit a hysteresis loop when tested at the fatigue limit stress, thus implying that the material can deform plastically each cycle without catastrophic failure occurring (although, as discussed in Chapter 2, slip-band cracking may have already occurred). This suggested [41] that the value of the nominal stress range just necessary to create a stress range at the notch root equal to that at the plain fatigue limit would be greater than that given by elasticity theory. To calculate the nominal stress range necessary to realize the plain fatigue limit stress range at the notch root, it is necessary to know the dynamic stress–strain characteristics of the material and the elastic–plastic strain distribution around the notch root. The ratio of the maximum stress to this nominal stress

TABLE 4.17

Reversed direct stress fatigue data for square specimens containing a transverse hole and cylindrical specimens containing a circumferential vee-notch [41]

Material	Tempera- ture (°C)	Calculated K_t		Experimental K_f	
		Hole $K_t = 2\cdot3$	vee-notch $K_t = 3\cdot5$	Hole $K_t = 2\cdot3$	vee-notch $K_t = 3\cdot5$
Austenitic steel	20	1·7	2·6	1·3	1·2
Austenitic steel	700	1·8	2·7	1·4	—
Austenitic steel	650	1·8	2·8	1·6	—
0·17% C steel	20	1·9	2·8	1·7	1·8
Copper	250	1·9	2·9	1·3	—
Aluminium alloy RR58	200	2·0	3·0	1·6	—
Copper	20	2·2	3·4	1·7	—
Aluminium alloy 56S	20	2·2	3·4	2·2	2·9
0·17% C steel	450	2·3	3·5	1·5	1·8
0·5% C steel	20	2·3	3·5	1·7	—
Nickel–chromium–molybdenum steel	20	2·3	3·5	2·2	—
Aluminium alloy 26S	20	2·3	3·5	2·2	2·8

will be less than K_t, and can be considered as an elastic–plastic stress concentration factor, which the experimentally determined value of K_f cannot be expected to exceed. Forrest [41] calculated K_f values for 9 materials estimated on this basis; these are shown in Table 4.17, where they are compared with experimental values. The elastic–plastic strain distribution in the vicinity of a notch was assumed to be similar to the elastic case, and was taken from photo-elastic data. The dynamic stress–strain characteristics were obtained by a method which uses plain direct stress specimens [42]. Except for the austenitic steel, 0·17% C steel and copper at 250 °C, the calculated K_f values are close to the K_t values (that is, the dynamic stress–strain curve is sensibly linear up to stress levels equal to the plain fatigue limit). In the case of these 3 materials, plasticity effects, however, do account for some of the discrepancy between K_f and K_t but, as the figures in Table 4.17 show, they can by no means be considered a complete explanation. It was suggested [41] that the remaining discrepancy was due to stress-gradient effects.

4.3.2.7. Notch sensitivity index. Because the conventional notched fatigue limits of some materials are greater than the corresponding plain fatigue limits divided by K_t, whereas those of other materials are either equal to or are not far removed from the corresponding plain fatigue limits divided by K_t, the former materials are sometimes referred to as notch insensitive and the latter as notch sensitive. It has been argued that this difference in behaviour arises because the former materials have the ability to deform plastically each cycle (presumably without leading to cracking), so reducing the maximum stress range at the notch root to a value less than the calculated elastic value. In addition, it has been suggested that the ratio of the increase of the actual stress range over the nominal stress range to the increase of the theoretical elastic stress range over the nominal stress range could be considered as a material constant. Thus, if the nominal stress at the notched fatigue limit is $\pm\sigma_n$

$$\frac{K_f\sigma_n - \sigma_n}{K_t\sigma_n - \sigma_n} = \frac{K_f - 1}{K_t - 1} = q,$$

where q is termed the notch sensitivity index of a material. If $K_f = K_t$, $q = 1$ and the material is said to be fully notch sensitive whereas, if $K_f = 1$, $q = 0$ and the material is said to be fully notch insensitive. However, it is clear from the experimental data that q depends not only on material but also on specimen size and notch geometry [43]. Nevertheless, notched fatigue data are often presented in terms of the notch sensitivity index despite the fact that the procedure of determining q from a batch of notched specimens, and then using this value of q to predict the fatigue limit of another batch of notched specimens of different geometry but of the same material may lead to a grossly misleading answer.

A finite-life notch sensitivity index q_a can be defined [40] so that

$$K_{fN} = K_s + q_a(K_f - K_s),$$

where K_{fN} = fatigue strength reduction factor at N cycles, K_s = static strength reduction factor, and K_f = fatigue strength reduction factor at 10^7 cycles.

Examination of experimental data for the usual type of laboratory specimen (holed, filleted, and grooved specimens) showed

$$q_a = \frac{(\log N)^4}{b + (\log N)^4},$$

where b is a material constant.

If N is greater than about 5×10^5, q_a can be taken as one, and therefore K_{fN} can be taken as K_f.

4.3.2.8. Change in notch root radius. The K_t value of a notch would decrease if its root radius over a small length of arc at the bottom of the notch in-increased under the maximum tensile stress in the applied loading cycle.

However, measurements [44] have shown that the change occurring in the notch root radius at stress levels corresponding to the fatigue limit or strength at long endurances (zero mean load) of a metallic alloy is too small to lead to a significant change in the value of K_t.

4.3.2.9. Volume of critically stressed material. The volume of material and free surface area at the notch root subjected to high cyclic stresses decrease, for a given notch depth, as the notch root radius decreases. It could be argued, therefore, that the chance of there being a relatively weak grain having a free surface at the notch root compared to that of there being one having a free surface on the usual type of plain specimen decreases as the notch radius decreases. Thus, the discrepancy between K_f and K_t would be expected to increase (that is, the notched specimen will become relatively stronger) as K_t increases. For example, an analysis of both rotating bending tests on plain specimens of different diameters and notched fatigue specimens [45] suggested that a decrease in fatigue strength accompanied an increase in volume of material subjected to at least 95 per cent of the maximum cyclic stress.

4.3.2.10. Other relationships. In addition to the K_f–K_t relationships mentioned above, K_f may be related empirically to the notch and specimen dimensions for a particular series of tests on a given material. For example, it has been suggested that the torsional fatigue limit σ_T of steel shafts of diameter D containing a fillet of radius ρ is given by

$$\sigma_T = a - bD + c(\rho)^{\frac{1}{2}},$$

where a, b, and c are constants [46]. Although these relationships can obviously have no general validity, they are often useful for practical design data purposes.

In the past, the brittle appearance of a fatigue fracture has prompted the suggestion that the fatigue limits of similarly notched specimens of different steels may be related to their static notched impact strengths (that is, either Izod or Charpy values). However, the fatigue limits of batches of similarly-shaped notched specimens of steels heat-treated to give similar tensile strengths but widely different impact strengths are found to be similar [47]. In addition, if the fatigue limits of batches of similar sharply-notched steel specimens are determined at various temperatures, there is no evidence of a sudden drop in the fatigue limit when the test temperature is below the ductile–brittle transition temperature. On the other hand, it has sometimes been reported [48] that, if impact tests are carried out on specimens containing, for example, a notch of similar shape to an Izod or Charpy vee-notch which have been cyclically stressed but not broken, either the subsequent impact value at a given temperature has been decreased or the brittle–ductile transition temperature raised. However, these effects are in general due to the formation of a crack at the notch root by the prior cyclic stressing which has not grown to cause complete failure (cracks at the notch root would be expected to have a marked effect on the subsequent impact value, especially at sub-zero temperatures) rather than to any embrittling of the material structure by the prior cyclic stressing [49].

4.4. Non-propagating cracks in notched specimens

Conventionally, K_f is based on the cyclic stress necessary to cause complete fracture of a notched specimen, although it has been known for some time that an unbroken notched specimen may contain a non-propagating fatigue crack. Early evidence supporting the existence of non-propagating fatigue cracks was obtained in 1949 when they were found in mild steel specimens [50], 12·7 mm outside diameter, containing a circumferential vee-notch 1·3 mm deep and 0·13 mm root radius, which had been tested at a nominal alternating stress equal to 45 per cent of the conventional notched fatigue limit for 8×10^7 cycles.

Since then, non-propagating cracks have been observed in a variety of materials such as various steels [37, 51–53], aluminium alloys [52, 54, 55], copper [22, 37, 54, 56], its alloys [54], and nickel alloys [54]. They have also been observed in carbon steel specimens tested in reversed torsion [56]. Typically non-propagating cracks are only observed when K_t exceeds some critical value (generally equivalent to the notch root radius, for a given notch depth, being below some critical value).

Referring back to the K_t—K_f values shown in Table 4.11, it can be seen that the cylindrical (43 mm outside diameter) circumferentially vee-grooved (5 mm deep, 0·05 mm root radius) mild steel specimens having a K_t value of 14 gave a K_f value of only 3·8. The plain fatigue limit of the mild steel used was ±215 MN m^{-2}; this value of K_f therefore, corresponds to a conventional notched fatigue limit of about ±57 MN m^{-2}. Subsequently [51], similarly-shaped notched mild steel specimens were tested in reversed direct stress at nominal cyclic stresses of ±26 MN m^{-2} and ±37 MN m^{-2} for various endurances up to 10^8 cycles. Both these stress levels are less than the conventional notched fatigue limit, and consequently all specimens remained unbroken after testing. However, metallurgical examination of the material around the notch roots in these unbroken specimens revealed the presence of small cracks having depths around the periphery varying from 0·025 mm to 0·05 mm, these depths being the same irrespective of whether the endurance was 0.05×10^6 cycles or 10^8 cycles. The inference is that the cracks formed and reached their maximum depths before 0.05×10^6 cycles, thereafter remaining dormant even in a specimen tested for an endurance of 10^8 cycles.

Rotating bending tests have been carried out [55] on 6061-T6 aluminium alloy vee-notched specimens (12 mm outside diameter, 1·9 mm deep notch, root radii varying between 0·005 mm and 12·5 mm) having K_t values ranging from 1·1 to 19. Replicas of the surface of the notch root taken at intervals

11

throughout a test showed that cracks were present early in a test, the nominal stress to initiate a crack being given by the plain fatigue limit divided by K_t. Non-propagating cracks (or cracks which did not grow to cause failure in 5×10^8 cycles) were present in specimens having K_t values greater than 1·6, which were unbroken after testing at stress levels between the corresponding conventional notched fatigue limit and the plain fatigue limit divided by K_t.

The results of tests to determine the conventional reversed direct stress fatigue limits of batches of mild steel and $4\frac{1}{2}\%$ Cu–aluminium alloy notched

TABLE 4.18

Root radius (mm)	K_t	Conventional notched fatigue limit or strength, 30×10^6 cycles (MN m⁻²)	K_f	State of material at notch root in unbroken specimens after testing
Aluminium alloy				
1·25	3·3	±46	3·2	Uncracked
0·5	4·9	±31	4·9	Uncracked
0·2	7·3	±23	6·5	Uncracked
0·1	10	±23	6·5	Cracked
0·05	14	±39	3·9	Cracked
0·013	27	±40	3·7	Cracked
Mild steel				
1·25	3·3	±66	3·3	Uncracked
0·63	4·4	±59	3·7	Not examined
0·25	6·6	±59	3·7	Cracked
0·1	10	±52	4·1	Cracked
0·05	14	±59	3·7	Cracked

specimens (43 mm outside diameter containing a circumferential vee-groove 5 mm deep), each batch of specimens having a different root radius [52], are shown in Table 4.18. Specimens, unbroken after testing, were examined for cracks.

The values of K_f for each material reach a maximum value at some particular value of K_t, say, $K_{t\ crit}$, those for mild steel then remaining sensibly constant, whereas those for the aluminium alloy decrease as K_t increases above $K_{t\ crit}$. Cracks, of reasonably uniform depth around the notch root periphery, were found in all specimens having K_t values greater than $K_{t\ crit}$ and unbroken after testing at stress levels either equal or just less than the conventional notched fatigue limit. On the other hand, no cracks were found in unbroken specimens having a K_t value less than $K_{t\ crit}$. By sectioning and metallurgically examining notched aluminium alloy specimens having a 0·05 mm root radius tested at ±31 MN m⁻² (that is, ±8 MN m⁻² below the conventional notched fatigue limit) after various endurances, a crack was found to reach its maximum depth after about 10^5 cycles [52].

The crack depths attained after endurances of at least 30×10^6 cycles in notched specimens of both materials, tested at various stress levels below their conventional notched fatigue limits, are shown on Fig. 4.4. They are seen to fall near the line representing the depth of material, measured in from the notch root, over which the stresses generated by the notch are equal to or greater than its plain fatigue limit, assuming no cracks are present and the specimen remains wholly elastic.

Work using cylindrical vee-notched specimens suffers from the disadvantage that only one value of the average crack-depth around the notch

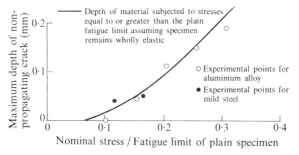

FIG. 4.4. Maximum depths of non-propagating cracks in vee-notched round bar aluminium alloy and mild steel specimens.

root periphery can be obtained from each specimen because a specimen sectioned for metallurgical examination cannot be restested. Thus, they cannot be used to provide definite proof that a crack found in an unbroken specimen is indeed dormant and not growing slowly. This difficulty can be overcome by using edge-notched plate specimens because these permit the direct observation of the behaviour of any cracks formed at the notch roots.

Reversed direct stress tests (zero mean stress) have been carried out [57] on mild steel (0·2% C) edge-notched plate specimens of the form shown on Fig. 4.5. The vee-notches were 5 mm deep and of various root radii, and all specimens were stress-relieved for 1 hour at 650 °C *in vacuo* after final machining. Measurements of the lengths of any cracks formed at the notch roots were taken at frequent intervals throughout a test; typical crack growth curves obtained from a batch of specimens having a 0·25 mm root radius and tested at different stress levels are shown on Fig. 4.6, the crack lengths plotted being the average of the 4 readings of crack length measured from the bottom of each notch on both sides and edges of the plate, at any instant. Even with a plate specimen, it is only possible to measure the lengths of the surface cracks visible on each face of the plate. However, as mentioned later in § 4.5.4 and in § 5.5 the shape of the crack front through the plate thickness, for slowly growing cracks, can be considered a straight line joining the ends of the two surface cracks visible on the opposite sides of the plate.

The crack growth curves obtained from the tests at ± 46 MN m^{-2} and ± 39 MN m^{-2} show clearly that cracks can form at the root of a notch, reach a maximum length after a certain number of cycles, in this case about 5×10^6, and then remain dormant for the remainder of the test, even though the nominal cyclic stress level on gross area is maintained constant throughout the test.

As well as the maximum alternating stress that would just not cause a crack to grow across a specimen, the maximum alternating stress that would

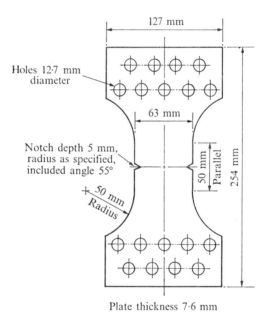

Plate thickness 7·6 mm

FIG. 4.5. Details of plate fatigue specimen [57].

just not initiate a crack at the notch root was determined for each batch of root radii tested, that is, 0·1 mm, 0·25 mm, 0·5 mm, and 1·3 mm. These two maximum stress levels are plotted against the corresponding K_t value of the notch on Fig. 4.7, the horizontal line (1) representing the maximum alternating stress that will just not propagate a crack across the specimen, curve (2) the maximum alternating stress that will just not initiate a crack at a notch root, curve (3) the plain fatigue limit divided by K_t, and curve (4) the conventional notched fatigue limit. If a vertical line is drawn through the point of intersection of line (1) and curve (2), the minimum alternating stress required to initiate a crack at the root of a notch having a K_t value to the left of the vertical line is greater than the minimum alternating stress required to cause it to grow. On the other hand, the minimum alternating stress required to initiate a crack at the root of a notch having a K_t value to the right of the

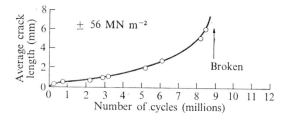

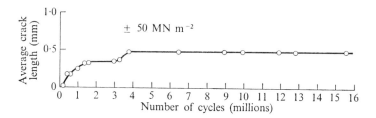

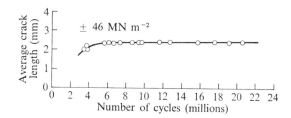

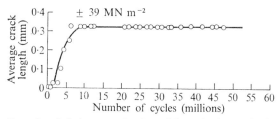

Fɪɢ. 4.6. Growth of fatigue cracks in mild steel plates. (Taken from Frost and Dugdale [57].)

vertical line is less than the minimum alternating stress required to propagate it across a specimen and hence non-propagating cracks are present in all specimens tested at stress levels between curve (2) and line (1).

The data in Fig. 4.7 are incorporated with other data obtained [58] on cylindrical mild steel specimens containing a circumferential vee-groove, to produce the diagrams shown on Figs. 4.8 and 4.9. These show the notched fatigue limits, based on either the stress to initiate a crack at the notch root (in the case of cylindrical notched specimens, this necessitated sectioning

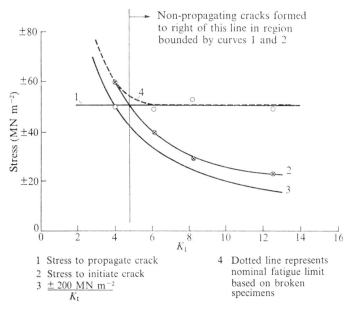

FIG. 4.7. Nominal alternating stress versus K_t for mild steel plates. (Taken from Frost and Dugdale [57].)

1 Stress to propagate crack
2 Stress to initiate crack
3 $\dfrac{\pm 200 \text{ MN m}^{-2}}{K_t}$

4 Dotted line represents nominal fatigue limit based on broken specimens

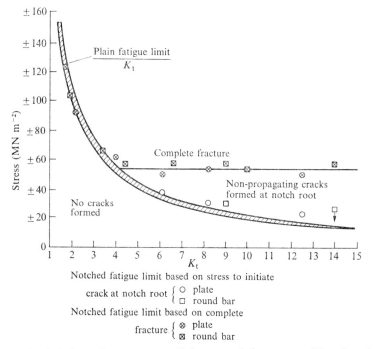

Notched fatigue limit based on stress to initiate
crack at notch root $\begin{cases} \bigcirc & \text{plate} \\ \square & \text{round bar} \end{cases}$

Notched fatigue limit based on complete
fracture $\begin{cases} \otimes & \text{plate} \\ \boxtimes & \text{round bar} \end{cases}$

FIG. 4.8. Nominal alternating stress versus K_t for reversed direct stress mild steel specimens having notches 5 mm deep.

unbroken specimens and examining the material at the root for the presence of cracks) or on complete fracture of the specimen, plotted against the corresponding K_t value for the notch. The data on Fig. 4.8 were obtained from both cylindrical (43 mm outside diameter) and plate (as Fig. 4.5) specimens containing 5 mm deep circumferential or edge vee-notches, of root radii ranging from 0·005 mm to 0·75 mm. All specimens were stress-relieved for 1 hour at

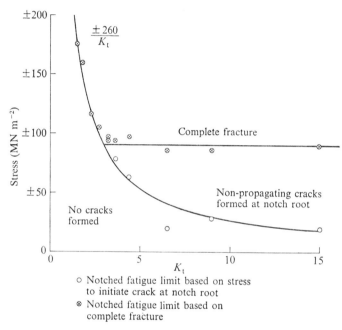

FIG. 4.9. Nominal alternating stress versus K_t for rotating bending mild steel specimens having notches 1·3 mm deep.

650 °C *in vacuo* after final machining and were tested in reversed direct stress. The data on Fig. 4.9 were obtained from specimens 12·7 mm outside diameter containing a circumferential vee-notch 1·3 mm deep and of root radii varying from 0·005 mm to 2·3 mm, stress-relieved after final machining and tested in rotating bending. The full-line represents the plain fatigue limit of the material divided by K_t; it is shown as a band on Fig. 4.8, covering a range of plain fatigue limits of from ± 200 MN m^{-2} to ± 230 MN m^{-2}. In the case of the 1·3 mm deep notches, when K_t exceeds a value of about 3, the notched fatigue limit based on completely broken specimens (that is, the maximum alternating stress that will just not cause a crack, formed at the notch root, to grow across the specimen) remains constant at about ± 90 MN m^{-2} and, likewise, in the case of the 5 mm deep notches, when K_t exceeded a value of about 4

the maximum alternating stress that will just not cause a crack to grow across a specimen was constant at about ± 54 MN m^{-2}, irrespective of the value of K_t. Thus, non-propagating cracks are present in all specimens containing 1·3 mm deep notches which are sufficiently sharp to initiate cracks at nominal stress levels below ± 90 MN m^{-2} and in all specimens containing 5 mm deep notches which are sufficiently sharp to initiate cracks at stress levels below ± 54 MN m^{-2}. Hence, increasing the notch depth decreases the stress level necessary to propagate a crack, formed at the root of a sufficiently sharp notch, across the specimen cross-section.

Similar diagrams to Figs. 4.8 and 4.9 have been reported for $4\frac{1}{2}$% Cu–aluminium alloy specimens [59] of the same geometries as used for the mild steel tests, that is, one diagram for notches 5 mm deep and the other for notches 1·3 mm deep. Non-propagating cracks were found in all specimens tested at or just below the conventional notched fatigue limits having a K_t value greater than 9 for the 5 mm deep notches and a K_t value greater than 5 for the 1·3 mm deep notches. The conventional notched fatigue limits reached minimum values of ± 19 MN m^{-2} and ± 39 MN m^{-2} for the 5 mm and 1·3 mm deep notches respectively, thus confirming that the minimum alternating stress required to propagate a crack formed at the notch root decreased as the notch depth increased. Unlike the non-propagating cracks found in the mild steel specimens, those in the aluminium alloy specimens were not always of uniform depth around the notch root periphery nor was their direction of growth always normal to the direction of loading. Examples of non-propagating cracks found in the two materials are shown in Figs. 4.10 and 4.11. The aluminium alloy specimens were not stress-relieved after machining the notch, and it is shown in § 6.3.4 that the presence of compressive residual stresses in the material at the notch root is a major factor in causing a crack at the notch root to be inclined to the loading direction. They are also probably responsible for the increase in conventional fatigue limit that was found with some of the aluminium alloy specimens having K_t values greater than 9 and 5 for the 5 mm and 1·3 mm deep notches respectively.

Similar tests on copper and nickel–chromium (En26) alloy steel notched specimens showed that non-propagating cracks were present in specimens tested either at, or just below, their conventional fatigue limits when, for a given notch depth, the value of K_t for the notch exceeded some particular value.

The experimental data described thus show that because a notched specimen is unbroken after testing it cannot be taken for granted that the material at the notch root is uncracked. When the notch geometry is such that a non-propagating crack is present in a specimen unbroken after testing at the conventional notched fatigue limit, this value will be determined by the maximum alternating stress that will just not cause the crack to grow and appears to depend on the notch depth.

4.5. The minimum alternating stress required to propagate a crack of a given length or depth at zero mean stress

The fact that certain notched specimens may contain non-propagating cracks when tested at stress levels either equal to, or just less than, their conventional notched fatigue limit implies that a batch of plain specimens containing cracks of similar size and shape should exhibit a definite fatigue limit. The relevant experimental data can be divided into four groups:

(1) that in which artificial cracks are produced in specimens;
(2) that in which fatigue cracks are produced in plain specimens by subjecting them to stress levels greater than their plain fatigue limit, the cracked specimens then being tested at a lower stress level;
(3) that in which fatigue cracks are grown in notched specimens to a given depth, the specimen then being remachined in order to remove the notch, so leaving a specimen containing a crack of known size;
(4) tests similar to (3), intended to reveal the relationship between crack size and fatigue limit.

4.5.1. Tests on specimens containing artificial cracks

Early data on the fatigue limit of cracked specimens were obtained on specimens containing artificial cracks [60, 61]. These were produced by compressing longitudinally cylindrical steel specimens containing a circumferential narrow vee-groove so as to completely close the groove. Some data are shown in Table 4.19. In general, the fatigue limit of cracked specimens is much less than that of the corresponding plain specimens and decreases as crack depth increases. Small quenching cracks in plain specimens of 0·6 % steel have been found to reduce the torsional fatigue limit by a factor of 2 [62].

4.5.2. Tests on plain specimens containing fatigue cracks

Cracked specimens have been produced [64] by subjecting 25 mm diameter mild steel, nickel–chromium alloy steel and $4\frac{1}{2}$% Cu–aluminium alloy plain specimens to rotating bending stresses greater than their respective fatigue limits, a test being stopped when a surface crack was visible to the naked eye; the resulting cracks were up to 7·5 mm deep. The cracked specimens were then retested at a lower stress level, in either rotating bending or reversed direct stress. After fracture, the outline of the initial crack was clearly visible on the fracture face (specimens which were unbroken at the end of a test were deliberately broken at a higher stress level so as to obtain the crack outline), and an approximate nominal stress along the crack front was based on the net uncracked area, taking into account the non-axiality of loading on this section. The points for each material, obtained by plotting this calculated nominal stress against the corresponding

TABLE 4.19

Rotating bending fatigue data for cylindrical specimens containing an artificial circumferential crack produced by hot-pressing notched blanks

Material	Condition	Plain fatigue limit (MN m^{-2})	Specimen diameter (mm)	Crack depth (mm)	Fatigue limit of cracked specimen (net area) (MN m^{-2})	Reference
0·44%C steel	Cold-pressed and stress-relieved	±215	20 81	2·5 10	±77 ±54	60
Chromium–vanadium alloy steel	Quenched and tempered	±650	5	2·5	±185	61
Mild steel	Annealed	±225	15	0·46 1·05 2·1	±165 ±113 ±96	63
0·45% C steel	Annealed	±295	15	0·79 0·94 2·5 3·3	±140 ±133 ±88 ±85	63
13% Cr steel	Quenched and tempered	±355	15	0·61 1·5 1·85	±147 ±158 ±93	63
Nickel–chromium alloy steel	Quenched and tempered	±450	15	1·0 1·65	±145 ±144	63

TABLE 4.20

Material	Plain fatigue limit (MN m^{-2})	Zero mean load fatigue limit of cracked specimen (MN m^{-2})	Repeated tension fatigue limit of cracked specimen (MN m^{-2})
Mild steel	±216	±85	1–185
Nickel–chromium alloy steel	±550	±200	1–230
4½% Cu–aluminium alloy	±155	±93	1–85

endurance, fall around a single curve similar in shape to a conventional S/N curve and exhibiting a definite fatigue limit. Additional tests [65], on similarly cracked specimens, subjected to a repeated tension loading cycle, also gave S/N curves exhibiting a definite fatigue limit. The values of the cracked specimen fatigue limits obtained are given in Table 4.20.

Small surface cracks about 1 mm in surface length were introduced into 2024-T4 aluminium alloy cylindrical plain specimens by testing at high stress levels, the cracks being detected by the evolution of hydrogen bubbles under a piece of transparent tape stuck on to the surface (see § 2.3.5). The fatigue strength $(5 \times 10^6$ cycles) of these cracked specimens was about one-half that of the original uncracked specimens. Although unbroken cracked specimens were only tested for about 3×10^6 cycles, there was no evidence of a crack growing during this period [66].

4.5.3. *Tests on specimens containing fatigue cracks grown at notches*

Crack size is more readily controlled when cracks are grown from sharp notches; for example, notched cylindrical carbon steel specimens [67], (18 mm outside diameter, containing a circumferential vee-groove 1·5 mm

TABLE 4.21

Steel	Plain fatigue limit (MN m^{-2})	Average crack depth (mm)	Fatigue limit of cracked specimens (MN m^{-2})
0·08% C	±190	0·5	±97
0·12% C	±224	0·25	±125
0·53% C	±263	0·25	±153
		3·0	±110

deep and 0·05 mm root radius) were tested in rotating bending at a nominal stress level sufficient to form a crack around the notch root. The crack depth was estimated from static deflection measurements on specimens which had been cycled for a known number of cycles and then sectioned to measure the corresponding crack depth. A test was stopped after an endurance that was estimated would result in a crack of a given depth being present at the notch root, the specimen then being re-machined to remove the notch, so leaving a cylindrical specimen containing a circumferential crack. The rotating bending fatigue limits of batches of specimens containing cracks of similar depths which had been stress-relieved at 700 °C for $\frac{1}{2}$ hour after the cracking and remachining procedure are given in Table 4.21. The nominal stresses used in estimating these fatigue limits were based on the net area of the specimen when the crack depth was small, and on a modified section modulus when the crack depth was large, which took into account the fact that tensile stresses are carried only by the net area, whereas compressive stresses are taken over the gross area. The results of additional tests [68] on similarly cracked nickel–chromium (1·3% Ni, 0·6% Cr) and chromium–molybdenum (1% Cr, 0·2% Mo) alloy steel specimens (14 mm outside diameter) are given in Table 4.22. It is seen that stress-relieving the cracked nickel-chromium alloy steel specimens reduced their fatigue limit below that of the corresponding non-stress-relieved specimens, presumably because the stress-relieving treatment reduced the magnitude of the compressive residual stresses induced at the crack tip during the cracking procedure.

Similar cracked specimens were obtained [69] by testing a batch of 0·18 % C sharply vee-notched cylindrical rotating bending specimens (10 mm outside diameter) at a nominal stress level just below their conventional notched fatigue limit for a stipulated endurance. Several of the tested specimens were selected at random and found to contain non-propagating cracks

TABLE 4.22

Steel	Plain fatigue limit (MN m^{-2})	Crack depth (mm)	Fatigue limit of cracked specimens (MN m^{-2})	Remarks
Chromium–molybdenum alloy steel	±455	0·4 1·0 2·0	±200 ±145 ±130	Not stress-relieved
Nickel–chromium alloy steel	±475	0·4 1·0 2·1	±208 ±162 ±140	Not stress-relieved
		0·4 1·0	±150 ±105	Stress-relieved

at the notch roots whose average depth around the periphery was between 0·1 mm and 0·2 mm. The remaining specimens were assumed to contain cracks of a similar depth, and these were re-machined to remove the notch. Their subsequent rotating bending fatigue limit was ±100 MN m^{-2} compared to that of ±200 MN m^{-2} for plain uncracked specimens. Some of the cracked specimens were induction hardened after cracking; their fatigue limit was increased to ±470 MN m^{-2} compared to a value of ±530 MN m^{-2} for induction-hardened plain specimens. This large increase in the fatigue limit of the cracked specimens was the result of compressive residual stresses induced in the material around the crack tip by the induction-hardening.

4.5.4. Tests to determine the relationship between crack length and the stress necessary for crack growth

The data given in §§ 4.5.1–4.5.3 suggest that a cracked specimen possesses a definite fatigue limit and that this value depends on the depth or length of the crack. The existence of a fatigue limit for a cracked specimen implies the existence of a corresponding maximum possible life for a broken specimen; this is usually of the order of 10^6–10^7 cycles. Various tests have been carried out [58, 59, 70] to obtain data that would enable a quantitative relationship to be established between crack length and the maximum value of the alternating stress (zero mean load) that would just not cause it to grow. Mild steel, nickel–chromium alloy steel, copper, and $4\frac{1}{2}\%$ Cu–aluminium alloy plate specimens, 63 mm wide and between 5 mm and 12·7 mm thick, having two opposite-edge vee-notches, 5 mm deep and 0·1 mm root radius (as Fig. 4.5), were subjected to a loading cycle sufficient to form and grow cracks from the notch roots, a test being stopped when cracks had grown to the required length. The specimens were then reprofiled to remove the edge-notches, so leaving a plate specimen containing two coplanar edge-cracks. Cracks were obtained between 0·25 mm and 6 mm long; it was considered that edge-cracks below 6 mm long could be considered as being in a plate of infinite width and nominal stresses could therefore be based on gross area. Except for the aluminium alloy plates, in which the initial cracks were formed by either a wholly compressive loading cycle or one in which the maximum nominal tensile stress did not exceed 15 MN m^{-2}, the plates were given a suitable stress-relieving heat-treatment (see Table 4.23) to minimize any residual stresses induced by either the cracking or reprofiling processes and then subjected to a given alternating (zero mean) stress, the subsequent crack growth behaviour being noted. Tests in which a crack did not grow were continued for at least 50×10^6 cycles. The initial crack outline was visible on the fracture face of a broken specimen and confirmed that an edge-crack was generally of uniform length through the specimen thickness. In those cases where it was not, the crack length was taken as the length of the longest line normal to the crack front from the edge of the plate. The longer of the two cracks present in each plate was taken as the effective crack length for that plate. Additional data were obtained from round bar specimens, 15 mm outside diameter, in which a crack was grown initially from a sharp vee-notch 2·5 mm deep, subjected to a wholly compressive loading cycle of appropriate magnitude. Sectioning a random selection of these specimens showed that cracks of depth around the periphery of up to 0·25 mm could be obtained. The remainder of the specimens were reprofiled so as to remove the notch and the cracked specimens tested in reversed direct stress. The experimental results for the nickel–chromium steel and the copper are shown on Figs. 4.12 and 4.13. In Fig. 4.12, the fatigue limits of batches of specimens containing cracks of similar lengths are plotted against the corresponding edge-crack length; in Fig. 4.13, all the experimental points are plotted, each point representing a test in which the crack either grew to failure or remained dormant.

For all 4 materials whether or not an edge-crack grew depended on the value of the parameter $\sigma_a^3 a$, where $\pm\sigma_a$ is the nominal alternating stress (zero mean load) based on the gross cross-sectional area and a, the length of an edge-crack whose value does not exceed 6 mm. If $\sigma_a^3 a > C$, a crack grows; if $\sigma_a^3 a < C$, a crack remains dormant, where C is an empirical material constant. Similar tests were carried out [54] on plate specimens, containing

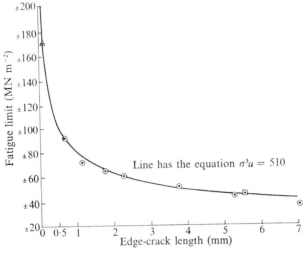

Plate specimens containing edge cracks

⊿ Cylindrical specimen containing small circumferential crack

⊟ Plate specimen containing 5 mm deep edge-notches

FIG. 4.12. Fatigue limit of nickel-chromium alloy steel cracked specimens versus edge-crack length. (Taken from Frost [70].)

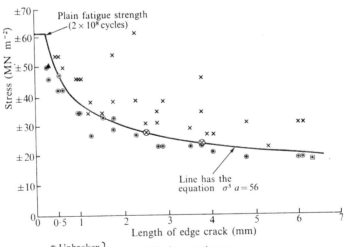

⊙ Unbroken ⎫ 53 mm wide plate specimens
× Broken ⎭

⊟ Fatigue limit of plate specimen containing 5mm deep notches

▲ Fatigue limit of cylindrical specimen containing small circumferential crack

⊗ Fatigue limit of cracked plates

FIG. 4.13. Alternating stress versus edge-crack length for copper plates. (Taken from Frost [70].)

edge-cracks of different lengths, of a further 8 materials. All plates were stress-relieved after cracking and then tested in reversed direct stress. It was assumed that crack growth behaviour was controlled by the value of the $\sigma_a a$ parameter, and when $\sigma_a^3 a$ was plotted against the logarithm of the corresponding endurance, the experimental points for a given material fell around a single curve having the form of a conventional S/N curve. The material constant C was taken as the value of $\sigma_a^3 a$ at which a curve became parallel to the abscissa.

Values of C for the 12 materials tested are given in Table 4.23; C has the

TABLE 4.23

Material	Stress-relieved 1 hour at	Tensile strength (MN m⁻²)	Plain fatigue strength, 50×10^6 cycles (MN m⁻²)	C	C/plain fatigue strength	ΔK_c Crack length 0·5–5 mm (MN m⁻³⁄²)	ΔK_c Crack length 0·025–0·25 mm (MN m⁻³⁄²)	Effective R (see § 4.6.1)
Inconel	600 °C *in vacuo*	655	±220	750	3·4	6·4		
Nickel	500 °C *in vacuo*	455	±140	700	5·0	5·9		−0·33
18/8 austenitic steel	600 °C *in vacuo*	685	±360	540	1·5	6·0		
Low-alloy Steel	570 °C *in vacuo*	835	±460	510	1·1	6·3		
Mild steel	650 °C *in vacuo*	430	±200	510	2·55	6·4	4·2	−0·53
Nickel–chromium alloy steel	570 °C *in vacuo*	925	±500	510	1·02	6·4	3·3	−0·93
Monel	500 °C *in vacuo*	525	±240	360	1·5	5·6		−0·21
Phosphor bronze	500 °C *in air*	325	±130	160	1·2	3·7		
60/40 brass	550 °C *in air*	330	±105	94	0·9	3·1		
Copper	600 °C *in vacuo*	225	±62	56	0·9	2·7	1·6	−0·54
½% Cu–aluminium alloy	—	450	±140	19	0·14	2·1	1·2	−0·73
Aluminium	320 °C *in vacuo*	77	±27	4	0·15	1·02		−0·24

units of $\sigma_a^3 a$, where σ_a is in MN m⁻² and a is in metres. The value of C is generally estimated to an accuracy of around 5–10 per cent and, at worst, ±20 per cent; this implies that the stress that will just not cause a crack of a given length to grow can be estimated to within ±7 per cent. This assumes that no residual compressive stresses are present ahead of the crack tip after the initial cracking procedure. Such stresses are inevitably introduced by the nature of the experimental techniques used. To grow a crack in the original notched plates, $\sigma_a^3 a$ must be greater than C yet, to determine the value of C, some specimens need to be tested after the removal of the notch at $\sigma_a^3 a$ values less than C. Any residual compressive stresses remaining after stress-relieving will tend to increase the value of C.

The data for plate specimens containing cracks 0·5–5 mm deep has also been analysed [71] using the fracture-mechanics approach (see §§ 5.2, 5.6.8, and 5.7), and the results expressed in terms of the range of stress intensity factor ΔK during the fatigue cycle. Because cracks were small compared to the plate width, ΔK was calculated using the expression [72] for an edge-crack in a semi-infinite plate, namely,

$$\Delta K = 1 \cdot 1 \sigma (\pi a)^{\frac{1}{2}},$$

where σ was taken as the range of tensile stress in the loading cycle on the assumption that a crack closed completely during the compression half of the loading cycle. The net section stresses involved were always well below general yield, so no plastic zone size-corrections were necessary. Values of ΔK were plotted against endurance and the critical value ΔK_c for crack growth to occur was obtained as a fatigue limit; the results obtained are given in Table 4.23. The uncertainty in the determination of ΔK_c was up to ± 20 per cent.

The data for the cylindrical specimens containing edge-cracks 0·025–0·25 mm deep were also analysed in a similar fashion, but whereas the same value of C had been found to apply to both the plate and cylindrical specimens, as seen in Table 4.23, the ΔK_c values were lower for these shorter cracks than for the longer cracks in the plate specimens.

Although data concerned with the effect of a mean stress on the cyclic stress needed to cause a crack to grow is discussed later in § 4.7, it is pertinent here to compare the cracked plate results in Table 4.23 with those given in Table 4.29 (§ 4.7.2), which show that in general the value of ΔK_c for the zero mean load cycle ($R = -1$) is similar to that for repeated tensile loading ($R = 0$). This confirms that, in general, a crack closes during the compression half of the loading cycle so that the effective value of R is never less than zero. In those cases where ΔK_c, for $R = -1$, is less than expected (in particular, for aluminium and for some of the data on crack lengths in the range 0·025–0·25 mm) it could be argued that the plastic zone at the crack tip effectively props the crack open at zero load, so that part of the compressive half of the loading cycle is required to close the crack, thus reducing the effective value of R below zero. Effective values of R for short crack lengths and soft materials at zero mean stress can be estimated by assuming that the true value of ΔK_c is the same as that for longer cracks or for $R = 0$, as appropriate: values obtained are shown in Table 4.23. For example, for the nickel–chromium alloy steel, the effective R is -0.93, implying that nearly all the compressive part of the loading cycle is used in closing the crack, so that the true value of ΔK is nearly twice that calculated from the tensile half of the cycle. On the other hand, there is evidence [73] that the plastic zones swept out by successive positions of the tip of a growing crack leave behind a stretched zone which acts as a wedge and causes the crack to close before the tensile load is completely removed, thus reducing ΔK.

The value of ΔK cannot therefore be readily calculated for zero mean stress loadings, and unfortunately values of ΔK_c based on the tensile half of the fatigue cycle are not independent of crack length. The use of the empirical parameter C, which seems to be independent of crack length, is therefore preferable when dealing with design problems. Values of C are based on cracks whose lengths are small compared to other specimen dimensions, as is usually the case in design problems involving the critical stress required to cause a crack to grow.

The major conclusion stemming from the data given in Table 4.23 is that neither the static strength nor the plain fatigue strength of a material is related to the critical cyclic stress required to cause a crack to grow. For example, there is little difference in the values of either C or ΔK_c for the 4 steels tested. However, those materials having a high Young's modulus E have a higher value of C (or ΔK_c) than those having a low E. Thus the nickel and ferrous alloys, which have the highest value of E of the materials tested, have the highest C (or ΔK_c) values, and these are followed in order of decreasing E by the copper alloys and then by the aluminium alloys. This is not unexpected, for whether or not a crack grows must depend on the amount it is opened and closed during the loading cycle. For a given σ_a and a, this will vary inversely as E, because the stress levels used are such that the body of the cracked plate deforms elastically.

It has been suggested [74, 75] that the cracked plate data can be reconciled by using the elementary structural unit concept ($\S$ 4.3.2.4). For example, the cracked mild steel data have been shown to be well represented by the equation

$$\sigma_c = \frac{S_0}{1 + 2(a/\rho_e)^{\frac{1}{2}}} \tag{4.1}$$

where σ_c is the fatigue limit of a plate containing an edge crack of length a, S_0 is the plain fatigue limit of the material, and ρ_e is an equivalent crack root radius, taken as 2 mm in order to make the equation fit the experimental results. The length ρ_e can be shown to be equivalent to the elementary structural unit A since this equation can be derived directly from the appropriate

equation for sharp-pointed notches having zero flank angle, given in §
4.3.2.4, namely,

$$K_f = 1 + \frac{K_t - 1}{1 + (A/\rho)^{\frac{1}{2}}}.$$

Writing

$$K_t = 1 + 2\left(\frac{a}{\rho}\right)^{\frac{1}{2}},$$

where ρ is the crack tip root radius, gives

$$K_f = 1 + \frac{2(a/\rho)^{\frac{1}{2}}}{1 + (A/\rho)^{\frac{1}{2}}}.$$

$(A/\rho)^{\frac{1}{2}}$ is large compared to 1, therefore

$$K_f = 1 + 2\left(\frac{a}{A}\right)^{\frac{1}{2}},$$

which is eq. (4.1) if $K_f = S_0/\sigma_c$ and $A = \rho_e$.

All of the suggested relationships are, of course, empirical in the sense that
a material constant must be derived from experimental data. However, it is
considered that the introduction of the plain fatigue limit into the relationship tends to mask a point of great practical significance, namely, that the
alternating stress required to just cause a crack of a given length to grow in a
steel has the same value irrespective of the tensile strength and plain fatigue
limit of the steel.

4.6. Interpretation of zero mean load notched fatigue data

4.6.1. Wrought materials

Discussion is limited to ductile homogeneous materials, in which surface
microcracks are initiated by continuing cyclic slip. A previous analysis [76]
of some of the experimental data given in § 4.3 and § 4.4 and other similar
analyses [77, 78] suggest that the results obtained by testing batches of either
plate or cylindrical notched specimens of similar over-all dimensions and
containing edge- or circumferential notches of various root radii but of constant depth may be represented by a diagram of the form shown on Fig. 4.14,
which is a generalized version of Fig. 4.7. Curve 1 on this diagram represents
the plain fatigue limit of the material divided by K_t, curve 2, the experimentally determined notched fatigue limits based on the alternating stress required
to initiate a crack at the notch root, and line 3 the conventional notched fatigue
limit, that is, the maximum alternating stress that will just not propagate a
crack formed at the notch root. The position of this line above the abscissa
varies with notch depth.

Consider, first, the nominal alternating stress required to initiate a crack
at the root of a notch, that is, curves 1 and 2. It is reasonable to postulate

that when the root radius of a notch is large compared to that at the tip of a crack, surface microcracks will form in the highly stressed region at the notch root by the same processes responsible for their formation on the surface of a plain specimen of the same material subjected to a cyclic stress greater than its plain fatigue limit. However, the volume of highly stressed material at the notch root must be such that not only does a surface microcrack form, but it is also able to develop to the necessary depth to enable it to grow as a

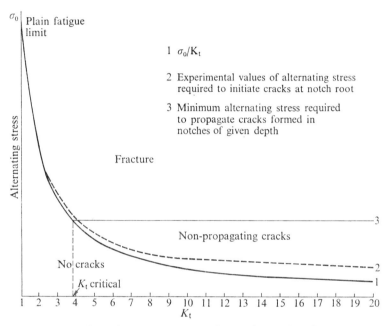

FIG. 4.14. Nominal alternating stress versus K_t diagram for a series of notched specimens having notches of different root radii but the same depth. (Taken from Frost [76].)

macrocrack under the action of the nominal stress range remote from the notch root. Thus, whereas in a plain specimen a microcrack is developing in a nominally uniform stress field which at all places is higher than the plain fatigue limit, in a notched specimen, a microcrack has to develop across a rapidly decreasing stress field. It follows therefore that, in order for it to be just able to develop, the stress at the surface of the notch root will need to be somewhat higher than that at the surface of a plain specimen in which a surface microcrack is just able to develop.

Because of the lower nominal stress over the cross-section, the length to which a microcrack must develop before it is able to grow as a macrocrack will be longer than in a plain specimen, but on the other hand, the effective length of the crack from the free surface is increased by the notch depth. This means that in all but shallow sharp notches, the nominal stress will generally be sufficient for a microcrack to grow as a macrocrack almost as soon as it is formed; it is certainly true for notches having K_t values lying to the left of the dotted vertical line on Fig. 4.14. It may be expected, therefore, that in this region, curves 1 and 2 will be close together, curve 2 tending to be somewhat higher than curve 1 because the surface stress may have to exceed that given by curve 1 if the microcrack is going to be able to develop to the macrocrack stage, but for a given K_t, the deeper the notch the more closely will curve 2 approach curve 1.

It may well be that the correlation between K_t and K_f, for K_t values lying to the left of the dotted line, achieved by the use of relationships (§ 4.3.2.4) based on the assumption that the fatigue limit stress must act over some finite element of material (defined by a length measurement in from the notch root) before cracking can occur, is a consequence of the fact that a microcrack must develop a small distance in from the notch root through a rapidly decreasing stress field. A further major cause of discrepancy between these curves can arise from the technique used for machining the notch which may both work-harden and induce compressive residual stresses into the material at the notch root. Work-hardening will result in an increase in the cyclic stress necessary to cause continuing cyclic slip, while induced residual compressive stresses will retard the development of a microcrack to the macrocrack stage by reducing the crack opening. Biaxial stress effects (§ 4.3.2.2) may also cause curve 2 to be higher than curve 1.

Consider now the conditions required to propagate a crack formed at the notch root. Fig. 4.14 implies that a crack formed at the notch root can only grow as a macrocrack, to cause complete failure of the specimen, if the nominal alternating stress lies in the area marked fracture bounded by curve 2 and line 3, bearing in mind that the position of line 3 above the abscissa depends on notch depth. For a given notch depth, the value of K_t at the intersection (sometimes called the branch point [77]) of either curves 1 or 2 and line 3 is given by

$K_{t\ crit}$ = plain fatigue limit/(minimum nominal alternating stress required to propagate a crack formed at the notch root)

Thus, for notches of a given depth having values of K_t less than $K_{t\ crit}$, the nominal alternating stress required to initiate a crack at the notch root is higher than the minimum propagation stress and all cracks which form will grow to cause complete failure of the specimen. For notches having K_t values greater than $K_{t\ crit}$, the minimum cyclic propagation stress (and hence the conventional notched fatigue limit) remains constant and is independent of the notch root radius. Non-propagating cracks will be present in all specimens having notches sufficiently sharp to initiate a crack at the notch root tested at all nominal stresses less than that represented by line 3.

In order to predict the position of line 3, it is necessary to know the effective crack depth a_a of a vee-notch containing a non-propagating crack and the value of the maximum nominal alternating stress that will just not cause a crack of a given length to grow. Experimental data on edge-notched plate specimens having root radii sufficiently sharp for non-propagating cracks to be present at the conventional notched fatigue limit showed that this value was equal to the maximum alternating stress that would just not propagate a crack whose length was equal to the notch depth plus length of non-propagating crack. Thus a_a can be taken as the notch depth plus the average length of the non-propagating crack formed at the conventional notched fatigue limit. It will also be assumed that the $\sigma^3 a = C$ relationship discussed in § 4.5.4 is applicable, although of course any other relationship, if shown to correlate the appropriate data, could equally well be used. Thus, whether or not a crack, formed at a notch root, grows will depend on whether $\sigma^3 a_a$ is greater or less than C, where $\pm\sigma$ is the nominal gross area cyclic stress applied to a specimen of such dimensions that a_a is small compared to specimen width or diameter. The length of the non-propagating crack formed at the conventional notched fatigue limit is generally small compared to the notch depth d, thus a_a can be taken equal to d, and non-propagating cracks will therefore be present in specimens tested at the conventional notched fatigue limit if

$$K_t > \frac{\text{plain fatigue limit}}{(C/d)^{\frac{1}{3}}}.$$

The conventional notched fatigue limit $\pm\sigma_n$ (that is, the position of line 3), based on net area, of a batch of specimens of finite dimensions containing a notch of K_t value greater than $K_{t\ crit}$ will be given by

$$\sigma_n = \alpha\left(\frac{C}{d}\right)^{\frac{1}{3}},$$

where α is a factor which depends on the ratio of notch depth to specimen diameter. If the specimen is large compared to the notch depth, $\alpha = 1$.

Consider now batches of vee-notched specimens of the materials given in Table 4.23, all having notches 2·5 mm deep and root radii sufficiently sharp that non-propagating cracks are present at the conventional notched fatigue limit, the other dimensions being such that $\alpha = 1$. K_t for these specimens is then given by

$$K_t = \frac{\text{plain fatigue limit}}{(C/0\cdot0025)^{\frac{1}{3}}}.$$

Values of K_t are given in Table 4.24; they are the maximum that can be attained (at zero mean load) for the notch depth considered, irrespective of notch root radius.

They indicate clearly why ignorance of the presence of non-propagating cracks has led to some materials, for example, the high-strength steel and aluminium alloys being termed notch-sensitive, whereas others, for example, copper and mild steel, are commonly referred to as notch-insensitive. A different notch depth would result in different K_t values but, of course, they would remain in the same relative order for the different materials. Thus, it is apparent that the procedure of carrying out fatigue tests on batches of specimens containing notches all of the same depth but of different root

T ABLE 4.24

Material	Plain fatigue strength, 5×10^7 cycles (MN m^{-2})	C	Calculated K_t
Inconel	±220	750	3·4
Nickel	±140	700	2·1
18/8 austenitic steel	±360	540	5·9
Low-alloy steel	±460	510	7·9
Mild steel	±200	510	3·4
Nickel–chromium alloy steel	±500	510	8·4
Monel	±240	360	4·7
Phosphor bronze	±130	160	3·3
60/40 brass	±105	94	3·1
Copper	±62	56	2·2
$4\frac{1}{2}\%$ Cu–aluminium alloy	±140	19	7·1
Aluminium	±27	4	2·4

radii, comparing the K_f values obtained with the corresponding K_t values and then concluding that the material is either notch sensitive or notch insensitive can be very misleading. For example, tests on copper specimens (Table 4.13) containing vee-notches 1·9 mm deep and of varying K_t values between 1·5 and 10 indicated that, irrespective of the K_t value, K_f did not exceed 1·5, and it was concluded [22], therefore, that the material was notch-insensitive. However, because non-propagating cracks must have been present in specimens unbroken after testing, it is clear that, had deeper notches of the same K_t values been tested, higher values of K_f would have been obtained.

The accuracy to which the C values given in Table 4.23 enable the conventional notched fatigue limits of sharply notched specimens to be estimated is illustrated by the results given in Tables 4.25 and 4.26. The calculated conventional notched fatigue limits were obtained from the equation

$$\sigma_n = \alpha \left(\frac{C}{d} \right)^{\frac{1}{3}},$$

and α was obtained by making the calculated mild steel values agree with the corresponding experimental values. This gave values of $\alpha = 1·2$ and

TABLE 4.25

Rotating bending fatigue data for 12·7 mm outside diameter specimens containing a circumferential 55° vee-notch 1·3 mm deep and root radius 0·0025–0·005 mm [54]

Material	Tensile strength (MN m^{-2})	Conventional notched fatigue limit (MN m^{-2})	
		experimental (net area stress)	calculated (net area stress)
Inconel	655	±100	±100
Nickel	455	±100	±99
Low-alloy steel	835	±89	±88
Mild steel	430	±89	±88
Monel	525	±77	±79
Phosphor bronze	325	±50	±60
60/40 brass	330	±42	±51
Copper	225	±35	±42
4½% Cu–aluminium alloy	450	±35	±29
Aluminium	77	±15	±17

1·25 for the 12·7 mm and 43 mm outside diameter specimens, respectively; they correspond to notch depth/specimen diameter ratios of 0·1 and 0·12 respectively.

It follows that a size-effect will become apparent if batches of geometrically similar notched specimens having a K_t value greater than $K_{t\ \text{crit}}$ are tested, for although all specimens will have the same K_t value, the notch depth will vary from batch to batch. Thus, the shallower the notch the higher the conventional notched fatigue limit and hence the lower the value of K_f.

An additional point arises in connection with line 3 on Fig. 4.14. As drawn, it implies that when non-propagating cracks are present in specimens unbroken after testing at the conventional notched fatigue limit, this value for a given notch depth is independent of notch root radius. However, the experimental data on the 4½% Cu–aluminium alloy shown on Tables

TABLE 4.26

Reversed direct-stress fatigue data for 43 mm outside diameter specimens containing a circumferential 55° vee-notch 5 mm deep and 0·05 mm root radius [54]

Material	Tensile strength (MN m^{-2})	Conventional notched fatigue limit (MN m^{-2})	
		experimental (net area stress)	calculated (net area stress)
Mild steel	430	±58	±57
18/8 austenitic steel	685	±62	±59
Nickel–chromium alloy steel	925	±58	±57

4.13 and 4.18 imply that this is not true, because the conventional notched fatigue limits of very sharply notched specimens are higher than those of less sharply notched specimens of equal notch depth even though non-propagating cracks are present in these latter specimens. However, this is believed to be due to residual compressive stresses induced in the material around the notch root during machining, since these aluminium alloys were tested with no prior stress-relieving treatment. It is reasonable to assume that higher residual stresses were induced in the sharper specimens due to the higher contact stresses involved in cutting the smaller radius, thus requiring a higher nominal alternating stress to make cracks grow. If the aluminium alloy specimens could have been fully stress-relieved after final machining, it is suggested that the results shown on Table 4.13 and 4.18 would have conformed to those shown on Fig. 4.14, that is, the conventional notched fatigue limits would have remained constant for K_t values greater than $K_{t\,\mathrm{crit}}$.

Although the results in Table 4.25 imply that if a notched specimen contains a non-propagating crack when tested at its conventional notched fatigue limit, it can be considered equivalent to a specimen containing a crack of length equal to the notch depth plus depth of non-propagating crack, the question arises why a non-propagating crack has a particular maximum length for, in most cases, the direction of the crack is normal to the loading direction, implying that it has grown over at least the latter part of its length as a macrocrack, that is, in Mode I in fracture-mechanics terms (§ 5.2.1).

Although a crack emanating from a hole or notch grows through a decreasing stress field, nevertheless for a given load the stress intensity factor normally increases continuously [7]. Hence in a fatigue test under constant load, the range of stress intensity factor during the fatigue cycle ΔK which for a zero mean load test is conventionally calculated from the tensile half of the fatigue cycle, will also increase continuously. If it is assumed that the critical value ΔK_c of ΔK necessary for crack growth is constant, there appears to be no mechanism by which a macrocrack can be arrested once it starts to grow. However, Table 4.23 shows that values of ΔK_c, for cracks in a plain specimen, calculated on the conventional basis, decrease at short crack lengths and, assuming that cracks at notches behave in a similar manner, these data suggest that behaviour can be represented schematically by the diagram shown in Fig. 4.15.

A crack growing as a microcrack will start to grow as a macrocrack as soon as $\Delta K \geqslant \Delta K_c$ and will continue to grow as long as $\Delta K \geqslant \Delta K_c$. Whether or not the crack stops and becomes a non-propagating crack depends on the relative shapes of the ΔK versus crack length and ΔK_c versus crack length curves. By differentiating eqn (5.1) (§ 5.2.2), it can be shown that the slope of the ΔK curve is given by

$$\frac{\mathrm{d}(\Delta K)}{\mathrm{d}a} = \frac{\Delta K}{2a},$$

where a is the over-all crack length, that is, macrocrack+microcrack+ notch (if any). The slope at a given ΔK, therefore, will be much greater (curve 1) for a crack growing in a plain specimen than for a crack growing in a notched specimen (curve 2) for which a includes the notch depth. The value of ΔK_c increases at first, and then becomes constant; the initial slope is greater for a hard material (curve 3) than for a soft material (curve 4).

In the case of a plain specimen (curve 1) ΔK is always greater than ΔK_c, so crack-arrest does not occur. However, for a notched specimen (curve 2)

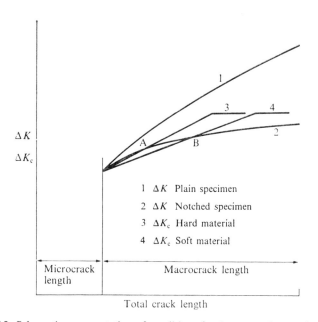

FIG. 4.15. Schematic representation of conditions for the arrest of a growing macrocrack.

$\Delta K = \Delta K_c$ at point A for a hard material and point B for a soft material so that a crack becomes non-propagating, the length of a non-propagating crack being shorter in a hard material than a soft material. This is indeed confirmed by the experimental data, non-propagating cracks in mild steel and copper notched specimens, for example, being much longer than in similar sharply notched high strength steel and aluminium alloy specimens.

4.6.2. Cast materials

Notched specimens of cast materials tend to give lower K_f values than those of similar shape made in wrought materials of the same tensile strength [9, 79]. If the cast material is one in which fatigue failure of a plain specimen is associated with the presence of inherent flaws, K_f may be much less than the K_t value of the notch, and for small shallow notches is not far removed from unity [80]; the deeper the notch and the larger the notch root radius, the more nearly will the K_f value approach K_t [9]. Defects in grey cast iron exist as graphite flakes so that, unless the size of the notch is large compared to the size of a defect, the addition of a further defect in the form of a mechanical notch makes little difference to the fatigue strength [81]. However, defects located at the root of a large notch are in a local high-stress field and hence could grow at nominal stresses less than that necessary in a plain specimen.

TABLE 4.27

Rotating bending fatigue data for notched cylindrical specimens
18 mm outside diameter containing a circumferential vee-groove
3·8 mm deep and 2·5 mm root radius; $K_t = 3\cdot5$ [83]

Cast iron	Plain fatigue limit (MN m⁻²)	Notched fatigue limit (MN m⁻²)	K_t
Ferritic flake	±85	±70	1·2
Pearlitic flake	±155	±110	1·4
Ferritic nodular	±210	±155	1·35
Pearlitic nodular	±300	±195	1·55

The rotating bending fatigue limits of grey cast iron specimens up to 23 mm diameter, containing a transverse hole whose diameter was less than a quarter of the specimen diameter, were only slightly less than that of the corresponding plain specimens [81]; larger holes, however, caused an appreciable decrease in the fatigue limit. Reference [82] gives the fatigue limits of a variety of differently-notched cast iron specimens, some showing little difference from the corresponding plain fatigue limits, others showing a significant difference. For example, the fatigue limits of grey cast iron specimens of 19 mm outside diameter, containing a circumferential vee-groove 5 mm deep, and having K_t values 1·5 and 3 were ±69 MN m⁻² and ±62 MN m⁻² respectively, compared to a plain fatigue limit of ±69 MN m⁻². However, the notched fatigue limit of 9 mm diameter specimens having a 1·5 mm diameter transverse hole in a grey cast iron of the same plain fatigue limit was ±45 MN m⁻². Table 4.27 gives some further results for various cast irons.

In general, therefore, the effect of a notch on the fatigue limit of a cast material or one containing known defects will depend on the size of the notch relative to the defect. If the notch is large, so that a volume of material containing many defects is subjected to stresses higher than the nominal stress, then the notched fatigue limit will be reduced. If, however, the notch size is comparable to the flaw size, then the addition of a further stress raiser will have little effect. It could be argued that, if the plain fatigue limit of a cast material is low compared to that of a wrought material of similar composition and tensile strength, the plain fatigue limit in the former case is determined by the cyclic stress necessary to cause cracks to grow from inherent flaws. Thus, the notched fatigue limit will depend on the size of the notch in relation to the flaw size as well as on its K_t value. Of course, if a flaw in a cast notched specimen is situated at the notch root and is lying in a direction normal to the loading direction, the effective flaw length is increased, and hence the notched fatigue limit is reduced. Even if the notched fatigue limit of a cast material were the same as that of similarly notched specimens of a similar wrought material, the cast material must exhibit the lower K_t value if the plain fatigue limit of the cast material is lower than that of the wrought material.

4.7. Effect of a mean load

4.7.1. Notched specimens

The analyses and data given in this section are applicable only to those notch geometries in which any crack formed at the notch root grows across the specimen to cause complete failure. The data given therefore illustrate the effect of a mean stress on the cyclic stress required to initiate a crack at the notch root. The behaviour of cracked specimens is discussed in § 4.7.2.

When notched fatigue specimens are subjected to a loading cycle in which the mean stress is not zero, various definitions of K_t are possible, based on the ratio of the plain fatigue limit to the conventional notched fatigue limit at either constant R (minimum load/maximum load) or constant mean stress, the mean stress being either the nominal stress or the actual stress at the notch root.

The effect of a mean stress on the plain fatigue limit (or strength at long endurances) of a material has been discussed in § 3.5; the effect of a mean stress on the fatigue limit of notched specimens follows the same general pattern in that a tensile mean stress reduces the fatigue limit and a compressive mean stress increases it. If the true values of the maximum alternating and mean stresses at the surface of the notch root are known, the interrelation between these two values would be expected to follow the same general trend as found with plain specimens of the same material. For example, if a specimen containing a notch of known K_t value remains wholly elastic at the stress levels under consideration, and the plain fatigue limits of the material under various mean tensile stresses conform to, say, the modified Goodman relationship, then

$$K_t \sigma_{nm} = K_t \sigma_{n0}\left(1 - \frac{K_t \sigma_m}{T}\right),$$

that is

$$\sigma_{nm} = \sigma_{n0}\left(1 - \frac{K_t \sigma_m}{T}\right),$$

where $\pm\sigma_{n0}$ is the nominal alternating stress at the zero mean load notched fatigue limit, $\pm\sigma_{nm}$ is the nominal alternating stress at the notched fatigue limit when a nominal tensile mean stress σ_m is applied, and T is the tensile strength of the material. However, owing to stress redistribution, the full value of $K_t\sigma_m$ may not be reached in a ductile material and σ_{nm}, therefore, will be greater than given by the above equation. In fact, the fatigue limits of notched

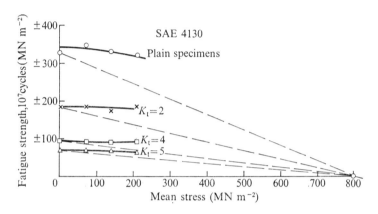

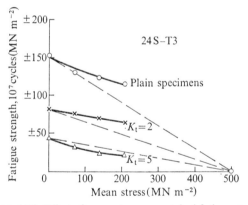

FIG. 4.16. Effect of mean stress on notched fatigue strength. (Taken from Grover, Hyler, and Jackson [14].)

ductile specimens tested at various nominal tensile mean stresses tend to fall on the safe side of a modified Goodman diagram employing nominal stresses and having as end-points the zero mean stress notched fatigue limit and the tensile strength of the material. This is illustrated by the results shown on Fig. 4.16; they were obtained [14] on edge-notched plate specimens of SAE 4130 steel (tensile strength 805 MN m^{-2}) and 24S-T3 aluminium alloy ($4\frac{1}{2}\%$ Cu, tensile strength 500 MN m^{-2}). Collected data [84] show that, with few exceptions, experimental fatigue limits fall on the safe side of a modified

Goodman line for both uniaxial and torsional stressing; those materials for which the Goodman line gives an unsafe prediction have high yield-stress/tensile-strength ratios [80], the true mean stress at the notch root being nearer to the elastic value than to the nominal stress.

Some experimental fatigue limits obtained on either cylindrical bars containing a circumferential vee-groove or plate specimens containing edge notches are compared in Table 4.28 with those predicted by both the nominal

TABLE 4.28

Material and reference	Plain fatigue strength and tensile strength (MN m^{-2})	K_t	Nominal mean stress (MN m^{-2})	Notched fatigue strength (MN m^{-2})		
				Experimental	Calculated	
					Goodman	Gerber
Aluminium alloy 14S–T [13]	±165 (5 × 10^7 cycles) 495	1·6	69	±125	±90	±101
			138	±103	±75	±95
			240	±90	±53	±79
			415	±48	±18	±32
		2·4	69	±69	±60	±68
			138	±55	±50	±63
			240	±48	±35	±52
			415	±34	±12	±21
		3·4	69	±48	±42	±48
			138	±34	±35	±45
			240	±28	±25	±37
			415	±28	±8	±15
Aluminium alloy 24S–T4 [13]	±172 (5 × 10^7 cycles) 505	1·6	69	±117	±92	±105
			138	±103	±79	±100
			240	±82	±56	±83
			415	±31	±19	±36
		2·4	69	±72	±62	±70
			138	±55	±52	±67
			240	±41	±37	±55
			415	±31	±13	±23
		3·4	69	±48	±43	±50
			138	±31	±37	±47
			240	±28	±26	±39
			415	±21	±9	±17
Aluminium alloy 75S–T6 [14]	±205 (10^7 cycles) 570	2	69	±90	±91	±102
			138	±66	±79	±97
			207	±59	±66	±90
		4	69	±28	±46	±51
			138	±21	±39	±48
			207	±21	±33	±45
		5	69	±24	±38	±41
			138	±17	±32	±39
			207	±16	±26	±36

TABLE 4.28 (*contd.*)

Material and reference	Plain fatigue strength and tensile strength (MN m⁻²)	K_t	Nominal mean stress (MN m⁻²)	Notched fatigue strength (MN m⁻²)		
				Experimental	Calculated	
					Goodman	Gerber
SAE 4130 steel [14]	± 330 (10^7 cycles)	2	69	± 185	± 152	± 164
			138	± 173	± 138	± 161
			207	± 185	± 123	± 155
		4	69	± 90	± 76	± 82
			138	± 90	± 69	± 81
			207	± 90	± 62	± 77
	805	5	69	± 69	± 61	± 66
			138	± 69	± 55	± 64
			207	± 62	± 49	± 61
Aluminium alloy 24S–T3 [14]	± 150 (10^7 cycles)	2	69	± 76	± 66	± 75
			138	± 69	± 55	± 70
			207	± 62	± 45	± 63
		4	69	± 35	± 32	± 37
			138	± 28	± 28	± 35
			207	± 28	± 22	± 31
	505	5	69	± 31	± 26	± 30
			138	± 24	± 22	± 28
			207	± 21	± 18	± 25
Magnesium alloy ($5\frac{1}{2}\%$ Zn, $0·66\%$ Zr) [13]	± 150 (5×10^7 cycles)	2·4	34	± 55	± 57	± 63
			69	± 48	± 50	± 61
			138	± 31	± 38	± 53
			207	± 28	± 25	± 41
			276	± 21	± 12	± 23
	345	3·4	34	± 48	± 40	± 44
			69	± 41	± 36	± 43
			138	± 24	± 27	± 37
			207	± 14	± 18	± 28
			276	± 10	± 9	± 16

mean stress Gerber and Goodman relationships, that is,

$$\sigma_{nm} = \frac{\sigma_0}{K_t}\left\{1 - \left(\frac{\sigma_m}{T}\right)^2\right\},$$

and

$$\sigma_{nm} = \frac{\sigma_0}{K_t}\left(1 - \frac{\sigma_m}{T}\right), \quad \text{respectively.}$$

where $\pm \sigma_{nm}$ is the nominal notched fatigue strength at a given endurance when a nominal tensile mean stress σ_m is present, $\pm \sigma_0$ is the plain fatigue strength (at the same endurance) of the material at zero mean load, and T is the tensile strength of the material

The use of σ_0/K_t instead of the experimentally-determined zero mean load notched fatigue strength σ_{no} gives a safer prediction, because K_t is generally greater than K_f (§ 4.3). In general, the Goodman relationship gives a safe prediction; the unsafe predictions for the 75S-T6 aluminium alloy are presumably associated with its high 0·1 per cent proof stress which allows the true

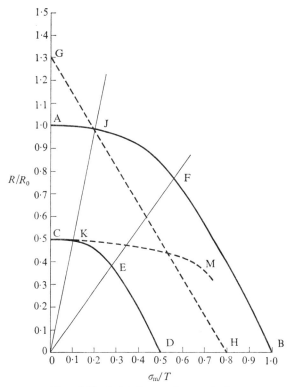

$$R/R_0$$

$$\sigma_m/T$$

FIG. 4.17. *R–M* diagram for notched specimens.

mean stress at the notch root to increase appreciably above its nominal value.

As with plain specimens (§ 3.5) notched fatigue data are often displayed on non-dimensional *R–M* diagrams [85]. Given the plain specimen *R–M* diagram (that is, curve AB on Fig. 4.17), the *R–M* diagram for a batch of notched specimens of the same material, provided they remain wholly elastic, is given by the curve CD, where on any line passing through the origin, OE = OF/K_t. The dotted line GH represents the condition for plain specimens that the maximum stress in the loading cycle is equal to the yield stress (or, say, 0·2 per cent proof stress); it intersects AB at J, the line OJ intersecting CD at K. Point K represents the nominal stress conditions at which the actual maximum tensile stress at the notch root is equal to the yield stress. Then, assuming that this maximum tensile stress does not increase appreciably with further increase in nominal mean stress until the plastic deformation extends over a large part of the specimen cross-section, the R–M diagram for the notched specimens does not depart greatly from a line parallel to the abscissa, that is, the curve CKM in Fig. 4.17. In fact, little error accrues from assuming that the initial part of KM is a straight line, parallel to the abscissa (as it would be for a non-work-hardening material), up to where it intersects the dotted line GH; its shape beyond this point is of little practical interest, the nominal mean stresses involved being outside the range of normal design practice. The value of σ_{nm} applicable to the curve CK is given by

$$\sigma_{nm} = \frac{\sigma_0}{K_t}\left\{1 - \left(\frac{K_t\sigma_m}{T}\right)^n\right\},$$

where $\pm\sigma_{nm}$ is the notched fatigue limit at a nominal tensile mean stress σ_m, $\pm\sigma_0$ is the zero mean load fatigue limit of plain specimens, T is the tensile strength of the material, n is 1 for the Goodman relationship and 2 for the Gerber relationship, and $K_t(\sigma_m + \sigma_{nm}) \leqslant Y$, where Y is the yield stress of the material. The value of σ_{nm} over the line KM, assuming it is a straight line parallel to the abscissa, is obtained by substituting for σ_m from this criterion, that is, $K_t(\sigma_m + \sigma_{nm}) = Y$, in the above equation.

Thus

$$\sigma_{nm} = \frac{\sigma_0}{K_t}\left\{1 - \left(\frac{Y - K_t\sigma_{nm}}{T}\right)^n\right\},$$

and σ_{nm} is independent of σ_m until the whole cross-section yields. These predictions are in agreement with experimental data [80, 85, 86].

4.7.2. Cracked specimens

The analyses and data given in § 4.7.1 are applicable only to those notch geometries in which any crack formed at the notch root grows across the specimen to cause complete failure.

As soon as a microcrack initiated at the root of a notch develops to such a depth that it can grow as a macrocrack, a superimposed tensile mean stress may enhance its growth rate, whereas a compressive mean stress will retard it. If the compressive mean stress is such that the crack faces never open, a crack initiated at the notch root (at a stress level less than the plain fatigue limit) is unable to grow across the specimen. Fig. 4.18 is the growth curve (crack length versus number of stress cycles) for a crack formed at the root of a 5 mm deep, 0·1 mm root-radius edge-notch, in a 63 mm wide mild steel plate tested at -120 ± 90 MN m^{-2}; it shows that the crack became dormant after about 4×10^6 cycles.

The effect of a tensile mean stress σ_m on the alternating stress σ_a, required to cause an edge-crack of length a to grow can be determined using the same techniques and methods of analysis used to determine the relationship at zero mean load (§ 4.5.4). The results can be expressed in terms of either C or ΔK_c; either parameter can be determined to within 10 per cent, and they are equally satisfactory means of correlating the data. If at zero mean load a crack merely remains closed during the compressive half of the loading cycle,

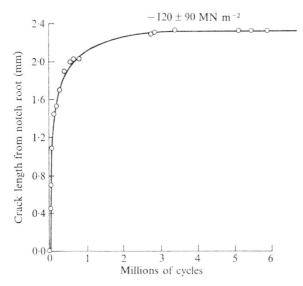

FIG. 4.18. Growth of a fatigue crack in an edge-notched mild steel plate subjected to a wholly compressive loading cycle.

the crack growth behaviour for the stress cycle $(0\pm P)$ would be the same as that for the stress cycle $(0-P)$, that is, $P/2\pm P/2$. Thus, for $\sigma_m = \sigma_a$, the value of ΔK_c (which is conventionally calculated ignoring compressive stresses) would be the same as for zero mean stress, but the value of C would be expected to be one-eighth of the value for zero mean stress. The results shown in Tables 4.29 and 4.23 in general confirm this (see § 4.5.4).

The results given in Table 4.29 show that C decreases steadily from its expected value (about one-eighth the zero mean stress value) at $R = 0$ to a minimum at some greater value of R. This minimum is given approximately [88] by

$$C = \frac{1 \cdot 8E^3}{10^{15}},$$

where E is Young's modulus in MN m^{-2}.

On the other hand, apart from the anomalous result for mild steel at $R = 0 \cdot 75$, values of ΔK_c decrease continuously without reaching any

TABLE 4.29

Critical stress required to cause a crack to grow

Material Stress-relieved 1 hour at	Tensile strength $(MN\ m^{-2})$	$R = \dfrac{\sigma_m - \sigma_a}{\sigma_m + \sigma_a}$	C $((MN\ m^{-2})^3 m)$	ΔK_c crack length 0·5–5 mm $(MN\ m^{-\frac{3}{2}})$
Mild steel	430	0·13	56	6·6
650 °C *in vacuo*		0·35	37	5·2
[87]		0·49	17	4·3
		0·64	14	3·2
		0·75	15	3·8
18/8 austenitic steel	665	0	65	6·0
4 hours at 500 °C		0·33	37	5·9
in vacuo		0·62	22	4·6
[88]		0·74	18	4·1
Aluminium	77	0	0·93	1·7
320 °C *in vacuo*		0·33	0·75	1·4
[88]		0·53	0·56	1·2
4½% Cu–aluminium	495	0	2·8	2·1
alloy (BS L65)		0·33	1·9	1·7
[88]		0·5	1·2	1·5
		0·67	0·6	1·2
Copper	215	0	4·7	2·5
600 °C *in vacuo*		0·33	1·9	1·8
[88]		0·56	1·4	1·5
		0·69	1·1	1·4
		0·80	1·1	1·3
Commercially pure titanium 700 °C *in vacuo* [88]	540	0·60	3·3	2·2
Nickel	430	0	93	7·9
2 hours at 850 °C *in*		0·33	65	6·5
vacuo [88]		0·57	28	5·2
		0·71	14	3·6
Low-alloy steel	680	0	79	6·6
650 °C *in vacuo*		0·33	32	5·1
[88]		0·50	19	4·4
		0·64	9	3·3
Monel	525	0	61	7·0
2 hours at 800 °C *in*		0·33	39	6·5
vacuo [88]		0·50	24	5·2
		0·67	12	3·6
Maraging steel†	2000	0·67	4.7	2·7
Phosphor bronze	370	0·33	14	4·1
550 °C in air		0·50	11	3·2
[88]		0·74	4	2·4

TABLE 4.29 (*contd.*)

Material Stress-relieved 1 hour at	Tensile strength (MN m^{-2})	$R = \dfrac{\sigma_m - \sigma_a}{\sigma_m + \sigma_a}$	C ((MN m^{-2})^{3}m)	ΔK_c crack length 0·5–5 mm (MN m$^{-\frac{3}{2}}$)
60/40 brass	325	0	14	3·5
550 °C in air		0·33	11	3·1
[88]		0·51	4	2·6
		0·72	3	2·6
Inconel	650	0	93	7·1
2 hours at 800 °C *in*		0·57	28	4·7
vacuo [88]		0·71	14	4·0

† Heat treated after fatigue cracking: 1 hour at 820 °C, air cooled, 3 hours at 480 °C.

apparent minimum, and ΔK_c in MN m$^{-\frac{3}{2}}$ units is given approximately [89] by

$$\Delta K_c = 3\cdot2 \times 10^{-5} E \left(\frac{\sigma_a}{\sigma_m}\right)^{\frac{1}{3}}.$$

Experimental values of ΔK_c are between two and five times the values which can be predicted theoretically; theoretical predictions and reasons for the existence of non-propagating cracks are discussed further in Chapter 5.

It is suggested in Chapter 5 that the length that a crack can grow in one stress cycle cannot be less than one lattice spacing. Thus, the fact that a crack of finite length can remain dormant under a finite stress range implies that the applied stress and crack length are insufficient to create a new surface at the crack tip at least one lattice spacing in length (that is, the change in crack tip profile under the stress range can be wholly accommodated by reversible deformation), and if a longer fresh surface is created it is able to rebond completely when the stress is reduced. It could be argued that the change in C or ΔK_c values at R values between zero and that corresponding to the minimum value of C arises from the fact that, for a crack of given length, the value of σ_a necessary to create a new surface at least one lattice spacing long increases as R increases or alternatively, that the bonding of freshly created surfaces is more effective as R approaches zero.

The lives of precracked specimens in which crack growth occurs may be greater than is possible at zero mean stress. This is because, although a tensile mean stress decreases ΔK_c, it generally does not affect the rate of crack growth for a given ΔK (§ 5.7). For a specimen tested under conditions where crack growth just takes place, the value of ΔK at the start of crack growth and the initial rate of crack growth will therefore be less than for a corresponding zero mean stress test, and the total life correspondingly greater.

For mild steel, the knee in the ΔK versus endurance curve moves from around 10^6 cycles at zero mean stress to around 10^7 cycles in the presence of a mean stress.

4.8. Effect of combined stresses

When a notched specimen is subjected to other than uniaxial stresses, the values of K_t and K_f will depend on how the stresses are defined. Consider, for example, a cylindrical bar containing a transverse hole, subjected to cyclic torsional stresses. A nominal cyclic maximum surface shear stress $\pm S$ will create a maximum cyclic tension–compression stress of $\pm 4S$ at points on opposite ends of the two diameters of the hole inclined at 45° to the longitudinal axis of the bar. Fig. 4.19 shows fatigue cracks growing along these 45° directions from two oil holes in a crackshaft journal subjected to torsional cyclic stresses. Because both other principal stresses are zero at the edge of the hole, the shear stresses at these points will be $\pm 2S$. Thus K_t could be defined as

(1) $\dfrac{\text{maximum principal tension stress at the edge of the hole}}{\text{nominal shear stress}} = \dfrac{4S}{S} = 4$

or

(2) $\dfrac{\text{maximum shear stress at the edge of the hole}}{\text{nominal shear stress}} = \dfrac{2S}{S} = 2,$

and the corresponding definitions of K_f would be

(1) $\dfrac{\text{uniaxial fatigue limit of plain bar}}{\text{torsional fatigue limit of holed bar}}$

or

(2) $\dfrac{\text{torsional fatigue limit of plain bar}}{\text{torsional fatigue limit of holed bar}}.$

Although the alternative K_t values are merely in a ratio of 2:1, this is not true for the corresponding K_f values, because the uniaxial plain fatigue limit may not be exactly twice the torsional plain fatigue limit.

The effect of a combined stress loading on the plain fatigue limit of a material was discussed in § 3.6. Most of the data described there were obtained on cylindrical bars subjected to in-phase bending and torsional loads and showed that in the case of wrought ductile steels the fatigue limits under various combinations of bending and torsional stresses could be represented by an ellipse quadrant, that given by the von Mises criterion being sufficiently accurate for practical purposes. However, the corresponding fatigue limits of both notched specimens of these steels and plain specimens of cast iron, a material in which failure is associated with the presence of inherent flaws, could not be represented by an ellipse quadrant but instead were represented by an ellipse arc, the ratios of the fatigue limits in torsion to those in bending being much higher than the values obtained from the plain wrought steel specimens. In particular, those for plain cast iron specimens approached unity in contrast to the average value of about 0·5 to 0·6 for the wrought steel plain specimens.

The maximum stress (or stress range) in a thin sheet specimen of infinite extent containing a central circular hole subjected to combined tension and shear stresses can be obtained [90] by considering the circumferential stress on the boundary of the hole. This is a principal stress, both other principal stresses being zero. Thus, if failure of a material was determined by any criterion of stress at a single point, failure of a holed specimen would always occur under identical conditions, that is, at one specific value of one principal stress, which alone differed from zero. This leads to the conclusion that failure of a holed specimen may be predicted simply from the geometry of the hole, without reference to the precise nature of the failure criterion. The circumferential tensile stress, at the periphery of the hole, due to the combined tensile stress σ and shear stress τ is given by:

$$\sigma - 2\sigma \cos 2\theta + 4\tau \sin \theta,$$

where θ is the angle measured from the axis parallel to the applied tensile stress. The circumferential stress has a maximum value of $\sigma + 2(\sigma^2 + 4\tau^2)^{\frac{1}{2}}$ at $\theta = \frac{1}{2} \tan^{-1}(-2\tau/\sigma)$. If $\pm\sigma_0$ is the plain fatigue limit in tension, the fatigue limit of the holed specimen is given by equating the maximum circumferential stress to this value, that is,

$$\sigma_0 = \sigma + 2(\sigma^2 + 4\tau^2)^{\frac{1}{2}}$$

which, on rearranging, gives

$$16\tau^2 + 3\left(\sigma + \frac{\sigma_0}{3}\right)^2 = \tfrac{4}{3}\sigma_0^2.$$

This is an ellipse having its centre at $\sigma = -\sigma_0/3$, $\tau = 0$ and intercepts on the tension axis of $\sigma = \sigma_0/3$ and $-\sigma_0$ and on the shear stress axis of $\tau = \sigma_0/4$ and $-\sigma_0/4$. The signs of σ and τ are irrelevant in the case of completely reversed stress cycles, and the failure conditions are given by the positive quadrant. Writing $\sigma_{0n} = \sigma_0/3$, $\tau_{0n} = \sigma_0/4$ (that is, the uniaxial plain fatigue limit divided by the theoretical stress concentrations for a hole in tension and shear respectively), the above equation becomes identical to the ellipse arc. Similarly [90] for a thin infinite sheet containing an elliptical hole, the fatigue limit of the specimen is

$$\sigma + (1+e)(\sigma^2 + 4\tau^2)^{\frac{1}{2}} = e\sigma_0,$$

where e is the ratio of the lengths of the minor to major axes. Writing $\sigma_{0n} = e\sigma_0/(e+2)$ and $\tau_{0n} = e\sigma_0/2(e+1)$ results in this equation becoming identical to the ellipse arc, e varying from 1 to 0, and τ_{0n}/σ_{0n} (that is, the ratio of the fatigue limit of the holed specimen in torsion to that in tension) varying from $\frac{3}{4}$ for a circular hole to 1 for the limit where a flat ellipse becomes a crack, and the analysis is appropriate for a material containing inherent flaws.

Combined bending and torsion tests [91] have been carried out on 7 wrought steels using tubular specimens, 11 mm outside diameter and 1·3 mm wall thickness, containing a transverse hole 1·1 mm diameter. The notched fatigue limits of each steel under different combinations of bending and torsion conformed to an ellipse arc:

$$\frac{\tau^2}{\tau_{0n}^2} + \frac{\sigma^2}{\sigma_{0n}^2}\left(\frac{\sigma_{0n}}{\tau_{0n}}-1\right) + \frac{\sigma}{\sigma_{0n}}\left(2-\frac{\sigma_{0n}}{\tau_{0n}}\right) = 1,$$

where σ_{0n} and τ_{0n} are the notched fatigue limits in pure bending and pure torsion respectively and σ and τ are the stress ranges due to bending and torsion at the notched fatigue limit of the combined stress loading. The average value of τ_{0n}/σ_{0n} for the seven steels was 0·8, a value which agrees well with the theoretical value of 0·75 for a circular hole; this confirms that an inherent flaw theory cannot apply to materials in general. However, cast iron is a material in which cracks grow from inherent flaws present as graphite flakes, and the combined bending and torsional fatigue limits of cast iron plain specimens conform to an ellipse arc having τ_{0n}/σ_{0n} ratios approaching unity; for example, two cast irons [92], Silal and Nicrosilal, gave τ_{0n}/σ_{0n} ratios between 0·9 and 1.

Tests on wrought steel cylindrical specimens [92] subjected to combined bending and torsion cyclic stresses and containing a circumferential vee-notch, 0·5 mm deep and about 0·013 mm root radius, gave values of τ_{0n}/σ_{0n} ranging from 0·8 to 1. However, although the values of K_t in pure bending and pure torsion were about 10 and 5, respectively, the experimentally determined K_f values were only between 1·2 and 2·5 in pure bending and between 1·2 and 1·8 in pure torsion. It was argued that these low K_f values were due to a size-effect and, if larger but similarly-shaped specimens had been tested, higher K_f values would have resulted. However, the specimens were not stress-relieved after machining, and work-hardening and induced residual compressive stresses could well have decreased the K_f values. In addition, although unbroken specimens were not examined metallurgically, it is very probable that non-propagating cracks were present at the root of notches in specimens tested at their conventional notched fatigue limits. If this were so, τ_{0n}/σ_{0n} would be expected to approach unity, as indeed it did for some of the materials tested. Thus, the fact that the fatigue limits of notched wrought steel specimens and plain specimens of cast iron fall around an ellipse arc, whereas similar results of plain specimens of homogeneous wrought ductile steels fall around an ellipse quadrant is due simply to the stress field created by either a mechanical or inherent metallurgical notch. Other interpretations of the ellipse arc are given in Reference [92].

4.9. Effect of temperature

In general, the effect of either decreasing or increasing temperature is to either raise or lower the notched fatigue limit of a material, but because the plain fatigue limit of the material also increases or decreases the ratio of the plain fatigue limit to the corresponding notched fatigue limit K_f does not vary widely, certainly not at sub-zero temperatures. Some results [93] from tests on either 6 mm or 12 mm diameter specimens containing a circumferential vee-notch 0·6 mm deep and 0·25 mm root radius showing that K_f does not change appreciably as the temperature is decreased to that of liquid air are given in Table 4.30.

TABLE 4.30

Material	Temperature (°C)	Plain fatigue limit (MN m^{-2})	Notched fatigue limit (MN m^{-2})	K_t	K_f
Aluminium alloy 24S–T	25	±175	±75	3·2	2·3
	−196	±315	±140		2·3
Commercially pure titanium	25	±505	±190	2·7	2·7
	−196	±690	±275		2·5

In general the value of K_f at elevated temperatures does not change appreciably from the corresponding room temperature value until the temperature is reached at which the plain fatigue limit decreases appreciably. For example, K_f values obtained on various aluminium and magnesium alloys [94] did not vary appreciably from the room temperature value for temperatures up to 150 °C but then tended to decrease below the room temperature value as the temperature was increased further. However, austenitic steel notched specimens [80] tend to give higher K_f values at temperatures above 650 °C than at room temperature. This could well be associated with the fact that the room-temperature K_f values of austenitic steels (and other materials which have similar work-hardening characteristics) are low because the material at the notch root is hardened and has beneficial residual compressive stresses induced into it by the machining process, thereby increasing the notched fatigue limit and decreasing the K_f value. However, soaking at a temperature of 650 °C and above will anneal the work-hardened material and relieve residual stresses; thus the notched fatigue limit will decrease at these temperatures proportionally more than the plain fatigue limit decreases due to general softening, thus resulting in an increased K_f value.

The general tendency for the K_f value to decrease at temperatures exceeding that at which the plain fatigue limit decreases markedly, probably results from the fact that intercrystalline cracking can occur due to grain-boundary sliding and both the plain and notched fatigue strengths depend on the time a crack takes to spread through the easy fracture paths provided by the intercrystalline voids in the body of the specimen. Thus, it is the general stress level necessary to provide these intercrystalline easy fracture paths, and not the sharpness of the notch, which is the major factor in determining the fatigue strength. The interaction of fatigue and creep mechanisms of failure in plain specimens subjected to both cyclic and static stresses was discussed in § 3.8.2. The problem is more complex in the case of notched specimens because, depending on the loading and temperature pattern applied to a notched specimen, the addition of a static tensile stress may either decrease or increase the life at a given cyclic stress. The life will be decreased if, at the elevated temperature, the static tensile stress facilitates grain-boundary cracking. However, if it were possible to have loading and temperature conditions such that a limited amount of creep strain sufficient to reduce the sharpness of the notch (for example, a hole may be elongated so that the maximum stress concentration at the edge of the hole is reduced) but insufficient to cause grain-boundary cracking could occur, then the life under a given cyclic stress could be increased.

The threshold stress necessary to grow a crack of given size is, in general, proportional to Young's modulus (§§ 4.5.4 and 4.7.2) so that temperature would only be expected to affect the value of ΔK_c if it affected Young's modulus. For example, Young's modulus for mild steel at 300 °C is little different from the room temperature value, and tests at 300 °C and zero mean stress [95] gave a ΔK_c of 7·1 MN m$^{-\frac{3}{2}}$ (Compare Table 4.23).

4.10. Effect of environment

Most notched fatigue tests are carried out in air; however, if tests are carried out in a different environment, this can affect any of the material parameters which control the behaviour of notched specimens as described in previous sections. This must be taken into account in the interpretation of notched fatigue data; it is often possible to deduce qualitative information on these parameters from test data. Corrosive environments which attack the specimen chemically generally cause time-dependent behaviour. The effect of environment on the stress required to initiate a crack is discussed in § 3.9 and on the rate of growth of fatigue cracks in § 5.9.4. Some data, obtained using the plate specimens described in § 4.5.4 [96], on the effect of environment on the stress necessary to grow a crack of given length are given in Table 4.31 using the parameter ΔK_c discussed in §§ 4.5.4 and 4.7.2.

If a chemically corrosive environment reduces the plain fatigue strength of a material, it would be expected to decrease the cyclic stress level necessary to initiate a crack at the root of a notch in the same material. Provided the corrosive medium can penetrate to the crack tip and is applied so that air has free access to the crack tip, the corrosive medium would also be expected to decrease the stress level necessary to just cause a crack of a given length to grow. As was the case with plain specimens, the corrosion notched fatigue strength will depend on testing speed; and because cracks will form at the

TABLE 4.31
Effect of environment on the value of ΔK_c

Material	Environment	R	ΔK_c (MN m$^{-\frac{3}{2}}$)
Mild steel	Air	−1	6·4
		0·64	3·2
	Brine (3 % NaCl w/w)	−1	<2·2
		0·64	1·15
	Tap water or SAE 30 oil	−1	7·3
	Tap water, SAE 5, 30 or 90 oil, dodecyl alcohol, butyl rubber coat	−1	8·2†
	Hydrogen peroxide	−1	6·4†
4½ % Cu–aluminium alloy (BS L65)	Air	−1	2·1
	Water or SAE 30 oil	−1	2·1†
	Brine or brine drip	−1	1·25†

† Estimated using data in Table 4.33.

root of a notch at even lower nominal stresses than in a plain specimen and may be able to grow at these low cyclic stresses, the corrosion notched fatigue strength (at a given endurance) will depend on specimen diameter.

If the corrosive environment is not too severe and the specimen contains a notch which is not too sharp, for example, a hole, the corrosion-fatigue strength, at moderate endurances, of notched specimens bears roughly the same relationship to the in-air notched fatigue strength as the corrosion-fatigue strength of plain specimens bears to the in-air plain fatigue strength. This is illustrated by the results given in Table 4.32 for plain and holed specimens [97] of SAE 3140 (1·3 % Ni, 0·6 % Cr) steel tested in either rotating bending or reversed torsion. The plain specimens were 7·6 mm diameter, the holed specimens 10 mm diameter and contained a transverse hole of 2 mm diameter. The corrosion-fatigue tests were carried out in a stream of tap water.

In the case of sharply notched specimens, cracks will form rapidly at a notch root and specimen behaviour will depend both on the stress necessary for crack growth and the subsequent rate of crack growth. For example, the corrosion fatigue strength at endurances up to 10^8 cycles of sharply notched specimens tested in brine can have very low values. The results on Fig. 4.20 for 19 mm diameter mild steel specimens [98] containing a circumferential vee-groove, 2·5 mm deep and 0·05 mm root radius, illustrate that

TABLE 4.32

Condition of material	Tensile strength (MN m⁻²)	Type of specimen	Fatigue strength, 10⁷ cycles (MN m⁻²)		Ratio $\dfrac{\text{in air}}{\text{in tap water}}$
			In air	In water	
Rotating bending					
Hot-rolled	835	Plain	±440	±230	1·9
		Holed	±215	±110	2·0
Quenched and tempered	1130	Plain	±620	±93	6·7
		Holed	±215	±62	3·5
Reversed torsion					
Hot-rolled	835	Plain	±300	±225	1·3
		Holed	±155	±93	1·7
Quenched and tempered	1130	Plain	±385	±225	1·7
		Holed	±210	±140	1·5

not only is the cyclic stress necessary to initiate a crack at the notch root reduced to a low level but so is the stress level to propagate such a crack when it forms. The specimens used were stress-relieved *in vacuo* at 650 °C after machining, the in-air specimens having non-corrosive mineral oil applied periodically to the notch so as to exclude atmospheric moisture, the corrosion

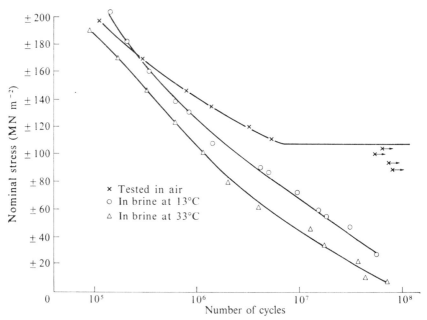

FIG. 4.20. *S/N* curves for vee-notched mild steel specimens tested in brine. (Taken from Dugdale [98].)

fatigue tests having an almost saturated solution of brine dripped slowly into the notch at a temperature of either 13 °C or 33 °C. The S/N curves on Fig. 4.20 show that a definite fatigue limit existed for the in-air tests, non-propagating cracks being found in all specimens unbroken after testing at or just below the conventional notched fatigue limit. However, there is no sign of either of the in-brine S/N curves flattening out to give a fatigue limit, an

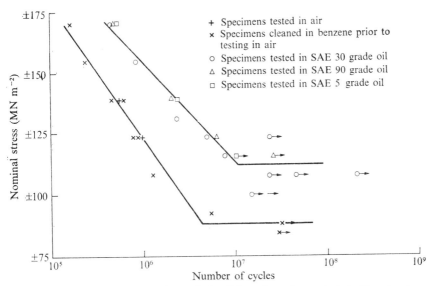

FIG. 4.21. S/N curves for sharply-notched mild steel specimens tested either in air or immersed in mineral oil. (Taken from Frost [99].)

alternating stress as low as ± 8 MN m^{-2} causing complete fracture in just less than 10^8 cycles. Thus, apart from causing cracks to be initiated at the notch roots at lower stress levels than are possible in air, the stress level necessary to cause a crack formed at the notch root to grow is reduced by the corrosive environment from ± 110 MN m^{-2} to a low value.

Further examples are given in Figs. 4.21 and 4.22, and the effects of various environments on the behaviour of notched fatigue specimens are summarised in Table 4.33. In all cases, the notches were sharp enough to cause rapid initiation of cracks at the notch roots.

Although it is appreciated that oil cannot act as a perfect barrier to air and moisture, it does appear to be able to restrict the air (oxygen) and moisture content of the environment at the crack tip to that in a fairly good vacuum, say, 10^{-5} mm Hg [99]. The tests in brine and the data given in § 5.9.4 show that, provided oxygen is kept away from the tip of a growing crack in a mild steel specimen, corrosive attack plays a minor role in determining the crack propagation characteristics. However, at stress levels corresponding to those at which a crack formed at the notch root would remain dormant in an oil environment (that is, all freshly created surfaces rebond during the compression half of the loading cycle), the chemical reactivity of brine is sufficient to prevent rebonding occurring and the crack is able to continue growing. In brine drip, the chemical reaction is more intense, but the results on Fig. 4.22 imply that in the case of mild steel the major role of the corrosive environment, at the test frequency used, is to prevent rebonding occurring

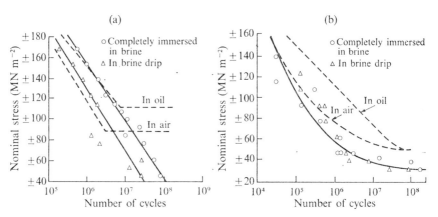

FIG. 4.22. S/N curves for sharply notched specimens tested either in a brine drip or completely immersed in brine. (a) Mild steel. (b) Aluminium alloy. (Taken from Frost and Greenan [99].)

rather than to chemically attack the material at the crack tip, because the crack propagation characteristics in brine are similar to those in air.

The supposition that prevention of free access of air to the crack tip improves the crack propagation characteristics of mild steel because some of the freshly created surfaces rebond at the crack tip is supported by tests in which a tensile mean stress is superimposed during the loading cycle. If rebonding is the operative mechanism, the crack growth characteristics would be expected to show a more marked improvement under a zero mean stress loading cycle than under a wholly tensile loading cycle in which the crack faces are never pressed together. On the other hand, if the minimizing of chemical attack is the reason for the improved crack growth characteristics in the absence of air, the improvement should certainly not be less under a wholly tensile loading cycle than at zero mean load. Measurement of the lengths of cracks growing from the roots of edge-notches in mild steel specimens [99] tested either immersed in SAE 30 grade mineral oil or in air showed that, when a tensile mean stress of sufficient magnitude to keep the loading cycle wholly tensile was imposed, the growth rate characteristics in oil were only slightly superior to those in air. It is interesting to note that, although ΔK_c for mild

TABLE 4.35

Rotating bending tests on sharply-notched specimens in various environments

Reference	Material	Reference environment	Environment	Effect on ΔK_c	Effect on rate of crack growth	Notes
98	Mild steel	Air	Saturated brine drip	Severely reduced	Increased	See text and Fig. 4.20.
100	SAE 4340 steel 17/7 stainless steel 6061 aluminium alloy Beryllium copper	Air	Dodecyl alcohol poured continually into notch		Decreased	Dodecyl alcohol prevented oxygen and moisture reaching the crack tip.
101	6% Al–magnesium alloy	High humidity air (>85% R.H.)	Low humidity air (<3% R.H.)		Decreased	Specimen life doubled at low humidity. Similar tests on plain specimens showed that fatigue strength at 10^7 cycles only slightly affected. Therefore humidity has more effect on the propagation of a crack than its initiation.
99	Mild steel	Air	SAE 5, 30 or 90 grade mineral oil	Increased by factor of about 1·3	Decreased	See Fig. 4.21. Plain and mildly notched specimens not affected, therefore stress to initiate a crack not affected.
99	Mild steel	Air	Dodecyl alcohol Water	Increased by factor of about 1·3	Decreased	Results similar to tests in oil.
99	Mild steel	Air	Coated with butyl rubber Hydrogen peroxide Coated with butyl rubber, then pin hole inserted	Unaffected	Unaffected	Shows that increased life in oil, water, dodecanol, and butyl rubber due to exclusion of atmosphere (presumably oxygen) from crack tip, and not due to mechanical action of fluid in crack.
99	Mild steel	Air	Brine Brine drip	Severely reduced Severely reduced	Decreased Unaffected	See Fig. 4.22(a). Sharp knee in S/N curve and fatigue limit disappear. Otherwise brine similar to oil results, and brine drip similar to air results.
99	4½% Cu–aluminium alloy	Air	Water	Unaffected	Unaffected	
99	4½% Cu–aluminium alloy	Air	SAE 30 grade mineral oil	Unaffected	Decreased	Scatter of test results very low in oil.
99	4½% Cu–aluminium alloy	Air	Brine Brine drip	Reduced by factor of about 0·6	Increased	See Fig. 4.22(b).

steel can be varied over a wide range simply by altering the environment (Table 4.33), values of ΔK_c for the carbon and low-alloy steels in air (Table 4.23) are insensitive to the metallurgical hardening techniques responsible for increasing their yield stress, hardness, and tensile strength.

Data given in § 5.9.4 show that moisture has a major influence on the crack propagation characteristics of aluminium alloys, whereas oxygen has little effect. This is confirmed by the test results for immersion in oil, which would exclude atmospheric moisture from the crack tip, and by the results for the two methods of brine application, where it is immaterial whether atmosphere is excluded from the crack tip. Unlike the mild steel, however, some definite corrosive attack does occur because the lives in both these corrosive environments are less than the corresponding in-air values. Again, in contrast with mild steel, the improvement in the crack growth properties of aluminium alloys when the atmosphere (moisture) is excluded from the crack tip is just as marked under a wholly tensile loading as at zero mean load [102]. This implies that the improvement is due to the minimization of chemical attack in the absence of moisture.

Environment will also play a part in determining the depths of non-propagating cracks found in certain sharply notched specimens. Non-propagating cracks found in aluminium alloy specimens are usually small, whereas those in mild steel specimens may be many times the notch root radius in length. From crack-opening considerations there is no reason why, once a crack has grown beyond the stress field generated by the notch, it should ever stop growing, provided that the nominal stress level is kept constant. However, it was pointed out in § 4.6.1 that, at short crack lengths, mechanical factors cause ΔK_c to first increase with crack length and then become constant, so that the length of a non-propagating crack at a notch is determined by the point of intersection of the ΔK_c versus crack length, and ΔK versus crack length curves. In general, a change of environment will modify the ΔK_c versus crack length curve and hence alter the length of a non-propagating crack. In particular, corrosive media will find it more difficult to reach the crack tip as a crack grows, both because of the greater distance involved and perhaps because the crack becomes choked by corrosion debris, particularly at low or zero mean stress.

Fig. 4.23 shows the fracture surface of a 6 mm thick cracked mild steel plate specimen which was tested completely immersed in brine consisting of a 3% (w/w) solution of NaCl, at a stress level of ± 26 MN m^{-2}. The initial crack length was 3·3 mm corresponding to $\Delta K = 3$ MN m$^{-\frac{3}{2}}$, whereas it is known (Table 4.33) that, when immersed in brine, cracks of this order of length can grow at a ΔK value as low as 2·2 MN m$^{-\frac{3}{2}}$. After $4 \cdot 10 \times 10^8$ cycles, the specimen was unbroken; fractographic examination showed that the crack had grown along the free surfaces to an approximately constant depth, leaving a central uncracked web approximately 1 mm wide. ΔK was calculated along this web, considering a lamina perpendicular to the web, using the equation [72] for symmetrical edge-cracks in a sheet, and was found to be $4 \cdot 2$ MN m$^{-\frac{3}{2}}$. ΔK_c at the web is, therefore, approximately double the minimum critical value, and it is clear that the method of test can have a significant effect on the value of ΔK_c obtained and that care must be taken to consider the effect of any change of crack-shape during a test.

4.11. Additional implications of a macrocrack length–cyclic propagation stress relationship

It is explained in Chapter 2 that, in a ductile metal, a surface microcrack penetrates into the body of the metal along certain crystallographic planes on which cyclic slip is continually occurring under the action of the resolved cyclic shear stresses created by the external loading cycle. When this loading cycle is of a uniaxial nature, a microcrack will at the same time be opening and closing owing to stresses acting across its faces, the amount of opening increasing as the crack size increases. However, until the microcrack reaches a depth at which the magnitude of the cyclic opening is sufficient to subject an element of metal immediately ahead of its tip to a tensile strain sufficient to fracture a length of metal which does not rebond completely during the compression half of the loading cycle, a microcrack can only continue to develop by the to-and-fro slip movements that created it initially. When the microcrack has penetrated to this critical depth, its subsequent growth rate characteristics depend on the magnitude of the cyclic opening, and its direction of growth becomes normal to the maximum cyclic tensile stress; in fracture-mechanics terms (§ 5.2.1) it grows in Mode I. Its rate of growth is now much faster than when it was growing as a microcrack, and it is to macrocracks that the growth parameters described both in this chapter and in Chapter 5 apply.

If it can be assumed that the $\sigma^3 a = C$ relationship (or any similar established relationship) predicts whether a macrocrack will or will not grow and it can be used to predict the behaviour of macrocracks smaller than those tested, an estimate of the depth a_c at which a microcrack changes into a macrocrack, at a given stress level $\pm \sigma_c$ (where σ_c is equal to or greater than the plain fatigue limit), can be obtained by substituting in $\sigma_c^3 a_c = C$, that is, $a_c = C/\sigma_c^3$, because this will give the maximum depth of macrocrack that will just not grow at $\pm \sigma_c$. Values of a_c for the materials given in Table 4.23, at values of σ_c equal to their plain fatigue limits (or strengths at 5×10^7 cycles) are given in Table 4.34.

The higher the value of σ_c, the smaller the value of the changeover length a_c. Because the rate of crack growth increases once the changeover length is exceeded, then, if the materials listed in Table 4.34 are tested at stress levels such that σ_c/σ (where σ is the plain fatigue limit) is constant, there will be more time for surface slip markings to develop and become more sharply defined on, for example, copper, aluminium, and nickel than on the high-strength steels and aluminium alloys, before a microcrack reaches the greater depth necessary for it to grow as a macrocrack [103]. The value of a_c can also be considered as the maximum depth of a surface scratch or flaw that can be tolerated without causing a decrease in the plain fatigue limit of the material.

Macrocrack growth rates are given in Chapter 5. These can be used to calculate the number of cycles required to grow a macrocrack from this changeover length to a length sufficient to cause complete fracture of a

TABLE 4.34

Material	Plain fatigue limit $(MN\,m^{-2})$	C	a_c (mm)
Inconel	±220	750	0·066
Nickel	±140	700	0·25
18/8 austenitic steel	±360	540	0·012
Low-alloy steel	±460	510	0·005
Mild steel	±200	510	0·064
Nickel–chromium alloy steel	±500	510	0·0043
Monel	±240	360	0·025
Phosphor bronze	±130	160	0·071
60/40 brass	±105	94	0·08
Copper	±62	56	0·024
$4\frac{1}{2}\%$ Cu–aluminium alloy	±140	19	0·007
Aluminium	±27	4	0·165

specimen. It is easily shown that, in a plain specimen tested just above its fatigue limit, the percentage of the life spent in growing a macrocrack is small compared with the number of cycles required to develop a microcrack to the changeover length.

If the cyclic stress applied to a plain specimen is sufficient to initiate continuing cyclic slip yet is insufficient to cause the resulting microcrack to penetrate to the changeover depth, it will remain dormant at this stress level. Examples were given in Chapter 2 of the presence of microcracks in slip bands on mild steel specimens which were unbroken after testing at their plain fatigue limit. Thus, the fatigue limit of such a material is determined by the cyclic stress necessary to develop a microcrack to the changeover depth a_c rather than by the cyclic stress necessary to just cause surface slip. If a microcrack reaches a grain boundary before reaching the changeover length, it may be held up because the slip characteristics of adjacent grains may be different. This could then lead to a dependence of the fatigue limit on grain size—the smaller the grain size, the higher the fatigue limit. However, if a microcrack reaches the changeover length and begins growing as a macrocrack before reaching a grain boundary, the grain boundary will have little or no effect on its development (it is now no longer dependent on the relative orientation of crystallographic slip planes), and thus the grain size will have no effect on the fatigue limit. As an example, the value of a_c for brass, shown in Table 4.34, is 0·08 mm, which implies that slip band cracks of this length could be present at the plain fatigue limit without growing, whereas larger ones could not, and that a grain size-effect should only be found with grain sizes less than 0·08 mm. Examination of 70/30 brass plain specimens [104], having grain sizes below 0·04 mm diameter, showed that microcracks were present in slip bands on specimens which were unbroken after testing at the plain fatigue limits. Assuming that the fatigue limit stress was equal to the cyclic stress necessary to just propagate a crack of depth equal to the grain size (equivalent to taking a_c at the plain fatigue as the grain size) gave a relationship between fatigue limit and grain size of $\sigma^{3\cdot5}a_c = C$. However, as predicted above, no microcracks were found in specimens having a grain size of 0·33 mm tested at the fatigue limit, nor did the fatigue limit conform to the proposed relationship.

If a material contains crack-like flaws longer than the relevant changeover length given in Table 4.34, the fatigue limit will be determined by the cyclic stress that will just not cause these flaws to grow rather than by the cyclic stress just necessary to cause continuing surface slip. Grey cast iron can be considered as a low-strength steel containing a random distribution of graphite flakes. These flakes act as flaws, and it is highly probable that some will meet the surface and lie normal to the loading direction. Assuming their lengths to be within the range 0·25–1 mm and substituting in $\sigma^3 a = 510$ gives σ in the region of ± 75 MN m^{-2} to ± 125 MN m^{-2}, which corresponds to fatigue limits found experimentally. The fact that the fatigue limit of grey cast iron is dependent on the cyclic stress required to grow cracks from graphite flakes rather than on the cyclic stress necessary to initiate a surface microcrack is illustrated by the data given in § 3.5. These data show that tensile mean stresses cause a greater proportional decrease and compressive mean stresses a greater proportional increase in fatigue strength than for the usual wrought steels, because the flaws cannot grow as macrocracks under a wholly compressive loading cycle. Thus, fatigue failure is not necessarily a surface phenomenon. Materials which contain inherent flaws will fail by the propagation of cracks from them if their length is such that the required cyclic stress for propagation is less than that required to initiate and develop a surface microcrack.

Values of the ratio C/(plain fatigue limit) are given in Table 4.23 for the various materials tested. If the design of a component, which in service will be subjected to dynamic loadings, is based on the plain fatigue limit, then one made of a material having a high value of this ratio has a better chance of operating successfully than one made of a material having a low value. This follows from the fact that, should surface cracks form owing to some unforeseen circumstance such as fretting, the cyclic stress required to propagate

14

these cracks will be a greater proportion of the design stress at higher values of this ratio. Therefore it can be considered as an inherent material factor of safety against fatigue failure.

The fact that the value of C (and ΔK_c) is about the same for plain carbon and low-alloy steels means that the stronger the steel, the more attention should a designer pay to the detail design of a steel component or structural member, especially if the design stress is taken as some fraction of either the tensile strength or plain fatigue limit. The reason for this is that, should the dynamic loadings experienced in service lead to the formation of surface cracks, the higher nominal design stress permitted in a stronger steel may enable a crack to grow that would not have grown in a lower stressed mild steel component.

References

1. HEYWOOD, R. B. *Designing by photo-elasticity.* Chapman and Hall, London (1952).
2. *Data sheets.* The Royal Aeronautical Society, London,
3. PETERSON, R. E. *Stress concentration design factors.* Wiley, New York (1953).
4. TIMOSHENKO, S. and GOODIER, J. N. *Theory of elasticity.* McGraw-Hill, New York (1951).
5. NISITANI, H. *Bull. J.S.M.E.* **11**, 947 (1968).
6. CREAGER, M. and PARIS, P. C. *Int. J. Fracture Mech.* **4**, 247 (1967).
7. PARIS, P. C. and SIH, G. C. *Symposium on fracture toughness testing and its applications*, p. 30. American Society for Testing Materials, S.T.P. 381 (1965).
8. SEELY, F. B. and SMITH, J. O. *Advanced mechanics of materials.* Wiley, New York (1952).
9. HEYWOOD, R. B. *Designing against fatigue.* Chapman and Hall, London (1962)
10. GROVER, H. J. *Proc. Am. Soc. Test. Mater.* **50**, 717 (1950).
11. TAYLOR, R. J. and GUNN, N. J. F. Min. of Supply, R.A.E. Rep. No. Met. 42 (1950).
12. BENNETT, J. A. and WEINBERG, J. G. *J. Res. natn. Bur. Stand.* **52**, 235 (1954).
13. LAZAN, B. J. and BLATHERWICK, A. A. Wright Air Development Centre, Tech. Rep. No. 52-307, (1952).
    BLATHERWICK, A. A. and LAZAN, B. J. Wright Air Development Centre, Tech. Rep. No. 53-181, (1953).
14. GROVER, H. J., BISHOP, S. N., and JACKSON, L. R. NACA Tech. Note 2390 (1951).
    GROVER, H. J., HYLER, W. S., and JACKSON, L. R. NASA Tech. Note D 111 (1959).
15. LEYBOLD, H. A. NASA Tech. Note D 439 (1960).
16. HYLER, W. S., LEWIS, R. A., and GROVER, H. J. NACA Tech. Note 3291 (1954).
17. DOLAN, T. J. and HANLEY, B. C. University of Illinois, Engineering Experimental Station Rep. No. 6 (1948).
18. MORKOVIN, D. and MOORE, H. F. *Proc. Am. Soc. Test. Mater.* **44**, 137 (1944).

19. OUCHIDA, H. *Proceedings of the 2nd Japanese Congress on testing materials* p. 14 (1959).
20. PHILLIPS, C. E. and HEYWOOD, R. B. *Proc. Instn mech. Engrs.* **165,** 113 (1951).
21. TEMPLIN, R. L. *Proc. Am. Soc. Test. Mater.* **54,** 641 (1954).
22. MANN, J. Y. *Jl. R. aeronaut. Soc.* **60,** 681 (1956); *Proc. Am. Soc. Test. Mater.* **60,** 602 (1960).
23. FINNEY, J. M. Dept. of Supply, Australian Defence Scientific Service, Aero. Res. Lab., ARL/SM Rep. No. 287 (1962).
24. MASSONNET, C. *Proc. Am. Soc. Test. Mater.* **56,** 954 (1956).
25. KARRY, R. W. and DOLAN, T. J. *Proc. Am. Soc. Test. Mater.* **53,** 789 (1953).
26. OBERG, T. T. and JOHNSON, J. B. *Proc. Am. Soc. Test. Mater.* **37,** 195 (1937).
27. SIEBEL, E. and STIELER, M. *Z. Ver. dt. Ing.* **97,** 121 (1955).
28. NEUBER, H. *Theory of notch stresses.* Edwards, London (1946).
29. KUHN, P. and HARDRATH, H. F. NACA Tech. Note 2805 (1952).
30. KUHN, P. *Colloquium on fatigue.* Springer-Verlag, Berlin (1956); *Current aeronautical fatigue problems*, p. 229. Pergamon Press, Oxford (1965).
31. AGERMAN, E. *Acta polytech. scand. Ser.* (*e*), No. 8 (1960).
32. SMEDLEY, G. P. and BATTEN, B. K. *Trans. NE. Cst. Instn. Engrs. Shipbldrs.* **77,** 293 (1961); *Int. Shipbldg Prog.* **8,** 105 (1961).
33. MINAMIOZI, K. and OKUBU, H. *J. Franklin Inst.* **249,** 49 (1950).
34. VITOVEC, F. H. *Schweizer Arch. Angew. Wiss. Tech.* **27,** 163 (1961).
35. MOORE, H. F. *Proc. Am. Soc. Test. Mater.* **45,** 507 (1945).
36. HIKATA, A. Government Mechanical Engineering Lab., Japan, Bull. No. 2 (1954).
37. ISIBASI, T. and URYU, T. *Rep. Res. Inst. appl. Mechs. Kyushu Univ.* **4,** 107 (1956).
    ISIBASI, T. *Trans. Japan Soc. mech. Engrs.* **22,** 144 (1956).
38. OUCHIDA, H. *Proceedings of the 2nd Japanese Congress on testing materials*, p. 14 (1959).
39. HEYWOOD, R. B. *Aircr. Engng.* **19,** 81 (1947).
40. HEYWOOD, R. B. *Designing against fatigue.* Chapman and Hall, London (1962).
41. FORREST, P. G. *International Conference on fatigue, Institution of Mechanical Engineers*, p. 171 (1956).
42. FORREST, P. G. and TAPSELL, H. J. *Engineering* **173,** 757 (1952).
43. PETERSON, R. E. and WAHL, A. M. *Trans. Am. Soc. Mech. Engrs.* **58,** A15 (1936).
44. YEN, C. S. and DOLAN, T. J. University of Illinois. Engineering Experimental Station Bull. No. 398 (1952).
45. KUGUEL, R. *Proc. Am. Soc. Test. Mater.* **61,** 732 (1961).
46. DOREY, S. F. and SMEDLEY, G. P. *International Conference on fatigue, Institution of Mechanical Engineers*, p. 247 (1956).
47. DOLAN, T. J. and YEN, C. S. *5th progress report on the behaviour of materials under repeated stress, University of Illinois, Engineering Experimental Station* (1948).
48. MACGREGOR, C. W. and GROSSMAN, N. *Weld. J. Easton* **27,** 132 (1948).

49. OATES, G., *J. Iron Steel Inst.* **204**, 991 (1966).
    LESSELLS, J. M. and JACQUES, H. E. *Weld. J.*, *Easton* **15**, 74 (1950).
50. JACQUES, H. E. Bureau of Ships, Navy Dept. Report No. SSC-31 (1949).
51. FENNER, A. J., OWEN, N. B., and PHILLIPS, C. E. *Engineering* **171**, 637 (1951).
52. FROST, N. E. *Engineer* **200**, 464 (1955); **200**, 501 (1955); *Aeronaut. Q.* **8**, 1 (1957).
53. MANN, J. Y. Dept. of Supply, Australia, Aero. Res. Lab. Struct. and Materials Note 256 (1959).
54. FROST, N. E. and GREENAN, A. F. *J. mech. Engng. Sci.* **6**, 203 (1964).
55. HUNTER, M. S. and FRICKE, W. G. *Proc. Am. Soc. Test. Mater.* **57**, 643 (1957).
56. ISIBASI, T. and MATAKE, T. *Proceedings of the 2nd Japanese Congress on testing materials*, p. 19. (1959).
57. FROST, N. E. and DUGDALE, D. S. *J. Mech. Phy. Solids*, **5**, 182 (1957).
58. FROST, N. E. *Proc. Instn. mech. engrs.* **173**, 811 (1959).
59. FROST, N. E. *J. mech. Engng. Sci.* **2**, 109 (1960).
60. PETERSON, R. E. *Trans. Am. Soc. Mech. Engrs.* **55**, 79 (1933).
61. HANKINS, G. A., BECKER, M. L., and MILLS, H. R. *J. Iron Steel Inst.* **133**, 399 (1936).
62. POPE, J. A. and BARSON, C. W. *International Conference on fatigue, Institution of Mechanical Engineers*, p. 557 (1956).
63. OUCHIDA, H. *Bull.* J.S.M.E. **1**, 233 (1958).
64. FROST, N. E. and PHILLIPS, C. E. *Proc. Instn mech. Engrs.* **170**, 713 (1956).
65. FROST, N. E. *Engineer* **203**, 864 (1957).
66. BENNETT, J. A. *Mater. Res. Stand.* **5**, 235 (1965).
67. ISIBASI, T. and URYU, T. *Rep. Res. Inst. appl. Mechs.*, *Kyushu Univ.* **2**, 65 (1953).
68. ISIBASI, T. and URYU, T. *Rep. Res. Inst. appl. Mechs.*, *Kyushu Univ.* **4**, 57 (1956).
69. NAKAMURA, H., AMAKASU, T., and UEDA, S. *Bull.* J.S.M.E. **1**, 227 (1958).
70. FROST, N. E. *J. mech. Engng. Sci.* **5**, 15 (1963).
71. FROST, N. E., POOK, L. P., and DENTON, K. *Eng. Fracture Mech.* **3**, 109 (1971).
72. PARIS, P. C. and SIH, G. C. *Symposium on fracture toughness testing and its applications*, p. 30. American Society for Testing Materials S.T.P. (1965).
73. ELBER, W. *Eng. Fracture Mech.* **2**, 37 (1970).
    CHENG, Y. F. and BRONNER, W. *Int. J. Fracture Mech.* **6**, 431 (1970).
74. LEVY, J. C. Discussion in [58].
75. HARDRATH, H. F. and McEVILY, A. J. *Crack propagation Symposium, Cranfield*, p. 231 (1961).
76. FROST, N. E. *J. mech. Engng. Sci.* **3**, 299 (1961).
77. ISIBASI, T. *Proceedings of the 6th Japanese National congress of applied Mechanics*, p. 71 (1956).
78. PETERSON, R. E. William M. Murray Lecture. *Proc. Soc. exp. Stress Analysis* **28**, 105 (1961).
79. FORREST, P. G. *Fatigue of metals*, Pergamon Press, Oxford, 1962.
80. FOUND, G. H. *Proc. Am. Soc. Test. Mater.* **46**, 715 (1946).

81. ISIBASI, T. *Mem. Fac. Engng. Kyushu Univ.* **13,** 71 (1952).
82. GROVER, H. J., GORDON, S. A., and JACKSON, L. R. *Fatigue of metals and structures.* Bureau of Aeronautics, Dept. of Navy (1954).
83. GILBERT, G. N. J. and PALMER, K. B. *J. Res. Dev. Br. Cast Iron Res. Ass.* **6,** 410 (1956).
84. SMITH, J. O. University of Illinois, Engineering Experimental Station, Bull. 334 (1942).
85. GUNN, K. W. *Aeronaut. Q.* **6,** 277 (1955).
   DIRKES, W. E. *Trans. Am. Soc. mech. Engrs.* **78,** 511 (1956).
86. DOYLE, W. M. and HOW, I. M. *Engng. Mater. Des.* **3,** 538 (1960).
87. FROST, N. E. and GREENAN, A. F. *J. mech. Engng. Sci.* **9,** 234 (1967).
88. FROST, N. E. and GREENAN, A. F. *J. mech. Engng. Sci.* **12,** 159 (1970).
89. POOK, L. P. and FROST, N. E. *Int. J. Fracture* **9,** 53 (1973).
90. COX, H. L. Min. of Supply, Aero. Res. Council, R and M No. 2704; *International Conference on fatigue, Institution of Mechanical Engineers,* p. 212 (1956).
91. THURSTON, R. C. A. and FIELD, J. E. DSIR Properties and Mechanics of Materials Committee Rep. PM No. 53; NPL Engineering Div. Rep. No. 447/50 (1950).
92. GOUGH, H. J., POLLARD, H. V., and CLENSHAW, W. J. Min. of Supply, Aero. Res. Council, R and M No. 2522 (1951).
93. SPRETNAK, J. W., FONTANA, M. G., and BROOKS, H. E. *Trans. Am. Soc. Metals,* **43,** 547 (1951).
94. FRITH, P. H. *Properties of wrought and cast aluminium and magnesium alloys at room and elevated temperatures.* H.M.S.O., London (1956).
95. POOK, L. P. and BEVERIDGE, A. A. *Fatigue at elevated temperatures,* p. 179. American Society for Testing Materials S.T.P. 520 (1973).
96. POOK, L. P. NEL Rep. No. 484 (1971).
97. DOLAN, T. J. *J. appl. Mechs.* **5,** A141 (1938).
98. DUGDALE, D. S. *Metallurgia* **65,** 27 (1962).
99. FROST, N. E. *Appl. Mater. Res.* **3,** 131 (1964).
   FROST, N. E. and GREENAN, A. F. *Environ. Eng.* **25,** 11 (1967).
100. HOLSHOUSER, W. L. and UTECH, H. P. *Proc. Am. Soc. Test. Mater.* **61,** 749 (1961).
101. SHIVES, T. R. and BENNETT, J. A. NASA Rep. CR-267 (1965).
102. BRADSHAW, F. J. and WHEELER, C. Min. of Aviation R.A.E. Tech. Rep. No. 65073 (1965).
103. FROST, N. E. *J. Mech. Phy. Solids* **9,** 143 (1961).
104. FORREST, P. G. and TATE, A. E. L. *J. Inst. Metals* **93,** 438 (1965).

5 | The growth of fatigue cracks

Notation

IN OTHER chapters, relatively few symbols have been used, and these are defined as they appear. A similar practice is followed in this chapter, but because of the large number of symbols involved, the more frequently used are only defined the first time they appear and are listed below for the convenience of readers.

a	half-length of internal crack, length of surface crack, semi-minor axis of ellipse
B	specimen thickness
c	(as subscript) critical value
D	material constant in crack growth equation
E	Young's modulus
f	(as subscript) final value
G	shear modulus
G_c	effective surface energy (both crack surfaces)
G_I	strain energy release rate (Mode I)
K_c	critical value of K_I
K	stress intensity factor (with subscripts I, II, III to denote mode)
K_{Ic}	K_c for plane strain conditions
K_{max}	maximum value of K_I during fatigue cycle
K_{mean}	mean value of K_I during fatigue cycle
K_{min}	minimum value of K_I during fatigue cycle
K_t	stress concentration factor
ΔK	range of K_I during fatigue cycle ($K_{max} - K_{min}$)
ΔK_c	critical value of ΔK for fatigue crack growth
m	exponent in crack growth equation
N	number of cycles
R	stress ratio ($\sigma_{min}/\sigma_{max}$)
r, θ	polar coordinates (Fig. 5.1)
r_p	plastic zone radius or length
W	specimen width
x, y, z	rectangular coordinates
Y	stress intensity factor coefficient
α	geometric correction factor
δ_c	critical value of crack opening displacement

ν Poisson's ratio
ρ notch root radius
σ gross stress
σ_a alternating stress
σ_m mean stress
σ_{max} maximum stress during fatigue cycle
σ_{min} minimum stress during fatigue cycle
σ_N net section stress
$\sigma_x, \sigma_y, \sigma_z$ stress components in the x, y, z directions
σ_Y yield stress (taken as the 0·1 per cent or 0·2 per cent proof stress)
τ gross shear stress
τ_Y yield stress in shear
0 (as subscript) initial value

The symbols given are, in general, in conformity with current usage in fracture mechanics literature. Symbols used by other authors have been altered when this is necessary to maintain a reasonably consistent scheme within the chapter. Numerical factors in certain equations have been altered to bring them into conformity with the convention that a represents the half-length, not the over-all length, of an internal crack. The conventional term $\pi^{\frac{1}{2}}$ which appears in the definitions of stress intensity factor (eqn (5.1)) is used throughout the chapter.

5.1. Introduction

It has been mentioned in Chapter 2 that, if the cyclic stress level is sufficiently high, a surface microcrack will spread across the surface and penetrate into the body of a material by continuing to-and-fro slip processes until it has reached such a size that it is able to grow as a macrocrack, that is, its growth behaviour will depend on the amount it opens and closes under the normal cyclic stress across its faces. To obtain a macrocrack in a specimen at a stress level less than the plain fatigue limit of a material, some form of notch must be introduced into the specimen so that the effective length of a crack formed at the notch root is increased to a value sufficient to grow directly as a macrocrack at the applied nominal stress level. This chapter discusses the speed at which a macrocrack grows and unless stated otherwise, it is implicit in any reference to fatigue crack growth that the crack has reached the macrocrack stage.

Until recent years, little effort had been devoted to the experimental determination of the laws governing the rate of growth of a fatigue crack; in fact, no accurate quantitative experimental data had been published prior to 1953, the year Head [1] published his theoretically derived relationship between crack length and number of stress cycles. This may have been due to the fact that the assessment of design stresses, in those cases where it was considered necessary to give due regard to the fatigue properties of a material, had been almost always based on the plain fatigue limit or strength of the material, as obtained from smooth laboratory specimens. Naturally, the purpose of these design stresses was to prevent the initiation of any cracks under the working loads by keeping all cyclic stresses below some critical value. However, it is only possible to do this when the components or structural members are of a relatively simple shape and the magnitude of the working loads precisely known. The need to produce components or members of complex shape, which are not uneconomic in their use of material, to operate under service conditions which are not precisely defined, has led to the possibility of cracks forming, even at relatively low nominal cyclic loads, usually as a consequence of fretting (§ 6.6) or in the locally highly stressed material around some discontinuity. This implies that some components and structural members, particularly those designed to have a limited life, must operate successfully even though they do contain fatigue cracks.

In some cases, modern inspection procedures have enabled small cracks to be detected in certain components at an early stage in their expected life. However, it has been stated [2] that a crack roughly 5–15 mm long is about the smallest flaw that can be readily detected during routine service inspection. In addition, the necessity to assume the existence of cracked members in engineering structures despite the efforts of designers to design fatigue-resistant structures is now generally accepted. Whether these cracks will grow and, if they do, the rate at which they grow will depend on material and the values of the applied nominal mean and alternating stresses. The selection of a material, from those which fulfill other necessary design considerations, giving the slowest rate of crack growth for a given external loading will lead to an increased margin of safety between routine inspections. Thus, a knowledge of the growth rate characteristics of a material, together with regular inspections, may enable a cracked component to have a long useful life before having to be replaced. A fail-safe design [3] (that is, a structure so designed that should cracks form they will not cause catastrophic failure under the working loads until one of them reaches a known length) implies that a limiting crack length can be established which must be detected by inspection if the crack is not to extend to cause failure before the next inspection. Therefore, designers should use all possible means to achieve the ideals of a low rate of crack propagation and a high residual static strength in the presence of a crack. Probably the best way of assessing the merits of a fail-safe design is by the length of inspection periods which it allows in relation to the weight involved.

Numerous, apparently-different 'laws' of fatigue crack growth have been described in the literature [4], and by making various plausible assumptions some of them can be derived theoretically. All the laws can be regarded as valid in the sense that they describe a particular set of fatigue crack growth data, and they can be used to predict crack growth rates in situations similar to those used to collect the data. It is sometimes possible to fit the same set of data to apparently contradictory laws; in such cases it is not possible to decide which law is the most 'correct'.

Since the end of World War II, the problem of brittle fracture has been studied extensively. It has been found that such low-stress (compared to the yield stress of the material) fractures always originate at flaws or cracks of various types. The fracture-mechanics approach to residual static strength in the presence of a crack makes use of the stress intensity factor K_I concept to describe the stress field at a crack tip; when K_I reaches a critical value K_c the crack extends, usually catastrophically. Values of K_I are known for a wide range of crack configurations [5–11], and the fracture-mechanics approach has proved useful in problems of material development, design, and failure analysis. In view of its success in dealing with static fracture problems, it is logical to use a similar general approach to analyse fatigue crack growth data. The availability of a master curve for a particular material relating fatigue crack growth rate and range of stress intensity factor enables a designer to predict growth rates for any cracked body configuration, and he is not limited to situations similar to those pertaining to the cracked specimen geometry used to generate the original data.

5.2. Linear elastic fracture mechanics

5.2.1. Modes of crack growth

There are three basic modes of crack surface displacement [5] which can cause crack growth; these are shown in Fig. 5.1.

I. *The opening mode.* The crack surfaces move directly apart.
II. *The edge sliding mode.* The crack surfaces move normal to the crack front and remain in the crack plane.
III. *The shear mode.* The crack surfaces move parallel to the crack front and remain in the crack plane.

The superimposition of these three modes is sufficient to describe the most general case of crack surface displacement. It is conventional to add the Roman numerals I, II, III as subscripts to various symbols to indicate the mode.

In fracture mechanics only the macroscopic mode of crack growth is considered; crack growth on 45° planes, often referred to as 'shear fracture', is a combination of Modes I and III, but is usually treated in calculations as if it were Mode I.

For strictly two-dimensional cases and thin-shell problems, only Modes I and II can exist. However, 'two-dimensional' is often taken to include examples of plates of finite (constant) thickness. Mode II displacements can only exist at internal or mathematically deep external cracks.

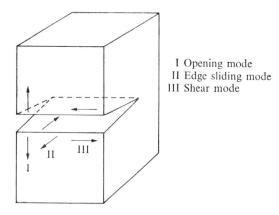

I Opening mode
II Edge sliding mode
III Shear mode

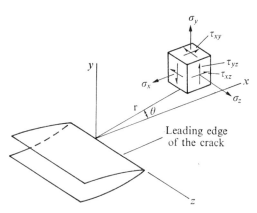

Leading edge
of the crack

FIG. 5.1. Basic modes of crack surface displacement, coordinates measured from the leading edge of a crack and the stress components in the crack-tip stress field. (Taken from Paris and Sih [5].)

5.2.2. Stress intensity factor

Crack surfaces are stress-free boundaries adjacent to the crack tip and therefore dominate the distribution of stresses in that area [5]. Remote boundaries and loading forces affect only the intensity of the stress field at the crack tip. These fields can be divided into three types corresponding to the three basic modes of crack surface displacement,, and are conveniently characterized by the stress intensity factor K (with subscripts I, II, III to denote the mode). K has the dimensions (stress) $\times$ (length)$^{\frac{1}{2}}$ and is a function of the specimen dimensions and loading conditions. In general, it is proportional to (gross stress) $\times$ (crack length)$^{\frac{1}{2}}$. Conventionally, K is expressed in MN m$^{-\frac{3}{2}}$.

In general, the opening mode intensity factor is given by

$$K_I = \sigma(\pi a)^{\frac{1}{2}}\alpha, \tag{5.1}$$

where σ is the gross tensile stress perpendicular to the crack (compressive stresses simply close the crack), a is crack length and α is a factor, of the order of unity, which depends on geometry and loading conditions; for engineering purposes α can often be taken as 1. Expressions for K_I for several configurations [5, 6, 10, 11] are shown in Fig. 5.2. The value of K_I for a crack at a sharp notch, in general, is equal to that for a crack of the same total length provided that the notch profile lies within an envelope having an included angle of 30° drawn from the crack tip [12].

When K is known, stresses and displacements near the crack tip can be calculated using standard equations [5]. Thus, for example, in Mode I, referring to Fig. 5.1 for notation (where u, v, w are displacements in the x, y, z directions), these can be written for plane strain as

$$
\left.
\begin{aligned}
\sigma_x &= \frac{K_I}{(2\pi r)^{\frac{1}{2}}}\cos\frac{\theta}{2}\left(1 - \sin\frac{\theta}{2}\sin\frac{3\theta}{2}\right) \\[6pt]
\sigma_y &= \frac{K_I}{(2\pi r)^{\frac{1}{2}}}\cos\frac{\theta}{2}\left(1 + \sin\frac{\theta}{2}\sin\frac{3\theta}{2}\right) \\[6pt]
\tau_{xy} &= \frac{K_I}{(2\pi r)^{\frac{1}{2}}}\sin\frac{\theta}{2}\cos\frac{\theta}{2}\cos\frac{3\theta}{2} \\[6pt]
\sigma_z &= \nu(\sigma_x + \sigma_y) \\[6pt]
\tau_{xz} &= \tau_{yz} = 0 \\[6pt]
u &= \frac{K_I}{G}\left(\frac{r}{2\pi}\right)^{\frac{1}{2}}\cos\frac{\theta}{2}\left(1 - 2\nu + \sin^2\frac{\theta}{2}\right) \\[6pt]
v &= \frac{K_I}{G}\left(\frac{r}{2\pi}\right)^{\frac{1}{2}}\sin\frac{\theta}{2}\left(2 - 2\nu - \cos^2\frac{\theta}{2}\right) \\[6pt]
w &= 0.
\end{aligned}
\right\} \tag{5.2}
$$

where G is the shear modulus and ν is Poisson's ratio.

Elastic stresses are inversely proportional to the square root of the distance from the crack tip, and become infinite at the crack tip. Provided that only one mode is present, the stress intensity factors due to different loadings can be superimposed by algebraic addition; if more than one mode is present, the individual stress components and displacements can be similarly superimposed.

Small-scale non-linear effects, such as those due to yielding, microstructural irregularities, internal stress, local irregularities in the crack surface,

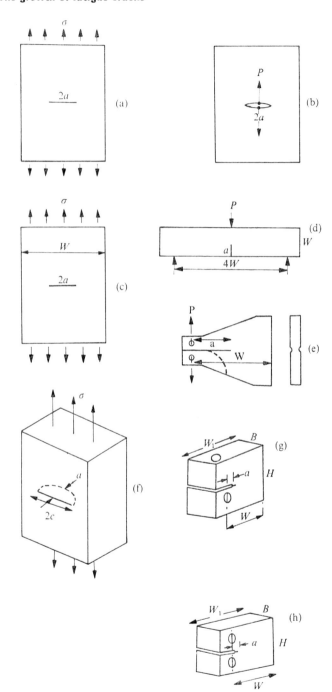

and 45° crack growth in thin sheets do not affect the general character of the stress field and can be regarded as being within the crack-tip stress field [5]. Similarly, the actual fracture process can be regarded as taking place within the stress field at the crack tip. The concept of stress intensity factor therefore provides a convenient mathematical framework for the study of fracture processes.

The representation of a crack tip stress field by a stress intensity factor is a basic concept in fracture mechanics. The term should not be confused with 'stress concentration factor' or 'stress intensification factor', which are terms used to describe the ratio between the maximum and nominal stress at a discontinuity.

It is found that, under increasing load, a crack will start to grow (provided that general yielding does not intervene) when K_I reaches a critical value (K_c), and will continue to grow as long as the loading conditions are such that $K_I \geqslant K_c$.

Fracture mechanics can also be applied to problems involving cracks intersecting or along the interfaces between dissimilar materials and to the fracture behaviour of glued joints and composite materials. The advanced analyses needed for these problems are less well developed, and in general only qualitative predictions of fracture behaviour are possible [7].

FIG. 5.2. Stress intensity factors for various configurations. References [5], [6], [10], and [11]. (a) Centre crack in infinite plate. Remote load. $K_I = \sigma(\pi a)^{\frac{1}{2}}$. (b) Centre crack in infinite plate. Point loads on crack surface. $K_I = P/\{B(\pi a)^{\frac{1}{2}}\}$. (c) Centre crack in plate of finite width. Remote load.

$$Y = K_I/\sigma a^{\frac{1}{2}} = 1 \cdot 77 + 0 \cdot 227(2a/W) - 0 \cdot 510(2a/W)^2 + 2 \cdot 7(2a/W)^3. \qquad 2a/W \leqslant 0 \cdot 7.$$

(d) Edge crack in plate loaded in three-point bend.

$$Y = K_I BW/6Pa^{\frac{1}{2}} = 1 \cdot 93 - 3 \cdot 07(a/W) + 14 \cdot 53(a/W)^2 - 25 \cdot 11(a/W)^3 + 25 \cdot 80(a/W)^4.$$

$$a/W \leqslant 0 \cdot 6.$$

(e) Constant K specimen.

$$K_I BW^{\frac{1}{2}}/P = 10 \cdot 9 \qquad 0 \cdot 2 \leqslant a/W \leqslant 0 \cdot 5.$$

(f) Semi-elliptical crack in semi-infinite body

$$K_I = \frac{1 \cdot 1\sigma(\pi a)^{\frac{1}{2}}}{\phi}, \qquad \phi = \int_0^{\pi/2} \left\{1 - \left(\frac{c^2 - a^2}{c^2}\right)\sin^2\theta\right\}^{\frac{1}{2}} d\theta.$$

(g) 'T-type WOL'. $W = 2 \cdot 55B$, $W_1 = 3 \cdot 20B$, $H = 2 \cdot 48B$. Thread $= \frac{1}{2}B$ diameter. Hole $= 0 \cdot 7B$ diameter. $K_I = YP/BW^{\frac{1}{2}}$, where $Y = 39 \cdot 7(a/W)^{\frac{1}{2}} - 294 \cdot 2(a/W)^{\frac{3}{2}} + 1118(a/W)^{\frac{5}{2}} - 1842(a/W)^{\frac{7}{2}} + 1159(a/W)^{\frac{9}{2}}$, and $0 \cdot 25 \leqslant a/W \leqslant 0 \cdot 8$. (h) 'CKS-type WOL.' $B = W/2$, $W_1 = 1 \cdot 3W$, $H = 1 \cdot 2W$. Holes $= B/2$ diameter. $K_I = YP/BW^{\frac{1}{2}}$, where $Y = 29 \cdot 6(a/W)^{\frac{1}{2}} - 185 \cdot 5(a/W)^{\frac{3}{2}} + 655 \cdot 7(a/W)^{\frac{5}{2}} - 1017(a/W)^{\frac{7}{2}} + 638 \cdot 9(a/W)^{\frac{9}{2}}$, and $0 \cdot 3 \leqslant a/W \leqslant 0.8$.

5.2.3. Crack direction

Irrespective of the initial crack orientation, a static [13, 14] or a fatigue [15] crack in an isotropic material usually tends to grow in Mode I. The favourable direction [13] is along a plane intersecting the crack tip and perpendicular to the greatest local tensile stress. This plane is often approximately the same as the one perpendicular to the maximum principal tensile stress in an uncracked specimen. For the two-dimensional case, the direction of initial crack growth is along a principal stress trajectory whose direction is given by [13, 14]

$$K_I \sin \theta = K_{II}(3 \cos \theta - 1).$$

If Mode III displacements are present, a preferred plane for crack growth will intersect the crack front at only one point, so that initially the crack may be constrained to a less favourable path.

5.2.4. Effect of yielding

An uncracked metal plate loaded in uniaxial tension is in a state of plane stress. The insertion of a crack does not affect the plate remote from the crack tip, which remains in plane stress, but the highly stressed material near the crack tip is prevented from contracting in the thickness direction by the material further away from the crack, and is therefore in a state of plane strain. In the interior of the plate there is a transverse stress $\sigma_z = \nu(\sigma_x + \sigma_y)$, where ν is Poisson's ratio. All the plate surfaces, however, will still be in a state of plane stress.

In a metal, the yield stress is exceeded near the crack tip, and a plastic zone develops; the approximate extent of this plastic zone can be estimated by substituting a yield criterion into the stress field equation. If the plastic zone is small compared with the plate thickness, transverse yielding is restricted and conditions near the crack tip still approximate to plane strain through most of the plate thickness. In fracture mechanics, this localized plane strain situation is called plane strain [16] (see Fig. 5.3) and exists in most metals [16], provided that the thickness is at least $2 \cdot 5 \ (K_I/\sigma_Y)^2$, where σ_Y is the yield stress (usually taken as the 0·2 per cent proof stress). A large plastic zone means that σ_z is not fully developed through the specimen thickness; when the plastic zone size becomes comparable with the thickness, yielding can take place on 45° planes, and the stress state near the crack tip changes to plane stress. This happens when the thickness $B \ll 2 \cdot 5 \ (K_I/\sigma_Y)^2$, and in fracture mechanics is referred to as plane stress.

The actual size and shape of the plastic zone depends on the plastic flow properties of the material [6], but its dimensions are proportional to $(K_I/\sigma_Y)^2$. The relaxation of stresses, caused by yielding inside the plastic zone, means that, to maintain equilibrium, the stresses outside the plastic zone must increase slightly. The plastic zone thus increases the effective length of the crack. This effective length increase, called r_p (a symbol for nominal plastic zone radius) is given approximately by [6]

$$r_p = \frac{1}{2\pi}\left(\frac{K_I}{\sigma_Y}\right)^2 \quad \text{for plane stress} \tag{5.3}$$

and

$$r_p = \frac{1}{6\pi}\left(\frac{K_I}{\sigma_Y}\right)^2 \quad \text{for plane strain,} \tag{5.4}$$

and is about half the extent of the plastic zone. These corrections are only applicable when the plastic zone is small compared to the specimen dimensions in the plane of the plate, and are therefore within the region where the

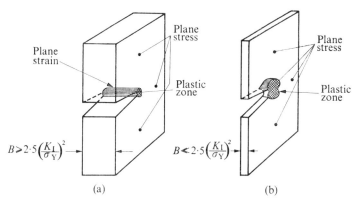

Plane strain

Plane stress

Plane strain

Plastic zone

Plane stress

Plastic zone

$$B > 2 \cdot 5\left(\frac{K_I}{\sigma_Y}\right)^2$$

$$B < 2 \cdot 5\left(\frac{K_I}{\sigma_Y}\right)^2$$

(a)   (b)

FIG. 5.3. Nomenclature for the state of stress in a cracked plate. (a) Plane strain. (b) Plane stress. (Taken from Pook [17].)

stresses are reasonably accurately described by the stress intensity factor. If the plastic zone becomes too large, which happens when the net section stress σ_N exceeds about $0\cdot8\sigma_Y$ [7], linear elastic fracture mechanics is no longer applicable. It is not always possible to define the net section stress unambiguously, and other criteria may be adopted [6]; for example, that the crack length and the net section ligament are both at least $2\cdot5\ (K_I/\sigma_Y)^2$.

5.2.5. Application to fatigue crack growth

In the analysis of fatigue crack growth data, the fatigue cycle is usually described by $\Delta K = (K_{max} - K_{min})$, where K_{max} and K_{min} are the maximum and minimum values of K_I during the fatigue cycle. It has been shown experimentally that ΔK rather than K_{max} has the major influence on fatigue crack growth [18] and that, if ΔK is constant, the fatigue crack growth rate is constant [19, 20]. The use of stress intensity factors has also proved valuable in the correlation of fatigue crack growth data for complex situations such as plate bending [21] and internally pressurized thin-walled cylinders [8, 22]. For many materials, subjected to a wholly tensile loading cycle, the rate of fatigue crack growth can be expressed by the equation

$$\frac{da}{dN} = D(\Delta K)^m, \tag{5.5}$$

where N is number of cycles, D is a material constant, and m is an exponent, usually about 3 or 4. If ΔK is below a certain threshold value, fatigue crack growth does not occur. Using a rigid plastic strip model [23] (that is, the cracked body becomes two elastic half planes joined together along a strip of rigid plastic material, with a void in the strip to simulate the crack), it has been shown that, on removal of a given load, the zone of reversed plastic yielding and change in strip deformation depend only on the decrement of load and not on the magnitude of the load prior to unloading. Thus, when subjected to a cyclic loading, the strip model predicts that the cyclic plastic deformation near the crack tip depends only on the load amplitude and not on its mean value. When this zone of reversed deformation is small, its magnitude depends only on ΔK, that is, the elastic stress intensity factor based on stress range. Eqn (5.5) applies only to an essentially elastic situation; corrections to K_{max} may be made for plastic zone sizes using eqns (5.3) or (5.4). Corrections to ΔK may be made for plastic zone sizes using these equations, but with K_I replaced by ΔK and σ_Y replaced by $2\sigma_Y$ [24]. The resulting correction to ΔK is usually small and often can be neglected. The minimum value of $K_I(K_{min})$ during the fatigue cycle equals $(K_{max}-\Delta K)$. For the case of a zero minimum load K_{min} would be expected to be zero, but if plastic zone corrections are applied, $K_{max} > \Delta K$ and K_{min} has a small positive value; the crack is effectively held open by the plastic zone, so that a small compressive load is required to close the crack and reduce K_{min} to zero. For an alternating load it is conventional to calculate ΔK on the assumption that the crack is completely closed on the compressive half-cycle, so that the effective load cycle is zero to maximum load. The effect of the plastic zone is to increase ΔK somewhat because the crack is actually open during part of the compressive half-cycle; the effect is more marked for short crack lengths. When a crack has grown for some distance, the permanent deformation adjacent to the crack surface, left behind by the passage of the plastic zone at the crack tip, may be sufficient to cause closure of the crack before the load has fallen to zero [25], thus reducing ΔK, particularly in thin sheets.

When a centre-crack specimen (Fig. 5.2(c)) is used, both K_{max} and ΔK increase with crack length, but the stress ratio R (minimum stress σ_{min}/maximum stress σ_{max}) remains constant; data are usually presented as plots of da/dN against ΔK for constant R. Constant K specimens, where K_I is independent of crack length (Fig. 5.2(c)) are particularly convenient, because all the parameters can easily be varied independently. Plotting data by different methods, for example, da/dN against ΔK for constant K_{mean} instead of

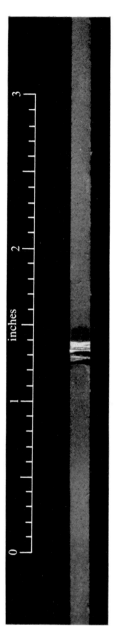

FIG. 5.4. Fracture face
of austenitic steel sheet.

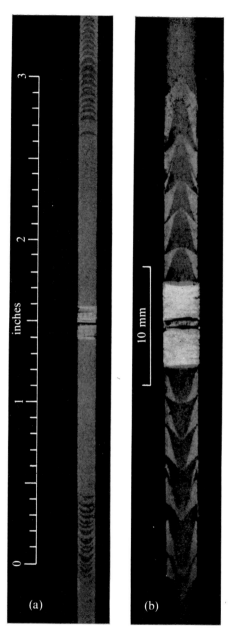

(a)   (b)

FIG. 5.5. Fracture faces of $5\frac{1}{2}\%$ Zn–aluminium
alloy sheets. (a) Tested at 31 ± 7.7 MN m^{-2}.
(b) Tested at 220 ± 23 MN m^{-2}. (Taken from
Frost [27].)

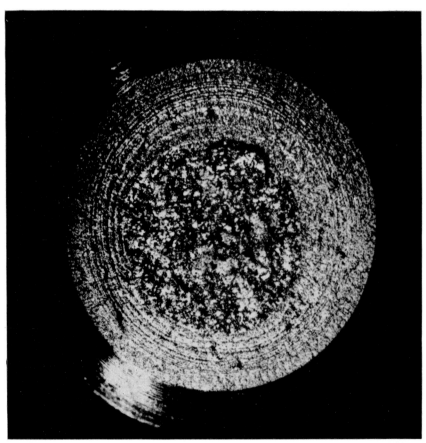

FIG. 5.6. Fracture face of a mild steel specimen. Stress programme: $\pm440\,\mathrm{MN\,m^{-2}}$, 5 cycles; $\pm31\,\mathrm{MN\,m^{-2}}$, 20 000 cycles. Total life 34·3 programmes. (Taken from Marsh [30].)

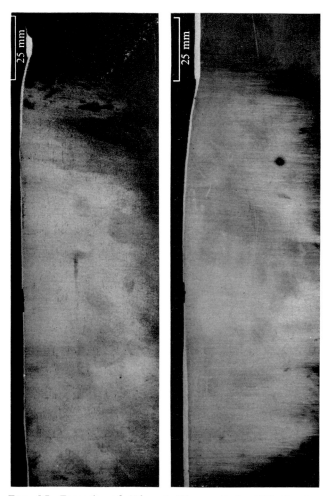

FIG. 5.7. Examples of 90° and 45° growth in $4\frac{1}{2}\%$ Cu–aluminium sheet. (Taken from Frost and Dugdale [35].)

FIG. 5.8. Fracture face of mild steel sheet tested at 193 ± 35 MN m^{-2}. (Taken from Frost [33].)

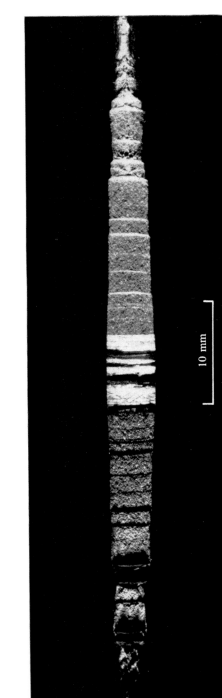

FIG. 5.10. Steps produced on fracture face of copper sheet due to repeated unloading and reloading. (Taken from Frost [33].)

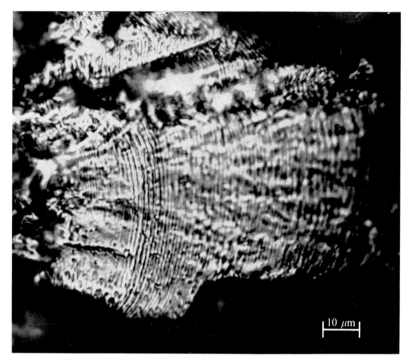

FIG. 5.11. Striations on fracture face of an L65 aluminium alloy specimen. Constant amplitude loading. Direction of crack growth left to right.

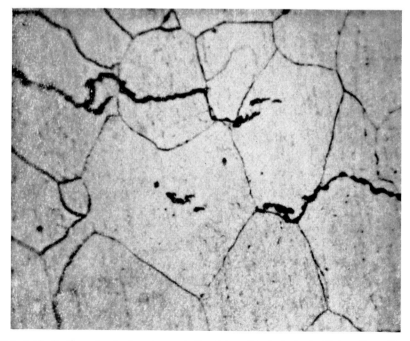

FIG. 5.12. Section ahead of main crack front in mild steel sheet. (Taken from Frost, Holden, and Phillips [59].)

FIG. 6.14. Vehicle fatigue testing on a road simulator facility.

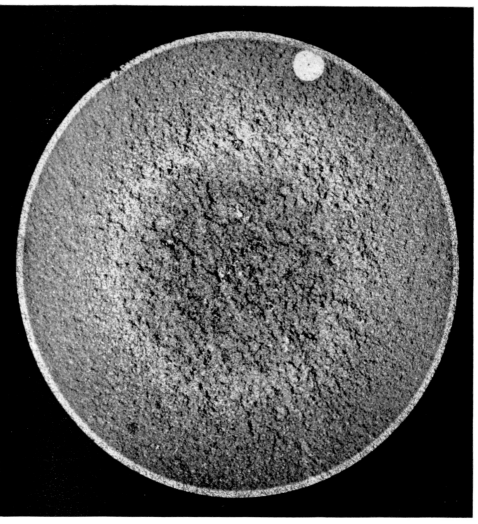

FIG. 6.18. Fatigue fracture face of carburized steel specimen, 25 mm diameter, showing origin of failure at centre of circular whitish area.

FIG. 6.23. Ring and clamping pad for fretting tests. The origin of the fatigue fracture can be seen beneath the end of the upper pad. (Taken from Field and Waters [240].)

constant R, can give a different impression of the fatigue crack growth properties of a material.

If the maximum cyclic load is such that general yielding occurs, it may still be possible to apply linear elastic fracture mechanics provided that the alternating load is small. In this case it can be argued that the unloading displacements during the first cycle, and all the subsequent cycles, will be essentially elastic so that it is possible to calculate ΔK, although K_{max} cannot be calculated. This argument has been found [26] to be justified for some materials because ΔK correlates data satisfactorily at stresses beyond general yielding.

5.3. Fractographic aspects of crack growth

5.3.1. Macroscopic appearance

The fracture faces produced on many metallic alloys by a continuously growing fatigue crack have, in general, a smooth matt appearance, free from markings visible to the naked eye; Fig. 5.4 shows the fracture face of an austenitic steel sheet produced by fatigue cracks grown from both ends of an initial central slit at 77 ± 32 MN m^{-2}. Some high-strength materials, such as the $5\frac{1}{2}\%$ Zn–aluminium alloy, exhibit quite distinct crescent-shaped markings, which become larger and more pronounced as ΔK and/or K_{max} increase. Examples of the fracture faces produced by a growing crack in this alloy at stress levels of $31 \pm 7 \cdot 7$ MN m^{-2} and 220 ± 23 MN m^{-2} are shown on Fig. 5.5(a) and (b) respectively. Each dark area on Figs. 5.5(a) and (b) is an element of fast fracture occurring in one stress cycle, whereas each light area corresponds to a period of fatigue crack growth, that is, it takes more than one stress cycle for the crack to traverse it. Confirmation of this composite growth behaviour is provided by the fact that 'clicks' may be heard during a crack growth test on the $5\frac{1}{2}\%$ Zn–aluminium alloy which correspond to bursts of fast fracture. Alternating light and dark areas may occur if the load cycle is varied systematically during a test. In general, the higher the load level the darker the fracture surface [28, 29]. Fig. 5.6 shows a specimen loaded in rotating bending at two different nominal stress levels.

5.3.2. Crack direction

The expected direction of crack growth in a uniaxially loaded sheet specimen is normal to the loading direction (§ 5.2.3) with the fracture face on a plane through the thickness at 90° to the plane of the specimen (termed 90° growth: Mode I); indeed in some materials, for example, zinc and titanium, this is what occurs. However, in other materials, such as steels, copper alloys, and aluminium alloys [18, 31–4], a transition to growth on a plane through the thickness inclined at approximately 45° to the plane of specimen (termed 45° growth: a combination of Modes I and III) usually takes place after an initial period of 90° crack growth. Examples of these two different types of fracture face are shown on Fig. 5.7. In some cases the fracture face may be on double shear (45°) planes instead of a single 45° plane.

The crack growth rate usually increases when the transition takes place [27], although occasionally a decrease is observed [36]. It has been shown experimentally [37–9] that the transition starts when the crack growth rate exceeds some critical value. The critical rate depends on the alloy and increases with sheet thickness and reduction of test frequency. Thus, for 2 mm thick 2024 aluminium alloy tested at 30 Hz the critical rate was 2×10^{-4} mm per cycle, which increased to about 4×10^{-4} mm per cycle when the frequency was reduced to $\frac{1}{3}$ Hz, and to 5×10^{-4} mm per cycle when the thickness was increased to 3 mm. As ΔK may be used to correlate crack growth rates, it may also be used to correlate the start of the transition [40, 41]. For most aluminium alloys the transition starts when ΔK exceeds about 10 MN m$^{-\frac{3}{2}}$. The start of the transition is only strongly affected by mean stress in materials, such as aluminium alloys, whose growth rate is affected markedly by mean stress; the transition then tends to start at lower ΔK values as mean stress is increased. In all materials the transition tends to be more abrupt as mean stress increases. An example of an abrupt transition at high tensile mean stress is given in Fig. 5.8; this shows the fracture face of a mild steel specimen tested at 193 ± 35 MN m^{-2}.

The plane of initial crack growth from a slit is independent of the orientation of the slit [39, 42]; an initial slit inclined through the thickness cannot force crack growth away from the 90° plane at low values of ΔK. Conversely, at high values of ΔK, crack growth may start immediately on a 45° plane. Although the transition appears to be associated with a change from plane strain to plane stress conditions, some attempts to correlate the transition with plastic zone-size have proved inconclusive [38, 43].

As theoretical (§ 5.6.8) and experimental results show that crack growth on a 45° plane is faster than on 90° planes, 45° planes are therefore energetically more favourable. However, rotation of the crack surfaces to 45° planes can only take place if a suitable mechanism is available. Growth on 45° planes only occurs in those materials in which the static tensile fracture of a piece of material of the same thickness as the crack-growth specimen occurs on a 45° plane through the thickness. If the static fracture occurs on a 90° plane (as it does, for example, with zinc and titanium), a fatigue crack grows on a 90° plane throughout. Both titanium and zinc have a close-packed hexagonal structure [44] and in sheet form tend to be textured, with the c-axis perpendicular to the plane of the sheet for titanium and parallel to this plane for zinc. Consequently, the sheets show normal anisotropy: properties are isotropic in the plane of the sheet, but are different through the thickness. This makes through the thickness yielding on 45° planes more difficult [45], and could account for the fatigue crack growth behaviour. More explicitly, tests on grain-oriented silicon iron [46] showed that the transition is suppressed for orientations in which no slip systems are available for yielding on 45° planes.

The types of fracture face described are typical of sheets whose thickness does not exceed about 3 mm; thicker sheets of similar materials may exhibit different types of fracture face. For example, although the growth rate characteristics of mild steel sheets, 2·5 mm, 7·6 mm, and 25·4 mm thick are not widely different [47], the appearance of the fracture face changes as the thickness increases. Initial growth occurs in all cases on a 90° plane but whereas with the 2·5 mm thick sheets subsequent growth is on a 45° plane, it is on a plane inclined at an angle of about 80° to 85° to the plane of the specimen in

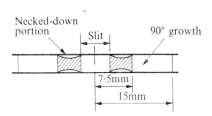

FIG. 5.9. Fracture face of mild steel sheet tested at 193 ± 39 MN m^{-2}. (Taken from Frost [33].)

the 7·6 mm thick specimens; it remains on a 90° plane throughout in the 25·4 mm thick sheets, although there are shear lips in regions corresponding to the 45° crack growth regions in the 2·5 mm thick sheets.

As only plane deformations are involved, even at relatively high stresses, the specimen thickness does not decrease significantly while a crack is growing on a 90° plane. For instance when high mean loads are applied to a sheet of a soft material such as mild steel or copper containing a slit, gross plastic deformation occurs around the ends of the slit, often resulting in the tip of the slit blunting and the material just ahead of it necking down. However, once a fatigue crack beings to grow on a 90° plane under a small alternating stress, the tip of the crack does not necessarily blunt excessively nor does the material ahead of the crack tip neck down. The sketch of the fracture face in the vicinity of the initial slit in a mild steel sheet tested at 193 ± 39 MN m^{-2} (Fig. 5.9) shows that, although the application of the mean stress results in the sheet thickness ahead of the slit necking down, once the crack starts growing on a 90° plane any reduction in sheet thickness is negligible. If the sheet is unloaded, re-application of the mean load causes the crack to open up over its whole length and its tip to blunt. Repeating this process during a crack growth test results in a series of steps being produced on the fracture face. Fig. 5.10 shows such steps produced on the fracture face of a copper sheet tested at 154 ± 15 MN m^{-2}.

5.3.3. Microscopic appearance

Since 1950 [48] a great deal of effort has been devoted to the microscopic examination of fatigue fracture surfaces, particularly since the advent of the electron microscope [49], and various collections of electron micrographs showing the details of the fracture faces created by a growing fatigue crack have been published [28, 49–51]. The most prominent features of fatigue fracture surfaces (particularly those created by cracks growing on 90° planes) are distinct line markings, parallel to each other and normal to the direction of crack growth. These are generally called striations; each striation corresponds to one load cycle. In general, striations are more clearly defined in ductile than brittle materials; for instance, in the stronger steels [52], striations are short and discontinuous and their successive positions not clearly defined. Examples of the striations clearly visible on certain areas of the fracture face of an L65 aluminium alloy specimen created by a fatigue crack growing under a constant amplitude loading cycle are shown on Fig. 5.11.

The presence of striations on a fracture surface is proof that failure was caused by fatigue [53], but they cannot always be found on all fatigue fracture surfaces, often because the microscope used has insufficient resolution. Striations varying in spacing from about 2·5 mm [54] to less than $2·5 \times 10^{-5}$ mm [55] have been observed on various materials. At high crack growth rates they tend to give way to ductile dimples [56].

On a microscopic scale, fatigue crack growth is often an irregular process. Examination of the fracture surfaces of 2024-T4 aluminium alloy [57] using a stereoscan microscope showed that the main fracture surface was irregular with numerous interconnected cracks intersecting the main crack; some of these cracks were at nearly 90° to the main fracture. Much earlier, a study [58, 59] of the shape of the front of a crack growing in a 3·2 mm thick mild steel sheet was made by examining sections on planes normal to the direction of crack growth so as to eventually intersect the crack front. This showed that the crack front bows forward slightly so that a section can be made with the leading part of the crack in the middle of the sheet thickness. In the region of the crack front, numerous apparently independent cracks were found (see Fig. 5.12). These cracks may be similar to those found in the aluminium alloy.

The one-to-one correspondence between striations and applied loads was first proved by Forsyth and Ryder [53] from an examination of the fracture surface of an L65 aluminium alloy wing spar which had been programme fatigue tested. Each programme consisted of loading the specimen to 83 MN m^{-2} and then superimposing upon this mean load 18 cycles of ±21 MN m^{-2}. The entire load was then removed. The specimen failed after 10 000 applications of this programme. Examination of the fracture surface showed coarse striations corresponding to the application of the 83 MN m^{-2} loads and, between each pair of these, 18 finer ones corresponding to the

± 21 MN m^{-2} loads. They also demonstrated the one-to-one correspondence between striation spacing and load application from tests on DTD 546 aluminium alloy; numerous investigators have since confirmed this correspondence [2, 28, 47, 51, 52, 54, 60–2]. Growth rates calculated from striation spacings at different distances from the centre line of a titanium sheet, together with values estimated from the actual experimentally determined growth curve are given on Fig. 5.13; they are seen to be in good agreement.

Crack propagation tests [52] on two batches of 7178 aluminium alloy ($6\frac{1}{2}\%$ Zn), one batch containing 0·38 per cent volume fraction of inclusions

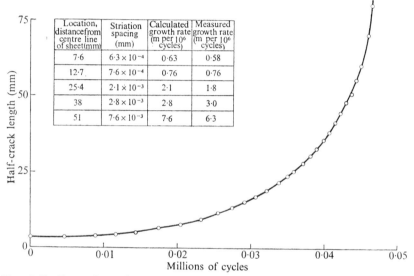

Location, distance from centre line of sheet (mm)	Striation spacing (mm)	Calculated growth rate (m per 10⁶ cycles)	Measured growth rate (m per 10⁶ cycles)
7·6	$6\cdot3 \times 10^{-4}$	0·63	0·58
12·7	$7\cdot6 \times 10^{-4}$	0·76	0·76
25·4	$2\cdot1 \times 10^{-3}$	2·1	1·8
38	$2\cdot8 \times 10^{-3}$	2·8	3·0
51	$7\cdot6 \times 10^{-3}$	7·6	6·3

FIG. 5.13. Comparison of measured crack growth rates and those estimated from the spacing of striations observed on the fracture face of a titanium sheet.

and the other batch 4·8 per cent showed that the measured macroscopic crack growth rate in the latter alloy was faster than in the former material. Measurements of striation spacing showed that the growth rate in the matrix was slower than the experimental macroscopic growth rates but metallurgical examination revealed that, in both batches of material, the crack front spurted forward when it reached a brittle second-phase particle or inclusion, so that the growth rate characteristics of each batch of material was a combination of fatigue growth through elements of matrix (and this was the same in both batches) plus the spasmodic elements of fast fracture through a brittle particle. The over-all macroscopic growth rate was faster, therefore, than that in the matrix as deduced from the striation markings and was faster in the batch containing the larger volume of inclusions, because these induced the greater number of fast fracture bursts of growth.

Macrocrack growth is not restricted to metals and metallic alloys. As mentioned in § 2.4, although the formation of surface microcracks by continuing to-and-fro cyclic slip is only possible in ductile metals, macrocracks are able to grow in materials in which the slip processes common to ductile metals do not occur. For example, visible boundaries (that is, striations) between regions exposed by successive increments of crack growth have been observed [64] in strain-crystallizing elastomers (natural rubbers) but not in non-crystallizing elastomers. These striations apparently arose from deviations from the straight crack path during a single extension and corresponded to a definite surface relief. The fracture surface of fatigue cracks grown from a central slit in sheets of polycarbonate (a crystalline thermoplastic) and polyethylene (a thermoplastic which is about 50 per cent crystalline) exhibited striation markings similar to those observed in metals [65]. The measured striation spacings gave a one-to-one correlation with the measured growth rate.

Various theories have been proposed to explain the mechanism responsible for striation formation. Forsyth [60, 63] considered that a striation was a ridge on the fracture face, and because the distance between two adjacent striations corresponds to the distance the crack front moves forward during one stress cycle, each increment of crack growth could be considered as a tensile test on an element of material of size corresponding to the striation spacing. Both cleavage fracture and plastic deformation would occur, the relative amounts depending on material and the crack tip stress, the striation produced being an indication of the local plastic strain of the element as it was fractured. Thus it follows that striations are most clearly revealed in ductile materials. At low stress levels he considered that a fracture face might appear featureless because either the spacing of the striations was too close to be resolved or the plastic deformation at the crack tip was too small to produce a detectable surface ridge. Christensen [2] also suggested that the mechanism of fatigue crack growth was simply a series of progressive minute static tensile fractures, striations being a consequence of the plastic deformation occurring at the crack tip as the crack spurted forward under the maximum tensile load in the cycle.

Laird and Smith [61] obtained direct evidence of striation profiles, which led them to suggest that striations are troughs in the fracture surface, not ridges as proposed by Forsyth; they subjected high-purity aluminium and nickel plain specimens to reversed direct stress amplitudes of magnitude sufficient to cause fracture in less than 10^4 cycles, and then examined the fracture faces. They found that, irrespective of endurance, striations were visible on the fracture face. Some tests were stopped, at various points around the loading cycle, when a specimen contained a well-defined crack, and the load held constant while the crack was filled with Lacomit. This was allowed to harden and so preserved the crack profile (at the given external load) when the load was removed. They found, by sectioning, that during the compression half of the loading cycle, the crack was completely closed, but as the loading entered the tensile half of the loading cycle, the crack began to open from the outside like a hinge, giving a profile similar to a sharp notch. When the tensile load reached its maximum value, the crack tip became rounded and pronounced ears formed in the apex of the rounded region or to one or both sides of it. On unloading and recompressing, the rounded-off crack tip came to a sharp tip as the fracture faces closed completely. The deformation ears also closed up and formed adjacent to each other on the opposing crack surfaces to give troughs which appeared as ripples on the fracture face. Microhardness tests taken on the aluminium specimens showed that a small region

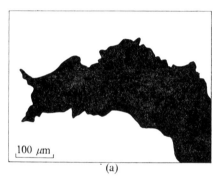 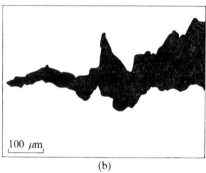

100 μm   100 μm

(a)   (b)

FIG. 5.14. Profile of crack tip in a loaded mild steel sheet.

at the apex of the rounded-off fatigue crack was as hard as the cup part of a static tensile fracture. The metal at the tips of cracks which had been sharpened by compression was equally hard. The authors considered that the deformation produced at the crack tip during each cycle resulted in extension of the crack, crack propagation being a continuous process and resulting from a miniature double-cup plastic separation repeated each cycle.

Fig. 5.14(a) shows an example of a blunted tip having two ears, similar to that described by Laird and Smith, found in a mild steel specimen in which the crack was filled with plastic steel whilst the maximum load was held constant. However, other sections revealed that the crack tip could be either blunted with only one ear or no ears or it could still retain a sharp profile as shown on Fig. 5.14(b).

Hertzberg and Paris [43] found that on the 90° growth portion of the fracture faces of 2024-T3 aluminium alloy sheets there were areas containing well-defined striations, areas in which the striations were less well defined, and areas having a rumpled appearance with no evidence of striations. As the examination of the fracture face was extended towards the 45° plane of fracture, fewer regions of striations were observed, while on the 45° growth fracture face itself no striations could be observed. Associated with this decreasing incidence of striations were an increasing number of elongated dimples, having their long axis perpendicular to the direction of crack growth, which were typical of static ductile fracture. The authors considered that a striation formed during the plane strain 90° growth stage, as a result of some mechanism producing slip motion in and out of the plane of the crack, thus producing a surface marking parallel to the advancing crack. This would arise because, in the case of plane-strain stressing, the planes of maximum shear stress ahead of the crack tip are perpendicular to the sheet and inclined at an angle of about ±60° or ±70° to the plane of the crack. However, during the plane stress or 45° growth stage, the planes of maximum shear are oriented at approximately 45° to the plane of the sheet. Thus, when slip now occurs, it will be in a direction from one surface of the sheet to the other, that is, the slip direction will be parallel to the leading edge of the crack front. Thus, no striations would form on the fracture faces produced by 45° growth because of the absence of slip processes moving in and out of the crack plane. However, striations whose spacing agrees with measured crack growth rates have been observed on 45° fracture planes in L73 aluminium alloy [54] although they were sparser than on the 90° fracture planes. The complete elastic–plastic analysis for 45° crack growth required to elucidate the situation is not available, but the crack surface displacements for a 45° crack are a combination of Modes I and III, which appears to account for the displacements necessary for striation formation during 45° crack growth.

McMillan and Pelloux [55] considered that striations were both ridges and troughs, that is, the surface had a microscopic sawtooth profile, cracking occurring only during the loading part of the cycle. During unloading, the fracture surfaces created during the previous loading cycle were heavily deformed near the crack tip, leading to the formation of the dark rumpled side of the striation and erasing in part, the bright appearance of the fracture face created during loading. They concluded that striation formation was a two-step process composed of crack extension on loading followed by striation definition through plastic flow and resharpening on unloading, the crystallography of the material accentuating the localization of this flow, leading to sharp, well-defined ridges and grooves.

Very large striations having a wave-shaped profile do sometimes occur on aluminium alloys and mild steel [54].

5.4. Metal physics aspects of crack growth

X-ray diffraction and thin-film electron microscopy examinations of cyclically stressed metallic specimens, described in Chapter 2, showed that cyclic stressing led to the formation of a sub-structure within the parent grains, but that this was not necessarily associated with the initiation of surface microcracks; it rather gave an indication of the stable cyclic structure produced by cyclic stressing.

The fracture faces of mild steel and aluminium sheets created by the slow growth of a fatigue crack have been examined [58] using a micro-beam X-ray diffraction technique [66] which depends for its application upon dislocations in the deformed metal being so distributed that they form arrays defining sub-grains which are relatively free of dislocations. It allows estimation of the size of the sub-grains, and their misorientation within the grains. The sub-grain structure appeared to be localized to within a depth of 50 μm from the fracture surface and was similar to that found in plain specimens subjected to relatively large cyclic plastic strains. The characteristics of the sub-grain structure are summarized in Table 5.1.

The cyclic sub-structure appeared to be associated with the accumulation of dislocations in regions of high density, interspersed with regions of low dislocation density. The final dislocation structure on the fracture face was independent of stress range, so that it was characteristic of the fracture condition at the crack tip and not of any intervening state of plastic deformation. There was no evidence that the sub-boundaries played a primary role in crack

TABLE 5.1

Specimen details	Characteristics of sub-structure deduced from X-ray reflection measurements	
	Average sub-grain size (μm)	Mean angle between sub-grains (degrees)
Fracture surface of aluminium sheet crack propagation specimen tested at $46\pm7\cdot5$ MN m^{-2}	4–6	13
Fracture surface of aluminium sheet crack propagation specimen tested at 46 ± 15 MN m^{-2}	4–6	13
Plain torsion specimen of aluminium tested for 6000 cycles at surface plastic strain amplitude of $\pm10^{-2}$	4–8	13
Plain torsion specimen of aluminium tested for 80 000 cycles at surface plastic strain amplitude of $\pm3\times10^{-3}$	4–8	13
Plain push–pull specimen of aluminium tested for 30 000 cycles at a plastic strain amplitude of $\pm8\times10^{-3}$	5–8	8–12
Fracture surface of mild steel sheet crack propagation specimen tested at 77 ± 38 MN m^{-2}	1–2	8–13
Fracture surface of mild steel sheet crack propagation specimen tested at 185 ± 46 MN m^{-2}	1–2	8–13
Plain push–pull specimen of iron tested for 30 000 cycles at a plastic strain amplitude of $\pm10^{-3}$	1–2	7–9

propagation; their significance in this respect was to emphasize the relatively low level of hardening attained at large cyclic strain ranges, so that a metal possessing this cyclic structure should flow readily. This was confirmed by measurements of the extension of plain specimens of aluminium subjected to relatively high cyclic stresses and low mean stresses. The creep rate exhibited by such a specimen was much greater than that of a specimen subjected to a static stress equal to the maximum stress present in the loading cycle. Thus, the fact that hardening mechanisms in the low dislocation-density regions within a sub-grain are restricted to intersection processes means that there can be only limited hardening at a crack tip, and favours continual blunting and resharpening at the crack front as a crack growth mechanism. The stacking fault energy of a material, because it affects intersection processes and jog formation, is consequently a more important crack growth factor than hardening by initial working or by grain-size control above the range of cyclic sub-grain sizes.

Examination of aluminium alloy fatigue specimens using thin-foil electron microscopy [67] showed that the dislocations near the tip of fatigue cracks depended on the type of alloy; in 1100–0 aluminium alloy they were distributed in a sub-grain structure. By contrast, a more uniform distribution of sub-grain loops was found in 2024-T4. In 7075-T6 the dislocations were tightly packed in a uniform distribution and showed little sign of motion or interaction. There was no correlation between the sub-grain structure and striations on the fracture surface. Dislocation densities 6 μm from the tips of fatigue cracks grown over 10^5–10^6 cycles ranged from 10^8 lines per mm² in the 1100–0 alloy to about 10^9 lines per mm² in the 7075-T6 alloy.

Thin-film examination of copper single crystals [68] subjected to a push–pull fatigue cycle which gave a life of about 10^6 cycles showed that fatigue cracks did not follow sub-grain boundaries; the sub-grain structure was somewhat finer than the striation spacing and was found to develop ahead of the growing fatigue crack.

It may be concluded that, although a sub-grain structure is formed ahead of a growing crack, it does not control the incremental length of growth which occurs each cycle; this appears to be non-crystalline in nature and a function of the macroscopic plastic strains which accompany the blunting and resharpening of the crack tip

5.5. Determination of fatigue crack growth rates

Plain cylindrical specimens are unsuitable for obtaining information on the rate of growth of a crack because only measurements of surface length are possible during a test whereas the growth rate will depend on the shape of the cracked area normal to the loading direction.

A suitable and commonly-used crack-propagation specimen is a long, wide, thin sheet (Fig. 5.15) loaded in the longitudinal direction. A sensibly uniform longitudinal stress is obtained across the test-section if the length is at least three times the width. Buckling of the sheet due to compressive loading is prevented by either superimposing on the alternating stress a tensile mean stress of sufficient magnitude to ensure that the loading is never compressive or by fitting guide plates. Care must be taken that the sheet is not so thin that buckling takes place even under entirely tensile loading (§ 5.9.1). A small central slit cut normal to the loading direction is generally used to initiate fatigue cracks.

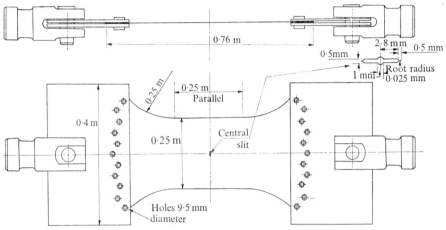

FIG. 5.15. Crack propagation test-piece. (Taken from Frost [27].)

Crack lengths are generally measured from the centre line of the sheet, thus giving 4 readings of half-crack length at any instant. If the sheet is thin, there is usually little difference between the 4 readings taken at any instant, and the average value is taken as the current half-crack length. In fact, should a half-crack on one side of the centre line grow more than that on the other side, so displacing the centre of the crack from the sheet centre line, there will be a tendency, depending on the rigidity of the end fixings, for tensile and compressive in-plane bending stresses to be superimposed on the material ahead of the now offset half-cracks, thus tending to even out their growth rates. A typical crack growth curve obtained from a 0·25 m wide specimen containing a central 6 mm long slit is shown in Fig. 5.16. As the crack length increases, the remaining area of material available to carry the applied loads becomes progressively smaller. Thus the external cyclic loading applied to a crack propagation specimen may be either maintained constant (that is, stresses based on gross areas remain constant) or it may be continually reduced so that either the stresses based on net uncracked area or the stress intensity factor remain constant throughout a test. Most experimental work is of the former type.

Several specimen designs based on fracture mechanics principles have been used to collect fatigue data. Bend (Fig. 5.2(d)) and wedge-opening loading (Fig. 5.2(g) and (h)) specimens are particularly suitable for heavy sections because they use relatively little material. Constant K specimens (Fig. 5.2(e)), where the stress intensity factor is independent of crack length, permit tests at constant K without alteration of the applied load, but the crack tends to deviate from a straight line and one or two side grooves must be used to constrain it. The side grooves increase the stress intensity factor by a factor

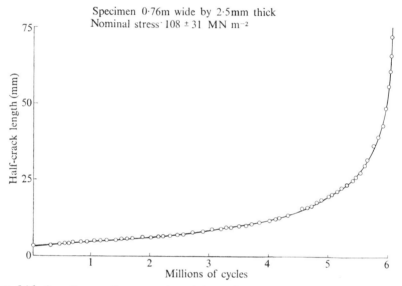

FIG. 5.16. Growth curve for a central crack in a mild steel specimen. (Taken from Frost [27].)

of approximately $(B/b)^{\frac{1}{2}}$ [69], where B and b are gross and net thickness. Any other configuration for which stress intensity factors are available can be used to collect data.

Even with a thin sheet specimen, crack length measurements can be taken only on two faces of the sheet, whereas, of course, the crack front is moving through the entire sheet thickness. Although on a microscopic scale the crack front may be a complex shape, on a macroscopic scale a slowly growing crack can be considered as growing in a direction normal to the loading direction and having a front which is a straight line joining the two ends of the visible surface cracks.

Apart from direct observation of the specimen surface, various other means of crack measurements have been developed, and these are summarized [70] in Table 5.2.

TABLE 5.2

Crack growth measurement techniques

Method	Usage	Advantages	Disadvantages
Microscopy techniques	Sheet and plate test-pieces. Photography sometimes used	Cheap. Easy installation.	Difficulty of crack tip location without stroboscopic light. Only surface measurements possible during test. Difficult to automate.
Mechanical methods	Rotating bend test pieces. Sheet, plate, and others depending on displacement gauge used	Use of compliance change which can be measured externally away from specimen.	Restricted to tests where compliance calibration (relationship between specimen stiffness and crack length) is known.
Acoustic methods	Applicable to most types of test-piece	Very small probe required, can be mounted easily; useful in low- and high-temperature tests.	Errors due to background noise and calibration is difficult
Electrical techniques	Continuity gauges usually used on sheet and plate samples, could be used for surface measurements on other test-pieces	Electrical signal gives easy automation.	Difficulty of connecting wire and foil gauges. Gauges must break when crack passes. Only surface measurement.
Eddy currents	Used on surface crack monitoring of sheet test-pieces; others should be possible.	Easily adapted to automatic process. Small probe which is not in contact with test-piece.	Not yet used on thicker samples, may only be useful for surface measurement. Expensive.
Electrical resistance or potential measurement	Used on sheet and plate test-pieces	Easily adapted to automatic process. Only four leads attached to specimen, therefore ideally suited for high- or low-temperature tests	Problems of insulating the test-piece. Initial calibration problem thought to be overcome.
Ultrasonics	Ideally suited to compact fracture toughness test-pieces. (Fig. 5.2).	Easily adapted to automatic process. Internal measurement of crack front.	Expensive compared to other techniques. Measurements restricted to thicker type test-pieces.

It has been mentioned in Chapter 2 that scatter in life of fatigue specimens is associated with the number of cycles required to initiate and develop a surface microcrack to the macrocrack stage. An example of the reproducibility that is possible in the case of macrocrack growth curves is shown on Fig. 5.17. The cracks were grown in two 18/8 austenitic steel sheets tested at 124 ± 62 MN m^{-2}.

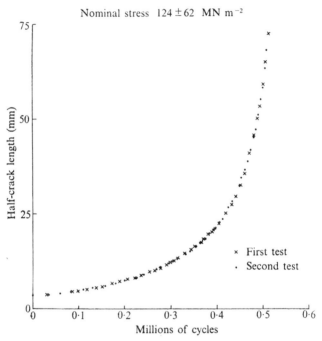

FIG. 5.17. Crack growth curves for 2 wide austenitic steel sheets. (Taken from Frost [71].)

A scatter in growth curves may become apparent at low stress levels and small crack lengths because the initial period of growth at these levels is somewhat erratic. It is always possible, of course, that at low stress levels compressive residual stresses induced during the preparation of the initial slit may be retarding the growth, whereas these stresses would tend to be swamped at higher stresses. This rather hesitant and erratic growth at short lengths and low stress levels should be borne in mind when analysing the crack growth data for a series of tests at different stress levels.

Crack growth rates are normally determined by drawing tangents to the experimentally determined crack length versus number of cycles curve. No completely satisfactory method of fitting a curve to the individual data points has yet been developed: subjective judgment is necessary in rejecting disparate points and assessing the smoothness of the fitted curve.

Fatigue crack growth data can be obtained indirectly [72] by consideration of the total life of a precracked specimen, such as the stress-relieved edge-cracked plate specimens used to determine the threshold stress necessary for fatigue crack growth (§§ 4.5.4 and 4.8.2). Assuming that the life of a broken edge-cracked plate specimen is occupied entirely by crack growth, the initial rate of crack growth can be obtained by integration of an appropriate expression for crack growth such as that given by eqn (5.5), namely

$$\frac{da}{dN} = D(\Delta K)^m.$$

Now eqn 5.1 gives

$$\Delta K = 2\sigma_a(\pi a)^{\frac{1}{2}}\alpha$$

hence

$$\frac{da}{dN} = D\{2\sigma_a\alpha(\pi)^{\frac{1}{2}}\}^m a^{m/2}$$

or

$$\frac{dN}{da} = \frac{a^{-m/2}}{D\{2\sigma_a\alpha(\pi)^{\frac{1}{2}}\}^m}.$$

Therefore

$$N = \int_{a_0}^{a_t} \frac{a^{-m/2}}{D\{2\sigma_a\alpha(\pi)^{\frac{1}{2}}\}^m}\, da$$

$$= \frac{a_f^{(1-m/2)} - a_0^{(1-m/2)}}{D(1-m/2)\{2\sigma_a\alpha(\pi)^{\frac{1}{2}}\}^m}.$$

That is

$$D = \frac{a_f^{(1-m/2)} - a_0^{(1-m/2)}}{N(1-m/2)\{2\sigma_a\alpha(\pi)^{\frac{1}{2}}\}^m}.$$

Using this value of D and taking a as a_0 to obtain the initial rate of crack growth, the term in braces cancels out and

$$\frac{da}{dN} = \frac{a_0 - a_f(a_0/a_f)^{m/2}}{N(m/2-1)} \qquad (5.6)$$

(when $m = 2$ this gives $da/dN = a_0/N \ln a_t/a_0$), where a_0 and a_t are the initial and final crack lengths, and N is the number of cycles the crack takes to grow from a_0 to a_t. The value of da/dN is not particularly sensitive to either a_t (provided it is reasonably large compared with a_0) or m. Data obtained using eqn (5.6) are in general in reasonable agreement (Fig. 5.18) with data obtained by conventional methods, but each specimen yields only one data point. The method has the advantage that no crack growth instrumentation is necessary, so that data on crack growth in difficult environments can readily be obtained.

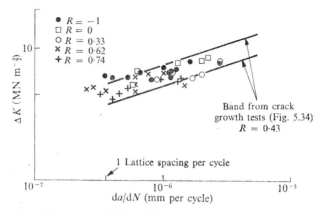

Fɪɢ. 5.18. ΔK versus da/dN for 18/8 austenitic steel. (Taken from Pook [72].)

5.6. Some fatigue crack growth theories

Although crack growth data could be presented simply as a series of curves of crack length plotted against number of cycles for different mean tensile and alternating stresses, it is more convenient to handle if presented as a mathematical relationship involving crack length, number of stress cycles, tensile mean stress, alternating stress, and a material constant. Several attempts have been made to derive such a relationship theoretically by treating the material as a continuum. All relate crack length and number of cycles; some offer a prediction of the stress dependence of the growth rate but in general, do not predict the material constant, which must be determined experimentally. A crack growth theory due to Valluri is mentioned in § 6.2.3.

All the theories discussed assume that crack growth is in Mode I, usually considering a central transverse crack, length $2a$, in an infinite sheet subjected to a remotely applied uniaxial stress σ. As examination of the fracture faces created by a moving crack (§ 5.3.3) shows that a fatigue crack moves forward each stress cycle, any theory of crack growth based on the assumption that a crack remains stationary for a certain number of cycles of stress, while the material ahead of the tip is conditioned in some way prior to fracture, is invalid.

5.6.1. Head's theory

Head's [1] theory was developed before treatments of plasticity near cracks were available and was based on various simplifying assumptions. A cracked body was regarded as consisting of a composite array of three types of continua. Taking infinitesimal elements of each of these types, material directly ahead of the crack was viewed as an array of independent, rigid-plastic tensile bars, each hardening linearly from a yield stress σ_Y to a maximum tensile stress σ_t at a modulus E_w, but without any Bauschinger effect. The material above and below the crack and rigid plastic bar array was regarded as an array of independent elastic tensile bars of modulus E, each carrying the remotely applied stress σ, which transmitted the load to the rigid-plastic bars both directly and through a third array of elements transmitting the load by shear. The properties of the shear elements and length of the elastic bars were selected so that the model gave the correct elastic opening at the centre of the crack. He considered the history of a small volume of material in line with the advancing crack and argued that, as the crack tip approached, it would begin to deform plastically, work-hardening progressively, until its ductility was exhausted, at which point it would fracture and become part of the main crack.

This model gave for an applied stress $\pm\sigma$, when $\sigma < \sigma_Y$

$$\frac{da}{dN} = \frac{2E_w\sigma^3a^{\frac{3}{2}}}{3E(\sigma_t-\sigma_Y)(\sigma_Y-\sigma)^2h^{\frac{1}{2}}}, \tag{5.7}$$

where $2h$ is the height of the rigid plastic elements in front of the crack.

Because $\sigma_Y \geqslant \sigma$, eqn (5.7) is equivalent to

$$\frac{da}{dN} \propto K_I^3.$$

Using this analysis, the plastic zone-size is given by [24]:

$$r_p = \frac{(ha)^{\frac{1}{2}}}{2} \frac{\sigma}{\sigma_Y-\sigma},$$

that is, r_p is proportional to K_I, rather than to K_I^2 (see § 5.2.4).

For a remotely applied stress greater than the yield stress, $\sigma \geqslant \sigma_Y$ the theory gave

$$\frac{da}{dN} = \frac{2E_w\sigma^3a^{\frac{3}{2}}}{E\sigma_t(\sigma_t^2-\sigma^2)h^{\frac{1}{2}}}.$$

Thus in a given test in which gross stresses are kept constant, $a^{-\frac{1}{2}}$ can be plotted linearly against the number of cycles; h must be obtained from the experimental data.

5.6.2. The geometrical similarity hypothesis

This is based [42] upon consideration of a small idealized transverse slit, in a perfectly elastic sheet of infinite extent, subject to plane stress and loaded in uniaxial tension. If a unit diagram is prepared in which dimensions are scaled by taking the slit length as unity, elastic theory shows that at any point defined by a vector drawn from the origin, the stress or displacement is the same regardless of the actual slit length. Dimensional analysis of all the parameters that have a bearing on the problem always gives the same result.

The same argument can be applied to a finite sheet, provided that the sheet width is large compared with the slit length, because stresses in the vicinity of the crack will only be slightly affected. If the sheet is thin compared with the slit length, stresses through the thickness can be assumed zero, so that sheet thickness has no effect. Provided that the structural dimensions of the material are small enough for it to be considered homogeneous, no lengths other than the slit length are involved, all other parameters being stresses. Thus, for a single loading up to a particular nominal stress, a stress configuration is attained in the vicinity of the slit which can be reduced to a unit diagram regardless of slit length. If fracture under a repeated loading is regarded as a continuous process where a crack has grown continuously from an initial length to its current length, not being arrested at any stage, there is only one independent variable of length to which the configurations of stress and strain can be referred, namely, the current crack length. It follows that the rate of propagation must be proportional to the current crack length.

However, in a ductile material, different configurations will only be similar if the material undergoes no change as the crack grows. If residual stresses are introduced during the first loading, then the second configuration at the increased crack length might not be the same as the first, because two values of length are now involved, or there might be independent length dimensions associated with the plastic zone always present ahead of a growing crack in a ductile material. However, both theory [73] and experiment [74] show that the length of the plastic zone ahead of a crack is directly proportional to the crack length. Thus, the existence of a plastic zone does not invalidate the geometrical similarity argument that the growth rate is proportional to the current crack length. A more detailed argument [75] showed that the argument only held if the material had a stable response to the load history.

The geometrical similarity hypotheses thus leads to the growth law

$$\frac{da}{dN} = Da$$

that is,

$$\ln\left(\frac{a}{a_0}\right) = DN,$$

where a_0 is the initial crack length.

Thus, in a given crack growth test on a sheet of finite width, in which the gross stresses are kept constant, $\ln(a)$ should vary linearly with the corresponding number of cycles N, until the crack reaches such a length that it can no longer be regarded as growing in an infinitely wide sheet. The coefficient D depends on both the mean and alternating stresses and on the material; it cannot be predicted, but must be obtained from analysis of experimental data.

5.6.3. Net area stress theories

Weibull developed a theory [76, 77] based upon consideration of a central transverse crack growing in a thin sheet of finite width subjected to a zero to tensile loading cycle. He argued that, as the crack length/sheet width ratio increased, the effective stress at the crack tip would also increase so that the rate of growth at a given crack length/sheet width ratio would depend only on the instantaneous value of the effective stress at the crack tip, that is,

$$\frac{d}{dN}\left(\frac{2a}{W}\right) = F\sigma_t^\beta, \tag{5.8}$$

where $2a$ is the over-all crack length, W is the sheet width, N is the number of cycles, σ_t is the effective crack tip stress, and F and β are constants. He assumed that the effective crack-tip stress σ_t depended only on the maximum nominal stress acting on the net uncracked area of the sheet σ_N, so that

$$\sigma_t = A\sigma_N^m, \tag{5.9}$$

where A and m are constants. Substituting eqn (5.9) in eqn (5.8) gave

$$\frac{d}{dN}\left(\frac{2a}{W}\right) = C\sigma_N^n, \tag{5.10}$$

where

$$C = FA^\beta \quad \text{and} \quad n = m\beta.$$

Substituting

$$\frac{d(2a)}{dN} = W\frac{d}{dN}\left(\frac{2a}{W}\right)$$

gave

$$\frac{d(2a)}{dN} = CW\sigma_N^n. \tag{5.11}$$

If a crack growth test is carried out in which the external loads are continually reduced as the crack grows so that the nominal net cyclic stress σ_N is maintained at a constant value throughout, eqn (5.11) can be integrated to give

$$2a = CW\sigma_N^n N.$$

Thus, in a constant net area stress crack propagation test on a sheet of finite width, the crack length should vary linearly with the number of cycles, irrespective of crack length. The material constant and stress dependence are not predicted and must be obtained from experimental data. However, for sheets of different width, the slope of the a versus N plots, at a given σ_N, should be directly proportional to the width W.

Eqn (5.10) can be applied to a constant gross area stress crack growth test by substituting

$$\sigma_N = \frac{\sigma}{(1-2a/W)},$$

where σ is the gross area stress. This gives

$$\frac{d(2a)}{dN} = \frac{C\sigma^n}{(1-2a/W)},$$

and thus

$$\left(1-\frac{2a}{W}\right)^{n+1} = C(n+1)\sigma^n(N_t-N),$$

where N_t = number of cycles at final fracture, that is, at $2a/W = 1$. Writing

$$\frac{1}{N_1} = C(n+1)\sigma^n$$

gives

$$\left(1-\frac{2a}{W}\right)^{n+1} = \frac{(N_t-N)}{N_1}.$$

Thus, in a constant gross area stress crack growth test on a sheet of finite width, $(1-2a/W)$ should vary linearly with (N_t-N) on logarithmic axes for all values of $2a/W < 1$.

Weibull's net area stress relationship can be deduced using fracture mechanics [78]. The stress intensity factor for a finite-width sheet can be written [5]:

$$K_I = \sigma(\pi a)^{\frac{1}{2}}\left(\frac{W}{\pi a}\tan\frac{\pi a}{W}\right)^{\frac{1}{2}},$$

but, in a Weibull test,

$$\sigma = \sigma_N\left(1-\frac{2a}{W}\right)$$

therefore

$$K_I = \sigma_N\left(1-\frac{2a}{W}\right)(\pi a)^{\frac{1}{2}}\left(\frac{W}{\pi a}\tan\frac{\pi a}{W}\right)^{\frac{1}{2}}$$

$$= \sigma_N\left(\frac{\pi W}{2}\right)^{\frac{1}{2}}f\left(\frac{2a}{W}\right).$$

The values in Table 5.3 show that over the range 0·2–0·7, $f(2a/W)$ is sensibly constant, and, as σ_N and W are constant throughout a Weibull test, K_I also remains sensibly constant.

McEvily and Illg [79, 80] also proposed a net area stress theory based on the assumption that the effective stress at the tip of a crack was given by the expression $K_N\sigma_{Na}$, where σ_{Na} was the alternating stress on the net uncracked area and K_N the effective stress concentration factor for the crack. Provided $K_N\sigma_{Na}$ was greater than the plain fatigue limit of the material, they postulated

TABLE 5.3

$2a/W$	0·1	0·2	0·3	0·4	0·5	0·6	0·7
$f(2a/W)$	0·36	0·46	0·50	0·51	0·50	0·47	0·42

that a crack would grow at a rate which was a function of the current value of $K_N \sigma_{Na}$, that is,

$$\frac{da}{dN} = f(K_N \sigma_{Na}).$$

K_N was derived from Neuber's equation (§4.3.2.4), for zero flank angle, that is,

$$K_N = 1 + \frac{K_t - 1}{1 + (A/\rho)^{\frac{1}{2}}},$$

where ρ is the crack tip radius and A is a material constant of the dimensions of length. K_t was based on the value for an ellipse in a sheet of finite width, namely,

$$K_t = 1 + (K_H - 1)\left(\frac{c}{\rho}\right)^{\frac{1}{2}},$$

where c is the length of the semi-major axis of the ellipse and K_H the elastic stress concentration factor for a hole of radius c in a sheet of the same width. Thus, K_N for a crack of length a equal to c was obtained by substituting for K_t, and assuming further that the effective crack root radius ρ was equal to the constant A gave

$$K_N = 1 + \tfrac{1}{2}(K_H - 1)\left(\frac{a}{A}\right)^{\frac{1}{2}}.$$

The functional relationship between growth rate and $K_N \sigma_{Na}$ and, incidentally, A could only be obtained from analysis of experimental data. This concept is equivalent [8, 81] to the use of stress intensity factors.

5.6.4. Accumulated strain hypothesis

Various hypotheses based on an element of material ahead of the crack tip fracturing when it has accumulated some critical amount of plastic deformation have been put forward. As an example [82] consider the case of a central crack transverse to the loading direction in a thin sheet subjected to a zero to maximum loading cycle, and assume that an elementary length of material ε ahead of the crack fractures as an entity when the average repeated tensile strain accumulated by the element reaches some critical value. Assuming that the average strain across the element is not appreciably different from that obtained by considering the material as wholly elastic, the average elastic stress across ε can be written as

$$\bar{\sigma} = A\sigma_{max}\left(\frac{a}{\varepsilon}\right)^{\frac{1}{2}},$$

where A is a factor depending on specimen and crack geometry and σ_{max} is the maximum gross area stress in the loading cycle. The average strain can therefore be written as

$$\bar{e} = \frac{A}{E}\sigma_{max}\left(\frac{a}{\varepsilon}\right)^{\frac{1}{2}},$$

where E is Young's modulus. Because the relationship between strain amplitude and number of cycles has been shown from constant strain amplitude fatigue tests on plain specimens to conform to [82] $\mathrm{d}N\bar{e}^n = C$, where C is a material constant, the rate of growth is given by

$$\frac{\mathrm{d}a}{\mathrm{d}N} = \frac{\varepsilon}{\mathrm{d}N} = \frac{\varepsilon(\bar{e})^n}{C}$$

$$= \frac{\varepsilon^{1-n/2}}{C}\left(\frac{A\sigma}{E}\right)^n a^{n/2}.$$

Thus, for a given test on a particular material, the growth rate is proportional to $a^{n/2}$, where n is obtained from constant strain amplitude data on plain specimens of the same material. At different stress levels the rate will be proportional to $(\sigma a^{\frac{1}{2}})^n$, that is, proportional to some function of the stress intensity factor.

5.6.5. Dislocation theories

In the case of a crack loaded in anti-plane strain (Mode III), the plastic zone at its tip can be conveniently represented by a continuously distributed array of infinitesimal dislocations on the crack plane. Theories based on dislocation arrays assume that crack growth will start when the accumulated plastic strain distribution at a crack tip exceeds a critical value, and continues as this value is exceeded at successive points ahead of the original crack tip. At some point in a theory it is then assumed that behaviour in Mode I is similar to behaviour in Mode III. In general, [83] such theories predict that the rate of crack growth is proportional to K_I^4. As an example Weertman's theory [84] took as a starting point a model [85] of a freely slipping crack subjected to an applied shear. In the model a crack of length $2a$ having plastic zones at either end was considered and dislocation theory used to calculate the displacement in the vicinity of the crack tips due to this shear stress. It was then shown that under certain conditions a crack lying normal to a tensile stress σ can be considered in a similar manner. It was assumed that, under cyclic loading, it would grow when the sum of the absolute values of cyclic displacement at the current crack tip exceeded some critical value D_1. For a repeated tensile loading 0 to $\sigma_{\max}$ such that $\sigma_{\max} \leqslant \sigma_Y$ an expression for D_1 in terms of a, σ_Y, $\sigma_{\max}$ and N (number of cycles) was derived. Consideration of the rate at which the crack grows per stress cycle in terms of this displacement sum finally lead to the expression

$$\mathrm{d}a = \frac{a^2\sigma_{\max}^4}{D_1 E \sigma_Y^3},$$

where $\mathrm{d}a$ is the extension per cycle, and E is Young's modulus. Therefore

$$\frac{\mathrm{d}a}{\mathrm{d}N} \propto (\sigma_{\max} a^{\frac{1}{2}})^4$$

but
$$\sigma_{\max}(\pi a)^{\frac{1}{2}} = K_{\mathrm{I}}$$

(or ΔK for the load cycle considered), that is,

$$\frac{\mathrm{d}a}{\mathrm{d}N} \propto K_{\mathrm{I}}^4.$$

5.6.6. Energy theories

The energy associated with the plastic zone at a crack tip is proportional to K_{I}^4, so that theories based on the energy required to operate the fracture mechanism in general, will predict that the rate of crack growth is proportional to K_{I}^4, in agreement with dislocation theories.

For instance, a theory can be based [24] on a rigid-plastic strip model where the cracked body becomes two elastic half planes joined together along a strip of rigid-plastic material, with a void in the strip to simulate the crack. Tracing the deformation history of a particular point ahead of the crack tip, from when the plastic zone first reaches it to the time it is reached by the crack tip, it is assumed that the separation occurs when the total absorbed hysteresis energy U per newly created surface area equals a postulated critical value U_c. Letting $\Delta U_y(x, 0)$ be the plastic displacements of the discrete surface of tensile yielding per load reversal when the crack tip is at $x = 0$, and assuming then that the growth rate is constant while crossing a zone w of reversed deformation, the growth rate is given by

$$\frac{\mathrm{d}a}{\mathrm{d}N} = \frac{4\sigma_{\mathrm{Y}}}{U} \int_0^w \Delta U_y(x, 0)\, \mathrm{d}x,$$

where σ_{Y} is the yield stress. This leads to

$$\frac{\mathrm{d}a}{\mathrm{d}N} = \frac{5\pi(1-\nu^2)\varepsilon_{\mathrm{Y}}\sigma_{\mathrm{Y}}}{96 U_c}\left(\frac{\Delta K}{\sigma_{\mathrm{Y}}}\right)^4,$$

where ε_{Y} is the yield strain, that is,

$$\frac{\mathrm{d}a}{\mathrm{d}N} \propto (\Delta K)^4.$$

5.6.7. Frost and Dixon's theory

Frost and Dixon [86] argued that the absence of evidence to support internal cracking ahead of the crack tip in a homogeneous material (internal cracking may occur in a material in which inclusions or other inhomogenities give rise to elements of fast fracture occurring in the growth process), together with the fact that crack growth cannot be considered merely a consequence of the slip process which lead to the initiation of a surface microcrack, lead to the conclusion that a crack grows because its tip profile is successively blunted and resharpened each stress cycle. The unloading half of the stress cycle is essential to the growth process for, unless the crack tip is resharpened each cycle, fresh surfaces cannot be created during the process of crack tip blunting when the load is re-applied. It is not necessary for the material to be unloaded to zero in order for the crack tip to resharpen, because compressive residual stresses of the order of the yield stress of the material will be induced at the crack tip as soon as an increment of load is removed from the maximum load applied [74]. These compressive residual stresses will tend to sharpen the crack tip. Thus the profile of a crack in a ductile material loaded from 0 to σ_1 will be different from that loaded from 0 to σ_2, where $\sigma_2 > \sigma_1$, and then unloaded to σ_1, because in the former case the crack tip will be blunted, whereas in the second case the compressive residual stresses induced during the unloading from σ_2 to σ_1 will tend to sharpen the crack tip.

Fresh surfaces can be created in two ways as the crack tip blunts. First, the deformation necessary to accommodate the blunted tip profile may not all be reversible so that, on removal of the load, some of the deformed material remains and adds to the crack length. Secondly, an element of material at the crack tip may cleave as soon as the load is applied, which will create fresh surfaces in addition to those created by irreversible deformation. The environment might also influence the amount that the crack grows each cycle, a corrosive environment increasing the increment of growth by chemically attacking the material at the crack tip, whereas an inert environment might result in a decrease in the increment of growth by allowing some proportion of the freshly created surfaces at the tip to rebond when the crack is unloaded. A valid crack growth theory must be based therefore on a detailed knowledge of the geometry of the changing crack tip profile in terms of the amount of cleavage and irreversible deformation which must occur to accommodate the loaded blunt profile, with due allowance being made for any rebonding of the freshly created surfaces, which may occur when the crack is unloaded. At the present time the development of such a theory is not possible, but Frost and Dixon [86] argued that, as a starting point, the geometry of the crack tip profile, for a given loading cycle, would be determined to a first approximation by the elastic opening of the crack. They considered the case of a central transverse crack of length $2a$ in an infinite plate undergoing a repeated stress cycle $0-\sigma$; changes in crack profile were assumed to follow broadly the pattern shown in Fig. 5.19. Under the stress σ, a crack in an elastic sheet opens up into an ellipse; the stress distribution around this ellipse was calculated using the elastic solution for an elliptical hole, and it was assumed that the part of the elliptical profile which was subjected to a tensile stress retained this length when the load was removed. The rate of crack growth was then given by

$$\frac{da}{dN} = \frac{\sigma^2 a}{E^2}\left(\ln\frac{4E}{\sigma} - 1\right).$$

A typical value of $(\ln 4E/\sigma - 1)$ was 8, so that

$$\frac{da}{dN} = \frac{8\sigma^2 a}{E^2}. \tag{5.12}$$

Writing eqn (5.12) in terms of the range of stress intensity factor, (for an infinite plate $K_I = \sigma(\pi a)^{\frac{1}{2}}$) gives

$$\frac{da}{dN} = \frac{8}{\pi}\left(\frac{\Delta K}{E}\right)^2. \tag{5.13}$$

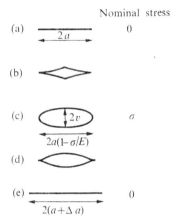

FIG. 5.19. Sequence of crack opening and closing under the repeated loading cycle $0-\sigma$. The sequence (a)–(e) is repeated for each successive cycle. (Taken from Frost and Dixon [86].)

This conforms with the assumption [24, 86] that, if continuum elastic variables alone control the extension per cycle at a crack tip,

$$\frac{da}{dN} \propto (\Delta K)^2,$$

a result which can be obtained using dimensional analysis and is an extension of the geometrical similarity hypotheses (§ 5.6.2). Any other result can be obtained only by the insertion of a characteristic dimension: in Head's theory (§ 5.6.1) the characteristic length for the rigid-plastic tensile bars ahead of the crack leads to a dependence on $(\Delta K)^3$. Frost and Dixon corrected eqn (5.12) for plasticity effects by the use of an experimentally determined relationship for estimating the total elastic–plastic strains around a crack in a non-work-hardening elastic–plastic material.

This leads to

$$\frac{da}{dN} = \frac{256\sigma_a^3 a}{E^2\sigma_Y},$$

where σ_a is the alternating stress and σ_Y the yield stress. The equation only holds when $\sigma_a > \sigma_Y/8$. The $\sigma_a^3 a$ dependence occurs because of the implicit introduction of the major axis of the ellipse as a characteristic length. This equation can be written as

$$\frac{da}{dN} = A\sigma_a^3 a. \tag{5.14}$$

Tomkins [87] has proposed a rather different elastic-plastic deformation theory based on a decohesion mechanism, which also leads to eqn (5.14).

Eqn (5.14) implies that any value of σ_a, no matter how low, will result in a positive value of da/dN. However, in §§ 4.5.4 and 4.7.2 it is shown that a minimum value of the parameter $\sigma_a^3 a (= C)$ must be exceeded before a crack of a given length will begin to grow. For mild steel, C tends to a minimum value of 14 as the mean stress is increased. If it is argued that a crack must remain dormant if the crack opening per cycle is insufficient to create a new surface length at the crack tip equal to one lattice spacing, substituting appropriate values in eqn (5.14), that is, $da/dN = 2.9 \times 10^{-7}$ mm per cycle, $A = 0.024 \times 10^6$ (Table 5.4, § 5.7) should give a value of $\sigma_a^3 a$ approaching 14. Hence, $2.9 \times 10^{-7} = 0.024 \times 10^{-6} \sigma_a^3 a$, and therefore $\sigma_a^3 a = 12$, a value which is surprisingly close to the experimentally determined value.

5.6.8. A fracture-mechanics crack growth theory

Frost and Dixon's theory can be re-expressed in fracture-mechanics terms [88] with eqn (5.13) derived directly from the stress and displacement fields around cracks and sharp notches. These predict that the crack opens up into a parabola. Following the original theory, consider the stress at the periphery of a parabolic notch having the same profile as this parabola. Unlike the original theory for an elliptic-shaped crack, peripheral stresses fall to zero at infinity. Thus, to formulate a growth law, a different fracture criterion is required. This is achieved by assuming that the part of the crack profile subjected to a tensile stress greater than the yield stress retains its length on unloading. For typical values of E/σ_Y, this leads to

$$\frac{da}{dN} = \frac{9}{\pi}\left(\frac{K_I}{E}\right)^2 \tag{5.15}$$

for plane stress and

$$\frac{da}{dN} = \frac{7}{\pi}\left(\frac{K_I}{E}\right)^2 \tag{5.16}$$

for plane strain. Values for the constants are only weakly dependent on E/σ_Y. This is very similar to Frost and Dixon's original result, but with the important generalization that its derivation does not depend on a particular geometry.

In the case of a completely tensile stress cycle, the resharpening on unloading means that, provided the crack has been growing for a number of cycles, the profile changes are independent of mean stress, so that K_I in eqs. (5.15) and (5.16) can be replaced by ΔK.

By assuming the von Mises yield criterion, the theory can be extended to Mode III or a combination of Modes I and III, but cannot be applied to Mode II. In Mode II, stresses and displacements are antisymmetrical about the crack plane; hence an increase in profile length on one crack surface is balanced by a decrease on the opposite surface. Crack growth on 45° planes can be treated by making some simplifying assumptions leading to

$$\frac{\mathrm{d}a}{\mathrm{d}N} \approx \frac{13}{\pi}\left(\frac{K}{E}\right)^2,$$

which implies a faster rate of growth than eqn (5.15).

If hard intermetallics or particles are present, as in high-strength aluminium alloys, the increased tendency of these to fracture as the maximum stress intensity factor during the fatigue cycle $K_{\max}$ increases results in mean stress dependence. A similar effect is produced by small-scale residual stresses [89] normal to the crack plane; these will locally increase or decrease the tensile mean stress, depending on their sign. Increasing the local tensile mean stress will not affect the rate of crack growth, but a decrease will cause the crack to slow or stop, thus decreasing the average growth rate. Increasing the over-all tensile mean stress will progressively overcome compressive residual stresses and increase the average growth rate.

As with Frost and Dixon's theory, the final eqn (5.15) implies that any value of ΔK, no matter how low, will result in a positive value of $\mathrm{d}a/\mathrm{d}N$. It has been shown experimentally (§§ 4.5.4 and 4.7.2) that a minimum value ΔK_c of ΔK is necessary for crack growth to occur, and that this appears to be associated with the minimum possible fatigue crack growth rate of one lattice spacing per cycle. Continuum mechanics provides only a rough guide to behaviour at crack growth rates of this order; nevertheless, for the zero to tension loading case ΔK_c can be estimated by substituting the lattice spacing into eqn (5.15). The resulting values are between one-fifth and one-half of those obtained experimentally.

5.6.9. Correlation with experiment

Experimental assessment of the validity of a fatigue crack growth theory is difficult: data can usually be found in the literature to either support or vitiate any particular theory. Thus the fact that experimental evidence is cited in support of a theory does not guarantee its validity. In addition, the theories mostly relate to a zero to tensile stress loading cycle, whereas much data, especially on sheet specimens, are obtained under the stress cycle $\sigma_m \pm \sigma_a$, where $\sigma_m > \sigma_a$. None of the theories predict the effect of a mean tensile stress.

The only crack growth data available to Head had been obtained from surface measurements of cracks in cylindrical rotating bending steel specimens [90, 91], of 7·6 mm and 15·2 mm diameter. However, he found that the data could be plotted linearly on $a^{-\frac{1}{2}}$ versus N axes, thus conforming to his proposed growth rate relationship. There are other data scattered throughout the literature which appear to conform to Head's relationship. For example, tests on constant width, clad 2024 aluminium alloy sheets [31] subjected to varying stress amplitudes at a constant mean tensile stress gave growth rates conforming to

$$\frac{da}{dN} = A a^{1·5} \sigma_a^{2·6}.$$

Under various mean stresses the growth rate found in sheet specimens, 160 mm wide, of $4\frac{1}{2}\%$ Cu (2024) and $5\frac{1}{2}\%$ Zn (7075) aluminium alloys were given by the equation

$$\frac{da}{dN} = A_1 \exp(-A_2 R)\sigma_{max}^3 a^{1·5}\left(1 + \frac{40a^2}{W^2}\right),$$

where A_1 and A_2 are constants, $R = (\sigma_m - \sigma_a)/(\sigma_m + \sigma_a)$, $\sigma_{max} = \sigma_m + \sigma_a$, and $(1 + 40a^2/W^2)$ is an empirical correction factor to allow for the influence of the crack length/sheet width ratio; again, these results conform with Head's theory.

Rotating bending tests using soft aluminium plain specimens [92], 0·4% C steel plain specimens [93] heat-treated to three different strength levels, and sharply notched chromium–nickel alloy steel specimens [94] gave data supporting the geometrical similarity hypothesis. For the aluminium, a test was stopped at intervals, and a replica of the surface taken to determine crack lengths after various numbers of cycles. For the 0·4% C steel, crack lengths were recorded photographically, whereas the chromium–nickel alloy steel specimens were removed from the fatigue machine after various endurances and broken, so that crack depth could be measured. In each case, it was found that the rate of crack growth at a given stress level was proportional to crack size.

Tests have been carried out on a wide range of materials using sheet specimens 254 mm wide by about 2·5 mm thick, containing a central transverse crack [27, 32–4, 42]. For half-crack lengths up to about 18 mm, the crack can be regarded as growing in an infinite sheet [42], and in this region it was found that the logarithm of the crack length varied linearly with the number of cycles (Fig. 5.20) thus implying $da/dN = Da$. The tests were carried out under the stress cycle $\sigma_m \pm \sigma_a$, where $\sigma_m > \sigma_a$, and the coefficient D was found to depend on σ_a^3, thus $da/dN = A\sigma_a^3 a$, where A was not markedly dependent on mean stress, except for the high-strength aluminium alloy (see Table 5.4, § 5.7).

Tests [77] on 2 mm thick $4\frac{1}{2}\%$ Cu– and clad $5\frac{1}{2}\%$ Zn–aluminium alloy specimens from 22 mm to 170 mm wide supported Weibull's net area stress theory. A zero to tension load cycle was used, and cracks were grown from a central notch whose over-all length was one-eighth of the sheet width. The net area stress was kept constant, and the crack length (measured from the sheet centre line) varied linearly with the number of cycles, including over-all crack lengths up to 60–80 per cent of the sheet width; slopes of

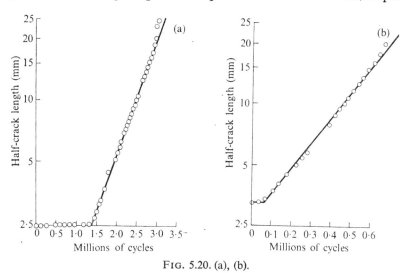

FIG. 5.20. (a), (b).

a versus N lines were proportional to sheet width as predicted. Some of the results are shown in Fig. 5.21. There was an initial period of slow crack growth in some tests, particularly in the $5\frac{1}{2}\%$ Zn alloy. The theory was also supported by constant net section stress tests on edge-notched mild steel plates [95] and centre-crack 0.25% C steel plates [96]. However, tests [39] on 160 mm wide by 2 mm thick 2024 aluminium alloy sheets with a central slit, 6 mm over-all length, using various net section stresses, showed that plotting crack length against number of cycles produced a curve. The theory implies that, if crack growth rate is expressed in the non-dimensional form $d(a/W)/dN$, it should be independent of sheet width, but tests [78] using various specimen widths showed that it was faster for wide sheets. McEvily and Illg's net area stress theory is supported by some crack propagation tests which were carried out on 51 mm and 305 mm wide thin sheets of $4\frac{1}{2}\%$ Cu– and $5\frac{1}{2}\%$ Zn–aluminium alloys [80]; each specimen had a small central hole to initiate fatigue cracks and was subjected to a zero to tension loading cycle. It was found that, by plotting the instantaneous value of $K_N\sigma_{Na}$ against the corresponding rate of crack growth, the points obtained from a series of tests at different maximum gross-area stresses on specimens of both widths of a

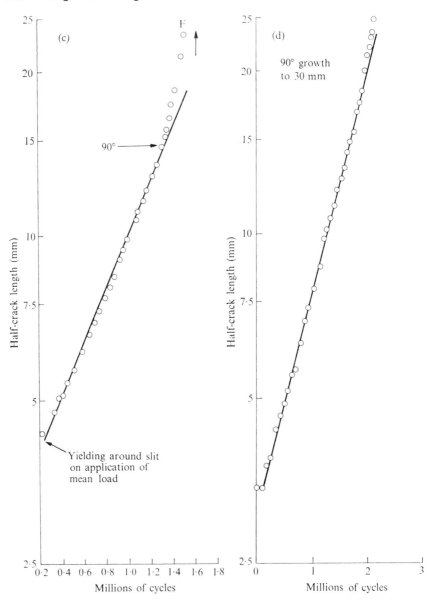

F IG. 5.20. Log half-crack length versus number of cycles for various materials. (a) Austeni-tic steel at 93 ± 43 MN m^{-2}. (b) Copper at 62 ± 31 MN m^{-2}. (c) Copper at 155 ± 23 MN m^{-2}. (d) Aluminium at 110 ± 12 MN m^{-2}. (Taken from Frost [32].)

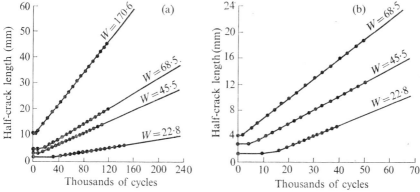

FIG. 5.21. Crack length versus number of cycles. (a) Tests on 24S−T ($4\frac{1}{2}$% Cu) aluminium alloy sheets of different width W(mm). Stress cycle 0–118 MN m⁻² on net section maintained constant throughout test. (b) Tests on 75S−T ($5\frac{1}{2}$% Zn) aluminium alloy sheets of different width W(mm). Stress cycle 0–118 MN m⁻² on net section maintained constant throughout test. (Taken from Weibull [77].)

given material fell around the same smooth curve. Their results for the $5\frac{1}{2}$% Zn–aluminium are shown on Fig. 5.22. The dotted line in each diagram has the equation

$$\log \frac{da}{dN} = 0\cdot000725 K_N \sigma_{Na} - 4\cdot067 - \frac{234}{K_N \sigma_{Na} - 234}.$$

Experimental data supporting the $(\Delta K)^4$ dependency of growth rate predicted by both dislocation and energy theories can be found in the literature.

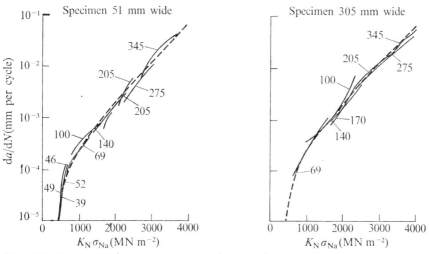

FIG. 5.22. Crack growth rate versus $K_N \sigma_{Na}$ for a $5\frac{1}{2}$% Zn–aluminium alloy. Figures on diagrams are the maximum stress in the loading cycle in MN m⁻². (Taken from Hardrath and McEvily [80].)

For example, tests [18] on steel, aluminium alloy, titanium, and magnesium sheet have shown that

$$\frac{\mathrm{d}a}{\mathrm{d}N} = D(\Delta K)^4,$$

where D is a material constant. A similar result was obtained for 70/30 brass thin-sheet specimens [97]; D had the same value for both the cold-rolled and annealed conditions. Some crack propagation tests [78] on 2024-T3 alclad sheets (3 mm thick), varying in width from 80 mm to 600 mm, have been carried out with a tensile mean stress of 78 MN m^{-2} and gross-area alternating stresses of ± 26 MN m^{-2}, ± 39 MN m^{-2}, and ± 64 MN m^{-2}. The results for each stress level in general confirmed the relationship $\mathrm{d}a/\mathrm{d}N = D(\Delta K)^4$, but D did not have the same value at each stress level.

On the other hand, data can be found in the literature which do not conform to this relationship. For example, data obtained from $2\frac{1}{2}\%$ Cu, $1\frac{1}{2}\%$ Mg aluminium alloy sheets [98], ranging in width from 76 mm to 508 mm and containing a small central transverse slit, could not be correlated adequately on a stress intensity factor basis.

The rate of growth of a fatigue crack from an edge-notch in the upper face of a 12·7 mm thick, 25·4 mm deep, beam has been measured [99] using an essentially repeated bending loading cycle. The value of the maximum stress intensity factor K_{max} necessary during the fatigue cycle to cause a crack to grow at a given rate in various different materials showed that, for a given growth rate, K_{max}/E (where E is Young's modulus) appeared to be a constant. For example, for a growth rate of $2·5 \times 10^{-4}$ mm per cycle, K_{max}/E had values varying only from $4·8 \times 10^{-5}$ m$^{\frac{1}{2}}$ to $6·5 \times 10^{-5}$ m$^{\frac{1}{2}}$ for various magnesium alloys, aluminium alloy, brass, titanium alloy, and steels, the growth rate for all materials being given by

$$\frac{\mathrm{d}a}{\mathrm{d}N} = 6·48 \times 10^{11} \left(\frac{K_{\mathrm{max}}}{E}\right)^{3·6},$$

where K_{max} is in MN m$^{-\frac{3}{2}}$, E is in MN m^{-2}, and $\mathrm{d}a/\mathrm{d}N$ is in mm per cycle. The results were taken as confirming the view that fatigue crack growth is a strain-controlled process.

A survey of the fatigue crack growth characteristics of structural steels with yield strengths ranging from 250 MN m^{-2} to 1320 MN m^{-2} [100] showed that these were largely independent of steel strength, as predicted by the fracture-mechanics crack growth theory. For ferrite–pearlite steels, the data all fell on one scatter band, whose lower limit was given by $\mathrm{d}a/\mathrm{d}N = 6·89 \times 10^{-9} (\Delta K)^3$, where $\mathrm{d}a/\mathrm{d}N$ is in millimetres and ΔK in MN m$^{-\frac{3}{2}}$. At a crack growth rate of 10^{-6} mm per cycle, the corresponding value of ΔK is 5·3 MN m$^{-\frac{3}{2}}$, which may be compared with a value of 6·2 MN m$^{-\frac{3}{2}}$ for the centre line of the scatter band for mild steel (Table 5.5, § 5.7). Similarly, the lower limit of the band for martensitic steels was given by $da/dN = 1 \cdot 36 \times 10^{-7} (\Delta K)^{2 \cdot 25}$; crack growth rates were somewhat faster than in the ferrite–pearlite steels.

5.7. Fatigue crack growth data for various materials

During the last fifteen years, numerous 'laws' of fatigue crack growth have been published [4]; some of these have been described in § 5.6. All are equally valid in the sense that their originator considered that they accurately represented a set of fatigue crack growth data, although other data can often be found to refute any particular theory. It is also usually possible to fit the same set of fatigue crack growth data to apparently contradictory crack propagation laws. The choice of a particular method of analysis is therefore a matter of the convenience with which the data can be subsequently applied to practical problems. On these grounds, the use of stress intensity factors is to be preferred. Once a master curve relating fatigue crack growth rate and range of stress intensity factor is available for a particular material, a designer can predict crack growth rates for any cracked body configuration, and is not limited to situations similar to those used to generate the original data.

A fracture-mechanics method of analysis using stress intensity factors is described below and illustrated by fatigue crack growth data for a wide variety of metallic materials obtained using 254 mm wide panels about 2·5 mm thick, subjected to the general tensile stress cycle $(\sigma_m \pm \sigma_a)$, where $\sigma_m > \sigma_a$, cracks being grown from both ends of a small transverse central slit. The results were originally analysed [27, 32–4, 42] using eqn (5.14), namely, $da/dN = A\sigma_a^3 a$ where a is the average half-crack length measured from the centre line of the sheet, and A is a material constant which may or may not depend on σ_m. Details of the materials concerned and the values of A obtained are shown in Table 5.4.

All the experimental data in references [27], [32–4], and [42] pertaining to cracks of over-all lengths of up to 100 mm were used in the fracture mechanics analysis [26]. Curves were fitted to the basic crack length versus number of cycles data for each specimen, and crack growth rates obtained from the appropriate slopes. The stress intensity factor for a central transverse crack in a sheet of finite width is given by:

$$K_I = \sigma(\pi a)^{\frac{1}{2}} \left\{ 1 - \left(\frac{2a}{W} \right)^2 \right\}^{-\frac{1}{2}},$$

where σ is gross area stress, W is specimen width and $\{1-(2a/W)^2\}^{-\frac{1}{2}}$ is Dixon's finite width correction [101]. Although other finite width corrections could be used for the values of $2a/W$ up to 0·4 used here, they do not differ by more than 1 per cent or 2 per cent from Dixon's. Owing to the large

17

TABLE 5.4

Material	Sheet thickness (mm)	Tensile strength (MN m⁻²)	Tensile mean stress, σ_m (MN m⁻²)	A†
Mild steel (0·05 % C)	3·25	325	31–201	0·024
Cold-rolled mild	2·03	695	77–108	0·033
steel (0·07 % C)			232–386	0·060
18/8 austenitic steel	3·43	665	77–139	0·016
			232	0·030
Copper, annealed	3·25	215	31–77	0·10
Copper, cold-rolled	3·25	310	31–185	0·10
Brass (70/30)	3·25	400	62–124	0·095
Titanium (99·9 %)	3·25	555	46–340	0·33
5 % Al–titanium alloy	3·05	835	124–432	0·22
15 % Mo–titanium alloy	3·25	1160	124–340	0·35
			425	0·60
Zinc (99 %)	2·16	125	15–46	3·5
Aluminium (99·8 %)	3·25	155	31–46	0·30
			77–108	0·54
Aluminium alloy HS30W	2·90	265	46	0·41
(solution treated)			124	0·76
Aluminium alloy HS30WP	2·90	310	46–77	0·92
			124–185	1·35
5 % Mg–aluminium alloy	3·25	310	46	0·71
			124	1·4
			170–185	2·2
4½ % Cu–aluminium alloy	4·06	480	31	0·41
(BS L71)	2·03		46–62	0·81
			232	3·3
			355	4·6
5½ % Zn–aluminium alloy	3·25	540	31–77	2·2
(DTD 687A) longitudinal		Initial growth	124	4·6
specimens			216–247	9·0
		Secondary growth	31–77	4·3
			124	13
5½ % Zn–aluminium alloy		Initial growth	46	2·2
(DTD 687A) transverse			124	5·4
specimens			232	16
		Secondary growth	46	4·9
			124	18

† $\mathrm{d}a/\mathrm{d}N$ in 10^{-6} mm per cycle, σ_a in MN m⁻², and a in metres.

amounts of data involved, the results obtained are plotted as scatter bands of $\mathrm{d}a/\mathrm{d}N$ against ΔK in the Figures. The boundaries of the bands are the approximate 90 per cent confidence limits for the data. The transition from crack growth on a 90° plane through the specimen thickness to crack growth on a 45° plane, which usually occurred as a crack grew, has been ignored in the analysis; the transition tends to increase the crack growth rate and contributes to scatter. The results only apply strictly to the sheet thickness used in the tests, but, because crack growth rates normally increase at the transition (§ 5.3.2), they will tend to be conservative if applied to thicker material.

A plastic zone develops at the tip of a crack in a ductile metal, its approximate radius r_p being given by the expression (eqn (5.3), § 5.2.4)

$$r_p = \frac{1}{2\pi}\left(\frac{K_I}{\sigma_Y}\right)^2$$

for plane stress, and one-third of this amount for plane strain. Provided that r_p is small compared with the half-crack length a and that the maximum net section stress σ_N does not exceed $0.8\sigma_Y$ (σ_Y = yield stress), the plastic zone has little effect on the over-all elastic stress field; if required, a correction can be made by adding r_p to a when calculating K_I. Assuming plane stress conditions are appropriate for the thin sheets tested, then $r_p \approx a/7$, for a gross stress $\sigma = 0.5\,\sigma_Y$, which can be regarded as small, and for the range of $2a/W$ used, the net section stress σ_N does not exceed $0.83\,\sigma_Y$. Data were regarded therefore as valid provided that the maximum gross stress $\sigma_{max} = \sigma_m + \sigma_a$ during the fatigue cycle did not exceed $0.5\,\sigma_Y$ (where σ_Y is taken as the 0.1 per cent proof stress).

A correction for the plastic zone can be made to ΔK using eqn (5.3), but with K_I replaced by ΔK and σ_Y by $2\sigma_Y$ (§ 5.2.4); this correction would not exceed 2 per cent for the present data. Even when there is general yielding on the net section, unloading deformations will be entirely elastic, provided that σ_a is small, so that ΔK can still be used in the analysis of fatigue crack growth rates. Data to which this argument could be applied but for which $\sigma_{max} > 0.5\sigma_Y$ are referred to as 'invalid'; in some cases, these fell within the valid data scatter bands. Bands, or parts of bands, containing only 'invalid' data are indicated by dotted lines on the Figures. For some materials, the data fell into more than one band depending on their validity and the value of the stress ratio $R = (\sigma_m - \sigma_a)/(\sigma_m + \sigma_a)$. Separate bands were also sometimes obtained for invalid data, depending on whether the maximum net section stress was near to or well above the yield stress. The bands were generally straight so that the expression $da/dN = D(\Delta K)^m$ (Eqn (5.5), § 5.2.5) could be used to represent the data. The centre line of each band was used to obtain values of both the exponent m in this expression, and ΔK for a crack growth rate of 10^{-6} mm per cycle; these are given in Table 5.5.

For many materials m is seen to be close to 3, which agrees with Head's theory (§ 5.6.1) and implies that $da/dN \propto \sigma_a^3 a^{1.5}$, compared with $da/dN \propto \sigma_a^3 a$ predicted by Frost and Dixon's theory (§ 5.6.7). The relatively slight differences between these two expressions explains why both the original method and the fracture mechanics method were equally successful in correlating a large body of data.

As crack growth does not take place unless a critical value of ΔK, that is, ΔK_c, is exceeded (§§ 4.6.1 and 4.7.2), a theoretical minimum crack growth

TABLE 5.5

Tests to determine rate of crack growth

Material	Tensile strength (MN m⁻²)	0·1 per cent proof stress (MN m⁻²)	Nominal R	Tests with $\sigma_{max} \leqslant 0.5\sigma_Y$	Tests with $\sigma_{max} > 0.5\sigma_Y$	m	ΔK for $\frac{da}{dN} = 10^{-6}$ mm per cycle (MN m⁻³⁄²)	Minimum crack growth rate (nm per cycle)		Lattice spacing (nm)
								Observed (lower limit of bands)	Calculated	
Mild steel (Fig. 5.24)	325	230	0·34	10 tests $R = 0.14$–0.54	46 tests $R = 0.06$–0.74	3·3	6·2	0·3	0·6	0·29
Cold-rolled mild steel (Fig. 5.35)	695	655	0·25	24 tests $R = 0.07$–0.43	1 test $R = 0.36$ $\sigma_N \approx \sigma_Y$ (top of band)	4·2	7·2			
			0·65	7 tests $R = 0.54$–0.76		5·5	6·4			
			0·84	5 tests $R = 0.75$–0.92	5 tests $R = 0.79$–0.92	6·4	5·2			
18/8 austenitic steel (Fig. 5.34)	665	195–225	0·43	2 tests $R = 0.43$	2 tests $R = 0.33$–0.37 $\sigma_N \approx \sigma_Y$	3·1	6·3	0·35	0·3	0·36
			0·45		15 tests $R = 0.18$–0.81 $\sigma_N > \sigma_Y$	3·2	4·0			

Material				Tests					
Aluminium (Fig. 5.23)	125–155	95–125	0.46	6 tests R = 0.33–0.60 20 tests R = 0.14–0.87 $\sigma_N > \sigma_Y$	2.9	2.9	0.5	0.3	0.4
5% Mg–aluminium alloy (Fig. 5.27)	310	180	0.44	5 tests R = 0.20–0.69	2.7	1.6			
			0.76	9 tests R = 0.60–0.92 $\sigma_N > \sigma_Y$	3.4	1.7			
Aluminium alloy HS30W (solution treated) (Fig. 5.28) (1% Mg, 1% Si, 0.7% Mn)	265	180	0.46	7 tests R = 0.20–0.71	2.6	1.9			
			0.66	4 tests R = 0.44–0.88 $\sigma_N \approx \sigma_Y$	3.5	1.8			
Aluminium alloy HS30WP (age hardened) (Fig. 5.30) (1% Mg, 1% Si, 0.7% Mn)	310	245–280	0.34	4 tests R = 0.25–0.43	3.9	2.6†			
			0.64	8 tests R = 0.50–0.78 $\sigma_N \approx \sigma_Y$ (top of band)	4.1	2.15			
			0.85	4 tests R = 0.82–0.88 4 tests R = 0.85–0.92 $\sigma_N > \sigma_Y$	4.2	1.6			
4½% Cu–aluminium alloy BS L71 (Fig. 5.31)	480	415)	0.30	8 tests R = 0.14–0.46	3.7	2.4	3.2	0.3	
4½% Cu–aluminium alloy clad BS L73 (Fig. 5.31)	435	370)	0.69	12 tests R = 0.50–0.88	4.4	2.1	0.5	0.1	
			0.86	11 tests R = 0.76–0.96 $\sigma_N > \sigma_Y$	4.7	1.55			

TABLE 5.5 (*Continued*)

Material	Tensile strength (MN m⁻²)	0·1 per cent proof stress (MN m⁻²)	Nominal R	Tests with $\sigma_{max} \leqslant 0.5\sigma_Y$	Tests with $\sigma_{max} > 0.5\sigma_Y$	m	ΔK for $\frac{da}{dN} = 10^{-6}$ mm per cycle (MN m⁻³⁄²)	Minimum crack growth rate (nm per cycle) Observed (lower limit of bands)	Calculated	Lattice spacing (nm)
5½% Zn–aluminium alloy clad DTD 687A (Fig. 5.32)	540	495	0·32	7 tests R = 0·20–0·45		3·7	1·75	2·5	2·4	
			0·64	22 tests R = 0·50–0·78	1 test R = 0·76 $\sigma_N \approx \sigma_Y$ (top of band)	4·2	1·8			
			0·90	11 tests R = 0·87–0·94	4 tests R = 0·82–0·84 $\sigma_N \approx \sigma_Y$ (top of band)	4·8	1·45			
Copper (annealed or cold-rolled)(Fig. 5.25)	215–310	26–215	0·34	17 tests R = 0·07–0·60	20 tests R = 0·08–0·82	3·9	4·3	0·4	0·013	0·36
Commercially pure titanium (Fig. 5.26)	555	440	0·48	18 tests R = 0·08–0·87	9 tests R = 0·04–0·94	4·4 (2·3)	3·1 (1·35)†	0·5	0·2	0·30(a)
5% Al–titanium alloy (Fig. 5.37)	385	735	0·56	10 tests R = 0·17–0·94	5 tests R = 0·63–0·86 $\sigma_N \approx \sigma_Y$	3·8 (2·5)	3·4 (1·5)†			0·47(c)
15% Mo–titanium alloy (Fig. 5.39)	1160	995	0·50	8 tests R = 0·28–0·71		3·5	3·0			
			0·88	8 tests R = 0·81–0·94		4·4	2·75			

† Extrapolated.

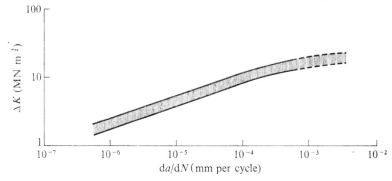

FIG. 5.23. ΔK versus da/dN for pure aluminium in longitudinal direction. (Taken from Frost, Pook, and Denton [26].)

rate can be calculated using the coefficients given in Table 5.5 by substitution of an appropriate value of ΔK_c (§ 4.7.2). The results obtained for all the materials for which data were available are shown in Table 5.5; the approximate slowest rate observed during a fatigue crack growth test and the lattice spacing for each material are shown for comparison. With the possible exception of copper, there appears to be a minimum possible crack growth rate of about one lattice spacing per cycle. Slower average crack growth rates would imply that crack growth was occurring over only a part of the crack front during one cycle, since an increment of less than one lattice spacing is not physically possible.

Johnson and Paris [102] have presented data for a $5\frac{1}{2}\%$ Zn–aluminium alloy which are claimed to show that average crack growth rates as low as 0·005 nm per cycle for $R \approx 0$ are possible. However, their data (Fig. 5.41, § 5.8) could equally well be interpreted as showing that $\Delta K_c = 2\cdot 2$ MN m$^{-\frac{3}{2}}$.

The data for aluminium (Fig. 5.23), mild steel (Fig. 5.24), and copper

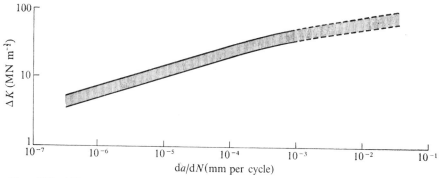

FIG. 5.24. ΔK versus da/dN for mild steel in longitudinal direction. (Taken from Frost, Pook, and Denton [26].)

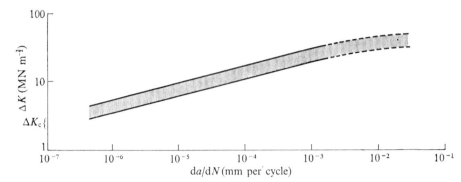

FIG. 5.25. ΔK versus da/dN for copper in longitudinal direction. (Taken from Frost, Pook, and Denton [26].)

(Fig. 5.25), fall into bands of similar shape, in each case the data fitting the band irrespective of the value of R or the validity of the data. This implies that the materials are not sensitive to mean stress and that the rate of growth is not affected by yielding on the net section, although at high values of ΔK the crack growth rate is faster than predicted by eqn (5.5), particularly for the invalid data at the top of each band. The behaviour of commercially pure titanium (Fig. 5.26) is similar except that there is a distinct discontinuity in

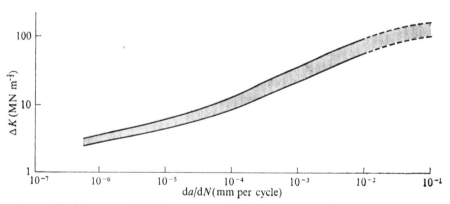

FIG. 5.26. ΔK versus da/dN for commercially pure titanium in longitudinal direction. (Taken from Frost, Pook, and Denton [26].)

the band at a growth rate of about 5×10^{-5} mm per cycle. The constants for the upper part of this band are shown in brackets in Table 5.5.

All the valid data for the 5% Mg–aluminium fall on the same band (Fig. 5.27) irrespective of the value of R, but the band for the invalid data, for which R was generally higher, is displaced to higher growth rates at high ΔK values, although it meets the valid band at low ΔK values. It is not clear whether this

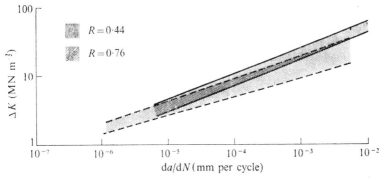

FIG. 5.27. ΔK versus da/dN for 5% Mg–aluminium alloy in longitudinal direction. (Taken from Frost, Pook, and Denton [26].)

displacement is caused by the increase in R or by yielding on the net section. The general behaviour of the aluminium alloy HS30W (Fig. 5.28) is similar to that of the 5% Mg–aluminium alloy except that the slope of both bands decreases at high ΔK values.

The centre lines of the bands from Figs. 5.23, 5.27, and 5.28 are compared on Fig. 5.29, which shows that all the valid data lie on the same band and can be represented by a 'master line' ($m = 2.7$, ΔK at 10^{-6} mm per cycle $= 1.7$ MN m$^{-\frac{3}{2}}$). All data that fall below this master line are invalid, and this suggests that in these materials yielding on the net section can increase the growth rate for a given ΔK value.

The valid data for the aluminium alloy HS30WP (Fig. 5.30), the $4\frac{1}{2}$% Cu–aluminium alloy (Fig. 5.31), and the $5\frac{1}{2}$% Zn–aluminium alloy (Fig. 5.32) all fall into distinct bands depending on the value of R, the rate of crack growth increasing as R increases. Invalid data all fall on the appropriate band, except that, in the case of the $4\frac{1}{2}$% Cu–aluminium alloy, the band for

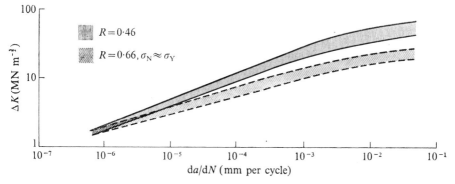

FIG. 5.28. ΔK versus da/dN for HS30W aluminium alloy in longitudinal direction. (Taken from Frost, Pook, and Denton [26].)

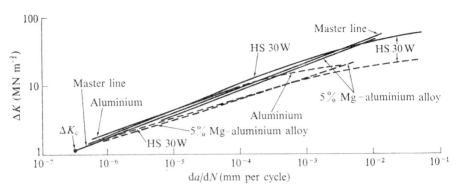

FIG. 5.29. Comparison of crack growth curves for aluminium and low-strength aluminium alloys. (Taken from Frost, Pook, and Denton [26].)

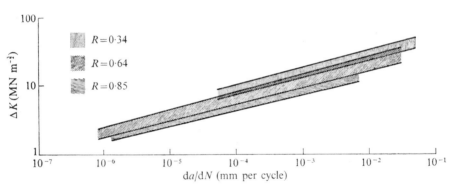

FIG. 5.30. ΔK versus da/dN for HS30WP aluminium alloy in longitudinal and transverse directions. (Taken from Frost, Pook, and Denton [26].)

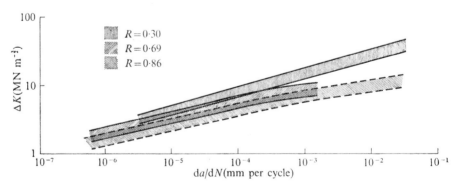

FIG. 5.31. ΔK versus da/dN for $4\frac{1}{2}$% Cu–aluminium alloy (BS L71 and L73) either clad or unclad, longitudinal direction. (Taken from Frost, Pook, and Denton [26].)

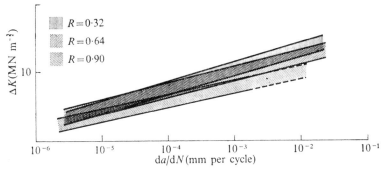

FIG. 5.32. ΔK versus $\mathrm{d}a/\mathrm{d}N$ for $5\frac{1}{2}\%$ Zn–aluminium alloy (DTD 687A) in longitudinal and transverse directions. (Taken from Frost, Pook, and Denton [26].)

invalid data is displaced slightly to higher crack growth rates at high values of R. The value of m varies from 3·7 to 4·8. The bands are compared with the master line for aluminium in Fig. 5.33; it is seen that, as ΔK is reduced, the bands meet the master line. It is clear that the mean stress sensitivity of the high-strength aluminium alloys is an inherent property of a particular alloy and is not due to net section yielding.

The limited number of tests at a single R value on the 18/8 austenitic stainless steel show that, provided the net area stress is not much above the yield stress, the behaviour (Fig. 5.34) is similar to that of mild steel. For the same R value, but with the net section stress well above the yield stress, the whole band is displaced to faster crack growth rates (Fig. 5.34), which again suggests that mean stress sensitivity can be caused by general yielding of the material.

The cold rolled mild steel (Fig. 5.35) behaves in a similar manner to the high strength aluminium alloys; the rate of crack growth increases as R

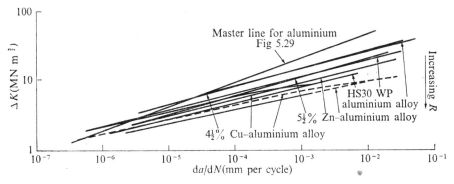

FIG. 5.33. Comparison of crack growth curves for high-strength aluminium alloys. (Taken from Frost, Pook, and Denton [26].)

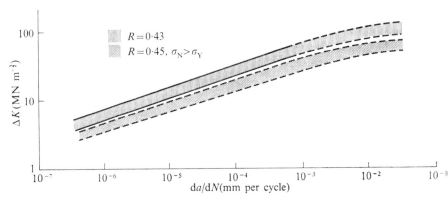

FIG. 5.34. ΔK versus da/dN for 18/8 austenitic steel in longitudinal direction. (Taken from Frost, Pook, and Denton [26].)

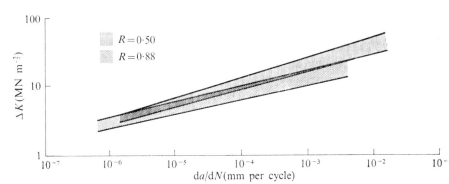

FIG. 5.35. ΔK versus da/dN for cold-rolled mild steel in longitudinal direction. (Taken from Frost, Pook, and Denton [26].)

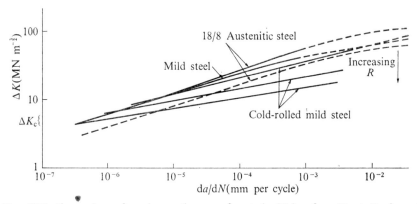

FIG. 5.36. Comparison of crack growth curves for steels. (Taken from Frost, Pook, and Denton [26].)

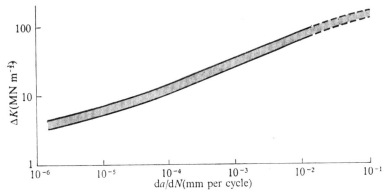

FIG. 5.37. ΔK versus da/dN for 5% Al–titanium alloy in longitudinal direction. (Taken from Frost, Pook, and Denton [26].)

increases, invalid data fall on the appropriate band and as ΔK is reduced, the individual bands meet the band for mild steel (Fig. 5.36).

The behaviour of the 5% Al–titanium alloy is similar to that of the commerically pure titanium (Figs. 5.37 and 5.38). In the case of the 15% Mo–titanium alloy, the crack growth rate increases as R increases (Fig. 5.39); at high ΔK the growth rate is faster than in pure titanium but the lower part of the band is similar to the lower part of the band for pure titanium (Fig. 5.38).

Most fatigue crack growth data are obtained by observation of fatigue cracks while they are growing. However, the initial rate of crack growth of a broken precracked specimen can be obtained by consideration of its total life (§ 5.5). Values of initial da/dN and initial ΔK were calculated from the results of the tests on edge-cracked plate specimens described in §§ 4.5.4 and

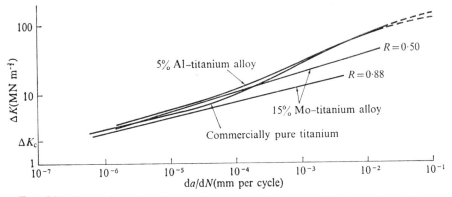

FIG. 5.38. Comparison of crack growth curves for titanium and titanium alloys. (Taken from Frost, Pook, and Denton [26].)

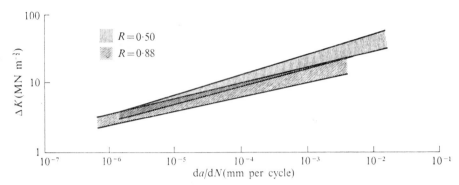

F IG. 5.39. ΔK versus da/dN for 15% Mo–titanium alloy in longitudinal direction. (Taken from Frost, Pook, and Denton [26].)

4.7.2 and, where sufficient data points were available, these were used to estimate m and ΔK for a crack growth rate of 10^{-6} mm per cycle. The values obtained [72] are shown in Table 5.6; in general, they apply to crack growth rates from about one lattice spacing per cycle up to about 3×10^{-5} mm per cycle. For similar materials they are in reasonable agreement with the test results obtained by conventional methods; see Table 5.5.

Because fatigue crack growth is a strain-controlled process, the behaviour of different metals would be expected to be similar if compared on the basis of strain instead of stress. This has been done in Fig. 5.40, where data for mild steel, copper, and titanium are compared on the basis of $\Delta K/E$, and shows this is indeed the case. Also included is a theoretical prediction (§ 5.6.8). High-strain fatigue crack growth is mentioned in § 6.1.5.

The growth behaviour of alloys, or of materials containing residual stresses,

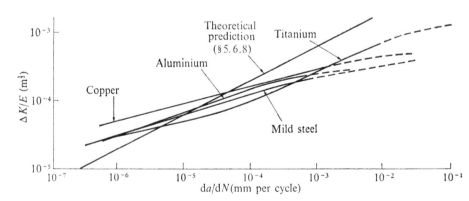

F IG. 5.40. Comparison of crack propagation curves on basis of $\Delta K/E$. (Taken from Frost, Pook, and Denton [26].)

TABLE 5.6

Fatigue crack growth data for various materials
(obtained indirectly—see § 5.5)

Material	Stress relief	Tensile strength (MN m⁻²)	R	m	ΔK for da/dN = 10⁻⁶ mm per cycle (MN m⁻³ᐟ²)
Mild steel	1 hour at 650 °C	430	−1, 0·13, 0·35, 0·49, 0·64	3·3	6·2
Low-alloy steel	1 hour at 570 °C	835	−1	3·3	6·2
	1 hour at 680 °C	680	0, 0·33, 0·50	3·3	5·1
			0·64, 0·75	3	3·5
Maraging steel	See footnote†	2010	0·67		
18/8 austenitic steel	1 hour at 600 °C	685	−1	3·1	6·3
	4 hours at 600 °C	665	0, 0·33, 0·62, 0·74		
Aluminium	1 hour at 320 °C	77	−1, 0, 0·33, 0·53	2·9	2·0
Copper	1 hour at 600 °C	225	−1	3·9	4·3
	1 hour at 700 °C	215	0, 0·33, 0·56, 0·69, 0·80		
Phosphor bronze	1 hour at 500 °C	325	−1	4	5·6
	1 hour at 550 °C	370	0·33, 0·50	3·9	4·3
			0·74		
60/40 brass	1 hour at 550 °C	330	−1	4	6·3
	1 hour at 550 °C	325	0, 0·33	3·9	4·3
			0·51, 0·72	4·4	3·6
Titanium	1 hour at 700 °C	540	0·60		
Nickel	1 hour at 500 °C	455	−1	4	8·8
	1 hour at 850 °C	430	0, 0·33, 0·57, 0·71		
Monel	1 hour at 500 °C	525	−1	4	6·2
	1 hour at 850 °C	525	0, 0·33, 0·50, 0·67		
Inconel	1 hour at 600 °C	655	−1	4	10·7
			0		
	2 hours at 800 °C	650	0·33, 0·57, 0·71	4	8·2

† Heat-treated 1 hour at 820 °C and air-cooled 3 hours at 480 °C; all heat-treatment after fatigue cracking.

can be regarded as a modification of the corresponding base metal behaviour. As R is increased both the crack growth rate and the value of the exponent m increase; as ΔK is reduced the curve of ΔK versus da/dN eventually meets the curve for the corresponding base metal. Macro-cleavage through brittle particles in the structure which do not permit the crack tip to blunt until it has passed right through them is believed to be responsible for the mean stress dependence of some materials, in particular the high-strength aluminium alloys. These materials, although having the same E as aluminium, exhibit faster crack growth rate characteristics which, moreover, are markedly dependent on the mean stress. The element of cracking per cycle in these alloys therefore may be determined by metallurgical as well as geometric considerations. The element of macro-cleavage occurring per cycle will be some function of inclusion size and spacing, as well as of mean and alternating stresses. Large inclusions widely dispersed could have the effect of making da/dN highly mean-stress dependent for small values of σ_a but much less mean-stress dependent for higher values of σ_a, whereas finely dispersed inclusions could make a material mean-stress dependent at all stress values. As mentioned in § 5.3, it has been found that the rate of crack growth in the matrix of two different aluminium alloys (determined from striation markings) was the same. The difference in over-all growth rates was due to the different amounts of cleavage cracking in the two alloys occurring each time the crack tip met a brittle second-phase particle or inclusion. This type of mean stress sensitivity should not be confused with the mean stress sensitivity due to net section yielding.

5.8. Threshold effects in fatigue crack growth

Provided that the increment of crack growth in each cycle is considerably greater than the atomic spacing, macrocrack growth can be regarded for most experimental and theoretical purposes, as taking place in a homogeneous continuum. However, if increments of crack growth of the order of the atomic spacing are to be considered, it is evident that a crack can no longer be regarded as growing in a continuum. An increment of crack growth of less than one atomic spacing is clearly impossible on physical grounds, and it follows that, if the applied cyclic stress is insufficient to cause crack growth at a rate of one atomic spacing per cycle, the crack simply opens and closes, and macrocrack growth does not occur. Discontinuities in fatigue crack growth behaviour associated with growth rates of the order of one atomic spacing per cycle are usually called threshold effects. Many of these are described under various other headings, and the more important are summarized below.

A crack will not grow under cyclic loading unless the range of stress intensity factor during a fatigue cycle ΔK exceeds a critical value ΔK_c. Values of ΔK_c for a wide range of materials are given in § 4.5.4, for zero mean load, and § 4.7.2, for completely tensile loadings. These were obtained by carrying out fatigue tests on precracked plates and plotting the results as ΔK against endurance. The resulting curves were similar in shape to conventional S/N curves, ΔK_c being the value of ΔK at which a curve becomes parallel to the abscissa. The parameter ΔK_c therefore, is analogous to the fatigue limit in tests on plain specimens. Results can also be presented in terms of the parameter C, which is the critical value of $\sigma_a^3 a$ necessary for fatigue crack growth. At zero mean load C provides a better fit to the experimental data than ΔK_c, and is to be preferred when making calculations. The existence of ΔK_c and C implies that a minimum cyclic stress is required to cause a crack of a given length to grow.

Unlike rates of fatigue crack growth which are comparatively unaffected (§ 5.7), values of ΔK_c decrease as the mean load is increased (§ 4.7.2) and are approximately proportional to $(\sigma_a/\sigma_m)^{\frac{1}{3}}$. Similarly, values of ΔK_c are in general more affected by changes in the environment (§ 4.10) than are rates of crack growth (§ 5.8.4).

The parameter C has been used to provide an explanation of the observed fatigue limits of notched specimens made from wrought material (§ 4.6.1). A microcrack initiates at the root of a notch when the local stress exceeds the plain fatigue limit of the material; therefore the stress to initiate a crack can be calculated from the stress concentration factor K_t and the plain fatigue limit. For a mild notch, the nominal stress is sufficient to cause a microcrack to propagate as a macrocrack, whereas, with a severe notch, the lower nominal stress needed to initiate a microcrack may be insufficient for macrocrack propagation, leading to the development of non-propagating cracks. When this happens, macrocrack growth only takes place when the nominal stress is increased to the minimum necessary corresponding to the total crack length (notch+microcrack). Thus, for mild notches the fatigue limit is determined by the stress necessary to initiate a microcrack whereas, for severe notches, the fatigue limit is determined by the stress necessary to propagate a macrocrack. Either C or ΔK_c can be used to explain the behaviour of materials such as flake cast iron, which contain inherent flaws (§§ 4.6 and 4.11).

The depth at which a microcrack developing in a plain specimen starts to grow as a macrocrack can also be calculated from C (§ 4.11). Values of this changeover depth at the plain fatigue limit vary from 0·005 mm to 0·25 mm (Table 4.34). This can be considered as the maximum depth of a surface defect which can be tolerated without affecting the fatigue limit of a material. The concept of changeover depth is important in explaining the effects of various types of surface treatment (§ 6.4), and fretting (§ 6.6). More general threshold concepts are used in explaining the effect of mechanical working (§ 6.3) and the behaviour of pressure cylinders (§ 6.5), welded joints (§ 6.8), and shrink-fit assemblies (§ 6.9).

18

When using normal experimental techniques, the minimum rate of crack growth which can be observed for most materials is of the order of one lattice spacing per cycle (§ 5.7). This minimum rate can be predicted (Table 5.5) by substituting an appropriate value of ΔK_c into the crack growth expression for the material concerned. The value of C can be predicted theoretically (§ 5.6.7) by assuming that it corresponds to a crack growth rate of one lattice spacing per cycle; a similar theoretical prediction for ΔK_c is somewhat less satisfactory (§ 5.6.8).

Carefully controlled experiments [102, 103] suggest that continuous crack growth at average rates of much less than one lattice spacing per cycle can sometimes be observed; some results for 7075-T6 aluminium alloy are shown in Fig. 5.41. These results should not be confused with initial hesitation in

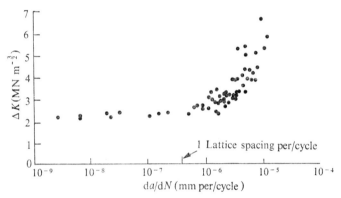

FIG. 5.41. Fatigue crack growth data for 7075-T6 aluminium alloy. (Taken from Johnson and Paris [102].)

crack growth, associated with changes in crack-front shape, sometimes observed at the start of a test (§ 5.5).

The data in Fig. 5.41 show a well-defined inflection at a growth rate of about one lattice spacing per cycle. To the left of the inflection, the rate of crack growth is nearly independent of ΔK, and it is clear that, if ΔK is reduced significantly below the value corresponding to a growth rate of one lattice spacing per cycle, growth stops. Data of this type can be used as an alternative method of obtaining ΔK_c values [103]. It seems that crack growth does not necessarily cease abruptly as ΔK is reduced, but that within a narrow band of ΔK values, crack growth only takes place on a part of the crack front during each cycle, producing very low average crack growth rates.

The inflection is not always as abrupt as shown in Fig. 5.41, and the crack growth equation $da/dN = D(\Delta K)^m$ is sometimes modified to allow for the change in shape as the threshold is approached; for example, the equation

$$\frac{da}{dN} = D\{(\Delta K)^m - (\Delta K_c)^m\}$$

was shown [104] to provide a good fit to data for a range of steels.

In the presence of a corrosive environment, (such as mild steel in brine, § 4.8.4), ΔK_c may be considerably reduced and the inflection suppressed, without having very much effect on crack growth rates of greater than one lattice spacing per cycle. Fig. 5.43 (§ 5.9.4) shows that under corrosive conditions crack growth can take place at average rates of very much less than one lattice spacing per cycle with corresponding values of ΔK well below that corresponding to a crack growth rate of one lattice spacing per cycle. When fatigue tested in air, copper corrodes extensively on the crack surfaces [105] and, from the data presented in § 5.7, its behaviour appears to be similar to mild steel in brine.

The existence of a threshold for fatigue crack growth means that a cracked structure, in general, will have a definite fatigue limit. For a given stress level, the crack must be above a minimum length for growth to occur, and from the form of eqn (5.18), § 5.10.2, it follows that there is a corresponding maximum number of cycles which can lead to fracture. For most situations, this is in the range 10^6–10^7 cycles. Under variable amplitude loading not all load cycles necessarily cause crack growth (§§ 5.9.3 and 6.8.3), so that the total number of cycles may be considerably greater, although the number of damaging cycles still cannot exceed 10^6–10^7 cycles. Of course, the slow crack growth rates possible in some corrosive environments would considerably increase the maximum possible number of cycles which can lead to failure.

5.9. Other factors affecting crack growth

5.9.1. Effect of thickness

Apart from the effects due to the transition from a 90° to a 45° plane (§ 5.3.2), thickness has little effect on the rate of crack growth, provided that the crack front is sensibly straight through the thickness. Some tests [38] on $4\frac{1}{2}\%$ Cu–aluminium alloy (2024-T3 alclad) sheet 100 mm wide, 0·6 mm to 4 mm thick showed that, at short crack lengths, the crack growth rates tended to increase with sheet thickness, but were not affected at longer crack lengths. Other tests on 2024-T3 aluminium alloy [43] from 1·62 mm to 3·2 mm thick and mild steel [47] sheets 254 mm wide and from 2·5 mm to 25 mm thick showed no significant effect.

It has been shown [102] that the crack growth rate may increase as the maximum stress intensity factor in the fatigue cycle $K_{\max}$ approaches K_c, the fracture toughness of the material. K_c in general decreases as the thickness increases, reaching a minimum K_{1c} under plane strain conditions

(§ 5.10.1). This change in K_c with thickness can cause a corresponding thickness effect at high crack growth rates [106] as illustrated in Fig. 5.42.

If a sheet is thin enough, buckling will take place, even under entirely tensile loading, with inflexions at the crack tips. The stresses at the crack tip, and therefore the stress intensity factors, are increased by a factor of approximately $(1-0.001\ 2a/B)^{-1}$ for a plate of thickness B containing a central

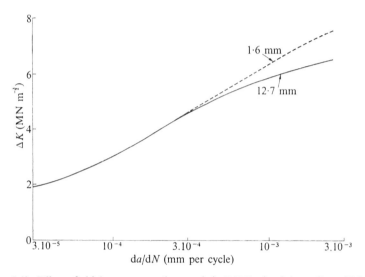

FIG. 5.42. Effect of thickness on crack growth in RR58 aluminium alloy. (Taken from Bradshaw [106].)

transverse crack of length $2a$, with a corresponding increase in crack growth rates [107]. This correction makes no allowance for the amount of buckling, which will vary with the applied stress.

5.9.2. Effect of test frequency

Available evidence suggests that the speed of loading has little effect on the growth rate characteristics of a material over the range 0·25–100 Hz: the growth rate is likely to be slightly faster at lower loading speeds.

Some tests [31] on 2024 aluminium alloy sheet specimens 160 mm wide by 2 mm thick showed that the rate of growth of cracks from a central slit was about 30 per cent faster at 0·33 Hz than those grown at 33 Hz. Further tests [108] on the same material at 150 °C showed that the growth rate was about 30 per cent faster than in a corresponding ambient temperature test: the growth rate at 0·33 Hz was again about 30 per cent faster than at 33 Hz. Other tests [43] on 2024-T3 aluminium alloy sheets, tested at either 83–133 Hz or 0·50–0·75 Hz, showed that the growth rate at the higher speed tended to be slightly lower than at the lower speed. Tests [32] on $4\frac{1}{2}\%$ Cu–aluminium alloy (BS L71) sheets showed no significant difference between the rate of growth for speeds of 33 Hz and 3·3 Hz. There is little difference [32–4] between the growth rate characteristics of mild steel, titanium, and copper sheets tested at 33 Hz or 0·33 Hz. Tests on DTD 5070A and DTD 683 aluminium alloys in various environments (§ 5.9.4) at 1 Hz and 100 Hz showed that, in general, frequency had little effect on crack growth rates, although there was some tendency for faster growth rates at the lower speed.

It is difficult to visualize frequency having any effect on growth rate (assuming that the environment is non-corrosive) other than that associated with the relevant stress–strain characteristics of the material at the crack tip. If at a low frequency the crack tip opening for a given external load is greater than that at a higher frequency, then obviously the length of fresh surface created each cycle will be greater, and thus the growth rate will be greater.

5.9.3. Effect of load changes

Residual compressive stresses will be left in the material ahead of a growing crack front if the maximum tensile stress in the loading cycle causing it to grow is increased for a number of cycles and then reduced to its original value. Thus in general, if the stress level is reduced, the subsequent initial growth rate will be less than expected from constant amplitude tests, and there may be some delay before crack growth restarts. However, if the stress level is increased, there will be no residual stress effect, and cracks will continue immediately at the expected rate. This behaviour has been confirmed by tests on aluminium alloy sheet specimens [59, 109]. Tests on thin-walled steel cylinders [110] showed that changing the stress level had no effect, irrespective of whether the stress was raised or lowered. This may be because the stress levels applied were of the order of the plain fatigue limit so that any compressive residual stresses resulting from a reduction in stress would be quickly relaxed in the soft mild steel used. In some out-of-plane bending tests [111], and some direct stress tests [112], there was a temporary increase in crack growth rate after an increase of stress level; this may have been associated with a change of crack-shape. Changes in crack-shape are often observed [113, 114] in tension tests when the load is altered.

In random-load tests [51] on 4 mm thick 2024-T3 aluminium alloy sheets, it was found that each striation could be correlated with a load application. The over-all rate of crack growth could be predicted within a factor of 2 by linear addition of increments of crack growth for each load level taken from constant amplitude data. A similar result was obtained from earlier work [115] on the same alloy. However, if load levels are divided up into programme load blocks, the actual rate of crack growth is sometimes much slower than that predicted by linear summation. This follows because in random-load tests there are not usually such drastic changes in stress amplitude as when programme load blocks are applied [51].

Previous fatigue cycling of unnotched sheets does not appear to affect the subsequent rate of growth of cracks from subsequently introduced slits as demonstrated by tests [116] on $4\frac{1}{2}\%$ Cu–aluminium alloy sheets.

5.9.4. Effect of environment

Most fatigue crack growth tests are carried out in air, and temperature and humidity are not normally controlled. However, environment may have a significant effect on fatigue crack growth rates, as discussed extensively [102, 117–19] by various authors.

Some data were given in § 4.10 from tests on sharply notched specimens, in which it was shown that cracks formed so quickly that the total life of a specimen could be regarded as consisting wholly of the propagation of a macrocrack. These tests show for copper and mild steel that excluding oxygen from the crack tip reduces the rate of crack growth, the effect being most marked for specimens subjected to a zero mean stress loading cycle. A possible explanation of these findings is that, in the absence of oxygen, the freshly created surfaces at the crack tip can partially rebond when the load is removed; this would be more marked in a zero mean load test in which the crack faces are pressed together during the compression half of the loading cycle than in a test with a tensile mean load. If oxygen is present, the freshly created surfaces oxidize, thus preventing rebonding and increasing the crack growth rate.

Conventional crack growth tests [120] have been carried out on 254 mm wide by 2·5 mm thick mild steel sheets containing an 8 mm over-all length sharp central transverse slit. A plastic bag was fixed around the test-section of the sheet and filled with SAE 30 grade mineral oil. Tests carried out at 77 MN m^{-2} mean stress and various alternating stresses (always less than the mean stress) show that for the initial crack growth (that is crack lengths up to about one-eighth the sheet width) the growth rate is some 25 per cent lower in the oil tests than in a corresponding in-air test.

As explained previously, crack growth does not normally take place at values of ΔK significantly less than that corresponding to a growth rate of one lattice spacing per cycle. However, this does not necessarily apply in the presence of a corrosive environment. For instance, Fig. 5.43 shows some data [72] for mild steel completely immersed in brine. These were obtained by an indirect method (§ 5.5) from the total lives of precracked plates. The data form an extension to the in-air scatter band and show crack growth taking place at average rates of much less than one lattice spacing cycle with corresponding very low values of ΔK. This is presumably because when an increment of crack growth occurs on part of the crack front, the corrosive environment prevents rebonding of the freshly created surface at the crack tip.

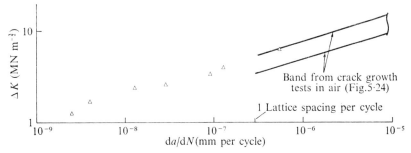

FIG. 5.43. ΔK versus da/dN for mild steel immersed in brine. (Taken from Pook, [72].)

The most extensive experimental results available are for aluminium alloys, and some of the data will be used to illustrate the general effects of environments. A series of tests [121] using 32 mm wide sheets containing a central transverse slit are summarized in Table 5.7, although the figures quoted do not in all cases represent adequately the complexity of the results. The range of stress intensity factor ΔK necessary for a crack growth rate of 10^{-6} mm per cycle and the value of the exponent m in the equation $da/dN = D(\Delta K)^m$ are quoted. In all tests the ratio of minimum to maximum stress R was 0·1. In general, exclusion of air from the crack tip increases the value of ΔK for a given rate of crack growth by about $1\frac{1}{2}$, corresponding to a decrease in crack growth rate for a given ΔK of about ten times. In the tests in a water vapour environment, the rate of crack growth is about the same as in air,

TABLE 5.7

Effect of environment on fatigue crack growth in two aluminium alloys [121]

Material	Environment	Test frequency (Hz)	ΔK for $da/dN = 10^{-6}$ mm per cycle (MN m$^{-3/2}$)	m
DTD 5070A $2\frac{1}{2}\%$ Cu, $1\frac{1}{2}\%$ Mg aluminium alloy	Air	1	1·6	2·5
	Air	100	2·25	3·5
	Vacuum	1	4·2	4·5
	Vacuum	100	4·2	4·5
	Water vapour	1	2·1	3·2
	Water vapour	100	2·1	3·2
	Nitrogen	100	4·2	4·5
	Oxygen	100	4·2	4·5
DTD 683 $5\frac{1}{2}\%$ Zn–aluminium alloy	Air	1	1·35	2·8
	Air	100	1·65	2·9
	Vacuum	1	2·85	3·7
	Vacuum	100	4·3	4·9
	Water vapour	1	2·8	5·9
	Water vapour	100	3·0	6·9
	Nitrogen	100	2·85	3·7
	Oxygen	100	3·2	4·2

which normally contains water vapour. This presence or absence of water vapour appears to be a principal factor affecting crack growth rates in aluminium alloys. This is probably because water vapour reacts with strained metal at the crack tip, resulting in the release of nascent hydrogen, which can diffuse into the material ahead of the crack tip. This could aid crack propagation in two ways: it could either collect in pockets, recombining to form molecular hydrogen whose pressure would strain the material in tension, or it could embrittle grain boundaries or intermetallic surfaces, so providing easy fracture paths. On the other hand, conventional hydrogen environments [122] do not appear to increase the crack growth rate. The dominating

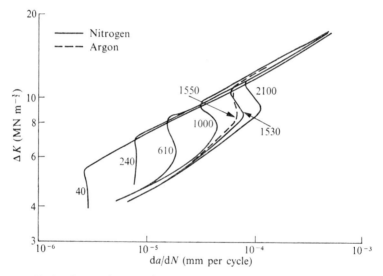

FIG. 5.44. Crack growth rates of 5070A aluminium alloy at different pressures of water vapour (N m^{-2}). (Taken from Bradshaw and Wheeler [121].)

influence of water vapour has also been demonstrated by other series of experiments [122–5]. In general, environment has less effect on crack growth rates at high growth rates, either in terms of numbers of cycles or time, because there is less time available for chemical processes to take place, and a much larger fresh surface is exposed by each cycle. In some cases, the da/dN versus ΔK curve for a corrosive environment is simply a modification of the curve for an inert reference environment. On the other hand, some material–environment combinations show two distinct curves, with a transition from one to the other which takes place at higher rates of crack growth as the severity of the environment increases. Fig. 5.44 shows some data [121] for DTD 5070A aluminium alloy in 1 atm of humid nitrogen or argon at 100 Hz. The amount of water vapour present determines a critical crack growth rate for the changeover from the curve for relatively dry nitrogen to relatively wet nitrogen, but once above or below the transition the level of water vapour does not appear to affect the crack growth rate.

It would thus seem that environments which can chemically corrode the material at the crack tip will increase the rate of crack growth, the effect being most pronounced at low crack growth rates. This is not unexpected, since the length of fresh surface produced by mechanical means will be small and the additional element of length due to corrosion can be a significant proportion. At high crack growth rates, the length of fresh crack surface produced each cycle will be large and, consequently, any additional element of length as a consequence of chemical attack will be less significant. Keeping oxygen away from the freshly created surfaces will prevent them from oxidizing, and they may then be able to rebond when the load is removed. This effect will be most marked when the crack faces are pressed together under a compressive load as in a zero mean load test.

5.9.5. Effect of stress state

Nearly all the experimental data available relate to the growth of a crack under a uniaxial tensile cyclic loading, the crack growing in a direction normal to the loading direction, that is, in Mode I. Under combined stress systems, the preferred direction of crack growth is Mode I, perpendicular to the maximum principal tensile stress. However, as explained in § 3.6.1, for solid specimens tested in pure torsion, fatigue cracks initiate on planes of maximum shear stress, and subsequently change to Mode I crack growth. This change is not readily achieved, because a preferred plane only intersects a shear plane at one point, and usually depends on the crack meeting obstacles. Soft, ductile metals may exhibit a considerable amount of growth on shear planes, that is, in Mode II and/or Mode III. The mechanism of such growth is obscure, presumably the same as that for development of a microcrack along a slip plane, but quantitative information on crack growth rates, in a form suitable for analysis using stress intensity factors, does not seem to be available.

Investigation of the direction of growth of a fatigue crack in mild steel specimens of square cross-section subjected to combined bending and torsional cyclic stresses [126] showed that only when the ratio of the maximum principal tensile stress to the maximum principal shear stress exceeded 1·6 did the crack follow a specific direction, and this was that of principal tension. Similar tests [127] on 3 high-strength wrought aluminium alloys and on commercially pure copper showed that cracks in the aluminium alloys followed directions normal to that of the principal tensile stress at the point under consideration, regardless of the ratio of the principal tensile stress σ to the maximum shear stress τ (in specimens stressed in pure torsion, the initial direction of growth at the point where a crack was initiated was in a maximum shear stress direction but further growth was normal to the principal tensile stress direction), but cracks in copper behaved similarly to those in mild steel in that there seemed to be a critical σ/τ ratio above which cracks grew normal to the σ direction and below which they grew parallel to the τ direction at the point under consideration. The value of this ratio was not determined precisely but appeared to be lower than that found for mild steel.

Some tests have been carried out [15] on 0·8 mm thick 7075-T6 aluminium alloy plates with crack starter slits inclined so giving a combination of Mode I and Mode II crack surface displacements. Initial fatigue crack growth

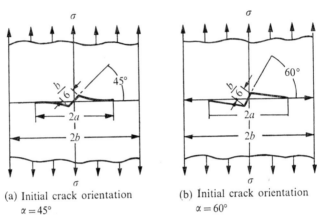

(a) Initial crack orientation
$\alpha = 45°$

(b) Initial crack orientation
$\alpha = 60°$

FIG. 5.45. Crack extension pattern of an initially slanted crack in a tension plate. (a) Initial crack orientation $\alpha = 45°$. (b) Initial crack orientation $\alpha = 60°$. (Taken from Iida and Kobayashi [15].)

was at an angle to the crack starter slit and continued along a curved path (Fig. 5.45).

Subsequent computer analysis based on actual crack trajectories showed that, in general, only Mode I crack surface displacements were present, although in the initial stages there was a small amount of Mode II displacement. Crack growth rates were generally similar to those obtained on conventional specimens, but the presence of even a small K_{II} increased the crack growth rate by 10–20 per cent. The direction of crack growth was always such that K_I was a maximum.

Cracks can grow under a purely compressive loading, provided that a tensile stress across the crack exists at some time during the fatigue cycle. For example, tests have been carried out on 7075–T6 aluminium alloy [128] under a zero to compression loading cycle using the specimen shown in Fig. 5.46. Loading this specimen in compression causes plastic flow at the notch or crack tip, and unloading creates a tensile residual stress of sufficient magnitude to cause crack growth; the fatigue crack growth data obtained is

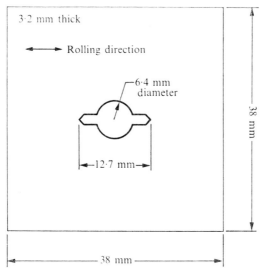

FIG. 5.46. Specimen geometry. (Taken from Hubbard [128].)

shown in Fig. 5.47. After the cracks had grown about 2·5 mm, further cracks developed in the tensile stress fields at the top and bottom of the hole.

It is usual in problems involving the bending of cracked plates to determine elastic stress fields in the vicinity of crack tips using fourth-order plate bending theory [5, 8, 129]. The resulting elastic stress fields are described by stress intensity factors K_B (for bending) and K_S (for shear). K_B is equivalent

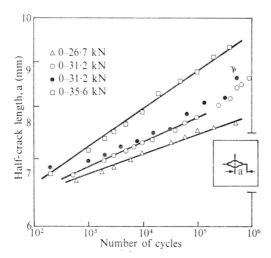

FIG. 5.47. Crack length versus number of cycles for notched specimens. (Taken from Hubbard [128].)

to K_I, and at the plate surface $K_B = K_I(3+\nu)/(1+\nu)$, and K_S is equivalent to K_{II}. There is no equivalent to K_{III}. Tests in cylindrical bending [21] on bare and clad 7075-T6 and 2024-T3 aluminium alloys in thicknesses ranging from 1·3 mm to 3·2 mm showed that the results could conveniently be correlated in terms of stress intensity factor, and that crack growth rates were the same as in tension, provided that the plastic zone-size in the crack plane was the same.

Only membrane stresses are present in an uncracked internally pressurized thin-walled cylinder. If a longitudinal crack is introduced, bending stresses and bulging develop in the vicinity of the crack. The stress conditions at the crack tip can be expressed conveniently by defining a resultant stress intensity factor [130] which has extensional K_I and bending K_B components. Using this resultant stress intensity factor, it was found that [22] the rate of fatigue crack growth in 203 mm diameter by 7·8 mm thick 6063-T6 and 89 mm diameter by 0·56 mm thick 6061-T4 aluminium alloy cylinders could be predicted from data for thin sheets in tension. The cylinders tested had constrained ends; however, stresses parallel to a crack do not affect the values of stress intensity factors, and, by implication, the fatigue crack growth rates. Tensile stresses parallel to a crack can increase K_c, and correspondingly reduce crack growth rates at high values of ΔK [131] as described in § 5.9.1. Tests on mild steel in a state of pure shear, obtained by loading thin-walled cylinders in torsion [132], showed that crack growth rates were initially the same as in uniaxial tension, but buckles which developed at longer crack lengths caused a corresponding increase (§ 5.9.1) in fatigue crack growth rates.

5.9.6. *Methods of increasing resistance to fatigue crack growth*

Conventional metallurgical techniques used for hardening metallic alloys do not in general result in an improvement of their fatigue crack propagation characteristics. Indeed, they generally lead to a deterioration, particularly if these characteristics are based on a stress value bearing a constant relation to the plain fatigue limit or tensile strength of the material. For example, if a steel were heat-treated in such a manner as to double its tensile strength (and its plain fatigue limit) there is no doubt that the ratio of the growth rate of a crack of a given length in the stronger steel to that in the softer steel would be greater than 2 if the alternating stress applied to the former steel was double that applied to the softer steel. The difference would be even greater in the case of hard and soft aluminium alloys.

Apart from structural techniques, such as those used in the aircraft industry, there are several methods by which the rate of crack growth in a structure or specimen subjected to a given loading cycle can be reduced.

When a crack is growing in a plate or sheet, its rate of growth can be retarded, sometimes to zero, by drilling holes at its ends. This has the effect of increasing the crack-tip root radius and hence reducing the stress concentration effect. It must be borne in mind, however, that for the configuration shown on Fig. 5.48, for example, the stress concentration factor at the edge of the hole is not 3, as for a central hole in a wide sheet, but has a value given by

$$K_t = 1 + 2\sqrt{\left(\frac{a}{\rho}\right)}.$$

Thus, unless the crack was initiated either at a stress raiser having a K_t value greater than the drilled configuration or as a result of fretting, the

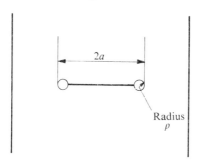

FIG. 5.48 Stopping holes.

crack will only be delayed temporarily, because further cracks will be initiated eventually at the edges of the stopping holes. The effect of stopping holes on the development of fatigue cracks in $4\frac{1}{2}\%$ Cu–aluminium alloy has been studied [133] using plates, 80 mm wide by 2 mm thick containing a central notch of the form shown on Fig. 5.49. The plates were subjected to the repeated loading cycle 0–78 MN m^{-2} until cracks had grown from both ends of the central notch to a length of 5 mm. Holes were then drilled through the plate at the positions shown on Fig. 5.49, and the specimens retested at 0–78 MN m^{-2}. Case (b) gave the longest life, provided care was taken to ensure that the crack tip was drilled out.

Experimental work described in § 5.9.3 shows that the application of an overload (either by an increase in cyclic stress or by a static tensile stress) may cause the growth rate under a subsequent lower cyclic stress to be reduced. This arises because removal of the overload induces compressive residual stresses into the material ahead of the crack tip, which tend to keep the crack tip closed. The amount the growth rate is reduced will depend on the material, the magnitude of the preload and the values of the subsequent nominal mean and alternating stresses. In certain cases, the application of the overload may result in the crack remaining dormant under the subsequent cyclic stressing; in other cases, the crack may grow at a reduced rate until it has passed through the zone of plastically deformed material created by the overload at the crack tip, when of course, it will grow subsequently at its expected rate. When a crack does continue growing at a reduced rate through the plastically deformed region created by the application of the overload, its direction of growth may no longer be normal to the loading direction and it may fork in an effort to avoid growing through this affected volume of plastically deformed material [134]. The effect of static overloading on the fatigue strength of notched specimens is discussed in § 6.3.4. A similar effect can be obtained by judicious spot-heating of parts of a structure

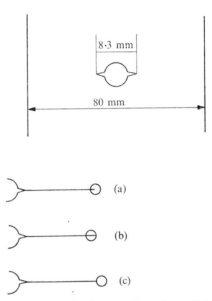

8·3 mm

80 mm

(a)

(b)

(c)

FIG. 5.49. Plate specimen and stopping hole configurations. (Taken from Wallgren and Rudin [133].)

[135, 136], to induce compressive residual stresses at crack tips; this technique can considerably improve the fatigue strength of a welded structure, which will normally contain crack-like defects, but the spot-heating procedure has to be selected on a trial-and-error basis.

If a material is sensitive to the environment in which it is operating, the rate of fatigue crack growth can be reduced by a suitable protective coating. To be effective, a coating must retain its integrity when a crack develops; even small punctures [120] destroy the protection given by a coating. The application of epoxy resins has been shown to be effective in increasing the fatigue lives of welded structures presumably because air is excluded from developing fatigue cracks (see §§ 6.8.5 and 5.9.4).

Reinforcing strips, suitably fixed to the surface of a sheet specimen both over the crack and along the expected line of crack growth, may reduce the growth rate, provided that they reduce the crack opening. As mentioned in

§ 5.10.2, this technique is often used in the aircraft industry. Wire reinforced material can be regarded as containing inherent reinforcing strips. Such material has been manufactured [137] by inserting either longitudinal high-strength steel wires or wire mesh between two sheets of a high-strength precipitation-hardening aluminium alloy in the softened condition, hot-rolling the sheets together, then solution-treating and ageing to restore the original properties of the sheets. Crack propagation tests were carried out on 165 mm wide specimens cut from these composite sheets in such a way that a sheet always had a set of wires running in the longitudinal direction, that is, parallel to the loading direction. A central transverse slit was introduced to initiate fatigue cracks, and it was found that the rate of crack growth at a given stress level could be some 2 to 4 times slower in a composite sheet than in a correspondingly loaded unreinforced sheet of the same aluminium alloy. Similar material consisting of commercially pure aluminium reinforced by 0·18 mm diameter stainless steel wire has been manufactured [138] using powder-metallurgy and flame-spraying techniques; again, the rate of fatigue crack growth was reduced substantially compared with the unreinforced material.

5.10. Fatigue cracks in structures

5.10.1. Residual static strength of cracked structures

A fatigue crack can form in a component or structural member, usually at a point of stress concentration or at a joint or in an area of fretting, or from some inherent defect, at relatively low nominal alternating stresses. If the magnitude of the nominal cyclic stress is sufficient, the crack will grow until the cross-sectional area of the component or member is so reduced that it can no longer support the maximum tensile stress due to both the imposed static and cyclic loads, and catastrophic failure occurs. Catastrophic failure can occur either before or after the average net area tensile stress reaches the yield stress of the material. In the latter case, fracture will occur in a ductile manner; in the former case, the fracture will occur in a brittle manner (that is, with no visible signs of gross plastic deformation). Complex fabricated structures invariably contain some small crack-like flaws that are either inherent in the material or introduced during fabrication. The operating life of such a structure will be dependent on the size of the initial flaws, their cyclic growth rate, and critical size under the operating loads. There is a growing realization among designers and engineers that the prediction of service life assuming no initial flaws in the structure is both unrealistic and dangerous.

Whether a metallic material fails in a ductile or brittle manner depends on certain conditions such as chemical composition, metallurgical treatments, shape of specimen (including notch configuration), the value of the stresses around the notch, temperature, and rate of deformation. Factors which delay the onset of plasticity, for example, low temperature, plane strain conditions, and increased rate of loading, make the material more susceptible to brittle fracture [139].

In practice, it is important to be able to predict either the residual static strength of a cracked member or alternatively, the length to which a crack may be permitted to grow before catastrophic failure occurs. If an actual crack is not present, cracks may form from either inherent or mechanical flaws by either the action of cyclic stresses or because the loading is such that the local stresses and restriction of strain at the notch root are sufficient to lead to a localized ductile fracture. If a crack is started at the root of a notch by, for example, a high impact loading, it may be able to run catastrophically at a low transverse tensile stress. Thus, in designing a safe structure, it is usual to assess the brittle fracture characteristics by replacing any discontinuity by a crack of equivalent length.

Linear elastic fracture mechanics, described in § 5.2, provides a convenient means of estimating either the nominal stress that will cause a crack to spread catastrophically or, alternatively, the maximum length a crack can be allowed to grow to under a fatigue loading.

It is found that, under increasing static load, a crack will start to grow (provided that general yielding does not intervene) when the opening mode stress intensity factor K_I reaches a critical value K_c, and will continue to grow as long as the loading conditions are such that $K_I > K_c$. Under certain conditions K_c can be regarded as a material property and is a convenient measure of the fracture toughness, or resistance to brittle fracture, of a material.

For a crack to grow under static loading two conditions are necessary and sufficient [140]: there must be sufficient stress available to operate a suitable mechanism of fracture, and the strain energy released by an increment of crack growth must equal or exceed the energy required to form the new crack surfaces. That is,

$$G_1 \geqslant G_c,$$

where G_1 is the strain energy release rate, and
G_c is the effective surface energy (both surfaces).
In metals, the true surface energy is small compared with the additional energy absorbed by the plastic deformation adjacent to the crack surface which always accompanies fracture. It can be shown that both these conditions are satisfied when $K_I \geqslant K_c$ [141], and that

$$K_I = (EG_I)^{\frac{1}{2}}$$

for plane stress. For plane strain E is replaced by $E/(1-v^2)$. K_c and G_c are similarly related, and therefore are equivalent measures of fracture toughness.

The value of K_c is normally a minimum under plane strain conditions, as shown schematically in Fig. 5.50; it can be considered a material property, denoted by K_{Ic}, in the same sense as the 0·2 per cent proof stress. The existence of K_{Ic} as a material property is the main justification for the application of linear elastic fracture mechanics to brittle fracture problems.

When a specimen containing a crack is loaded, the crack tip opens without extension of the crack. This movement is called the crack opening displacement and is associated with the development of the plastic zone. Its critical value δ_c when the crack starts to grow is roughly constant [142, 143] and

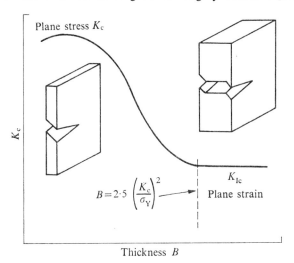

$$B = 2 \cdot 5 \left(\frac{K_c}{\sigma_Y} \right)^2$$

FIG. 5.50. Relationship between thickness and K_c.

approximately equals G_c/σ_Y; δ_c is used as a measure of toughness for low-strength steels and has the advantage that it still has meaning at and beyond general yield [143]. Standard methods of measuring K_{Ic} and δ_c have been developed [144, 145].

The shear lips [146] which develop on specimen surfaces (Fig. 5.50) are a result of plastic flow. Shear fracture is associated with yielding under plane stress conditions, which initially exist only at the plate surfaces, and extend progressively as the crack grows until the full width of the shear lip is reached. During the development of shear lips, the crack tends to bow forward in the plate interior. Even where there is a fully developed shear fracture, there is always an initial portion of square fracture roughly triangular in shape. Plane stress does not necessarily produce shear fracture; for example, beryllium and some titanium alloys show square fractures, irrespective of the state of stress. When the crack front has a complicated shape, only average values of G_I or K_I can be calculated, through the thickness. Various aspects of yielding at crack tips have been discussed by a number of authors [5, 6, 24, 142, 146, 147].

19

The stress intensity factor concept can be applied to moving cracks [5, 148]. When K_I exceeds K_c a crack will start to grow, and will continue to grow provided that K_I is at least equal to K_c. Any energy in excess of that required to form new crack surfaces causes the crack growth rate to accelerate towards a theoretical limit; as this is approached, surplus energy causes surface roughening, crack branching, and possibly shattering. If K_c increases with crack speed, the crack speed adjusts itself so that $K_c = K_I$. Provided the rate of increase of K_I is known, the strain rate for any point near the crack tip can be calculated with the aid of eqn (5.2), which gives the relationship between K_I and stresses at points near a crack tip. Similarly, the strain rate can be calculated for a propagating crack from the value of K_I and the crack speed. Increases in both the rate of increase of K_I and crack speed cause an increase in strain rate near the crack tip, but the relationships are not simple. The situation is further complicated by the presence of a plastic zone, and for some purposes it is convenient to compare stress rates [16] (rate of increase of stress) rather than strain rates. The stress rate is a maximum at the leading edge of the plastic zone. For plane stress the maximum stress rate $\dot{\sigma}$ at a stationary crack with constant rate of load increase is given by

$$\dot{\sigma} = \frac{2\sigma_Y}{t},$$

where t is the time from zero load. For a crack propagating at velocity V and under plane stress conditions $\dot{\sigma}$ is given by

$$\dot{\sigma} = \frac{\sigma_Y V}{2r_p},$$

where r_p is given by eqn (5.3).

If the material is strain-rate sensitive, the problem is further complicated by the increase in σ_Y at high strain rates, because the value of σ_Y is itself a function of $\dot{\sigma}$. However, most high-strength materials are not particularly strain-rate dependent, so that K_c is only slightly affected by the value of $\dot{\sigma}$. Mild and similar steels are markedly strain-rate sensitive, and crack initiation is more difficult than crack propagation [16, 149], particularly above the transition temperature. The relationship between K_c and $\dot{\sigma}$, above the transition temperature, is shown schematically in Fig. 5.51. At low loading rates, mild steel is too tough to obtain a value for K_c using specimens of practical size, but if a crack is initiated by any means it will accelerate rapidly towards the crack speed associated with the minimum K_c, and is not readily arrested. The decrease in K_c at high loading rates, with the associated increase in σ_Y means that much smaller specimens will behave in an essentially elastic manner [150], and explains the importance of impact loads as a cause of brittle fractures. The K_c required to initiate a crack can also be considerably reduced by metallurgical changes (for example, that associated with welding) and by local cooling.

In the past, the problem of brittle fracture was tackled by empirical methods based on service experience, and a great many tests were devised [151, 152], the best known of which is the Charpy impact test. Until the advent of fracture mechanics there was no really satisfactory method of assessing the fracture toughess of high-strength materials (say, greater than

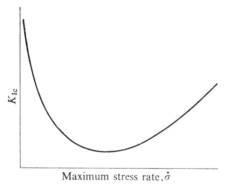

FIG. 5.51. Relationship for low-strength steels between maximum stress rate and K_{Ic}.

1000 MN m^{-2} for steels and 300 MN m^{-2} for aluminium alloys), but the determination of K_{Ic} is now an established method of assessing such materials [153].

Methods of measuring toughness are needed for the development of new materials, for quality control during material production, and to provide design information. The determination of K_{Ic} is now being used for material development, and its use is being planned for quality control and specification purposes. One particular value of K_{Ic} is that it can be used readily to measure the toughness at any area of interest (for example, at or near welds) by suitable orientation of the test-specimen and positioning of the initial crack.

In principle, application to design problems is straightforward [154, 155]. The relationship between K_{Ic}, applied stress σ, and initial flaw size a at the start of crack growth can be written in the general form

$$K_{\mathrm{Ic}} = \sigma(\pi a)^{\frac{1}{2}}\alpha, \tag{5.17}$$

where α is a correction factor for the geometry of the flaw and structure. Thus, if any two factors (that is, flaw size, applied stress or K_{Ic}) are known, it is possible to determine the value of the third necessary to avoid brittle fracture. The plastic zone increases the effective flaw size, and a correction should be included if it is a significant proportion of the flaw size. Eqn (5.17) only holds under essentially elastic conditions (see § 5.2.4) where failure occurs at a stress below general yield. If the material is too thin for fully-developed plane strain conditions (Figs. 5.3 and 5.50) K_{Ic} in eqn (5.17) is replaced by the value of K_c appropriate to the thickness.

In practice there are considerable difficulties in applying this approach. First, accurate values of α in eqn (5.17) for three-dimensional bodies are only available for a few simple crack-shapes in regular bodies; at present this is the biggest obstacle to a more widespread application of fracture mechanics in design. Secondly, the loadings on the structure may not be sufficiently known for accurate estimates of stress level to be made. Thirdly, flaw size often cannot be accurately determined using the available non-destructive testing techniques, and lastly, there may be considerable scatter in the toughness of a material, particularly in the vicinity of welds. Despite these shortcomings, fracture mechanics has been successfully applied to a number of design problems involving the strength of cracked structures, especially in the aerospace industry [156, 157], and has proved particularly valuable in failure analysis.

Low- and medium-strength steels which at room temperature fail in a ductile manner (that is, irrespective of crack length, the net area stress at fracture is always above the yield stress) may fracture in a brittle manner if the temperature is lowered below their transition temperature. When such steels are to be used in structural applications, one design philosophy is to select a steel whose transition temperature is well below the operating temperature. Thus should a crack form, it will not grow catastrophically at a stress lower than the yield stress. Transition temperatures are usually estimated from the energy absorbed by small standard sized (usually 10 mm square) Izod or Charpy vee-notched specimens broken at different temperatures in a standard impact machine, but unfortunately the brittle–ductile transition temperature of a given material varies with specimen size and notch or crack configuration. However, although the transition temperature determined by the standard Charpy test cannot be taken as applying to the same steel when used in the form of large fabricated thick plates (in fact, it will be unsafe because the transition temperature increases with increasing specimen size), the standard impact test is useful for comparing the behaviour of one material with another. Thus, if the service behaviour in bulk form of one material is known, a rough guide to the expected behaviour of the other materials can be obtained, although care is again needed since it does not necessarily follow that, because the transition temperature of one steel as determined in a Charpy test is, say, 30 °C lower than some other steel, this difference will be maintained when the steel is in a more massive form [150]. In order to determine the transition temperature, or a similar parameter, on specimens more representative of structural members, various other tests have been devised [158].

Just as the growth of a fatigue crack can be retarded by the presence of residual compressive stresses, so can the propagation of a brittle crack [159]. Pre-stressing a flawed structure at temperatures above its transition temperature induces compressive residual stresses in the vicinity of flaws. An extensive review of available evidence [160] indicates that, in general, this increases the resistance of a structure to brittle fracture at temperatures below its transition temperature, or at least is not harmful.

A knowledge of the static strength of a thin sheet of material containing a central crack is of importance in aircraft structural work and is often referred to as the residual static strength. A considerable amount of data has been accumulated relating to the strength of these thin cracked panels. Fatigue cracks are either grown from a central hole or slit, and the static strength determined when the crack has grown to the required length, or a slit is cut with a fine sawblade to simulate a crack. Generally, the results of tests on thin sheets containing cracks of different lengths are shown on diagrams in which the breaking stress on either gross or net area, expressed as a fraction of the tensile strength of the material, is plotted against the corresponding crack length, expressed as a fraction of the sheet width. Results of such tests can also be expressed in terms of the fracture mechanics parameter K_c, but sheets are generally thin so that they are in a state of plane stress and techniques to measure the plane stress K_c are not yet well developed [17], although progress is being made [161].

An indication of the strengths of some cracked sheet materials is shown on Fig. 5.52; they were obtained [3] on sheets, 250 mm wide by 1·6 mm thick containing a narrow, central saw-cut. An ideal material would obviously be one in which the stress on net area at failure was never less than the tensile strength of the material, that is, the experimental points would lie on the straight line joining the unit coordinates on Fig. 5.52. The fracture face of nearly all thin cracked sheets of various materials is in line with the crack and is generally on a plane at 45° through the thickness. In a few materials, such as titanium and zinc (both hexagonal metals), the fracture face is on a 90° plane through the thickness, as is fatigue crack growth (§ 5.3.2).

In some design problems (such as the designing of aircraft fuselages and pressure vessels) it is useful to know the value of the critical longitudinal crack length in a thin-walled cylinder subjected to a given internal pressure. Owing to the different geometries, the extrapolation of the critical crack length in a cylinder at a given hoop stress, from that in a cracked sheet specimen of the same thickness as the cylinder wall thickness subjected to the same nominal tensile stress, will be unsafe, becoming more so the smaller the diameter of the cylinder. Various semi-empirical methods of predicting the failure pressure have been derived for failures at below general yield [156, 162–4]. Recent theoretical developments [8] have resulted in the application of fracture mechanics to this type of problem [165].

Hydraulic pressure tests carried out on 1·5 m diameter, 25·4 mm wall thickness, steel cylinders containing longitudinal, through-the-thickness, sealed defects of from 76 mm to 610 mm long [163], showed that the hoop stress at failure decreased with increasing slit length according to the relationship $\sigma_{\mathrm{h}}^3 a^2 = \text{constant}$, where σ_{h} is the nominal hoop stress at failure and a is the slit length. For crack lengths of 150 mm and greater, the hoop stress at failure was below the yield stress of the steel used.

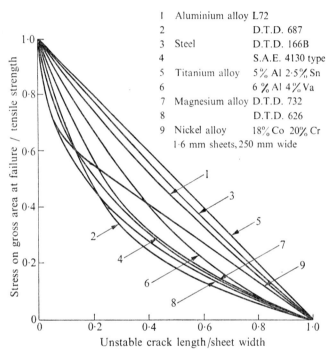

1	Aluminium alloy	L72
2		D.T.D. 687
3	Steel	D.T.D. 166B
4		S.A.E. 4130 type
5	Titanium alloy	5% Al 2·5% Sn
6		6 % Al 4% Va
7	Magnesium alloy	D.T.D. 732
8		D.T.D. 626
9	Nickel alloy	18% Co 20% Cr
	1·6 mm sheets, 250 mm wide	

FIG. 5.52. Static strength of cracked sheets. (Taken from Harpur [3].)

In aircraft structures, stringers are often affixed to a sheet parallel to the loading direction, and this can increase the breaking load of a cracked sheet [153]. The effect of stringers on the residual static strength of cracked thin sheets has been discussed by various authors [5, 166, 157], and fracture-mechanics methods are being applied to this type of problem [157], often in conjunction with computer stress analysis [167].

Stringers parallel to the crack can also increase strength. For example, fracture tests were carried out on both flat and curved 1·0 mm thick 914 mm wide $4\frac{1}{2}$% Cu–aluminium alloy sheets [168], the former having a central slit 165 mm long and the latter a slit 203 mm long, cut normal to the loading direction. Stringers were riveted to the sheets to that they ran in a direction parallel to the crack. The curved specimens were bolted into a special fixture,

TABLE 5.8

Specimen	No stringers	Stringers attached
Flat	170 MN m^{-2}	220 MN m^{-2}
Curved	105 MN m^{-2}	160 MN m^{-2}

and a hoop stress was created by air pressure. The gross area stresses at catastrophic failure are given in Table 5.8.

5.10.2. Estimation of service life

Consider a mild steel member in a structure subjected to cyclic loads of such a magnitude that cracks form early in the life due, for example, to fretting at either a rivet or bolt hole. The life of the structure will therefore depend primarily on the number of cycles required for the crack to grow to such a size that it results in catastrophic failure of the structure. The fact that the fatigue crack growth characteristics of steels of different strength do not vary widely means that, if a steel plate of higher tensile strength (and thus higher plain fatigue strength) is substituted for the original mild steel plate, the service life will not necessarily be increased for, if cracks now form, they will spread just as quickly in the stronger steel as in the mild steel. In fact, if the permissible working stress in the plate is increased in proportion to the increased tensile strength of the stronger steel, the service life of the joint in the stronger steel can be expected to be less than the one made in mild steel. This argument applies even more forcibly in the case of the aluminium alloys because, with these alloys, the crack growth characteristics tend to deteriorate with increasing tensile strength of the alloy.

In design considerations, both the fatigue crack growth rate and the static fracture characteristics must be taken into account. In general, materials of low ductility have a poor resistance to the onset of fast or brittle fracture (see § 5.10.1), but good ductility does not necessarily indicate a high resistance to fatigue crack growth.

The number of cycles required for a crack to grow from some initial length a_0 to the final length a_f at which failures takes place can be calculated readily if fatigue crack growth data is available in stress intensity factor form [135, 136, 153, 154, 169–72]. By substituting eqn (5.1) in (5.5) and integrating, the number of cycles needed to grow a crack from a_0 to a_f can be obtained. It is assumed that a_0 is above the minimum length necessary for crack growth at the stress level involved (§§ 4.5 and 4.7). If the data for mild steel (Fig. 5.24) are used and certain simplifying assumptions are made, including taking α in eqn (5.1) as 1, then the number of cycles N is given by [169]

$$N = \frac{64\,600}{(\Delta\sigma)^3}\left(\frac{1}{\sqrt{a_0}} - \frac{1}{\sqrt{a_f}}\right) \times 10^6, \qquad (5.18)$$

where $\Delta\sigma$ is the range of stress in MN m^{-2} during the fatigue cycle but neglecting any compressive stresses, and a_0 and a_t are in metres. Usually a_t will be large compared with a_0, and eqn (5.18) can be further simplified to

$$N = \frac{64\,600}{(\Delta\sigma)^3\sqrt{a_0}} \times 10^6.$$

Using this type of equation, diagrams relating N, $\Delta\sigma$, and a_0 can be derived readily. Such diagrams are being prepared for various design situations [153, 173] and are finding increasing use for applications such as estimation of the maximum flaw size which can be tolerated in a structure; they are likely in the future to help form the basis of design codes.

In internally pressurized thick-walled cylinders, it has been found (§ 6.5) that there is good agreement with experimental results if the initial flaw size is taken as that which will just grow at the fatigue limit of the material and the initiation period is ignored.

The fatigue strength of welded structures at endurances above about 10^5 cycles is usually found to be independent of the tensile strength of the parent metal. Welded structures usually contain cracks or crack-like flaws, and the fatigue life is determined by the number of cycles required to propagate an existing crack to the critical size for failure and not by the time required to initiate a crack (§ 6.8.3). The fatigue crack propagation characteristics of all steels are very similar; this also applies to weld metals used on constructional steels [174]. It is not surprising therefore that the fatigue strength of welded structures at long endurances is independent of tensile strength.

Although there is a large amount of information available on the fatigue strength of welded joints [135], there is little quantitative information available on the rate of fatigue crack propagation in welded structures partly because of the difficulty of determining stress intensity factors for cracks in complex structures [171, 172].

Fracture-mechanics analyses (§ 6.8.2) of the results of a large number of tests on butt welds containing defects have shown that the fatigue life can be predicted using fatigue crack growth data. When compared on a stress intensity factor basis, fatigue crack growth rates in civil engineering structures have been found to be the same as in conventional test-specimens [171]. A fracture-mechanics analysis [172] has given a satisfactory explanation of the King's Bridge failure at Melbourne [175].

The accurate estimation of service life is of particular importance for aircraft structures. Despite the availability of computer stress analysis [167], stress systems are, in general, too complex [166] for theoretical estimation, and reliance is placed on extensive testing of representative structures under simulated service loading histories (§ 6.2). There have been a number of investigations of the effects of various design features on the rate of growth of fatigue cracks initiated in a built-up section generally representative of some part of an aircraft structure [114, 176–8].

For example, the growth of fatigue cracks in box beams, fabricated from either $4\frac{1}{2}\%$ Cu (2024-T3) or $5\frac{1}{2}\%$ Zn (7075-T6) aluminium alloy and subjected to a repeated bending moment, has been studied [176]. The beams were supported at two points, 2·44 m apart, and loaded through two loading points, 0·61 m apart, thus subjecting this central 0·61 m length test-section to a constant bending moment. The tension covers of the beams were cambered to compensate for shear lag effects, the compression covers being designed to ensure that the tension cover would fail first under a static loading. All the beams were 0·51 m wide and had eight longitudinal stringers or stiffeners on each cover. In two beams of each material, the stiffeners were riveted to the cover, in a third they were resin-bonded, and in a fourth the tension cover and stiffeners were integrally machined from a thick plate. All the beams were subjected to a cyclic bending loading sufficient to induce a nominal stress cycle in the tension cover plate of 90 ± 45 MN m^{-2}. The number of stress cycles required to initiate a crack from a 12·7 mm long by 6·35 mm wide rectangular hole cut centrally in the tension cover was roughly the same in similar beams of either material, but for a given beam design, cracks grew more rapidly in those made of the 7075 alloy than in those made of the 2024 alloy. Crack growth in those beams having riveted stringers was interrupted each time the crack passed under a rivet head. The growth rate in beams of a given material was fastest in those having integral stiffeners and lowest in those having bonded stringers, although the growth rate in these latter beams was dependent on the effectiveness of the bond. Similar tests [177] were carried out on 9 different beam designs, made of the same two alloys, subjected to a nominal cyclic bending stress in the tension cover of 90 ± 45 MN m^{-2}. Six beams had stiffeners bonded and two had an integrally machined stiffened cover plate. These confirmed that in beams of similar construction, cracks grew faster in those made of the 7075 alloy than in those made of the 2024 alloy. In beams of either material, the growth rate in those having riveted stringers was slower the closer the spacing of the rivets. The fastest growth rate again occurred in covers having integral stringers (because no barriers to crack growth were present), and the slowest growth rate occurring in covers having bonded stringers in which there were no rivet holes in the critical section.

References

1. HEAD, A. K. *Phil. Mag.* **44**, 925 (1953); *J. appl. Mech.*, **78**, 407 (1956).
2. CHRISTENSEN, R. H. *Crack propagation Symposium, Cranfield*, p. 326 (1961).
3. HARPUR, N. F. *Crack propagation Symposium, Cranfield*, p. 442 (1961).
4. CHRISTENSEN, R. H. and HARMON, R. B. *Fatigue crack propagation*, p. 5 American Society for Testing Materials, S.T.P. 415 (1967).

5. PARIS, P. C. and SIH, G. C. *Symposium on fracture toughness testing and its applications*, p. 30. American Society for Testing Materials, S.T.P. 381 (1965).

6. BROWN, W. F. and SRAWLEY, J. E. *Plane strain crack testing of high strength metallic materials*. American Society for Testing Materials, S.T.P. 410 (1966).

7. ERDOGAN, F. *Eng. Fracture Mech.* **4**, 811 (1972).

8. ERDOGAN, F. and KIBLER, J. J. *Int. J. Fracture Mech.*, **5**, 229 (1969).

9. ROOKE, D. P. and CARTWRIGHT, D. J. *A compendium of stress intensity factors*, *H.M.S.O.*, London. To be published.

SRAWLEY, J. E. and BROWN, W. F. *Symposium on fracture toughness testing and its applications*, p. 133. American Society for Testing Materials, S.T.P. 381 (1965).

SIH, G. C. (Ed.) *Methods of analysis and solution of crack problems*. Noordhoff, Leyden (1973).

SIH, G. C. *Handbook of stress intensity factors*. Lehigh University (1973).

TADA, H., PARIS, P. C., and IRWIN, G. R. *The stress analysis of cracks handbook*. Del Research Corporation, Hellertown, Pa. (1973).

10. MOSTOVOY, S., CROSSLEY, P. B. and RIPLING, E. J. *Jnl Mater.* (*US*). **2**, 661 (1967).

11. WESSEL, E. T. *Eng. Fracture Mech.* **1**, 77 (1968).

12. GROSS, B. and MENDELSON, A. NASA Tech. Note D-6040 (1970).

13. ERDOGAN, F. and SIH, G. C. *J. bas. Engng.* **85**, 519 (1963).

14. COTTERELL, B. *Intn. J. Fracture Mech.* **2**, 526 (1966).

15. IIDA, S. and KOBAYASHI, A. S. *J. bas. Engng.* **91**, 764 (1969).

16. KENNY, P. and CAMPBELL, J. D. *Prog. Mater. Sci.* **13**, 135 (1967).

17. POOK, L. P. Min. of Tech. NEL Rep. No. 465 (1970).

18. PARIS, P. C. PhD. Thesis. University of Lehigh (1962).

PARIS, P. C. and ERDOGAN, F. *Trans. Am. Soc. mech. Engrs. J. bas. Engng.* **85**, 528 (1963).

PARIS, P. C., GOMEZ, M. P. and ANDERSON, W. E. *Trend Eng.* (*Univ. Wash.*) **13**, 9 (1961).

19. SWANSON, S. R., CICCI, F., and HOPPE, W. *Fatigue crack propagation*, p. 312. American Society for Testing Materials S.T.P. 415 (1967).

20. DONALDSON, D. R. and ANDERSON, W. E. *Crack propagation Symposium*, *Cranfield*, p. 375 (1961).

21. ERDOGAN, F. and ROBERTS, R. *International Conference on fracture, Sendai, Japan*, Vol. 1, p. 341 (1965).

22. CATANACH, W. M. and ERDOGAN, F. *Second International Conference on fracture, Brighton*, p. 765 (1969).

23. RICE, J. R. *International Conference on fracture, Sendai, Japan*, Vol. 1, p. 283 (1965).

24. RICE, J. R. *Fatigue crack propagation*, p. 247. American Society for Testing Materials, S.T.P. 415 (1967).

25. ELBER, W. *Eng. Fracture Mech.* **2**, 37 (1970).

LINDLEY, T. C. and RICHARDS, C. E. Preprint from *Conference on mechanics and mechanics of crack growth, Cambridge*, Paper 11 (1973).

26. FROST, N. E., POOK, L. P. and DENTON, K. *Eng. Fracture Mech.* **3**, 109 (1971).

27. FROST, N. E. *International Conference on fracture, Sendai, Japan*, Vol. 3, p. 1433 (1965).
28. JACOBY, G. H. *Exp. Mech.* **5,** 65 (1965).
29. LONGSON, J. Min. of Aviation, R.A.E. Rep. No. Struct. 267 (1961).
30. MARSH, K. J. Min. of Tech. NEL Rep. No. 373 (1968).
31. SCHIJVE, J. Nat. Aero. and Astro. Res. Inst., Amsterdam, Rep. No. MP 195 (1960).
32. FROST, N. E. *J. mech. Engng. Sci.* **1,** 151 (1959).
33. FROST, N. E. *J. mech. Engng. Sci.* **4,** 22 (1961).
34. FROST, N. E. and DENTON, K. *Metallurgia* **70,** 113 (1964); DSIR, NEL, Rep. No. 157 (1964).
35. FROST, N. E. and DUGDALE, D. S. DSIR, MERL Rep. No. PM 218 (1957).
36. SWANSON, S. R., CICCI, F., and HOPPE, W. *Fatigue crack propagation*, p. 312. American Society for Testing Materials S.T.P. 415 (1967).
37. BROEK, D. and SCHIJVE, J. Nat. Aero. and Astro. Res. Inst., Amsterdam, NRL-TR, M2111 (1963).
38. BROEK, D. and SCHIJVE, J. Nat. Aero. and Astro. Res. Inst., Amsterdam, NLR-TR, M2129 (1963).
39. BROEK, D., DeRIJK, P., and SEVENHUYSEN, P. J. Nat. Aero. and Astro. Res. Inst., Amsterdam, NLR-TR, M2100 (1962).
40. WILHEM, D. P. *Fatigue crack propagation*, p. 363 American Society for Testing Materials S.T.P. 415 (1967).
41. WALKER, E. K. *Effects of environment and complex load history on fatigue life*, p. 1. American Society for Testing Materials, S.T.P. 462 (1970).
42. FROST, N. E. and DUGDALE, D. S. *J. Mechs. Phy. Solids* **6,** 92 (1968).
43. HERTZBERG, R. W. and PARIS, P. C. *International Conference on fracture, Sendai, Japan*, Vol. 1, p. 459 (1965).
44. ROBERTS, W. T. *J. less-common Metals* **4,** 345 (1962).
45. LARSON, F. R. *Trans. Am. Soc. Metals* **57,** 620 (1964).
46. RICHARDS, C. E. *Acta metall.* **19,** 583 (1971).
47. FROST, N. E. and DENTON, K. *J. mech. Engng. Sci.* **3,** 295 (1961).
48. ZAPPFE, C. A. and WORDEN, C. O. *Trans. Am. Soc. Metals* **43,** 958 (1961).
49. *Electron fractography.* American Society of Testing Materials, S.T.P. 436 (1968).
50. PHILLIPS, A., KERLINS, V. and WHITESON, B. V. *Electron fractography handbook*. Air Force Mat. Lab., Wright Patterson Air Force Base, Ohio, Tech. Rep. ML-TDR-64-416 (1965).
51. McMILLAN, J. C. and PELLOUX, R. M. N. *Fatigue crack propagation*, p. 505. American Society for Testing Materials, S.T.P. 415 (1967).
52. PELLOUX, R. M. N. *Trans. Am. Soc. Metals* **57,** 511 (1964).
    PELLOUX, R. M. N. and McMILLAN, J. C. *International Conference on fracture, Sendai, Japan*, Vol. 2, p. 547 (1965).
53. FORSYTH, P. J. E. and RYDER, D. A. *Aircr. Engng.* **32,** 96 (1960).
54. POOK, L. P. Hawker Siddeley Aviation Ltd. Unpublished report (1962).
55. McMILLAN, J. C. and PELLOUX, R. M. N. Boeing Scientific Research Lab. Document, D1-82-0558 (1966).
56. PLUMBRIDGE, W. J. and RYDER, D. A. *Acta. metall.* **17,** 1449 (1969).

57. ERHARDT, K. and GRANT, H. J. *Second International Conference on fracture, Brighton*, p. 702 (1969).
58. HOLDEN, J. *Phil. Mag.* **6,** 547 (1961).
59. FROST, N. E., HOLDEN, J., and PHILLIPS, C. E. *Crack propagation Symposium, Cranfield*, p. 166 (1961).
60. FORSYTH, P. J. E. *Crack propagation Symposium, Cranfield*, p. 76 (1961).
61. LAIRD, C. and SMITH, G. C. *Phil. Mag.* **7,** 847 (1962).
62. SCHIJVE, J. Nat. Aero. and Astro. Res. Inst., Amsterdam, NLR-TR, M2122 (1964).
63. FORSYTH, P. J. E. *The physical basis of metal fatigue*. Blackie, London (1969).
64. ANDREWS, E. H. *J. appl. Phys.* **32,** 542 (1961).
65. MCEVILY, A. J., BOETTNER, R. C., and JOHNSON, T. L. *10th Sagamore Army Materials Research Conference on fatigue* (1963).
66. HIRSCH, P. B. and KELLAR, J. N. *Acta. crystallogr.* **5,** 162 (1952).
   HIRSCH, P. B., CAY, P., and KELLY, A. *Acta. crystallogr.* **7,** 41 (1954).
67. GROSSKREUTZ, J. C. and SHAW, G. C. *Fatigue crack propagation*, p. 226. American Society for Testing Materials S.T.P. 415, (1967).
68. KLESNIL, M. and LUKÁŠ, P. *Second International Conference on fracture, Brighton*, p. 725 (1969).
69. FREED, C. N. and KRAFFT, J. M. *J. Mater.* **1,** 770 (1966).
70. NICHOLSON, C. E. Unpublished BISRA report (1969).
71. FROST, N. E. DSIR, NEL Rep. No. PM 287 (1959).
72. POOK, L. P. *Stress analysis and growth of cracks*, p. 106. American Society for Testing Materials, S.T.P. 513 (1972).
73. DUGDALE, D. S. *J. Mech. Phys. Solids* **8,** 100 (1960).
74. DIXON, J. R. *Int. J. Fracture Mech.* **1,** 224 (1965).
75. LIU, H. W. *Trans. Am. Soc. mech. Engrs. J. bas. Engng.* **83,** 23 (1961).
76. WEIBULL, W. SAAB Aircraft Co., Tech. Note 25, 1954; Aero. Res. Inst., Sweden, FFA Rep. 65 (1956); FFA Rep. 86 (1960).
77. WEIBULL, W. *Crack propagation Symposium, Cranfield*, p. 271 (1961).
78. SCHIJVE, J., NEDERVEEN, A., and JACOBS, F. A. Nat. Aero. and Astro. Res. Inst., Amsterdam, NLR-TR, M2142 (1965).
79. MCEVILY, A. J. and ILLG, W. NACA Tech. Note 4394 (1958).
   ILLG, W. and MCEVILY, A. J. NASA Tech. Note D52 (1959).
80. HARDRATH, H. F. and MCEVILY, A. J. *Crack propagation Symposium, Cranfield*, p. 231 (1961).
81. BARROIS, W. AGARD, Rep. No. 412 (1962).
82. ISIBASI, T. *Proceedings of the 1st Japanese Congress on testing materials*, p. 37 (1958).
83. HEALD, P. T. and BILBY, B. A. *Fracture toughness of high-strength materials: theory and practice*, p. 63. ISI Publ. No. 120, Iron and Steel Institute (1970).
84. WEERTMAN, J. *International Conference on fracture, Sendai, Japan*. Vol. 1, p. 154 (1965).
85. BILBY, B. A., COTTRELL, A. H., and SWINDEN, K. H. *Proc. R. Soc.* A**272,** 304 (1963).
86. FROST, N. E. and DIXON, J. R. *Int. J. Fracture Mech.* **3,** 301 (1967).

87. TOMKINS, B. Preprint for *Conferences on mechanics and mechanisms of crack growth*, Cambrige, Paper 10 (1973).
88. POOK, L. P. and FROST, N. E. *Int. J. Fracture* **9**, 53 (1973).
89. POOK, L. P. *J. mech. Engng. Sci.* **11**, 343 (1969).
90. MOORE, H. F. University of Illinois, Engineering Experimental Station Bull. No. 165 (1927).
91. DEFORREST, A. V. *J. appl. Mech.* **58**, A23 (1936).
92. HUNTER, M. S. and FRICKE, W. G. *Proc. Am. Soc. Test. Mater.* **56**, 1038 (1956).
93. CUMMINGS, H. N., STULEN, F. B., and SCHULTE, W. C. Wright Air Development Centre, Rep. No. 58-43 (1958).
94. LANGE, E. A., CROOKER, T. W., and MOREY, R. E. U.S. Naval Research Lab., Washington, NRL Rep. 6065 (1964).
95. URYU, T. *Proceedings of the 1st Japanese Congress on testing materials*, p. 1 (1958); *Proceedings of the 3rd Japanese Congress on testing materials*, p. 43 (1960).
96. ROLFE, S. T. and MUNSE, W. H. *Weld. J., Easton.* **28**, 252s (1963).
97. MCEVILY, A. J., BOETTNER, R. C., and BOND, A. P. *J. Inst. Metals* **93**, 481 (1965).
98. ROOKE, D. P., GUNN, N. J. F., BALLET, J. T., and BRADSHAW, F. J. Min. of Aviation, R.A.E. Tech. Rep. No. 64025 (1964).
99. PEARSON, S. *Nature* **211**, 1077 (1966).
100. BARSOM, J. M. *Damage tolerance in aircraft structures*, p. 1. American Society for Testing Materials, S.T.P. 486, (1971).
101. DIXON, J. R. *J. R. aeronaut. Soc.* **64**, 141 (1960); **66**, 320 (1962).
102. JOHNSON, H. H. and PARIS, P. C. *Eng. Fracture Mech.* **1**, 3 (1968).
103. PARIS, P. C., BUCCI, R. J., WESSEL, E. T., CLARK, W. G., and MAGER, T. R. *Stress analysis and growth of cracks*, p. 141. American Society for Testing Materials, S.T.P. 513 (1972).
104. KLESNIL, M. and LUKÁŠ, P. *Eng. Fracture Mech.* **4**, 77 (1972).
105. WADSWORTH, N. J. and HUTCHINGS, J. *Phil. Mag.* **3**, 1154 (1958).
106. BRADSHAW, F. J. Private Communication.
107. DIXON, J. R. and STRANNIGAN, J. S. *Second International Conference on fracture, Brighton*, p. 105 (1969).
108. SCHIJVE, J. and DERIJK, P. Nat. Aero. and Astro. Res. Inst., Amsterdam, NLR-TR, M2138 (1965).
109. HUDSON, C. M. and HARDRATH, H. F. NASA Tech. Note D960 (1961).
110. ENDO, T. *Proceedings of the 7th Japanese Congress Testing Materials*, p. 108 (1964).
111. PLUNKETT, R. and VISWANATHAN, N. *J. bas. Engng.* **89D**, 55 (1967).
112. MATTHEWS, W. T., BARATTA, F. I., and DRISCOLL, D. W. *Int. J. Fracture Mech.* **7**, 224 (1971).
113. RYMAN, R. J. *Aircr. Engng.* **34**, 34 (1962).
114. TROUGHTON, A. J. and McSTAY, J. *Current aeronautical fatigue problems* p. 429. Pergamon Press, Oxford (1965).
115. CHRISTENSEN, R. H. Douglas Missiles and Space Systems Division, Paper No. 3279 (1965).

116. O'NEILL, P. H. Min. of Aviation, R.A.E. Tech. Rep. No. 66100 (1966).

117. ACHTER, M. R. *Fatigue crack propagation*, p. 181. American Society for Testing Materials, S.T.P. 415 (1967).

118. WEI, R. P. *Eng. Fracture Mech.* **1**, 633 (1970).

119. HARTMAN, A. and SCHIJVE, J. *Eng. Fracture Mech.* **1**, 615 (1970).

120. FROST, N. E. *Appl. Mater. Res.* **3**, 131 (1964).

121. BRADSHAW, F. J. and WHEELER, C. *Int. J. Fracture Mech.* **5**, 255 (1969).

122. BRADSHAW, F. J. and WHEELER, C. Min. of Aviation, R.A.E. Tech. Rep. No. 65073 (1965).

123. CHRISTENSEN, R. H. *Trans. Am. Soc. Metals* **57**, 373 (1964).

124. SCHIJVE, J. Nat. Aero. and Astro. Res. Inst., Amsterdam, Rep. MP 219 (1963).

125. HARTMAN, A. and JACOBS, F. A. Nat. Aero. and Astro. Res. Inst., Amsterdam, NLR-TN, M2123 (1964).
     HARTMAN, A. *Int. J. Fracture Mech.* **1**, 167 (1965).

126. COX, H. L. and FIELD, J. E. *Aeronaut. Q.* **4**, 1 (1952).

127. FIELD, J. E. Private communication.

128. HUBBARD, R. P. *J. bas. Engng.* **91D**, 625 (1969).

129. SIH, G. C., PARIS, P. C., and ERDOGAN, F. *J. appl. Mech.* **29**, 306 (1962).

130. FOLIAS, E. S. *Int. J. Fracture Mech.* **1**, 104 (1965).

131. KIBLER, J. J. and ROBERTS, R. *J. Engng. Ind.* **92B**, 727 (1970).

132. POOK, L. P. *Int. J. Fracture Mech.* **8**, 118 (1972).

133. WALLGREN, G. and RUDIN, E. Min. of Aviation, R.A.E. Library Translation No. 703.

134. CHRISTENSEN, R. H. *Appl. Mater. Res.* **2**, 197 (1963).

135. GURNEY, T. R. *Fatigue of welded structures*. Cambridge University Press (1968).

136. WATKINSON, F., BODGER, P. N., and HARRISON, J. D. *Fatigue of welded structures Conference, Brighton*. p. 97 (1970).

137. FORSYTH, P. J. E., GEORGE, R. W., and RYDER, D. A. *Appl. Mater. Res.* **3**, 223 (1964).

138. PATON, W. Min. of Tech., NEL Rep. No. 346 (1968).

139. COTTRELL, A. H. *Proc. R. Soc.* **A276**, 1 (1963); *Trans. metall. Soc.*, *A.I.M.E.* **214**, 132 (1958).

140. COTTRELL, A. H. *The mechanical properties of matter*. Wiley, New York (1964).

141. IRWIN, G. R. *J. appl. Mech.* **24**, 361 (1957).

142. WELLS, A. A. *Br. Weld.* **12**, 2 (1965).

143. DOBSON, M. O. (Ed.) *Practical fracture mechanics for structural steel*. Chapman and Hall, London (1969).

144. BRITISH STANDARDS INSTITUTION. *Methods for plane strain fracture toughness* (K_{Ic}) *testing*. DD 3 (1971).

145. BRITISH STANDARDS INSTITUTION. *Methods for crack opening displacement* (COD) *testing*. DD 19 (1972).

146. HAHN, G. T. and ROSENFIELD, A. R. *Application related phenomena in titanium alloys*, p. 5. American Society for Testing Materials, S.T.P. 432 (1968).

147. BEGLEY, J. A. and LANDES, J. D. *Fracture toughness*, p. 1. American Society for Testing Materials, S.T.P. 514 (1972).
148. COTTERELL, B. *Int. J. Fracture Mech.* **4**, 209 (1968).
149. DVORAK, J. and VRTEL, J. *Weld. J. Easton.* **45**, 272s (1966).
150. RADON, J. C. and TURNER, C. E. *J. Iron Steel Inst.* **204**, 842 (1966).
151. BOYD, G. M. (Ed.) *Brittle fracture in steel structures*. Butterworth, London (1970).
152. TIPPER, C. F. *The Brittle fracture story*. Cambridge University Press (1962).
153. IRON AND STEEL INSTITUTE. *Fracture toughness*. ISI Publ. No. 121, Iron and Steel Institute (1969).
154. TIFFANY, C. F. and MASTERS, J. N. *Symposium on fracture toughness testing and its applications*, p. 249. American Society for Testing Materials, S.T.P. 381 (1965).
155. COLLIEPRIEST, J. E. and KIZER, D. E. *Metals Engng. Q.* **9**, 43 (1969).
156. CRICHLOW, W. J. and WELLS, R. H. *Fatigue Crack Propagation*, p. 25. American Society for Testing Materials, S.T.P. 415 (1967).
157. WILHEM, D. P. *Fracture mechanics guide lines for aircraft structural applications*. Northrop Corporation Aircraft Division Tech. Rep. AFFDL-TR-69-111 (1969).
158. ROBERTSON, T. S. and HUNT, D. M. West of Scotland Iron and Steel Institute, Paper No. 456 (1953).
     PELLINI, W. S. and PUZAK, P. P. U.S. Naval Research Lab. Rep. No. 5920 (1963).
     COTTRELL, C. L. M. and TURNER, M. J. *J. Iron Steel Inst.* **200**, 380 (1962).
159. ROLFE, S. T. and HALL, W. J. *Weld. J., Easton* **38**, 169s (1959).
160. NICHOLS, R. W. *Br. Weld. J.*, **15**, 21 (1968); **15**, 75 (1968).
161. FREED, C. N., SULLIVAN, A. M., and STOOP, J. U.S. Naval Research Lab. Rep. No. 7374 (1972).
162. WILLIAMS, D. Min. of Aviation, R.A.E. Tech. Note 289 (1960); *Crack Propagation Symposium, Cranfield*, p. 303 (1961).
163. IRVINE, W. H., QUIRK, A., and BEVITT, E. *J. Br. Nucl. Energy Soc.* **3**, 31 (1964).
     BEVITT, E., COWAN, A., and STOTT, A. L. *J. Br. Nucl. Energy. Soc.* **3**, 16 (1964).
164. COX, H. L. and OWEN, N. B. *Aeronaut. Q.* **12**, 1 (1961).
165. ERDOGAN, F., KIBLER, J. J., and ROBERTS, R. *First International Conference on pressure vessel technology, Delft*, p. 771 (1969).
166. ROMUALDI, J. P. *Crack propagation Symposium, Cranfield*, p. 287 (1961).
     HUNT, R. T. *Current aeronautical fatigue problems*, p. 287. Pergamon Press, Oxford (1965).
     FIGGE, I. E. and NEWMAN, J. C. *Fatigue crack propagation*, p. 71. American Society for Testing Materials, S.T.P. 415 (1967).
167. KHOL, R. *Mach. Des.* **40**, 136 (1968).
     ZIENKIEWICZ, O. C. *The finite element method in structural and continuum mechanics*. McGraw-Hill, New York (1967).
168. FRISCH, J. *Trans. Am. Soc. Mech. Engrs. J. bas. Engng.* **83**, 32 (1961).
169. HASLAM, G. H. *J. mech. Engng. Sci.* **13**, 130 (1971).

170. HARRISON, J. D. *Second International Conference on fracture, Brighton*, p. 777 (1969).
171. FISHER, J. W. *Fatigue of welded structures Conference, Brighton*, p. 135 (1970).
172. MADISON, R. B. *Application of fracture mechanics to bridges*. Ph.D. Thesis, Lehigh University (1969).
    MADISON, R. B. and IRWIN, G. R. *J. struct. Div. Am. Soc. civ. Engrs.* **97,** 2229 (1971).
173. BRAITHWAITE, A. B. M., RICHARDS, K. G., and HARRISON, J. D. *Weld. Inst. Res. Bull.* **11,** 261 (1970).
174. MADDOX, S. J. *Metal Constr. Br. Weld. J.* **2,** 285 (1970).
175. *Report of Royal Commission into the Failure of Kings Bridge*. Presented to Parliament of Victoria, Melbourne 1963. A. C. Brooks, Government Printers, Melbourne (1963).
176. HARDRATH, H. F., LEYBOLD, H. A., and LANDERS, C. B. NACA Tech. Note 3856 (1956).
177. HARDRATH, H. F. and LEYBOLD, H. A. NACA Tech. Note 4246 (1958).
178. WHALEY, R. E. and KURZHALS, P. R. NASA Tech. Note D543 (1960).
    PETERSON, J. J. NASA Rep. No. CR333 (1965).
    CAPRIOLO, I. *Current aeronautical fatigue problems*, p. 325. Pergamon Press, Oxford (1965).

Notes on various other aspects of fatigue

PREVIOUS chapters have discussed the initiation and development of micro-cracks and their subsequent propagation as macrocracks. This chapter is divided into sections, each of which deals with some practical aspect of fatigue behaviour such as, for example, the fatigue strength of welded joints, low-endurance fatigue, cumulative damage, and the fatigue strength of pressurized containers.

Although each section has a central theme, there is inevitably some overlap between sections. Material has had to be allocated, therefore, to a particular section on an arbitrary basis, in some cases. However, it is hoped that the assembly of these sections into a single chapter will emphasize that despite their differing themes each section contains data whose interpretation can only be rationalized in terms of the fatigue crack initiation and propagation phenomena discussed in previous chapters.

6.1. Low-endurance fatigue

6.1.1. Introduction

The plain and notched fatigue limits, or fatigue strengths at long en-durances, of different materials have been discussed in Chapters 3 and 4, respectively. However, a knowledge of the fatigue limit of a material gives no indication of the life that may be expected from a specimen tested at a stress level greater than the fatigue limit. Such information may be required in designing a component or structural member which it is known will be subjected to a finite number of loadings during its lifetime. Gas cylinders, gun barrels, aircraft undercarriage assemblies, and various other aircraft components are examples of members which are subjected to only a limited number of stress reversals in their working life. Obviously, if both static and fatigue design considerations can be satisfied by considering the component life to be restricted to a stipulated number of loading cycles after which it is taken out of service, a more efficient and economic use of material is achieved than if the component is designed to have an infinite life. A gas cylinder, for example, if filled once a day will be subjected to only 18 250 loading cycles in 50 years; a design stress based on the value of the repeated internal pressure giving failure after 100 000 loading cycles should have a sufficiently large built-in safety factor. The region covering lives of components or specimens of up to about 10^5 cycles has come to be known as low-endurance fatigue or low-cycle fatigue.

Some suggested relationships defining the finite-life region of the S/N curve have been given in § 3.1. Such expressions are restricted to direct stress loadings because local plastic deformation may take place each cycle in

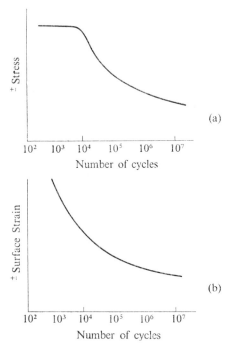

FIG. 6.1. Diagrammatic S/N curves.

specimens tested at stress levels above the fatigue limit. To be applicable to cyclic bending tests, it is necessary for the life to be related to a true surface stress, calculated from the applied bending moment and the known dynamic stress–strain characteristics of the material. If the bending stress is calculated from the applied bending moment assuming that the specimen remains elastic, the specimen life is greater than in a direct stress test at the same stress level.

The S/N curve, obtained by plotting the results of a series of direct stress, zero mean load, constant stress amplitude tests on plain specimens of a given material on the usual stress-range–log-endurance axes, flattens out at very short endurances (see Fig. 6.1(a)) implying that, if a specimen does not break when the first tensile loading (quarter-cycle) is applied, it will survive at least several hundred cycles. Because the amount of plastic deformation occurring each cycle may vary with testing speed, the shape of the S/N diagram, especially at high stress levels may vary markedly with testing speed; such tests may need to be carried out at a very low testing speed in order to avoid specimen heating. The flattened shape of the S/N curve in the low-endurance region implies that small changes in stress level will result in large changes in life. This, together with the fact that it is difficult to plot meaningful S/N curves for bending tests, has led to tests being carried out in which the strain range rather than the stress range is maintained constant. If the results of constant strain amplitude tests, whether these be uniaxial direct strain, bending, or torsion [1] are plotted on strain-range–log-endurance axes, the experimental points fall around a smooth curve of the form shown in Fig. 6.1(b), implying that fracture can occur after any number of cycles. This difference in behaviour between constant-strain and constant-stress amplitude tests arises because, in the latter tests, work-hardening reduces progressively the plastic strain range imposed on the specimen, whereas, in the former tests, a given cyclic strain amplitude is forced on the specimen irrespective of the magnitude of the external load necessary to achieve the stipulated strain amplitude.

Although annealed materials work-harden when cyclically deformed plastically, cold-worked materials can strain-soften when thus cycled. Constant strain amplitude tests [2] on various steels, titanium alloys, aluminium alloys, and other materials, in which the peak stress levels attained were measured throughout a test, showed that whether a material work-hardened or work-softened depended on the ratio of its static tensile strength to its yield stress. If this ratio exceeded 1·4, a material would work-harden; if less than 1·2, a material would work-soften.

Constant strain amplitude tests may be carried out in two ways: either the total strain range or the plastic strain range experienced by the specimen is maintained constant through the test (see Fig. 6.2). It has been argued that, because cyclic plastic strain is responsible for fatigue damage, the use of this quantity is more likely to lead to a correlation of the data than the use of the total strain amplitude. On the other hand, it can be argued that, for practical design purposes, it is the total strain amplitude that will be known, and thus correlation of the data in terms of total strain amplitude will be of direct practical use. This latter point is certainly true if the designer is interested in lives in the region of 10^5 cycles, because the plastic strain component of the total strain range will be small, and it would be impractical to carry out tests at such small plastic strain ranges. Several reviews of low-endurance fatigue have been written [3–6].

6.1.2. Total strain amplitude tests

Various investigators [3, 7, 8] have carried out constant total strain amplitude tests on a wide range of materials representing the results by equations

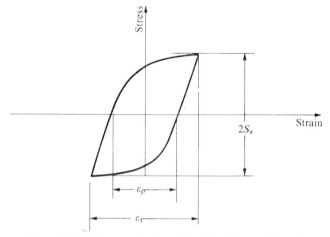

FIG. 6.2. Cyclic stress–strain relationship (hysteresis loop).

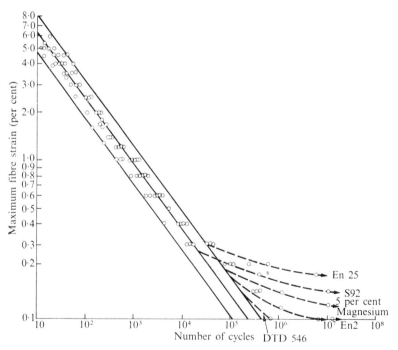

FIG. 6.3. Constant maximum fibre strain amplitude reversed bending tests on steels and aluminium alloys. (Taken from Low [7].)

of the form

$$\varepsilon_t N^m = C,$$

where ε_t is the total strain range, N the number of cycles to failure, and m and C are material constants. Results of plane bending tests on mild steel, aluminium alloy, and alloy steel specimens [7] are shown in Fig. 6.3; for strain amplitudes between ± 0.4 per cent and ± 5 per cent, the data can be represented by

$$\varepsilon_t N^{0.41} = 0.30,$$

where ε_t is here the maximum fibre total strain range.

Reversed plane bending tests on 16 steels [8] gave results fitting a similar relationship over the endurance range $5 \times 10^3 – 10^5$ cycles; values of m and C, however, varied as shown in Table 6.1.

TABLE 6.1

Type of steel	m	C
Carbon and manganese steels, up to 1·5% Mn	0·42	0·44
Low-alloy steels, 1·5–2·0% total alloy content	0·27	0·10
Complex alloy steels, 2·5–4·0% total alloy content	0·21	0·06

The total strain range–life relationship of 30 widely different metallic alloys tested in reversed direct loading over the range $10–10^6$ cycles has been found to conform to the expression [9]

$$\varepsilon_t = 3.5 \frac{S_t}{E} N^{-0.12} + \varepsilon_f^{0.6} N^{-0.6},$$

where S_t is the tensile strength of the material, E is Young's modulus, ε_f is the fracture ductility, that is, $\ln (A_0/A_f)$, where A_0 and A_f are the original and final cross-sectional areas of a static tensile test-specimen, ε_t is the total strain amplitude, and N is the life. As a rough guide, it was suggested that most materials when subjected to a total strain range of 0·01 would survive approximately 10 000 cycles. Another similar rule-of-thumb relationship [10] states that most materials will survive a total strain range of 0·02 for approximately 1000 cycles.

6.1.3. Plastic strain amplitude tests

Data relating the endurance to the plastic strain amplitude may be obtained either directly from tests in which the hysteresis loop width, that is, the plastic strain range (Fig. 6.2), is maintained constant or by calculating the plastic strain component of the total strain, in a constant total strain amplitude test. Coffin and others [11] found that the data obtained from reversed direct constant plastic strain amplitude tests, designed to give failures in up to about 10^5 cycles, on aluminium, copper, 0·1% C steel, nickel, 18/8 austenitic steel, titanium, and aluminium alloys conformed to the relationship

$$N^{\frac{1}{2}}\varepsilon_p = C, \tag{6.1}$$

where ε_p is the plastic strain amplitude and C a material constant. It was also found that, if the static fracture ductility ε_f (that is, $\ln (A_0/A_f)$) was taken as the value of ε_p corresponding to $N = \frac{1}{4}$ cycle, this point lay near the line drawn through the fatigue data. Some results of tests on aluminium, titanium, and aluminium alloy are shown on Fig. 6.4. The life over which the

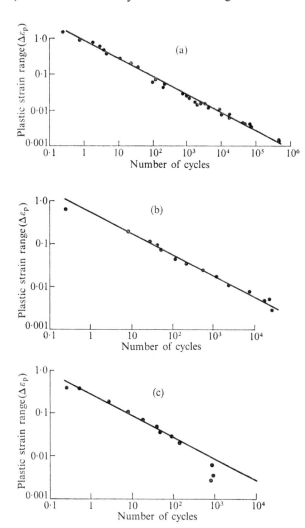

FIG. 6.4. Plastic strain range versus cycles to failure. (a) Aluminium, commercially pure. (b) Titanium, commercially pure. (c) $5\frac{1}{2}\%$ Zn–aluminium alloy. (Taken from Coffin [11].)

linear relationship is valid varies with material, being about 10^5 cycles for aluminium and 18/8 stainless steel, about 10^3 cycles for the high-strength aluminium alloys, and about 10^2 cycles for copper. It was also shown [11] that both room-temperature constant total strain amplitude data [7] and similar data [12] on 3 steels (18/8 austenitic, 13% Cr, 3% Cr–Mo) at temperatures up to 500 °C, when re-analysed in terms of the plastic strain range component ε_p, conformed to eqn (6.1).

Coffin argued that, because the fatigue data extrapolated back to the fracture ductility ε_f (given by $\ln (A_0/A_f)$), the value of C for a particular material in eqn (6.1) could be obtained by putting $\varepsilon_p = \varepsilon_f$ when $N = \frac{1}{4}$, that is, $\varepsilon_f/2 = C$. Thus eqn (6.1) becomes

$$N^{\frac{1}{2}}\varepsilon_p = \varepsilon_f/2. \qquad (6.2)$$

It was also suggested [13] that, when tests were carried out at elevated temperatures, ε_f could be replaced by an equivalent ductility ε_f' which depended both on temperature and strain rate. From analysis of experimental data it was found that a master curve could be plotted relating ε_f' and a parameter $T(7\cdot95-\log \dot\varepsilon_p)$, where T is the absolute temperature and $\dot\varepsilon_p$ the plastic strain rate. Thus, knowing T and $\dot\varepsilon_p$ for a given set of test conditions, ε_f' could be obtained from the master curve and the low-endurance fatigue life obtained from the equation

$$N^{\frac{1}{2}}\varepsilon_p = \varepsilon'/2. \qquad (6.3)$$

While eqns (6.2) or (6.3) are useful for representing fatigue data, it has been suggested that they could be converted to a form more adaptable to elastic design procedures. Making the assumption that, although the structure to be designed undergoes some plastic deformation, elastic stress analysis can be applied to determine the strains so produced, it was shown [14, 15] that in many cases the strains (but not the stresses) so calculated were good approximations to those actually obtained. These strains are related to material behaviour for design purposes by the use of eqn (6.2), thus

$$S_a = \frac{E\varepsilon_f}{4N^{\frac{1}{2}}}+S_0,$$

where S_a is the applied stress amplitude and S_0 the stress amplitude at the fatigue limit. Experimental evidence [16] from low-endurance fatigue tests on 12 structural materials showed that a reasonable correlation was obtained. Other stress–endurance relationships in the low-endurance range are reviewed by Landgraf [5].

Manson [2, 14, 17, 18] presented an analysis of direct loading constant plastic strain amplitude tests for 30 materials of widely differing static properties [9] showing that in all cases the endurance up to about 5×10^4 cycles was related to the plastic strain range by the relationship

$$\varepsilon_p N^{0.6} = C,$$

where C was given by $\varepsilon_t^{0.6}$ and ε_t, the fracture ductility is given by $\ln (A_0/A_t)$. He suggested that the results conformed to this relationship, and not eqn (6.1), because N had been taken as the number of cycles to complete fracture of the specimen (that is, separation of the specimen into two pieces), whereas eqn (6.1) was based on endurances at which cracks were first visible on the specimen surface. It is now accepted that the value of the exponent in eqn (6.1) is not a universal constant; it varies with material, environment, and the criterion adopted for failure [6, 19].

The numerous attempts [6, 9, 16, 17, 20–4] to interpret the constant C in terms of the monotonic fracture ductility ε_t have been summarized by Landgraf [5]. The relationship between stress, plastic strain, and plastic strain energy during a low-endurance fatigue test has been studied by Morrow [6]. He attempts to relate the life to the total plastic strain energy generated, that is, C is made a function of the integrated areas of the hysteresis loop up to the point of failure.

6.1.4. Mode of fracture and the effect of mean strain

The ability of a material to withstand a few cycles of large strain amplitude depends on the ductility of the material and how this is decreased by subsequent work-hardening. For example, reversed direct constant strain amplitude tests [25] on $4\frac{1}{2}\%$ Cu–aluminium specimens in which cyclic strains between ±0.3 and ±0.12 were applied, caused fracture in from 1 cycle to 7 cycles. The material work-hardened rapidly in the first $1\frac{1}{2}$ cycles, but thereafter the hysteresis loop on a true-stress–log strain basis showed negligible change. However, static tensile tests on duplicate specimens, which had been subjected to the same strain amplitudes as the fatigue specimens for only a part of the total life, showed that the ductility decreased steadily with increasing number of cycles until its value was equal to the applied value at which point fracture occurred.

The appearance of a fatigue specimen broken after a short number of cycles may therefore be more characteristic of a static tensile fracture than a typical fatigue fracture, the latter being obtained only if the loading cycle is such as to produce a failure in excess of some minimum life value. For example, it has been suggested [3, 26] that copper and aluminium alloy zero mean load specimens must have lives of at least 4000 cycles and 100 cycles, respectively, if typical fatigue fractures are to be obtained.

Both reversed direct stress and repeated tension short endurance constant stress amplitude tests carried out on mild steel, $5\frac{1}{2}\%$ Zn-aluminium alloy, and annealed and cold-rolled copper specimens showed [27] that the test-section of both mild steel and copper specimens subjected to a stress level approaching their tensile strengths extended permanently each cycle; even in a zero mean load test, the extension was not cancelled out during the compression half of the cycle. The final fracture was typical of a necked-down static tensile fracture. All zero mean load specimens failing before 100 cycles and repeated tension specimens failing before 5000 cycles exhibited a necked-down fracture. This phenomena of steady extension was termed 'cyclic creep'; it could be prevented in a zero mean load test by continually adjusting the load limits, very small tensile or compressive mean loads making the specimen either elongate or contract. No $5\frac{1}{2}\%$ Zn–aluminium alloy specimens exhibited cyclic creep but no repeated tensile stress specimens which survived the first loading cycle failed before 6000 cycles although failures of zero mean load specimens occurred at all endurances down to 20. It appeared that true fatigue failure occurred in a constant stress amplitude test only if the specimen did not deform permanently. If permanent deformation occurred, failure was due to cyclic creep, this leading to a discontinuity in the S/N curve of the material.

In constant strain amplitude tests on the same three materials, it was found that if a tensile mean strain was present, a reversal of the sign of the stress occurred in straining the specimen back to the lower strain limit, the magnitude of the compressive stress increasing rapidly each cycle until it was equal to the tensile stress corresponding to the maximum tensile strain in the cycle. Thus, although a test was nominally a repeated tensile strain test, it was, in fact, fulfilling the conditions of a reversed direct constant stress amplitude test. This point is illustrated by the results [28] given in Table 6.2 from repeated unidirectional tests on specimens of two steels. A specimen was bent to a maximum fibre tensile strain of 0·5 per cent, measurements being taken in each cycle of the peak bending moment required to reach this strain and then to restraighten the bar.

Several empirical relationships have been suggested for relating life to both the range of strain and the mean tensile strain. One such relationship [23, 29]

TABLE 6.2

Cycle number	620 MN m^{-2} tensile strength steel		460 MN m^{-2} tensile strength steel	
	Bending moment (N m)	Equivalent mean and range (N m)	Bending moment (N m)	Equivalent mean and range (N m)
1	0 to 162	81 ± 81	0 to 81	41 ± 41
2	-48 to 156	54 ± 102	-65 to 85	10 ± 75
3	-58 to 154	48 ± 106	-67 to 87	10 ± 77
500	-88 to 128	20 ± 108	-87 to 95	4 ± 91
1000	-101 to 115	7 ± 108	-87 to 95	4 ± 91

applicable to various carbon steels and aluminium alloys is

$$N^{\frac{1}{2}} = \left(\frac{\varepsilon_t - \varepsilon_m}{\varepsilon_t}\right),$$

where N is the number of cycles to fracture, ε_t the total strain range, ε_m the mean tensile strain, and ε_f the fracture ductility.

Constant strain amplitude tests [4] on mild steel specimens at both zero mean strain and with a superimposed tensile mean strain showed that the relationship

$$N^m \varepsilon_{pt} = C$$

applied to tensile strain cycles, where ε_{pt} was the tensile plastic strain range in the cycle. For tests intermediate between zero mean strain and repeated tensile strain, it was found that

$$\frac{1}{m} = 1 - 0 \cdot 86r,$$

where r is the ratio of compressive to tensile plastic strain range. Thus for zero mean strain tests, $r = -1$ and

$$N^{0.54} \varepsilon_{pt} = C,$$

whereas, for a repeated tensile strain cycle, $r = 0$ and

$$N \varepsilon_{pt} = C.$$

6.1.5. Notched specimens

In general [3], the results of short endurance constant nominal stress amplitude tests on notched specimens give an S/N curve of similar form to that for plain specimens, except that it is displaced to the left and can cross over that for plain specimens at very short endurances (see Fig. 6.5). The fact that the nominal stress amplitude required to cause fracture in a given short endurance may be higher for a notched than for a plain specimen is a consequence of the triaxial stress system generated across the minimum section of the former specimen. This reduces the plastic deformation and the onset of necking in this region, thus leading to an increased tensile strength (based on original net area) compared to that obtained on a plain specimen of the same minimum cross-sectional area. The initial flat portion of the S/N curve for notched specimens may also be much shorter than for plain specimens, probably because the material at the notch root is restrained by the bulk of the specimen and tends to undergo constant strain amplitude cycling even though the specimen as a whole is subjected to a nominal constant stress amplitude loading cycle. Several workers [30] have found that the constant nominal stress amplitude S/N curve for notched specimens may cross that for smooth specimens somewhere in the region of 100–1000 cycles.

In the case of sharp notches, cracks form quickly at high stress levels, and the life of a specimen is spent wholly in crack propagation; the life of a specimen or component therefore bears little relationship to the K_t value of the notch. It depends on the distance the crack must traverse to cause complete failure. The rate of growth of a crack at these high stress (or strain) levels cannot be predicted using the crack growth relationships discussed in Chapter 5 because these are applicable only as long as the bulk of the specimen remote from the crack tip is deforming elastically. A rough estimate can be made in

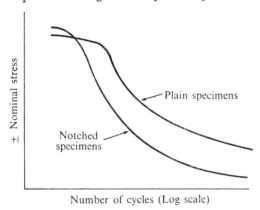

FIG. 6.5. Diagrammatic S/N curve for notched specimens.

the case of a crack growing under a constant strain amplitude by converting the strain to an equivalent elastic stress, and using one of the crack growth relationships discussed in Chapter 5. (In the case of a notched specimen, the initial crack length must be taken as the notch depth and the crack length subsequently measured from the free surface.) This approach is equivalent to assuming that the strain distribution is the same above and below general yielding, and has been used to predict static failure [31]. It is more likely to be successful when the crack length is small compared with other dimensions. Fatigue crack growth data in the fully plastic region have been successfully correlated using displacements calculated from slip-line fields [32], and with measurements of the crack opening displacement (COD) at the crack tip. Some results for mild steel [33] are shown in Fig. 6.6; the rate of crack growth is roughly proportional to (COD)². The application of COD to static failures is described briefly in §§ 5.2 and 5.10.

Morrow and his co-workers [34, 35] have developed an analysis of notched fatigue behaviour in the low-endurance region by considering the local stress-strain response at the notch. Changes in nominal stress ΔS and nominal strain Δe are related to corresponding changes in local stress $\Delta \sigma$ and local strain $\Delta \varepsilon$ by the relationship

$$K_f(\Delta S \Delta e E)^{\frac{1}{2}} = (\Delta \sigma \Delta \varepsilon E)^{\frac{1}{2}}.$$

They claim that life predictions for notched members may be made by this analysis from smooth specimen data, but this can presumably only apply if the whole life of a specimen is spent in initiating and developing a microcrack. When this is so, the Morrow approach would seem to be merely a quantitative alternative to obtaining the endurance from a smooth specimen plastic-strain–endurance curve. Hence, the life of a mildly notched specimen ($K_t \approx 2$

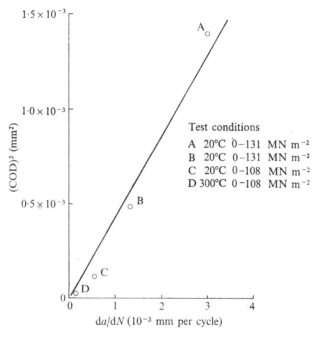

FIG. 6.6. High-strain fatigue crack propagation rates as a function of crack opening displacement. Tests carried out at 20 °C and 300 °C in repeated tension on mild steel plates $1\cdot83$ m $\times 0\cdot91$ m $\times 12\cdot7$ mm containing a central sharp $0\cdot23$ m slit. (Taken from Edmondson, *et al.* [33].)

or 3) can be obtained from this curve using the appropriately factored plastic strain. It must be emphasized that this approach applies only to specimens with smooth well-prepared surfaces. Although a component with an as-forged finish would display the same stress–strain response as a polished component, the life of the as-forged component would be spent wholly in propagating a macrocrack and therefore should be estimated by fracture mechanics methods.

6.1.6. Discussion

When a material fractures after a small number of loading cycles the failure may be either as in a conventional static tensile test or as in a conventional fatigue test.

In a constant true stress amplitude test, tensile failure can only occur during the first cycle because, if the specimen can sustain the maximum stress in the first cycle without fracturing, it will be able to do so in subsequent cycles until a surface crack develops and grows to such a size that the uncracked area can no longer carry the maximum load. If, however, the specimen necks-down on the first cycle and the load is not adjusted to maintain the initial stress on the reduced area, it is then possible for the specimen to break as a tensile fracture on the second or any subsequent cycle. On the other hand a tensile fracture can occur during any cycle in a constant strain amplitude test provided that the material is still continuing to cyclically work-harden. A specimen will fail during this work-hardening stage if the ductility of the material is reduced below the strain level being forced on to the specimen; it will fail as would a specimen of similar material work-hardened to the same reduced ductility tested in static tension. However cyclic work-hardening is usually completed early in the life and, provided the cyclic ductility of the material is still greater than the imposed strain amplitude, fracture can only occur by the initiation and propagation of surface cracks. This is supported by the fact that, as in tests at stress levels near the fatigue limit (Chapter 2), the life of a specimen subjected to a high strain amplitude is increased by machining away the surface [36]. However, the type of surface cracking at high stress or strain levels may be different from that at low stresses; grain-boundary cracking may be more common than slip-band cracking. High cyclic strain amplitudes also result in the grains of a material developing a characteristic sub-structure (see also § 2.2, § 2.3.6, and § 5.4) and, although there is no experimental evidence that this structure promotes internal crack-ing, the material flows more easily under a superimposed mean stress than it would in its initial uncycled condition. For example, it was found [37, 38] that the cyclic creep rate of plain specimens subjected to large cyclic strains and low mean stresses was many times larger than occurred in a static creep test at a load equal to the maximum value in the loading cycle applied for a comparable time. This would seem to support the argument that the cyclic structure does not promote a fracture mechanism but rather inhibits work-hardening, so permitting the material to extend under a mean stress until a necked-down fracture occurs.

The experimental data presented suggest that the life of a plain specimen tested in low-endurance fatigue is given by $\varepsilon N^m = C$, where ε is the strain range and m and C are constants for a particular material and testing condi-tions. When ε is expressed as the plastic strain range ε_p and the number of cycles to failure N defined by the presence of visible surface cracks, then m has a value of about $\frac{1}{2}$ for all materials. The value of N over which this rela-tionship is valid depends on material, and it could be argued that it corre-sponds to the number of cycles required to develop a surface crack to the stage where it can spread rapidly. Indeed May [39] (see §§ 2.4 and 6.2) shows that his model of surface cracking when modified to apply to a specimen subjected to a constant plastic strain amplitude leads to an $\varepsilon_p N^m = C$ relationship.

On the other hand, the fracture faces of short endurance, high strain amplitude specimens exhibit striations immediately adjacent to the point of crack initiation, suggesting that a crack commences growing as a macro-crack at a very early stage in the life [40]. The general relationship $N^m \varepsilon = C$, where ε may be either total or plastic strain range, is the type of relationship that would be expected if low-endurance fatigue failure under a given strain amplitude is essentially a crack-propagation problem. Since the growth rate of a crack is a function of its length and the nominal strain range in the bulk of the material, we can take

$$\frac{\mathrm{d}a}{\mathrm{d}N} = A\varepsilon^b a^c.$$

If we consider $c = 1$, then $\ln(a_t/a_0) = A\varepsilon^b N$, where a_t is the crack length at final fracture and a_0 the length at which a surface crack can be first considered a macrocrack. For a given series of tests $\ln(a_t/a_0)$ will be sensibly constant and thus

$$\varepsilon^b N = \text{constant}$$

or

$$\varepsilon N^m = \text{constant}.$$

The relationship would not be expected to hold below the plastic strain range at which the number of cycles spent in developing a microcrack to the macrocrack stage becomes a significant proportion of the total life.

It has been suggested that a relationship of the form $N^{\frac{1}{2}}\varepsilon_p = C$ could be obtained [41] by equating the total plastic work at fracture absorbed in a fatigue specimen to the plastic work absorbed by a tensile specimen up to the point of fracture. However, any argument that a specimen subjected to a given plastic strain range fractures when it has absorbed some critical amount of work is invalidated, at least for fatigue failure, by the fact that the life of a specimen is increased by machining a thin layer from the surface and in these circumstances is determined only by its original size and the frequency and depth of surface machining, irrespective of the work done in deforming it plastically each cycle.

It must be borne in mind that few engineering components behave like plain polished specimens, so that data applicable only to such specimens are of limited use. In finite-life design situations, cracks will be present in notched components long before complete failure occurs. For sharply notched com-ponents and constant amplitude stress levels such that the net area maximum nominal stress is less than 80 per cent of the yield stress, life should be calcu-lated from crack growth rate data. At higher stress levels estimates of ex-pected life may be made along the lines indicated in § 6.1.5. For components containing less severe stress concentrations and for variable amplitude loading conditions, the only certain way of determining the life is to carry out a fatigue test on the component itself, simulating service loadings as closely as possible.

6.2. Fatigue under varying stress amplitudes

6.2.1. Introduction

Whereas specimens tested in conventional fatigue machines are subjected to a cyclic stress of constant amplitude throughout their lives, most structural members and machine components are subjected in service to cyclic loadings of varying amplitude, the variation in stress level following either a regular or random pattern. To be absolutely confident that fatigue cracks will never form in these members or components, a designer must ensure that at no point in them is there a cyclic stress, created by the external loading, having an amplitude greater than that at the plain fatigue limit of the material. This procedure, however, may lead to an over-conservative design, particularly if high loads in service occur only very occasionally. If the design is such that stresses greater than the plain fatigue limit are allowed to occur, the component will not have an infinite life because the cumulative effect of these high stress cycles will eventually cause failure, but the total endurance necessary for this to happen may be many times the required service life of the component. However, to design a component for a finite life when it is subjected to stress cycles of varying amplitude, an acceptable method of predicting life under such conditions is necessary. The investigation of fatigue under varying stress amplitudes has come to be known as the study of cumulative damage, because of the early interest in how fatigue 'damage' at various stress levels accumulated; a fatigue test in which the stress amplitude is varied in some manner during a test is often termed a cumulative damage test.

Many early investigations were carried out employing very simple tests in which the amplitude of the cyclic loading applied to the specimen varied between two stress levels in a regular manner; the assumption was that the mechanism of damage accumulation elucidated from such tests could then be applied to more realistic stress histories as met in service applications. Such two-level tests could be:

Step tests where a specimen is tested at a given stress $\pm S_1$ for a given number of cycles n_1 which is less than the expected life N_1 at that stress level. The stress is then changed to $\pm S_2$, and the test is continued at this stress level until either the specimen fractures or the test is stopped.

Repeated block tests where a specimen is subjected alternately to $\pm S_1$ for n_1 cycles, and to $\pm S_2$ for n_2 cycles, until either the specimen breaks or the test is stopped.

More complicated cumulative damage tests have included step or block tests involving more than two stress levels, programme tests in which a specimen is subjected to a block test consisting of a number of stress levels, the number of cycles for which each stress level is applied in each block being in proportion to an actual load distribution which a particular component experiences in service, randomized multi-stress level block tests in which the order of application of a given stress level and the associated number of cycles is random, and random loading tests in which the amplitude of each stress cycle varies in a random manner between zero and a fixed maximum value.

6.2.2. The Palmgren–Miner rule and early experimental work

Many attempts have been made to predict the life of a specimen in a cumulative damage test, and many data have been accumulated for the purpose of either deriving appropriate empirical relationships or to prove or disprove theoretical predictions. Palmgren [42], in predicting the life of ball

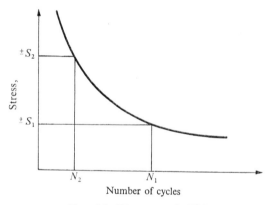

FIG. 6.7. Diagrammatic S/N curve.

bearings, assumed that damage was accumulated linearly with number of revolutions. Similarly, Miner [43] suggested that, in a fatigue test, damage of a specimen at a given stress level could be considered to accumulate linearly with the number of stress cycles, failure occurring when the accumulated damage reached some critical value. Thus if a specimen, stressed at $\pm S_1$, has a life of N_1 cycles, the damage after n_1 cycles will be n_1/N_1 of the damage at failure. Applying this argument to a two-level step test on a material for which the constant stress amplitude S/N curve is as shown on Fig. 6.7 (that is, the lives at $\pm S_1$ and $\pm S_2$ are N_1 and N_2 and the damage per cycle at $\pm S_1$ is D/N_1 and at $\pm S_2$ is D/N_2, where D is the damage at final fracture) and in which the total number of cycles the specimen has been subjected to at $\pm S_1$ and $\pm S_2$ are n_1 and n_2, respectively, gives the damage D at fracture as

$$D = \frac{Dn_1}{N_1} + \frac{Dn_2}{N_2},$$

and therefore

$$1 = \frac{n_1}{N_1} + \frac{n_2}{N_2}.$$

Similarly, for a multi-level test,

$$1 = \frac{n_1}{N_1} + \frac{n_1}{N_2} + \frac{n_3}{N_3} + \frac{n_4}{N_4} + \ldots = \sum \frac{n_i}{N_i},$$

where the ratio of the number of cycles at a given stress level to the expected life at the same stress level, that is, n_i/N_i, is termed the cycle ratio. The above equation, that is, $\sum (n_i/N_i) = 1$, is referred to either as the linear cumulative damage law or as the Palmgren–Miner law or just simply as Miner's law.

The physical reality of the damage D at any instant in the test is not defined, but it could be argued that it is a measure of the growth of a crack across the specimen, its value at failure corresponding to the point at which the crack is sufficiently large to cause catastrophic failure.

Consider a specimen where the total life is spent in propagating a crack across the section at a rate given by $da/dN = B(\Delta K)^m$, where $\Delta K = 2S(\pi a)^{\frac{1}{2}}\alpha$ (see § 5.2), and assume that no residual stresses are induced into the material ahead of the crack tip by changes in stress level, so that the growth rate is not dependent on stress history. If the specimen contains an initial crack of length a_0 and catastrophic failure occurs at crack length a_f, then the life under a constant stress amplitude of $\pm S_1$ is given by

$$N_1 = \frac{1}{B2^m S_1^m \pi^{m/2}\alpha^m \left(\frac{m}{2}-1\right)} \left(\frac{1}{a_0^{(m/2-1)}} - \frac{1}{a_f^{(m/2-1)}}\right),$$

which may be written

$$N_1 = \frac{k}{S_1^m}\left(\frac{1}{a_0^M} - \frac{1}{a_f^M}\right),$$

and similarly under $\pm S_2$ by

$$N_2 = \frac{k}{S_2^m}\left(\frac{1}{a_0^M} - \frac{1}{a_f^M}\right).$$

Now consider the specimen subjected to $\pm S_1$ for n_1 cycles, failure occurring after n_2 cycles at $\pm S_2$. If a_1 is the crack length after n_1 cycles, then

$$k\left(\frac{1}{a_0^M} - \frac{1}{a_1^M}\right) = S_1^m n_1$$

and

$$k\left(\frac{1}{a_1^M} - \frac{1}{a_f^M}\right) = S_2^m n_2.$$

Substituting for S_1 and S_2

$$k\left(\frac{1}{a_0^M} - \frac{1}{a_1^M}\right) = \frac{n_1}{N_1} k\left(\frac{1}{a_0^M} - \frac{1}{a_f^M}\right)$$

and

$$k\left(\frac{1}{a_1^M} - \frac{1}{a_f^M}\right) = \frac{n_2}{N_2} k\left(\frac{1}{a_0^M} - \frac{1}{a_f^M}\right).$$

Hence, adding,

$$\frac{n_1}{N_1} + \frac{n_2}{N_2} = 1.$$

The Palmgren–Miner rule is derivable therefore from consideration of simple fatigue crack propagation.

Not unexpectedly, the results of cumulative damage tests often do not conform to the predictions of the linear damage law. Even in simple two-level step tests, for example, the life of a specimen is found to depend on the order in which the stresses are applied. One reason for this can be illustrated by reference to the crack growth analysis given above. If S_2 is smaller than S_1, compressive residual stresses will be induced in the material around the crack tip when the stresses are changed, and the crack growth rate will be less than expected until the crack has passed through the affected zone (§ 5.9.3). Thus, the life of the specimen will be longer than that predicted from the linear damage law. On the other hand, if S_2 is greater than S_1, the linear damage law might be expected to give a reasonable prediction of specimen life if the major part of this is spent in crack propagation, as is so for sharply notched speci-mens. For plain specimens, however, where the bulk of the life is spent in initiating and developing a microcrack, the value of $\sum (n/N)$ in simple two-level step tests tends to be above unity for low–high stress tests, presumably because understressing effects at the low stress tend to strengthen the material (§ 2.3.4). Conversely, in high–low stress tests on plain specimens the value of $\sum (n/N)$ is often found to be less than unity, since the high stress develops a microcrack further than would have been achieved by the crack growing solely under the low stress for a comparable proportion of its life. There is in fact no physical reason for assuming that damage accumulation in the micro-crack initiation and development stage should be linear and therefore additive. Indeed, it has been shown that different processes of microstructural damage exist at different levels of cyclic strain [44, 45]. However, even within a rela-tively small range of cyclic strain, the differences in the processes of micro-crack initiation and macrocrack propagation make it improbable that a simple additive rule such as the Palmgren–Miner rule would provide an accurate prediction.

A large number of simple two-level tests were carried out on a wide variety of materials and specimens by numerous investigators [46–57] in the period up to 1960. A wide range of values for $\sum (n/N)$ was obtained, although most values lay between 0·3 and 3·0 and the trends described above began to become obvious. As a variation, two-level tests of a somewhat different nature were carried out by several investigators [58]. These involved testing a plain specimen at a stress level greater than its plain fatigue limit for a given number of cycles and then retesting it at the fatigue limit stress. If the specimen did not break at this latter stress level, it was assumed that no damage had been caused by the previous higher stressing whereas, if the specimen did break, it was considered that the previous stressing was damaging. By varying the initial testing conditions, a damage line could be constructed which indicated the maximum number of times that a stress level above the fatigue limit could be applied to the specimen which would not result in damage detectable by retesting at the fatigue limit. A further variation on this procedure is to subject a batch of specimens of a given material to the same initial stressing (greater than the plain fatigue limit) for the same number of cycles and then use this batch of tested specimens to determine an S/N curve. Series of S/N curves corresponding to various initial stressing conditions can be obtained in this manner, an estimate of the effectiveness of the initial stressing in damaging the material being obtained by comparing these S/N curves with the S/N curve for the virgin material [59]. A simple method for obtaining these damage S/N curves was proposed [60] for a material whose S/N curve exhibited a sharp knee, a fatigue limit, and a linear finite-life region, based on the assumption that, whatever the initial damage treatment, the knee of the S/N curve occurred always at the same number of cycles. Thus two fatigue tests on specimens subjected to a given initial stress level for a certain number of cycles were sufficient to define the S/N curve for this damage treatment. Data on SAE 4130 steel gave fair agreement with the suggested analysis. In 1965 an extension of this work [61] involving a cumulative damage relationship applicable to two-level tests was published and, as recently as 1969, new work on damage lines [62] was reported. It is difficult to justify such work since the test conditions are so far from realistic service conditions, and it does not seem possible to extrapolate the methods readily to other than the two-level situation.

6.2.3. Other prediction methods

The inaccuracy of the linear cumulative damage rule led to a number of alternative methods being proposed to predict the life under varying stress amplitudes, some wholly empirical, others with some physical basis. Reviews of cumulative damage theories have been given by Kaechele [63] and Swanson [64].

Various investigators [49, 65, 66] have suggested that there is a power-law relationship between damage and the cycle ratio (that is, $D \propto (n/N)^a$). Thus, in a constant stress amplitude test, the damage curves for stress amplitudes $\pm S_1$ and $\pm S_2$ are given by curves OAP and OBP respectively on Fig. 6.8. In the case of a simple two-step test, the transition from one stress to another will occur at a given D value which depends on n/N. Thus, in a high $(\pm S_1)$–low $(\pm S_2)$ stress test the damage path is OABP and the cumulative cycle ratio $\sum (n/N) = n_1/N_1 + (1 - n_2/N_2)$, while in a low–high test the path

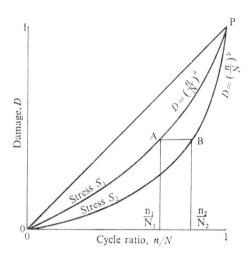

FIG. 6.8. Representation of power-law relationship between damage and cycle ratio.

followed would be OBAP and $\sum (n/N) = n_2/N_2 + (1 - n_1/N_1)$. At a given value of D, $(n_1/N_1)^a = (n_2/N_2)^b$, where $b > a$; thus for a high–low stress test

$$\sum \frac{n}{N} = \frac{n_1}{N_1} - \left(\frac{n_1}{N_1}\right)^{a/b} + 1,$$

which is less than unity, and for a low–high stress test

$$\sum \frac{n}{N} = \frac{n_2}{N_2} - \left(\frac{n_2}{N_2}\right)^{b/a} + 1,$$

which is greater than unity.

The method therefore reproduces the qualitative trends shown by testing plain specimens [67] but not those applying to test-pieces where the major part of the life is spent in crack propagation. If $a = b = 1$, the equations reduce to the linear damage law $\sum (n/N) = 1$.

Corten and Dolan [68] suggested that damage might be started at numerous places on the surface of a specimen, the number of damage nuclei m depending on stress level. Considering the case of a two-step block test, as illustrated on Fig. 6.9, they argued that, if N_1 and N_2 were the lives of specimens tested at constant stress amplitudes $\pm S_1$ and $\pm S_2$ respectively and r_1 and r_2 were coefficients depending on stress level, the total damage D was given by

$$D = m_1 r_1 N_1^{a_1} = m_2 r_2 N_2^{a_2}.$$

In the two-level test they assumed m_1 damage nuclei were initiated at the higher stress S_1, subsequent damage proceeding at both S_1 and S_2 as shown on

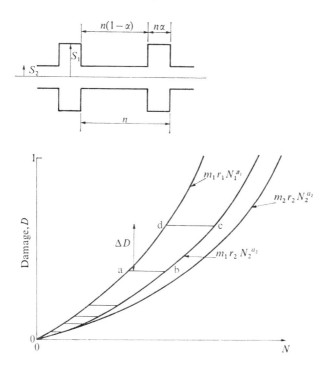

FIG. 6.9. Corten and Dolan damage–cycle relationship for a two-level loading test. (Taken from Corten and Dolan [68].)

Fig. 6.9. (Earlier investigators [69] had also suggested that a characteristic number of crack nuclei are initiated by the initial stress level, further damage at other stress levels being confined primarily to propagation of these initial cracks.) By a process of summing damage increments, equating the total damage to the damage at failure in a constant amplitude test at S_1, and incorporating some simplifying assumptions based on numerous two-level block tests on hard drawn steel wire, the theory predicts the life N in a two-level test as

$$N = \frac{N_1}{\alpha + R^{1/a}(1-\alpha)},$$

where α defines the block length (Fig. 6.9), $R = r_2/r_1$, and a_1 and a_2 are taken as equal to a.

Although the authors incorporated a nucleation period for initiating damage, their experimental data conformed to the theory if this was considered negligible and if $R^{1/a}$ was taken as $(S_2/S_1)^d$. Hence

$$N = \frac{N_1}{\alpha + (S_2/S_1)^d(1-\alpha)}.$$

It is interesting to note that the linear damage law would predict, for a two-step block test,

$$N = \frac{N_1}{\alpha + (N_1/N_2)(1-\alpha)},$$

and if the finite-life portion of the constant stress amplitude S/N relationship of the material can be plotted linearly on log–log axes, that is,

$$\frac{N_1}{N_2} = \left(\frac{S_2}{S_1}\right)^b,$$

then this equation can be written

$$N = \frac{N_1}{\alpha + (S_2/S_1)^b(1-\alpha)}.$$

Thus Corten and Dolan's parameter d may be interpreted as the inverse slope of a hypothetical S/N curve (whose finite-life portion is assumed to be linear on log–log axes) which allows for the interaction between high and low stress levels and which, if used in place of the experimental S/N curve in conjunction with the linear cumulative damage law, enables the life in a two-level block test to be predicted. Corten and Dolan's two-level data on steel gave a value of $d \approx 6{\cdot}6$ compared to a value of the inverse slope of the constant stress amplitude data on log–log axes of about $7{\cdot}5$.

The use of a hypothetical S/N relationship together with a linear damage accumulation law means that the proposed stress-level–endurance relationship could be written for a multi-level test as

$$N = N_1 \Big/ \left\{ \alpha_1 + \alpha_2 \left(\frac{S_2}{S_1}\right)^d + \alpha_3 \left(\frac{S_3}{S_1}\right)^d + \ldots \alpha_i \left(\frac{S_i}{S_1}\right)^d \right\},$$

where $\alpha_1, \alpha_2, ..$ are the proportions of the stresses at $S_1, S_2, \ldots$, for example, the number of cycles n_1 at S_1 is $\alpha_1 N$. The experimental work was extended to other materials and to the application of repeated stress blocks of arbitrary shape. It was suggested that if d was determined experimentally from two-level tests (that is, the hypothetical S/N curve was determined from two-level tests) the same value of d could be used to predict the life of a specimen in a multi-level test. Marsh [70–3], however, found that the value of d (the inverse slope of the hypothetical log–log S/N curve) obtained from two-level tests could not always be used to predict the life in more complicated block tests and in fact would lead to unsafe predictions in some circumstances. Nevertheless he concluded that the concept was useful, provided an appropriate value was assigned to d, which depended on the type of cumulative damage test being performed. Thus, although the method could provide considerably better predictions than the Palmgren–Miner rule, these predictions were not necessarily safe, experience being required in the use of the rule and considerable caution being necessary in its application to extreme stress histories. It was also pointed out that the Corten–Dolan hypothesis applied only when all stress levels were above the plain fatigue limit. If some of these stresses were below the fatigue limit, it was necessary to construct a hypothetical S/N diagram having a fatigue limit lower than the true S/N diagram. This then took into account the fact that, in the block tests, some stress levels below the fatigue limit could cause damage. In the case of tests on both plain and notched mild steel specimens, the fatigue limit of the hypothetical S/N curve needed to be assigned a value about 80 per cent of the conventional fatigue limit.

Freudenthal [74] carried out six-level block tests, in which the applied load sequences were randomized, on high-strength aluminium alloys, and found that $\sum (n/N)$ had values between 0·1 and 0·6. He argued that the reason the linear damage law predicted unsafe lives in multi-level tests was its inherent assumption that there were no interaction effects between one stress level and another. He too suggested therefore, that the stress interaction between stress levels in a block test could be incorporated by using the linear damage law in conjunction with a fictitious spectrum-dependent S/N curve. As Corten and Dolan, he assumed both the constant stress amplitude and fictitious spectrum-dependent S/N curves could be plotted linearly on log–log axes and found that, once this latter curve had been established by consideration of the experimental data, it enabled the life of specimens of the same material but under different stress levels and block loading to be predicted.

May [75] attempted to predict the life of a specimen in a random-load test using his model of crack initiation described in § 2.4. According to this model, surface notches were formed in a specimen subjected to a constant stress amplitude, by randomly distributed slip, the fraction of notches f, which after t cycles had depths between z and $(z+\mathrm{d}z)$, being given by $f = F \exp(-z/\alpha t)$, where F was a slowly varying function of z and t, α being a constant for a given test. The total number of notches with depths greater than some critical value of z, say Z, was of the form $A \exp(-Z/\alpha t)$, where A was another slowly varying function and had a large numerical value. May supposed that all notches deeper than Z were liable to give rise to cracks, the probability of any fatigue cycle generating a crack of depth Z being written as $PA \exp(-Z/\alpha t)$, where P was a constant. When cracks reached a depth Z he assumed they then grew so rapidly that this expression could be taken as the mortality rate of the specimens, the life of a specimen being given by the value of t at which $Z/\alpha t$ ceased to be small, say when $Z/\alpha t = K$. Both α and Z depended on the plastic strain range ε induced by a given stress level; α was taken proportional to ε, Z inversely proportional to ε. Thus, for a specimen subjected to a constant plastic strain range ε_i, $\alpha_i = a\varepsilon_i$ and $Z_i = C/\varepsilon_i$. The life therefore is given by $N_i = Z_i/K\alpha_i$, that is,

$$N_i \varepsilon_i^2 = C/aK = C',$$

where a, C, and C' are constants. This is the relationship found experimentally by Coffin (see § 6.1). May now considered the case of a random succession of stress levels, a fraction p_i having a plastic strain range ε_i. He assumed that the growth of surface notches was as in a test at constant ε, except that the constant α was replaced by an average value $\bar{\alpha} = a \sum_i p_i \varepsilon_i$. Thus the total number of notches of depth greater than Z after t cycles was written as $A \exp(-Z/\bar{\alpha}t)$. He considered next that the probability of any fatigue cycle generating a crack was given by the product of the fraction of the cycles p_i having a plastic strain ε_i and the number of notches with depths greater than $Z_i = c/\varepsilon_i$, that is, the mortality rate was written

$$AP \sum_i p_i \exp(-Z_i/\bar{\alpha}t).$$

The life of a specimen was given by the value of t at which this expression ceased to be small. It was considered that this relationship gave good correlation with appropriate experimental data.

Fuller [76] proposed a simple empirical method for predicting the life of a specimen under variable amplitude loading conditions based on the apparent rotation of the constant stress amplitude S/N curve, which has been observed in many two-level tests, to form the S/N curve applicable to varying-amplitude conditions. Thus the variable-amplitude S/N curve is defined by its slope, which is in some ratio to that of the constant-amplitude curve. This ratio is considered to be solely determined by the shape of the stress block applied. When extended to random loading conditions, the only information required to predict endurances is the constant-amplitude S/N curve and the cumulative probability distribution of the stress spectrum. The further assumption, in the case of random loading, that the constant-amplitude curve should be approximated by a straight line at its steepest slope results in the predicted relationship also being a straight line. No information is given about the fatigue limit of the random loading curve. The method has allowed a reasonable correlation of some experimental data [64, 76] but has given poor agreement in the case of other data [77].

Valluri [78] attempted to predict endurances under varying amplitude fatigue conditions based on the growth of the crack responsible for ultimate failure. On a semi-intuitive basis, the expression for crack growth was derived as:

$$\frac{1}{C}\log\frac{a}{a_0} = S^2\left(\frac{S}{S_i/K_n}-1\right)^2\left(1-\frac{S_m}{S}\right)^2 N,$$

where S is the stress amplitude, S_m is the mean stress, S_i is the fatigue limit, N is the endurance, a_0 and a are the initial and final crack lengths, and C is an empirical constant. K_n is defined as the natural (plastic) stress concentration factor for the stress in the plastic zone at the crack tip but is used as an additional empirical constant, having a value between 1 and 3·5, to give the best agreement between theory and experiment. This crack growth expression is used for defining equivalent damage at different stress levels, and, in particular, at a specific reference stress level S_r.

Making use of an equation for the probability distribution function of the peak amplitudes (see § 6.2.5) the total equivalent number of cycles at this reference stress, corresponding to the r.m.s. stress σ_q, acting per unit time is derived by a process of integration. This is converted to a non-dimensional equivalent time at the reference state, corresponding to the state q and these times summed for all values of σ_q to obtain the total equivalent time at the reference state t_{er}. The crack growth expressions are then used to show that the number of cycles n_r at the reference stress to grow a crack which would be critical for catastrophic failure at the stress S_{q1} is

$$n_r = \frac{\log(S_u/S_{q1})^b}{C\left\{S_r\left(\frac{S_r}{S_{mi}/K_n}-1\right)\left(1-\frac{S_m}{S_r}\right)\right\}^2},$$

where S_u is the tensile strength, S_{q1} is the residual strength of the specimen after n_r cycles at the stress S_r, S_{mi} is the fatigue limit at mean stress S_m, and b is the exponent describing the static strength of ductile materials. If ω_r is the reference frequency, $t_r = n_r/\omega_r$ and thus the actual time t_a at which the residual strength S_q is reached is given by $t_a = t_r/t_{er}$. Finally the probability of failure at t_a is given by $P(f) = \{1-\phi(S_{q1})\}$, where $\phi(S_{q1})$ is the cumulative probability of the distribution function for the r.m.s. stress σ_q.

The solution of the random fatigue problem is then claimed to be the following process. Given an r.m.s. stress versus frequency curve, compute t_a, as described, for various values of S_q ranging from S_u to S_{mi}/K_n. A curve of t_a against probability of failure $P(f)$ at t_a, can be plotted for the given r.m.s. stress versus frequency curve. This is repeated for different r.m.s. stress versus frequency curves to derive curves of r.m.s. stress versus cycles to failure with associated probabilities, or alternatively, by considering equal probability curves, the associated r.m.s. stress versus cycles to failure curves can be obtained. It is clear that the process described is one of great complexity, which is most unlikely to be used by even a sophisticated designer.

The equations also involve numerous numerical constants so that a reasonable fit to experimental results is to be expected. Nevertheless, the approach is interesting as an attempt to work from first principles, although the crack growth relationships would be better expressed in terms of stress intensity factors.

6.2.4. Programme loading to simulate service conditions

The simple step-tests described above bear little resemblance to the type of loading variations that occur in practice. To obtain a loading pattern or spectrum more like the practical situation, it is necessary to record the load spectrum on a particular component or member while operating under service conditions. The load spectrum can then be simulated by an applied loading pattern consisting of a number of stress levels applied for numbers of cycles which are in proportion to the service distribution. A very large number of programme loading fatigue tests have been carried out by various investigators both on relatively simple specimens (see, for example, References [79–87]) and on actual components and structures [88–97] motivated mainly by the inaccuracies of prediction methods. Schijve [98] for example, has reviewed cumulative damage problems in aircraft. While some form of prediction method (of whatever accuracy) is necessary at the preliminary design stage, if optimum design is required for economy, reliability, or safety, there is little alternative to testing prototype components under a reasonably close simulation of service conditions. This is particularly so in the field of aircraft components, and a great deal of effort has been expended to record [88, 99–104] service load spectra and use these data to define programme loading tests. Much more limited work has been done in other fields of engineering, but spectra for motor vehicles [97, 105], bridges [106, 107], and cranes [108–11] have been suggested.

Certain trends have become established. It has been shown that constant amplitude fatigue tests do not necessarily produce the same types or even locations of failure in a component as occur in service, whereas programme loading tests generally achieve a reasonable simulation of service failures. For example, both constant amplitude tests and multi-level block loading tests simulating the gust-load spectrum experienced by transport aircraft were carried out [94] on a number of joints consisting of $4\frac{1}{2}\%$ Cu–aluminium alloy lugs held at each end in tapered steel side straps by means of five in-line bolts. The holes in the side plates and lug were reamed to size, some joints being assembled dry and others having all individual parts greased before assembly. Although the endurances of dry and greased joints were similar in the constant stress amplitude tests, the average endurance of a greased joint in a programme test was more than three times that of a dry joint. Thus, because there was no significant difference in lives of dry and greased joints when subjected to a constant stress amplitude, the different endurances of dry and greased joints when tested under a programmed block loading could not be predicted by the linear or any other damage law. It was suggested that the explanation may lie in the different fretting actions occurring in the two types of test. These results show clearly that the behaviour of built-up members cannot always be expected to follow the same behaviour pattern as simple laboratory specimens. A survey of programme loading tests on notched light alloy specimens and structures has shown [112] that, whereas tests at zero mean load often result in dangerous predictions by the Palmgren–Miner rule (that is, values of $\sum (n/N) < 1$), the presence of a tensile mean stress, as is usual in aircraft structures, usually results in conservative predictions (that is, values of $\sum (n/N) > 1$), thus making this simple rule safe in this field for preliminary design purposes. The marked effect that occasional large overload cycles can have on endurance has been discussed by several investigators and is particularly important in the ground–air–ground transition in aircraft [73, 82, 112, 113].

One of the earliest proponents of programme loading testing was Gassner [114], who, with his co-workers, has carried out extremely extensive test programmes on a wide range of specimens and components. He suggested that the loading pattern experienced by transport vehicle components, such as springs and steering arms and also the loads on military aircraft wings and undercarriages conform to a 'binomial' probability distribution, that is, the cumulative probability distribution of stress amplitudes can be plotted linearly on binomial probability paper or, alternatively, the ratio of stress amplitude to maximum stress amplitude on a quadratic scale can be plotted linearly against the cumulative number of occurrences on a logarithmic scale. This distribution, known as the *LBF Normal* or *Binominal* distribution, is essentially similar to the cumulative probability distribution of peaks in narrow-band Gaussian random vibration (the Rayleigh distribution) or that of wide-band Gaussian random vibration in that there are few high stresses and many low stress amplitudes. The comparison, in terms of the more usual peak stress to r.m.s. stress ratio S/σ is shown in Fig. 6.10 (random waveforms are discussed in the next section). Similarly, Gassner suggested that the loadings on civil transport aircraft wings followed a 'logarithmic binomial' distribution which is essentially the same as the gust-loading distribution for aircraft wings formulated by Taylor [99]. The LBF Normal distribution has been the basis of a very large number of tests simulating service loading conditions in which the continuous distribution curve is replaced by an eight-level programme block as, for example, in Fig. 6.11, and it is claimed that such tests give a very good correlation with service endurances of a wide range of components.

This approach has been further extended to the concept of the life function. This is essentially an S/N curve obtained under variable-amplitude conditions, namely, the LBF Normal programme, and can be plotted linearly on a

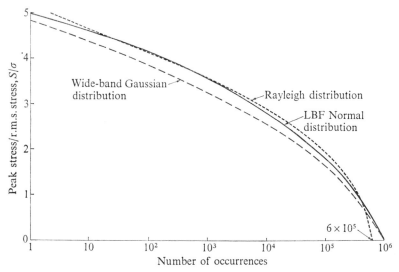

FIG. 6.10. Comparison of various stress distributions. (Taken from Marsh [73].)

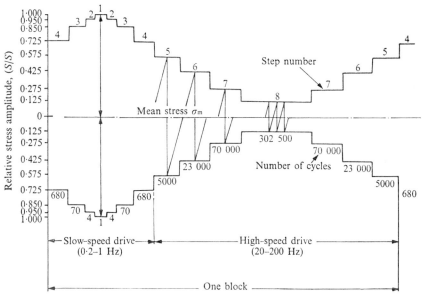

FIG. 6.11. Typical eight-level block programme to the LBF Normal distribution. (Taken from Gassner and Schütz [114].)

log–log basis in terms of $\bar{S}$, the maximum stress amplitude in the programme which occurs approximately once in 10^6 cycles. (This corresponds to about 5 times the r.m.s. stress amplitude.) For a given probability of failure P_s, stress ratio R, and stress concentration factor K_t, the life function is defined by the slope of the line k in the relationship $\bar{N} = C/(\bar{S})^k$, where $\bar{N}$ is the total number of cycles to failure. Fig. 6.12 shows a life function for 2024-T3

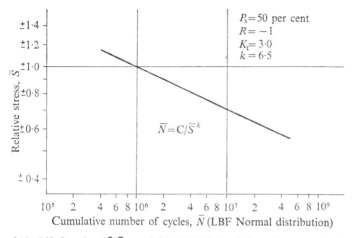

FIG. 6.12. Life function ($\bar{S}/\bar{N}$ curve) for 2024-T3 aluminium alloy on a relative stress scale. (Taken from Gassner and Schütz [114].)

aluminium alloy. Life functions for various values of R and K_t thus form design data which can be used for the design of structural parts under randomly varying amplitude conditions. The process can be extended to other stress probability distributions, such as gust-loading distributions, by building up the required distribution from a summation of several LBF Normal distributions of appropriate different $\bar{S}$ values and applying a linear damage accumulation process. This is essentially using the Palmgren–Miner rule based on a different S/N curve from the conventional constant amplitude curve, namely, one 'conditioned' by being derived from appropriate variable amplitude tests. The method is claimed to give only slightly conservative results when applied to aluminium alloy specimens of $K_t = 3.1$ subjected to a gust-load distribution.

6.2.5. Random loading

In practice, many components are subjected to an array of stress cycles which is more variable in amplitude than a succession of repeated blocks. Some improvement in simulating these loading histories can be achieved using testing machines having several different load channels controlled by punched tape, using short blocks, and randomizing the order of blocks. Such tests give results approximating to random loading tests [73, 115]. In many cases, however, it may be preferable to make use of an actual random process, such as the output of a white noise generator, as the basis for the simulation, applying this output to a suitable vibrator.

It should be noted that the term random loading as conventionally applied to fatigue tests is inexact. Any testing machine must have a finite applicable load, and therefore the amplitude of any stress peak is only random between zero and some upper limit. In general, the order of application of the stress amplitudes does approximate to a random distribution but is influenced to some extent, sometimes considerably, by the inertia of the moving parts of the testing machine. In regular block tests, either at zero mean stress or with a fixed superimposed mean stress, the alternating stress varies sinusoidally about a known mean level (that is, the ratio of the number of zero crossings to the number of peaks is always unity), but this need not be the case in a random loading, because now both the stress range and mean stress may vary every cycle. The analysis of a random stress–time waveform thus presents some difficulties, whereas in a multi-level block test the cycle ratio n/N is always known whatever the number or order of application of blocks of cycles, so that it is relatively easy to sum the n/N values in a given test. In fundamental work, therefore, signals used in random loading tests are often passed through an appropriate filter to provide a narrow-band frequency distribution, that is, the ratio of the number of zero crossings to the number of peaks (the *irregularity factor*) approaches unity. Tests can then be carried out at either zero mean stress or any given mean stress, and the concept of cycles to failure is retained. The amplitude of the random stress waveform is defined by its root mean square value σ.

Probability distributions of random waveforms may be considered in terms of the *probability density function* $p(S/\sigma)$, which is the probability that the magnitude of the stress S will lie between two given values (this quantity is usually normalized by dividing it by the r.m.s. value σ) or, more usually, in terms of the *cumulative distribution function* $P(S/\sigma)$, which is the probability that the magnitude of S will exceed a certain value. It can be seen therefore that $P(S/\sigma)$ is equal to the area under the curve of $p(S/\sigma)$ versus S/σ obtained by integrating between S/σ and ∞.

The two distributions normally encountered in fatigue work are the Gaussian or Normal distribution and the Rayleigh distribution. Gaussian describes a random function whose instantaneous value is described by the Gaussian probability density function as shown in Fig. 6.13(a) and given by the equation

$$p\left(\frac{S}{\sigma}\right) = \frac{1}{\sqrt{(2\pi)}} \exp\left(\frac{-S^2}{2\sigma^2}\right).$$

By integrating and combining positive and negative values, the cumulative distribution function (Fig. 6.13(b)) is given by

$$P\left(\frac{S}{\sigma}\right) = \frac{2}{\sqrt{(2\pi)}} \int\limits_{S/\sigma}^{\infty} \exp\left(\frac{-S^2}{2\sigma^2}\right) \mathrm{d}\left(\frac{S}{\sigma}\right).$$

This distribution applies to the instantaneous values of both broad-band (that is, the irregularity factor is less than unity) and narrow-band (that is, the irregularity factor approximates to unity) random vibration.

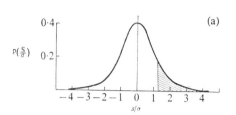
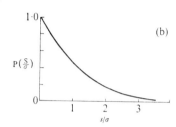

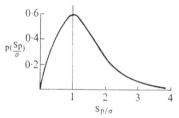
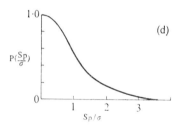

FIG. 6.13. Probability distributions. (a) Gaussian probability density. (b) Gaussian cumulative distribution function. (c) Rayleigh probability density. (d) Rayleigh cumulative distribution function.

When the distributions of peak values are considered, the two statistical functions may differ from those for instantaneous values. For broad-band Gaussian vibration, the distribution of peak values is normal, giving curves for $p(S/\sigma)$ and $P(S/\sigma)$ as before. However, for narrow-band Gaussian vibration the distribution of peak values S_p becomes the Rayleigh distribution. In this case the probability density as shown in Fig. 6.13(c) is

$$p\left(\frac{S_p}{\sigma}\right) = \frac{S_p}{\sigma} \exp\left(\frac{-S_p^2}{2\sigma^2}\right),$$

and the cumulative distribution

$$P\left(\frac{S_p}{\sigma}\right) = \exp\left(\frac{-S_p^2}{2\sigma^2}\right),$$

which can be seen to be of the same form as the probability density function for instantaneous values. The curve thus appears as in Fig. 6.13(d).

Many investigators have carried out tests in which a waveform approximating to the Rayleigh distribution of peaks is applied, determining σ/N curves instead of the conventional S/N curves; Swanson [116] has given an excellent review of random load testing. One of the earliest investigations [117] was reported in 1956 and several investigators [64, 72, 77, 84, 117–22] have loaded simple specimens either in bending or in direct stress by means of an electromagnetic vibrator fed by a filtered signal from a random noise source. The other main method of obtaining a Rayleigh distribution of stress peaks is to apply a random noise source to a resonant constant amplitude fatigue machine so that the stress amplitudes are modulated by a slowly randomly varying waveform [123, 124]. This results in an irregularity factor of unity, whereas the vibrator methods typically result in an irregularity factor of about 0·96, but it might be argued that the degree of randomness is less than occurs in many service applications.

When plotted as σ/N curves, random loading tests often give shorter endurances than the corresponding constant amplitude tests [118, 120], particularly in the case of steels [72, 77], where it appears that the fatigue limit of the random loading tests is roughly equal to the constant amplitude fatigue limit (in terms of conventional peak stress amplitude) divided by the ratio of highest peak stress to the r.m.s. stress amplitude of the random waveform. The knee in the random load σ/N curve, as might be expected, occurs at longer endurances than in constant amplitude tests. The ratio of the highest peak stress amplitude to the r.m.s. stress amplitude is known as the *clipping ratio*, particularly in American work; other investigators use the term *crest factor*, extending the more usual definition to include random waveforms. The former term seems possibly more suitable for random fatigue loading. Clipping ratios of $3\frac{1}{2}$–4 are common in the literature, although in some situations, such as vibrations in components of nuclear power reactors, where endurances up to 10^{12} cycles are of interest, clipping ratios as high as 5 have been employed [125]. A wide range of values for $\sum (n/N)$ in random loading tests has been recorded, no clear trends appearing. However, Swanson lists [116] some 30 different investigations, covering various materials and types of specimens, in approximately two-thirds of which the Palmgren–Miner rule gives optimistic predictions ($\sum (n/N) < 1$).

An interesting approach to random loading testing was proposed [123] in which a σ/N curve derived from narrow-band stationary random loading tests was used as the basis for a linear damage summation prediction of the results of tests synthesizing a gust spectrum by blocks of random loading of three different r.m.s. levels. The method is thus similar to and contemporary with Gassner's approach, mentioned earlier, except that random loading is the method of 'conditioning' the basic data rather than ordered programme blocks. The tests, on aluminium alloy loaded-hole lug specimens, showed that, although the method gave better predictions than the Palmgren–Miner rule, these predictions were still conservative and in some cases gave values of $\sum (n/N)$ up to about 3.

6.2.6. Servo-hydraulic testing methods

In recent years the approach to variable amplitude testing has been revolutionized by the advent of the hydraulic loading actuator controlled by a high-response electromagnetic servo-valve. Sophisticated control equipment allows virtually any load waveform to be applied; the input may be from a function generator or random noise source, from punched paper tape programming units or from magnetic tape recordings of service loading histories. The system is normally operated under closed loop control in either the load-control, deflection-control, or strain-control modes; here the actual value measured by a load cell, deflection transducer or strain gauge is compared continuously with the desired value, and continuously corrected. Single actuators may be used in conventional testing machine frames (see also Appendix 5) for uniaxial fatigue tests on materials specimens and simple components or multi-channel systems may be used for testing complete structures under realistic simulations of service loading conditions.

Numerous investigators, particularly in the aeronautical engineering field, have carried out such tests on simple specimens [82, 108, 126–9] or on a variety of components and structures such as vehicle wheel spindles [130], wing panels [95, 112], crane jibs [131], vehicle bodies or frames [132–5], and in many other applications.

There has been a great deal of discussion in recent years, particularly in the field of aeronautical fatigue, about the relative merits of block programme testing and random loading testing or testing using service–recorded stress histories. Gassner [136] claimed that a good agreement with service experience could be achieved using ordered block programme testing, provided that the mean load remained essentially constant and that the programme simulated a stationary random process, but he agreed that such testing could give very optimistic results when there was a varying mean stress situation. In general, it would seem preferable in programme tests to use blocks containing small numbers of cycles and to randomize the order of the blocks [73, 137] to approximate as closely as possible to the random process. Nevertheless, using servo-hydraulic equipment, it is possible to duplicate a recorded service-loading history exactly (although such an approach is necessarily more expensive than carrying out programme loading tests using less sophisticated equipment), and if the achievement of an optimum design is important, it may be desirable that such service loading tests on full-scale prototypes be carried out.

It is interesting to consider the alternatives to service loading tests on full-scale structures. The designer may attempt to predict the endurance of the structure from constant amplitude fatigue data on, for example, appropriate joint specimens. This approach involves the following factors:

(1) the availability of such data at the correct mean stress;
(2) since such data are often only available for $R = 0$ or $R = -1$ (where R is the stress ratio), the use of a mean-stress/alternating-stress relationship to estimate the relevant S/N curve;
(3) the use of a cumulative damage prediction method of dubious accuracy;
(4) knowledge of the load history in service;
(5) an accurate stress analysis of the structure to translate applied loads into stresses in the relevant regions of the structure (making allowance for possible multi-axial stressing) in order to apply the uniaxial stress fatigue data available.

Alternatively, tests could be carried out on relatively simple representative joint specimens under uniaxial stressing, but applying a service stress history; this is relatively straightforward using a direct-stress servo-hydraulic fatigue machine with suitable programming facilities. To use this data, the designer requires

(a) knowledge of the load history in service, and
(b) an accurate stress analysis, as before.

This alternative approach has, therefore, eliminated the first three factors noted in the previous approach, together with any errors or assumptions incorporated in them. Finally, service loading tests on the full-scale structure may be carried out. This approach requires knowledge of the load history but eliminates all the other factors. It has, therefore, the major advantage, if loads are applied to the structure in the manner in which they occur in service, that stress conditions throughout the structure are necessarily correctly simulated, eliminating the translation by means of stress analysis from small specimen data to the full-scale structural behaviour. It is, however, probably the most expensive approach.

It is clear, from the above discussion, that one factor is common to all approaches, namely, the requirement for knowledge of the service load history. This becomes, therefore, the most important aspect of the process; it is also the aspect about which least information is available for most engineering structures. Just as the advent of high-frequency response servo-hydraulic actuators made service-loading fatigue tests on large structures feasible, so the availability of sophisticated strain-recording equipment simplifies the strain-history data-collection problem. Nevertheless, data collection over long periods presents many difficulties and, with the exception of the field of aircraft fatigue, relatively little work of this nature has been carried out.

6.2.7. Structural fatigue tests on vehicles

In the particular case of vehicle structures, a different approach from the load-controlled tests generally used can be made, that is, the deflection-controlled inertial loading fatigue test. If the vehicle structure is mounted on actuators at the wheel points, and random waveforms simulating the statistical distribution of deflections due to the road surface profile used as inputs, the fully laden structure can be stressed in the correct fashion by inertial loading, just as it is in service. Instead of running the vehicle along a rough road, the rough-road input is brought to the vehicle. Fig. 6.14 shows an installation involving, initially, four fast response actuators mounted on a large sprung concrete block, to enable commercial vehicles of two-axle design and gross vehicle weight up to about 300 kN to be tested in this manner; a commercial vehicle cab and chassis is shown undergoing a durability test.

The basis of the road-simulator approach to vehicle fatigue testing is that the vehicle is subjected to a (random) succession of deflections at the wheel points, stresses in the structure being induced by inertial loading just as they are in service. The actuators are operated therefore under closed-loop deflection control, the input being a deflection waveform simulating the deflection of the wheel centres caused by the road or track. There are two methods of providing this deflection input. First, a vehicle may be instrumented to record accelerations at the wheel spindles when driven over the required road or track surface, these accelerations being double-integrated to produce a deflection waveform corresponding to the response of a particular vehicle with particular tyre and suspension characteristics. If a different vehicle is to be tested over the same road or track, further recording must be carried out. It is also necessary that a roadworthy prototype vehicle be available for recording; the use of merely 'similar' vehicles may introduce considerable errors if recordings derived from them are used as inputs to a vehicle of different dynamic characteristics.

The second approach is to derive the deflection history of the vehicle from the random amplitude profile of the road or track itself. The road profile is statistically defined in terms of the spectral density [116] of road surface displacements, measured either by surveying methods or by vehicle-mounted profilometer devices. This approach has the advantage that, once a given type of road or test track has been measured, the input derived from this can be applied to any vehicle, that is, it is fundamentally a more basic approach. The input to the vehicle may be derived in two ways. First, the input at the tyre may be derived from direct analogue recordings of road or track profile deflections, either directly from a profilometer or by digital–analogue conversion of surveyed data. Secondly, the tyre input may be synthesized from analogue (or perhaps ultimately digital) random signal sources, shaping the spectral density by means of filters to that of the desired road or track profile. It is necessary to obtain the correct cross-correlation between near- and off-side. In both cases, if the vehicle is loaded through the wheel spindles, the data must be transformed to allow for tyre characteristics.

The same type of facility may also be used for determining the dynamic characteristics of vehicle structures and for ride simulation studies.

6.2.8. Accelerated testing

One major advantage of laboratory full-scale fatigue testing is the possibility of a considerable reduction in the time necessary to carry out a fatigue evaluation compared with field studies. In some cases, such as service loading tests on a mobile crane jib [131], the test time can be greatly reduced simply by leaving out dead time, that is, applying load cycles consecutively without intervening delays. Again, provided that elevated temperatures or stresses in the region of gross yielding are not involved, the testing of relatively simple rigid components can be accelerated simply by increasing the frequency of cyclic loading, since frequency as such has no effect on fatigue strength over the normal range of frequencies encountered. Difficulties occur, however, in the testing of complex structures, since changing the frequency content of the input may excite resonances, resulting in different stress distributions within the structure from those observed in service. Thus, in general, the testing of complex structures such as vehicle structures may necessarily be restricted to 'real time' testing. To achieve rapid test results, two accelerating procedures are possible, namely, increasing the over-all stress level of the test to give shorter endurances or omitting very small amplitude stress cycles, which may be present in large numbers, from the stress history.

Traditionally, vehicle manufacturers increase stress levels by testing on a more severe road surface, such as Belgian pavé or corrugations, and this procedure has been carried over to laboratory simulations; the manufacturers rely on experience to interpret the endurance on the test track in terms of corresponding endurance under normal road conditions. The pavé stress history however, besides being more severe, has different spectral characteristics from those of normal roads, and it may not follow that structural failures caused by pavé testing will necessarily occur in service. The alternative is to use normal road-surface stress histories with the r.m.s. stress level increased to obtain suitably short endurances. This, again, raises problems in interpreting the results of such a higher stress level test.

The remaining approach, that of editing the stress history to remove 'non-damaging' small amplitude stress cycles, has been and is being pursued in the aircraft and railway engineering fields. In fact, the problem of what amplitude stress cycles can be ignored has been studied as long as variable amplitude fatigue tests have been carried out. The difficulty in complex structures incorporating bolted, riveted, or welded joints is that much of the life is spent in macrocrack propagation (that is, from crack lengths of a few hundredths of a millimetre); in these circumstances, regardless of the tensile strength of the steel, very low stresses may contribute to propagation if a crack of sufficient length is present. It is most important, therefore, that any basic work designed to explore the omission of small-amplitude stress cycles is carried out on specimens representative of the real structure. Plain polished specimens where the fatigue strength is dominated by the microcrack initiation phase may give misleading results.

6.2.9. Discussion

The engineering designer needs, at the preliminary design stage, some method of estimating the behaviour of a component under varying stress amplitudes. This he may do by means of the Palmgren–Miner rule or by some more complex method. The latter methods are either too cumbersome for ready use, restricted to certain conditions or materials, or, while giving more accurate predictions (for example, the hypothetical S/N curve methods), require considerable experience to be used with confidence. The Palmgren–Miner rule is widely considered as inaccurate and, in many situations, dangerous. However, when considering cumulative-damage rules, it is important to consider what is meant by damage in a cumulative-damage test. The life of any specimen, subjected to any type of loading cycle, is the sum of the number of cycles required to initiate and develop a surface microcrack to the necessary depth for it to grow as a macrocrack and the number of cycles required for the macrocrack to grow across the specimen cross-section. In a plain specimen, there is no metallographic evidence to suggest that a surface microcrack progresses linearly with number of cycles or, even if it does at one stress level, that it will continue doing so at another stress level, as is assumed by the linear damage law. Indeed, it is known that the scatter in lives of specimens subjected to the same constant stress amplitude is associated with the initiation and development of microcracks, and therefore it is not unreasonable to suppose that this scatter will be increased under conditions of varying stress amplitudes. In addition, if the specimens are subjected to numerous low-stress cycles, coaxing phenomena (§ 2.3.4) which occur in some materials will tend to retard the development of a microcrack at a higher stress level. However, with sharply notched specimens in which the life is spent in growing a macrocrack, damage assessed in terms of crack length or depth which increases with increasing number of cycles can be considered a physical reality. Indeed, it has been shown that, if no residual stresses are induced in the material ahead of the crack tip, the life of a specimen, spent wholly in propagating a macrocrack under a varying stress cycle, can be predicted from the linear damage law. However, it is known that, when the stress level is reduced from a higher value, residual compressive stresses are induced in the material ahead of the crack tip which will retard the subsequent growth rate. Depending on the change in stress level, the material, and whether or not the residual stresses are relaxed at the lower stress level, the crack growth rate at this latter stress may be abnormally slow or may even be reduced to zero, so resulting in the high values of $\sum(n/N)$ often found when sharply notched specimens are tested in simple high–low two-level tests. In multi-level block or random loading tests, the change in stress level is often not so drastic as in a two-level test, and residual stresses may not only be of smaller magnitude but may be more easily relaxed, thus giving values of $\sum(n/N)$ more nearly equal to unity. However, except in simple block tests in which the stress levels are not widely different (that is, there is little deviation from a constant stress amplitude test), the use of the linear damage law to predict the behaviour of plain specimens in a cumulative damage test in most cases can lead to unsafe predictions.

Nevertheless, the linear cumulative damage rule has the great advantage of simplicity in application. Used with intelligence and with some knowledge of the factors affecting its accuracy (as reviewed by Edwards [138], for example) it can still perform a valuable function in the preliminary design stage. Indeed, Jacoby [129] in a survey of 400 values for $\sum(n/N)$, including all types of materials and structures, all types of tests, and all types of stressing, shows that the density distribution histogram is centred on the value $\sum(n/N) = 1$. He concludes that $\sum(n/N) = 0\cdot3$ would give a safe prediction in 95 per cent of all cases. Excluding the results of rotating bending tests gives an asymmetric histogram of 340 results, the mode being again $\sum(n/N) \approx 1$; in this case 70 per cent of all results gave values of $\sum(n/N) \geqslant 1$, that is, safe predictions.

Thus, at the early stages of design, the Palmgren–Miner rule, despite its inaccuracies, still serves a useful function. At the other extreme, to achieve optimum design for strength, reliability, or safety, there seems little alternative to full-scale testing of components and structures under realistic simulations of service loading conditions; this can best be carried out using modern servo-hydraulic testing equipment.

6.3. Effect of mechanical working

6.3.1. Introduction

Residual stresses are induced in a specimen of a ductile material whenever it is unloaded from a previous loading which has resulted in a non-uniform stress distribution over a cross-section and the maximum stress in one or more but not all regions of the cross-section has exceeded the yield stress of the material. Thus a plain bar of material may have residual stresses induced into the surface layers on unloading, provided it has been bent or twisted in a particular direction to such a degree that the surface layers deform plastically but the core remains elastic. Residual stresses will be induced around a notch after removal of a uniaxial loading of such a magnitude that the material in the vicinity of the notch deforms plastically, yet that remote from the notch remains elastic. If the elastic–plastic stress distribution over the specimen cross-section due to an applied load is known, the residual stress distribution after unloading to zero can be estimated by subtracting the elastic stress distribution due to the applied load, since deformations on unloading will be elastic. Residual stresses considered here are due solely to differences in macroscopic deformations, some of which are reversible and others not; they are not to be confused with any microscopic stresses which may arise in a polycrystal whose individual grains have different stress–strain characteristics. Experimental procedures for assessing the magnitude of residual stresses include X-ray diffraction measurements and measurements of the change in curvature of strips cut from the unloaded deformed specimen. A survey of methods for determining the magnitude of residual stresses is given by Almen and Black [139].

6.3.2. Effect of work-hardening

Because plastic deformation is necessary for producing residual stresses, that material which has deformed plastically will be work-hardened. Thus, any change in the fatigue strength of a material which has had residual stresses induced in its surface layers will be a consequence of both the residual stresses and the increased hardness due to work-hardening.

To obtain an indication of the amount that the plain fatigue limit of a material may be increased (or decreased) by work-hardening alone, fatigue tests can be carried out on specimens cut from material which has been plastically deformed uniformly over its cross-section by a direct stress loading. Because there is no stress gradient across the specimens, there can be no residual stress field on unloading. Materials having a high rate of work-hardening, such as mild and austenitic steels, show the greatest change in fatigue limit with cold-work. For example [140], fatigue tests on specimens cut longitudinally from mild steel cylindrical blanks, which had been compressed to various nominal compressive plastic strains, showed (Fig. 6.15) that the fatigue limit increased from a value of ± 250 MN m^{-2} for the as-received bar to a maximum value of ± 350 MN m^{-2} at a nominal compressive pre-strain of about 50 per cent. Pre-strains above this value did not result in any further increase in fatigue limit; in fact, the fatigue limit dropped drastically to a value of about ± 270 MN m^{-2}. However, the hardness of a specimen did not show a corresponding decrease, and it was suggested that the excessive cold-work caused incipient cracking, so resulting in the drop in fatigue limit. It has been reported [141] that the fatigue strength (10^7 cycles) of a titanium alloy could be increased by about 30 per cent by pre-straining in tension to 10 per cent of the fracture strain. However, only smaller additional increases in fatigue strength occurred for pre-strains up to 60 per cent. On the other hand, the fatigue limits of alloy steels cut from pre-strained blanks show little difference from that of the unworked material; for example, the fatigue limit [140] of nickel–chromium steel (tensile strength 1000 MN m^{-2})

specimens cut from blanks compressed to 50 per cent plastic strain was only increased by about 10 per cent. Copper and copper alloys exhibit an increase in tensile strength and fatigue strength at short endurances with increasing cold-work, but the improvement over unstrained material becomes smaller the longer the endurance at which the fatigue strength is estimated. The softer aluminium alloys show some improvement in fatigue strength with

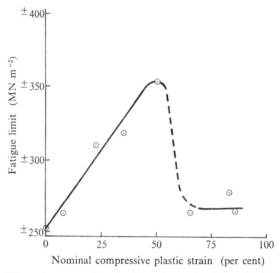

FIG. 6.15. Effect of compressive plastic strain on the fatigue limit of mild steel. (Taken from Frost [140].)

increasing cold-work but there is some evidence that the high-strength aluminium alloys may have their fatigue strengths at long endurances reduced by about 10–20 per cent by quite moderate amounts (for example, 10 per cent) of either uniform tensile or compressive pre-strain [142]. However, in general, the scatter in results with these alloys is such as to mask minor changes of this order; Fig. 6.16 shows data obtained on specimens cut longitudinally from $4\frac{1}{2}\%$ Cu–aluminium alloy blanks pre-loaded in compression to give various amounts of plastic strain.

6.3.3. Effect of residual stresses

Experimental data on the effect of mechanically induced residual stresses have been obtained on plain specimens which have been bent or twisted, and then straightened or untwisted, and on notched specimens which have been loaded and unloaded.

Residual stresses were induced into the surface layers of plain specimens [143] by bending and restraightening 12·5 mm square 0·17% C steel and

$4\frac{1}{2}\%$ Cu–aluminium bars. The steel specimens were bent to produce a surface plastic strain equal to six times the elastic yield point strain, annealed at 650 °C and restraightened; the aluminium alloy specimens were bent to give a surface plastic strain of twice the elastic strain at the 0·2% proof stress, but were not heat-treated before restraightening. Estimates of the values of the surface residual stresses (tensile on one face and compressive on the other

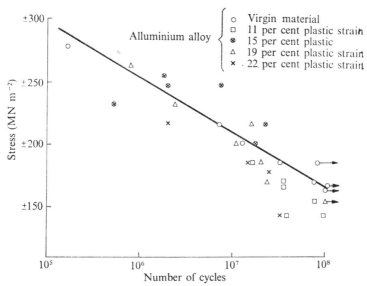

FIG. 6.16. Effect of compressive plastic pre-strain on fatigue strength of an aluminium alloy.

face) obtained from strain gauges attached to the surface of a restraightened specimen which was then cut in half down its longitudinal axis were 100 MN m^{-2} and 115 MN m^{-2} for the mild steel and aluminium alloy respectively. Both stress-free and restraightened specimens were tested in reversed plane bending, and it was found that the presence of the tensile residual stresses reduced the fatigue limit of the mild steel from ± 230 MN m^{-2} to ± 205 MN m^{-2} and the fatigue strength (10^7 cycles) of the aluminium alloy from ± 206 MN m^{-2} to ± 150 MN m^{-2}. By sectioning specimens which had been cyclically stressed for differing endurances, it was also found that the magnitude of the surface residual stress in the mild steel was relaxed to quite a low value after a relatively small number of stress cycles, thus accounting for the small decrease in fatigue limit. On the other hand, little relaxation of the surface residual stress occurred in the aluminium alloy until after 10^7 cycles, when the experimental results appeared to indicate that stressing beyond 10^7 cycles could result in an appreciable relaxation.

Many workers have found that the fatigue limit of a batch of notched specimens which have been loaded in tension sufficiently to deform the material

TABLE 6.3

Condition of material	Condition of specimens	Fatigue strength, 2×10^7 cycles (MN m^{-2})		
		Zero mean load	93 MN m^{-2} tensile mean stress	185 MN m^{-2} tensile mean stress
Naturally aged	No pre-load	± 73	± 50	± 46
	Pre-loaded	± 89	± 73	± 46
Fully heat-treated	No pre-load	± 73	± 50	± 46
	Pre-loaded	± 89	± 73	± 58

plastically in the vicinity of the notch, thereby inducing residual compressive stresses in this region on unloading, may be increased markedly. Conversely, similar specimens pre-loaded in compression prior to fatigue testing, thereby inducing tensile residual stresses in the region around the notch root, may have their fatigue limit lowered. For example, the notched fatigue strength (10^7 cycles) of $5\frac{1}{2}\%$ Zn–aluminium alloy specimens (12 mm deep and 0·05 mm root radius) was increased [144] from ± 63 MN m^{-2} to ± 145 MN m^{-2} by applying a static tensile stress of 570 MN m^{-2} prior to fatigue testing, whereas applying a static compressive stress of similar magnitude resulted in the fatigue strength decreasing to ± 28 MN m^{-2}. Applying a static tensile stress of 390 MN m^{-2} to 4% Cu–aluminium alloy specimens containing a circumferential vee-notch 1 mm deep and 0·1 mm root radius increased the rotating bending fatigue strength (5×10^6 cycles) from ± 58 MN m^{-2} to ± 123 MN m^{-2} [145]. The results of fatigue testing [146] notched $4\frac{1}{2}\%$ Cu–aluminium alloy plate specimens (51 mm wide by 5·1 mm thick, containing a central hole 6.4 mm diameter) which had been loaded statically, prior to testing, to a tensile stress on net area equal to 80 per cent of the material's 0·1 per cent proof stress are given in Table 6.3.

Prior to fatigue testing at 140 ± 54 MN m^{-2}, $5\frac{1}{2}\%$ Zn–aluminium alloy specimens (20 mm diameter, containing a 4·8 mm diameter transverse hole) were loaded to give various values of pre-stress [147]. These pre-stresses, expressed as a percentage of the 0·1 per cent proof stress (460 MN m^{-2}), and corresponding endurances are given in Table 6.4.

The high-strength aluminium alloy data referred to so far imply that the subsequent fatigue stressing does not relax the induced residual stresses, and

TABLE 6.4

Pre-load stress on net area (%)	0	0	$+81$	$+90$	$+103$	$+111$	$+112$	-26	-43	-70	-90
Endurance (millions of cycles)	0·46	0·18	0·47	0·78	3·33	8·21	0·19	0·17	0·07	0·05	0·05

they are therefore able to influence the subsequent fatigue strength. However, relaxation of induced residual stresses may occur in softer alloys with the consequence that such residual stresses have little effect on the subsequent fatigue strength. For example, 1% Mg–aluminium alloy (in either the softened, tensile strength 177 MN m^{-2}, condition or the hardened, tensile strength 320 MN m^{-2}, condition) plate specimens, 76 mm wide and having two opposite edge-notches, 18 mm deep and 2·5 mm root radius, were preloaded to a nominal net area stress equal to 80 per cent of the yield stress of the material, prior to fatigue testing in plane bending [148]. The magnitude of the maximum induced residual stress in the material at the notch root was determined by X-ray diffraction techniques at intervals throughout a test. The fatigue strength (10^7 cycles) of the softened plates was unaffected by either a tensile or a compressive pre-loading, but that of the hardened plates was increased from ±59 MN m^{-2} to ±76 MN m^{-2} by a tensile pre-load and reduced to ±42 MN m^{-2} by a compressive pre-load. These results were consistent with the residual stress measurements taken because, whereas the values of the initially induced residual stresses in the plates of the hardened material were unaltered by the subsequent fatigue stressing during the entire life of a specimen, those in the plates of the softened material were relaxed completely in the first few loading cycles.

Surface residual stresses were induced in high-purity aluminium cylindrical specimens (5·5 mm diameter by 32 mm gauge length) by applying either a static plastic twist of 80° or a cyclic plastic twist amplitude of $\pm10°$ for 1000 cycles [149]. The specimens were then subjected to a cyclic plastic twist amplitude of $\pm\frac{1}{4}°$, the maximum torque values in each cycle being noted. The end-point torque asymmetry created by the pre-loading was found to be removed after a very few loading cycles, and it was concluded that the introduction of residual stresses by plastic straining could not improve the fatigue strength of the aluminium because they would be removed quickly (usually in less than a few hundred cycles) by subsequent cycles of plastic strain of quite moderate amplitudes.

Residual stresses may be relaxed similarly in soft steels, whereas they may not be in harder steels. For example, rotating bending fatigue tests were carried out [150] on notched specimens (20 mm outside diameter, having either a semicircular notch of 2·5 mm radius or a vee-notch 3·8 mm deep and 0·025 mm root radius) of 3 steels (0·2% C, 0·4% C, and 4% Ni) which were pre-loaded by applying either a static tensile or compressive loading prior to fatigue testing. The vee-notched specimens were pre-loaded to the 0·1 per cent proof stress of the material multiplied by the area of the minimum cross-section; the semicircular notches were pre-loaded so that the notch width was either extended or decreased by 0·125 mm. The fatigue limits of the semicircular notched carbon steel specimens were unaffected by the pre-loading, but those of the corresponding nickel steel specimens were increased by the tension pre-loading and decreased by the compression pre-loading. The fatigue limits of the vee-notched nickel steel specimens were also increased by the tension and decreased by the compression pre-loadings. The vee-notched carbon steel specimens were stress-relieved at 650 °C, which resulted in their fatigue limit being reduced to about one half of that of as-machined specimens. Pre-loading was carried out only on these stress-relieved specimens; the fatigue limit of those which had been statically pre-loaded in tension was increased to a value about equal to that obtained on the as-machined but not pre-loaded specimens whereas compressive pre-loading had little, if any, effect on the fatigue limit of the stress-relieved specimens. Similarly, it was found [145] that pre-loading 0·2% C steel specimens containing a hole had no significant effect on the subsequent fatigue strength.

The effect of residual stresses induced by surface mechanical working processes, such as surface-rolling or shot-peening, on fatigue strength has also been widely studied because these processes induce biaxial compressive residual stresses in all free surfaces, unlike the bending and restraightening technique which induces tensile and compressive residual stress in opposite faces, the former tending to decrease the fatigue limit. For this reason, cold-straightening bars can lead to a deterioration of their fatigue properties. Shot-peening [151] induces a biaxial compressive stress of half the yield stress or more in a surface layer 0·1–0·5 mm deep.

Much of the relevant data has been obtained from steel specimens but a similar pattern of behaviour occurs in the case of all ductile materials. For example, it was found [152] that the rotating bending fatigue limits of steel, brasses, and aluminium alloys were all improved by shot-peening. Shot-peening and surface-rolling $4\frac{1}{2}$% Cu–aluminium alloy specimens [153] increased their rotating bending fatigue strength (10^7 cycles) by 20–30 per cent but had no effect on their reversed direct stress fatigue strength; this point is discussed in § 3.4. Several investigators [154–6] found that shot-peening increased the fatigue strength of hardened spring steel, there being some evidence that the highest fatigue strength was obtained by polishing the finally peened surface. Other examples of an increase in the fatigue strength due to peening have been given [157], and extensive data on a wide range of materials and peening processes are available [158]. Peening is useful in increasing the fatigue strength of components having a surface produced other than by machining, such as extruded and forged surfaces or steel surfaces which have been decarburized. For example, the plane bending fatigue strength of $4\frac{1}{2}$% Cu–aluminium alloy specimens having as-extruded surfaces [159] was improved by shot-peening with aluminium alloy shot; this was used instead of the conventional steel or chilled iron spherical particles in order to avoid iron contamination of the surface. Processes similar to shot-peening or surface-rolling, such as vapour-blasting, barrel-tumbling, and buffing have been reported as increasing the fatigue strength of both plain and notched specimens of the high-strength aluminium alloys [160, 161].

The plane bending fatigue limit was determined [162] of strip specimens of a 6% Al-titanium alloy having residual stresses, ranging from 430 MN m^{-2} tension to 740 MN m^{-2} compression, induced in both surfaces by either grinding (tensile residual stresses) or shot-peening (compressive residual stresses). It was found that the fatigue limit was increased by compressive residual stresses and decreased by tensile residual stresses as indicated by the equation

$$F_s = F_p - \frac{S}{10},$$

where F_s is the semi-range of the fatigue limit of a treated specimen, F_p is the semi-range of the fatigue limit of the annealed material, and S is the magnitude of the surface residual stress measured in the direction of the fatigue load.

Various grinding procedures were employed [163] to induce surface residual stresses, parallel to the grinding direction, of from $+70$ MN m^{-2} to -700 MN m^{-2} in flat bars of AISI 52100 (1% C, 1¼% Cr, Rockwell C59) steel. The fatigue limit in reversed plane bending increased from ±430 MN m^{-2} to ±680 MN m^{-2} as the surface residual stress changed from $+70$ MN m^{-2} to -700 MN m^{-2}. Measurements of the residual stresses in specimens tested at the fatigue limit showed that they were not relaxed by the cyclic stresses.

Contact pressure is more easily controlled in the surface-rolling process than in shot-peening, and can attain higher values. Because of these higher possible contact pressures, a deeper surface layer of material can be worked by rolling than by peening. Almen and Black [139] give many examples of the possible increases in the fatigue limit of shafts due to cold-rolling. Rolling is, however, particularly effective in increasing the fatigue limit of notched specimens or components, for example, cold-rolling the journal and web fillets of crankshafts [164]. The significant increase in fatigue limit that can result from cold-rolling the roots of screw threads is mentioned in § 6.10.

6.3.4. Discussion

The effect of a residual stress on the fatigue limit of a material is similar to that of a superimposed static mean stress (see § 3.5), except that a mean stress is maintained constant throughout a test by means of an external load, whereas a residual stress may be relaxed by any subsequent cyclic plastic deformation induced by the cyclic stressing. Obviously, if the magnitude of the cyclic stressing is sufficient to relax the residual stresses early in the test, they can have little effect on the subsequent fatigue strength. It follows therefore that induced residual stresses have the greatest effect on the fatigue strength of notched components where the applied nominal stresses are less than the plain fatigue limit of the material, the effect increasing with both notch sharpness and the yield-stress/fatigue-limit ratio of the material. Unrelaxed residual stresses would not be expected to have a pronounced effect on the minimum alternating shear stress required to initiate and develop a microcrack but may affect profoundly the subsequent propagation of macrocracks. Thus, residual compressive stresses of sufficient magnitude and depth will prevent a macrocrack opening and so either retard its growth or cause it to remain dormant until the stress level is raised. On the other hand, tensile residual stresses will open a crack, so making its subsequent propagation easier, in situations where this results in an increase in the tensile stress range. Compressive residual stresses will, for a given stress range, increase the changeover length between the microcrack and macrocrack growth stages. Thus, if the stress level applied to either a plain specimen having high compressive residual stresses induced in the surface layers or a notched specimen having high compressive residual stresses induced around the notch root is such as to cause it to break after a long endurance, it is found that the crack has to grow an appreciable distance as a microcrack in order to penetrate the volume of material influenced by the residual stresses, before finally growing as a macrocrack normal to the loading direction. This results in a fracture face having a marked shear lip extending in, either from the surface of the plain specimen or from the bottom of the notch in the notched specimen.

If residual compressive stresses affect only a very thin surface layer, which for a given cyclic loading and material is less than the depth at which a microcrack changes to a macrocrack (see § 4.11), a surface microcrack will be able to grow through it (under the action of resolved cyclic shear stresses) at a stress level either equal to or only slightly greater than that required to develop it to the same depth in a material in which residual stresses are absent. It follows therefore that, if the fatigue limit of either plain or notched specimens is increased markedly by the introduction of surface compressive residual stresses, in all probability microcracks will have formed in the surface layers but will have been prevented from growing. The slope of the finite-life portion of their S/N curves will be flatter than those of corresponding untreated specimens because, once a crack has penetrated the affected layer of material, its growth rate at a given stress level will be as in an untreated specimen, the difference in life being the number of cycles necessary for the crack to penetrate the affected layer. This difference will become less the higher the cyclic stress level for, in addition to it now being easier for a microcrack to reach the macrocrack stage, there will be a greater tendency for the residual stresses to be relaxed.

Whether or not residual stresses are relaxed depends on the magnitude of the subsequent cyclic stressing in relation to the yield stress of the material. It has been argued [51, 165, 166] that residual stresses will be relaxed if, when added to the external stresses acting in the same direction, the resulting value of the maximum resolved shear stress exceeds the yield shear stress of the material; they will be reduced to such a value that the sum of the external and residual stresses equals the yield stress. Residual stresses are therefore relaxed more easily in a material which exhibits a wide hysteresis loop at stresses equal to and just above its plain fatigue limit (for example, mild steel and soft metals in general) than in one whose fatigue limit is much less than the yield or 0·1 per cent proof stress (for example, high-strength aluminium alloys and stronger steels).

If the fatigue limit of a batch of rolled or peened specimens (either plain or notched) has been determined, with runouts being obtained at endurances greater than, say, 10^8 cycles, there are no obvious reasons why the beneficial effects due to the induced compressive residual stresses should be diminished in a specimen tested at or below the fatigue limit stress level, no matter how long the test is continued, since any relaxation of the residual stresses would be expected to occur early in the life. Certainly, if this has not occurred prior to 10^8 cycles it is difficult to visualize any mechanism whereby it can happen subsequently. In practice, the loading cycle may vary, and if the component should be overloaded for a period of time, the resulting higher cyclic stresses may enable the crack to grow through the compressive residual stress field and also partially relax the residual stresses.

In the case of plain specimens, the effect of residual stresses is less pronounced in reversed direct stress tests than in bending tests; the reasons for this have been discussed in § 3.4. As mentioned in § 4.6, compressive residual stresses are most effective in increasing the fatigue limit of notched specimens, particularly when they are induced at the roots of sharp vee-notches by cold-rolling. This is because the unrolled notched fatigue limit is low, and even though the notched fatigue limit may be doubled for example, by cold-rolling, the nominal stress will still be low compared to the plain fatigue limit of the material, the bulk of the specimens therefore deforming elastically. In many cases, non-propagating cracks will be present at the root of sharp notches when tested at the unrolled notched fatigue limit (§ 4.6); the cold-rolling must therefore be severe enough to ensure that the compressive residual stresses are induced to a depth greater than that to which these non-propagating cracks penetrate. Provided this is done, the nominal stress can be increased markedly before either the crack can penetrate through the affected layer or the residual stresses are relaxed.

Shot-peening and surface-rolling tend to roughen the surface and, if carried out incorrectly, may induce small surface cracks. Polishing a thin layer from the worked surface may therefore sometimes result in an additional increase in fatigue strength. Obviously, the beneficial effects produced by these processes will be lost if a component is heat-treated after working. However, rolling of crankshaft fillets is a common practice and, because these may operate at engine oil temperatures, it is necessary to restrict this temperature [167] to a value which does not cause relaxation of the residual stresses.

The beneficial effects of surface-working processes, especially surface-rolling, should be utilized by a designer whenever there is the slightest doubt that fatigue cracks may be initiated at a discontinuity or notch. The improvement in the fatigue limits of screw threads, welded joints, shrink-fit assemblies, platings, and specimens subjected to fretting that can result from surface-working are discussed in later sections.

6.4. Surface treatments

Various types of surface treatment are frequently applied to metals to improve their corrosion resistance, appearance, and wear resistance. These include metal platings, anodizing, and metallurgical treatments such as nitriding. They may be applied alone or in combination either with each other or with mechanical treatments, such as shot–peening, described in § 6.3.

6.4.1. Metal platings

Chromium is sometimes deposited electrolytically on to a load-carrying steel member either to provide a hard wear-resistant surface or to build up a worn or undersized region. Nickel and cadmium electro-deposited coatings are often used to improve resistance to corrosion. The effect of such coatings, particularly electro-deposited chromium, on the fatigue strength of the steel substrate has been studied in some detail; Hammond and Williams [168] have reviewed the subject. As deposited, chromium contains internal cracks and tensile residual stresses whose magnitude depends on the plating conditions. The value of the tensile residual stress may also depend on the thickness of the plating; the values given in Table 6.5 were obtained [168] by

TABLE 6.5

Thickness of plating (mm)	0·0025	0·0075	0·013	0·025	0·15
Residual tensile stress (MN m^{-2})	970	510	116	77	77

plating a high-strength steel from a standard solution (250 g l^{-1} chromic acid, 2.5 g l^{-1} sulphuric acid) at 2150 A m^{-2} and 50 °C. No further decrease in residual stress occurred with deposits thicker than 0·15 mm. It was found that chromium plating reduced the fatigue limit of stronger steels by a larger proportion than it did that of weaker steels; the percentage changes, due to a 0·15 mm thick chromium plate, in the fatigue limits of steels of various tensile strengths are shown on Fig. 6.17. In the case of high-strength steels, the reduction in fatigue limit was found to be independent of plating thickness over the range 0·025–0·3 mm. Some further results [169] showing the effect of plating thickness on the fatigue limit of a chromium plated 0·3% C, 1% Cr

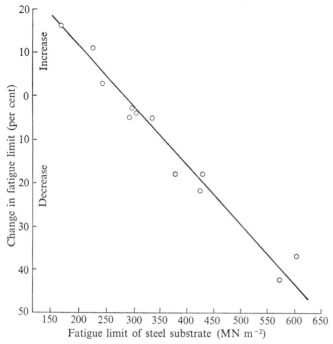

FIG. 6.17. Percentage change in the fatigue limit of a steel due to a 0·15 mm chromium plating. (Taken from Hammond and Williams [168].)

steel in either the normalized or the hardened and tempered condition are given in Table 6.6. The specimens, 7·6 mm diameter, were plated in a sulphate bath at 70 °C with a current density of 10 800 A m^{-2} and then tested in rotating bending. It was also found that heating the plated specimens at between 200 °C and 300 °C prior to testing decreased the fatigue limit but heating at 440 °C increased it. The effect of various heat-treatments on the rotating bending fatigue limit of chromium plated 0·3 % C steel specimens having a 0·125 mm thick plating are shown in Table 6.7 [170].

The effect of post-plating heat-treatments on the rotating bending fatigue limit of chromium-plated 1200 MN m^{-2} tensile strength steel (plain fatigue

TABLE 6.6

	Fatigue limit (MN m^{-2})					
	Thickness of plating (mm)					
Condition of steel	0	0·0025	0·025	0·1	0·23	Ground to 0·23
Normalized	±300	±255	±225	±255	±280	±260
Hardened and tempered	±640	±400	±420	±340	±310	±400

23

limit ±570 MN m^{-2}) specimens having platings either 0·025 mm, 0·15 mm, or 0·3 mm thick has been studied [168]. The fatigue strength (10^7 cycles) of as-plated specimens was about ±340 MN m^{-2}, irrespective of plating thickness but, whereas baking at 200 °C for 1 hour had little effect on the fatigue strength of the 0·025 mm thick plating, it decreased that of the 0·15 mm and 0·3 mm thick platings to ±230 MN m^{-2} and ±120 MN m^{-2} respectively. However, baking at higher temperatures resulted in a less drastic decrease in fatigue strength and, in fact, baking at 500 °C caused the fatigue strength to increase above the as-plated value, reaching values of ±570 MN m^{-2},

TABLE 6.7

Condition	Fatigue strength, 10^7 cycles (MN m^{-2})
Unplated	±245
Plated	±250
Plated and heated at 250 °C for 1 hour	±200
Plated and heated at 420 °C for 1 hour	±235
Plated and heated at 500 °C for 1 hour	±245

±500 MN m^{-2}, and ±400 MN m^{-2} for the 0·025 mm, 0·15 mm, and 0·3 mm thick platings respectively. It was argued that the fatigue strength was altered by these post-plating heat-treatments because they changed both the magnitude and sign of the residual plating stresses. For example, the 77 MN m^{-2} residual tensile stress present in a 0·025 mm thick plating was increased to 120 MN m^{-2} after baking at 250 °C (1 hour) but decreased to zero after baking at 430 °C. Baking at higher temperatures induced compressive residual stresses in the plating, these reaching a value of 300 MN m^{-2} at a baking temperature of 600 °C. Unfortunately, there are practical limitations to post-baking treatments; first, the tempering temperature of the steel substrate must not be exceeded and, secondly, the wear resistance characteristics of chromium plate deteriorate if softened (for example, baking at 600 °C can cause a drop in hardness from 900 HV to 400 HV).

Because plated chromium contains inherent cracks, its fatigue limit will be determined by the maximum cyclic stress that will just not cause a crack to grow. Thus, compressive residual stresses will tend to keep the cracks closed and so enhance the fatigue limit, whereas tensile residual stresses will tend to lower the cyclic stress necessary to cause a crack to grow and hence lower the fatigue limit. Indirect evidence that the fatigue limit of plated chromium depends on the cyclic stress to grow an inherent crack is provided by the results [168], given in Table 6.8, obtained from fatigue tests at various mean stresses on 1200 MN m^{-2} tensile strength alloy steel specimens in both the unplated and plated (0·15 mm thick) condition. It is seen that, whereas the fatigue limits of the unplated specimens change only slightly with increasing compressive mean stress, those of the plated specimens show the marked increase typical of the behaviour of cracked specimens, namely the fatigue limit increases so that the range of tensile stress (that controlling crack growth) remains roughly constant. The decrease in fatigue limit with increasing tensile mean stress is also more marked with the plated than unplated specimens, behaviour which would be expected if the former contained inherent cracks.

TABLE 6.8

Mean stress (MN m^{-2})	Fatigue limit (MN m^{-2})	
	Unplated	Plated
-310	± 630	± 590
-155	± 620	± 460
0	± 590	± 340
155	± 540	± 215
310	± 460	± 155
460	± 385	± 120
620	± 340	± 120
770	± 295	± 120

Hammond and Williams [168] observed that specimens with chromium platings thicker than 0·025 mm all had a fatigue limit of about ± 340 MN m^{-2}, independent of plating thickness. (This presumably implies that the maximum size of plating flaw is about 0·025 mm, so that platings thicker than this have, in themselves, no effect.) They therefore argued that the fatigue limit of a plated steel specimen would be equal to that of the steel substrate if this were less than ± 340 MN m^{-2} and would increase as the fatigue limit of the substrate increased, but could not exceed ± 340 MN m^{-2}. This arises because a crack growing in a plating such as chromium or nickel which forms an interatomic bond with a steel substrate, can pass directly into the its steel, the tensile strength of the steel having little or no influence on its growth characteristics (Chapter 5).

Because the fatigue strength (at long endurances) of aluminium alloys is less than that of chromium, the fatigue strength of a chromium-plated aluminium alloy specimen would not be expected to be different from that of the substrate. Indeed, it has been found [171] that hard chromium platings between 0·03 mm and 0·1 mm thick had little effect on the fatigue strength (at long endurances) of various aluminium alloy specimens.

Nickel plating, like chromium plating, causes a reduction in the fatigue limits of steels, the higher the tensile strength of the steel and the higher the tensile residual stress in the plating the greater the reduction in fatigue limit.

The results [165], given in Table 6.9, on nickel-plated steel specimens illus-trate this latter point. It has also been found that the fatigue limit of nickel-plated steel specimens is increased if the tensile residual stress is reduced by varying the conditions of the plating process [172]; tensile residual stresses, varying from 90 MN m^{-2} to 550 MN m^{-2}, depending on bath conditions have been reported [173].

It has been found [168] that, contrary to the behaviour of chromium plating, low-temperature baking of nickel plating on medium- and high-strength steels did not significantly affect the as-plated fatigue limit. The fatigue limit of nickel plating was shown to be increased by electroplating the steel substrate with 0·125 mm of tin, followed by a flash of copper before

TABLE 6.9

Specimen	Residual stress in nickel plating (MN m^{-2})	Fatigue limit (MN m^{-2})
Unplated steel	0	±310
Nickel-plated steel	−42	±310
Nickel-plated steel	+175	±200

plating with nickel [174]. For example, the fatigue limit of SAE 4330 steel was reduced from ±540 MN m^{-2} to ±310 MN m^{-2} by 0·025 mm thick nickel plate but, with tin and copper undercoats, the fatigue limit was in-creased to ±420 MN m^{-2}.

Platings, other than chromium and nickel, usually have little effect on the fatigue limits of low- and medium-strength steels. However, they can reduce the fatigue limits of stronger steels. For example, it has been reported [168, 175] that cadmium plating can reduce the fatigue limit of high-strength steels by about 10–15 per cent, but has little effect on the fatigue limit of low- and medium-strength steels. It has been suggested that this reduction in strength is associated mainly with the degree of absorption and diffusion of hydrogen liberated at the steel surface during the plating procedure [175]. However, although hydrogen will be liberated during the electroplating pro-cess and may diffuse into the steel substrate, it seems generally accepted that it has no effect on the fatigue limit of low- and medium-strength steels and little effect on that of high-strength steels, although it may cause a decrease in the fatigue strengths of high-strength steels at short endurances [168, 176, 177].

Electroplated zinc has been found to have no effect on the fatigue limits of steels having tensile strengths up to 1150 MN m^{-2} [168]. On the other hand, hot-dipped zinc coatings (galvanizing) can result in a serious reduction in fatigue limit. Thus, whereas the rotating bending fatigue limits of various carbon steels were not affected by electroplated zinc coatings [178], hot-dip galvanizing decreased the fatigue limit of a high-strength steel by up to 50 per cent, the decrease being less pronounced for steels of lower tensile strength. The reason for this different behaviour is that electroplated zinc does not produce discontinuities of a size sufficient to grow directly as cracks into the substrate. On the other hand, hot dipping produces a brittle intermediate layer of diffused iron–zinc which may crack at stress levels less than the fatigue limit of the steel substrate thus producing cracks which can penetrate the substrate directly.

The fatigue limit of high-strength steel specimens having either 0·025 mm thick copper or lead electroplatings are given in Table 6.10: copper causes a 20 per cent reduction and lead no significant decrease [179].

TABLE 6.10

Plating	Fatigue limit (MN m^{-2})
Unplated steel	±760
Copper plate	±600
Lead plate	±730

In an attempt to find out how an electro-deposited coating affected the fatigue limit of the substrate, copper, silver, and aluminium specimens were plated with each of these metals in turn [180]. It was concluded that the results obtained could not be explained solely on a basis of hairline cracks and residual stresses in the plating but that corrosion and oxidation effects played a significant role.

Because failure of a plated specimen necessitates the growth of a crack from the plating into and through the steel substrate, the introduction of compressive residual stresses into the surface of the substrate by, for example, shot-peening or rolling, retards the rate of growth of a crack in the substrate and hence increases the fatigue limit of the plated specimen as a whole. For example, it was found [181] that chromium-, nickel-, and cadmium-plated SAE 3140 specimens, which were shot-peened prior to plating, had higher fatigue limits than those which had not been shot-peened. Rotating bending fatigue tests [168] on high-strength alloy steel specimens which had been shot-peened prior to chromium plating (0·15 mm thick) showed that the fatigue limit of the plated specimens increased with increasing intensity of peening and that, provided the intensity of peening was sufficiently high, the fatigue limit of the plated specimens could be restored to that of the unplated steel. Baking at 200 °C, which reduced the fatigue limit of plated, unpeened specimens, had little effect on the fatigue limit of specimens shot-peened prior to plating. The fatigue limit of cadmium-plated high-strength steel specimens shot-peened prior to plating was found to be equal to that of the steel itself

[175]. Shot-peening either before or after nickel plating was found to increase the fatigue limit of steels, the greater increase being obtained by shot-peening after plating [172]. Shot-peening roughens the surface of the substrate and, because this roughness persists after plating, especially with thin platings, it is often eliminated by fine-grinding either the shot-peened substrate prior to plating or the finished plating. Careful grinding, whether done before or after plating, was found to have no significant effect on the subsequent fatigue limit [168]. Nitriding the steel substrate prior to plating also increases the fatigue limit of a plated specimen. However, the fatigue limit of chromium-plated nitrided specimens appears to decrease with increasing plating thickness [168]; it was suggested that the compressive stresses induced by nitriding were not as efficient at preventing cracks present in the chromium plating from growing into the substrate as those induced by shot-peening.

Summarizing briefly, it would seem that, in the case of those platings which make an interatomic bond with the substrate, the fatigue strength of the plated member depends on the discontinuities and residual stresses developed during the plating process. Because the crack growth characteristics of steels are similar, once the stress level exceeds that necessary to cause a crack in the plating to grow, the strength of the steel substrate will make little difference to the fatigue limit of a plated specimen. Any method, such as inducing high compressive stresses in the surface layers of the substrate, that prevents the growth of these inherent cracks will improve the fatigue strength of the plated specimen; similar effects are observed in sprayed coatings [182].

6.4.2. Anodizing

Anodizing is an electrolytic bath process for producing a hard anti-corrosive abrasion-resistant oxide surface layer on aluminium alloys. Because load carrying members are sometimes anodized, the fatigue strength of anodized aluminium alloy (generally the high-strength alloys used in aircraft construction) specimens has been studied by several workers. It was concluded [183] from rotating bending tests on anodized specimens of a cast (1·3 % Cu, 5 % Si) and 3 wrought (4 % Cu, $4\frac{1}{2}$ % Cu, and $5\frac{1}{2}$ % Zn) aluminium alloys that a 3 per cent chromic acid anodizing process giving a coating 0·0025–0·005 mm thick had little effect on the subsequent fatigue strength (10^7 cycles), but that a 15 per cent sulphuric acid process giving a coating 0·0125–0·025 mm thick, although having little effect on the fatigue strength at 10^7 cycles, caused a slight reduction in the life at higher stress levels. However, it was found subsequently [184] that, although thin coatings of the type used previously had no effect on the rotating bending fatigue strength of $5\frac{1}{2}$ % Zn–aluminium alloy specimens, thicker coatings, 0·1 mm thick produced by the chromic acid process and 0·025–0·05 mm thick produced by the sulphuric acid process, resulted in a 35 per cent reduction in the fatigue strength at 10^8 cycles.

If a particular anodizing process produces a coating which causes a re-duction in fatigue strength, it has been found that the fatigue strength can be restored by sealing the coating by immersing in a boiling dichromate solution. Rotating bending $4\frac{1}{2}\%$ Cu–aluminium alloy specimens having a hard anodic coating (sulphuric acid bath, $0\cdot025$–$0\cdot05$ mm thick) suffered a decrease in fatigue strength (10^7 cycles) of 40–50 per cent [185]. However, sealing the anodic coating in a boiling dichromate solution improved the fatigue strength to within 5 per cent of that of the virgin material. It was also found [184] that, although sealed anodic coatings $0\cdot025$ mm thick reduced

TABLE 6.11

Specimen condition	Fatigue strength, 10^8 cycles ($MN\,m^{-2}$)	
	BS L40	DTD 683
As-turned	±173	±182
As-turned + chromic acid anodizing	±179	±165
As-turned + acid pickling + anodizing	±179	±180
As-turned + caustic soda pickling + anodizing	±190	±200

the fatigue strength at short endurances of Alclad sheets, they had no signifi-cant effect on the fatigue strength at 10^8 cycles. A $0\cdot05$ mm thick anodic coating reduced the fatigue strength (10^7 cycles) of a 3% Al, 1% Zn, 3% Mn magnesium alloy by about 25 per cent and a $0\cdot03$ mm coating by about 10 per cent [186].

Prior to anodizing, it is usual to pickle the aluminium alloy substrate. The effect of either acid or caustic soda pickling prior to chromic acid anodizing on the rotating bending fatigue strength of the aluminium alloys BS L40 ($4\frac{1}{2}\%$ Cu) and DTD 683 ($5\frac{1}{2}\%$ Zn) has been studied [187], the results being given in Table 6.11. Of all the pickling solutions tested, the caustic soda pickle prior to anodizing gave the highest fatigue strength. Anodizing without pickling appeared to be beneficial in the case of the $4\frac{1}{2}\%$ Cu alloy but detri-mental in the case of the $5\frac{1}{2}\%$ Zn alloy. Further results of the effects of pickling and anodizing treatments on the fatigue strength of aluminium alloys are discussed by Harris [188].

6.4.3. Metallurgical surface-hardening techniques
There are three main metallurgical techniques commonly used to produce a hardened surface layer on steel, namely, induction or flame-hardening,

carburizing, and nitriding. They all harden the surface and produce metallurgical structure volume changes which induce high compressive residual stresses in the surface layer.

Flame-hardening consists of heating the surface above the critical temperature of the steel and then quenching to produce a hard martensitic surface layer containing high compressive residual stresses; it has been shown [189] that flame-hardening can produce a hardened layer more than 3 mm thick on a 0.4% C steel, the surface hardness increasing from 180 HV to 580 HV. The

TABLE 6.12

Quenching medium	Surface compressive residual stress ($MN\ m^{-2}$)	Fatigue limit ($MN\ m^{-2}$)
Furnace-cooled	0	± 280
Oil at 80 °C	-200	± 295
Water at 0 °C	-340	± 325
Salt solution at -5 °C	-340	± 340

largest increase in fatigue limit is produced when sharply notched specimens are so treated. For example, the fatigue limit of 0.45% C steel specimens containing a sharp shoulder was increased from ± 115 MN m^{-2} to ± 355 MN m^{-2} by flame-hardening the material in the region of the shoulder. The rotating bending fatigue limit of notched specimens (56 mm outside diameter, containing a circumferential vee-notch 6 mm deep and 0.6 mm radius) was increased from ± 85 MN m^{-2} to ± 340 MN m^{-2} and ± 560 MN m^{-2} by flame-hardening the material at the notch to a depth of 3.3 mm and 5 mm respectively [190], using high-speed direct gas heating. A practical difficulty when flame-hardening plain specimens, as opposed to notched specimens, is to obtain a uniformly hardened surface. Care is also needed in the case of complicated shapes to ensure that only surface compressive residual stresses are produced and that no complementary tensile residual stresses exist at a free surface.

Quenching alloy steel specimens from their tempering temperature induces surface residual compressive stresses and hence improves their fatigue limit [191]. Plain 0.34% C steel bars heated to their critical temperature and quenched in different media, thus inducing different surface compressive stresses, gave subsequent rotating bending fatigue limits as in Table 6.12 [192].

Both carburizing and nitriding produce a hardened layer on the surface of suitable steels. The former process consists of heating the steel in a carbon-bearing environment and then quenching; the latter consists of heating in an

TABLE 6.13

	Fatigue strength, 10^7 cycles (MN m^{-2})		
Condition of specimens	Rotating bending	Cyclic torsion	Reversed direct stress
Un-nitrided	±560	±310	±525
Nitrided	±740	±400	±525

ammonia environment so that nitrogen combines with certain elements in the steel. Nitriding has the advantage that it is not essential to quench, so minimizing any distortion, but it is beneficial to lap or hone the finally hardened surface in order to remove a brittle surface skin. Carburizing can give a thicker hardened case (typical thicknesses 0·7–2·5 mm) than nitriding (0·1–0·5 mm), the former having a surface hardness of about 700 HV, the latter 850 HV. Both processes give rise to high surface compressive residual stresses. The magnitude of these depends on the ratio of the core area to the case area; quoted values of these compressive stresses range from 230 MN m^{-2} to 620 MN m^{-2} and 310 MN m^{-2} to 1150 MN m^{-2} for carburizing and nitriding respectively [34, 193, 194]. As might be expected, both carburizing and nitriding can lead to an increase in the plain fatigue limit. However, as discussed previously in § 3.4, the fatigue limit of plain specimens having a hardened surface layer will only show an increase over that of untreated specimens when tested in cyclic bending or torsion, little or no effect occurring in direct stress. In general, the bending or torsional fatigue limit of plain specimens may be increased by about 20–100 per cent by either nitriding or carburizing, the amount depending on specimen size, case depth, and tensile strength of the base steel, the higher the tensile strength, the less the increase in fatigue limit. Data obtained [195] on nitrided chromium–nickel–vanadium steel specimens given in Table 6.13 illustrate these points. Other investigators [194, 196] have confirmed that nitriding did not increase the direct stress fatigue limit.

The results in Table 6.14 [197] show the need to quench after carburizing if the maximum increase in fatigue limit of rotating bending specimens is to be obtained. These results were obtained on 7·6 mm diameter

TABLE 6.14

Heat treatment	Case depth (mm)	Fatigue limit (MN m^{-2})
None—as received	0	±193
Carburized at 910 °C, air-cooled	0·5	±280
Carburized at 910 °C, oil-quenched	2·0	±555
Carburized at 910 °C, oil-quenched	0·5	±415

0·2% C steel (SAE 1020) specimens; they also show that the fatigue limit increases as the case depth increases. The results [198] given in Table 6.15 show that the reversed bending fatigue limit of nitrided chromium–molybdenum steel plain specimens increases with time of nitriding (that is, case depth), the shortest time giving a case depth of about 0·1 mm, the longest time a case depth of 0·75 mm; the effect is much less pronounced than for the results given in Table 6.14, presumably because the steel used in the latter tests was much stronger. In repeated torsion, the plain fatigue limit of a 1150 MN m^{-2} tensile strength alloy steel [199] was increased from 0–600 MN

TABLE 6.15

Nitriding conditions	Fatigue limit (MN m^{-2})
None, as received	±510
10 hours at 485 °C	±590
22 hours at 485 °C	±590
72 hours at 485 °C	±630

m^{-2} to 0–1000 MN m^{-2}, an increase of 66 per cent, by carburizing to a depth of 0·375 mm.

The effect of a moderately hardened surface layer has been discussed in § 3.4. However, when the surface layer is very hard compared to the core material, the resistance to cyclic slip may be so high that it is easier for cracks to develop from flaws or discontinuities just below the hardened layer than for surface cracks to be initiated. In any case, if surface cracks are initiated, the surface compressive residual stresses may be sufficiently high to prevent them developing to the macrocrack stage at stress levels less than that necessary to grow cracks from flaws situated just below the hardened layer. In fact it is found that, in general, failure of case-hardened plain specimens does originate from a point below the hardened case. Examination of the fracture face of such a failed specimen shows that the origin of failure is at the centre of a small circular whitish area situated close to the case and core boundary. A photograph of a fracture face in which failure originated at the centre of a circular white area, below a carburized surface layer, is shown on Fig. 6.18.

Cracks grow from inclusions or discontinuities just below the hardened layer in preference to those situated elsewhere because the compressive residual stresses in the case are balanced by tensile residual stresses in the material just below the case. These tensile residual stresses aid the development of a crack while, in a bending test, the boundary position between the core and case is the part of the core subjected to the highest stresses. The whitish circular area visible on the fracture face represents the path of a crack growing radially outwards from an inclusion or discontinuity at its centre, the whitish appearance being due to the fact that until the crack has grown through the hardened layer and broken the free surface of the specimen, the atmosphere is excluded from the fracture faces. Once the crack front breaks the free surface, air is admitted to the remainder of the crack front, and the subsequent fracture face takes on its normal in-air appearance. The diameter of the white spot depends on the distance of the failure origin from the free surface, which in turn depends on the depth of the hardened layer. The deeper the case and the higher the residual stresses in it, the longer the life at a given stress level. It is for this reason that the S/N curve of heavily case-hardened specimens flattens out very gradually to a fatigue limit, failures after 30–60×10^6 cycles being a common occurrence.

It is not possible to predict quantitatively the fatigue limit of a case-hardened steel specimen; it depends on the method of stressing, the hardness of the surface, the magnitude of the induced compressive residual stresses, the ratio of the hardness of the surface to that of the core, and the ratio of the case depth to specimen diameter. Maximum fatigue limits have been quoted [200] corresponding to values of this latter ratio of 0.01–0.2, depending on the steel and case-hardening technique. The fatigue limit also depends on the size and distribution of discontinuities in the steel, since these factors determine the surface hardness level above which it is easier for a crack to grow from a sub-surface discontinuity than for a surface crack to initiate and develop. Use of a cleaner steel (that is, one containing fewer and smaller discontinuities) results in a higher fatigue limit. Little or no effect occurs in direct stress cyclic loadings because, as discussed in § 3.4.1, once the fatigue limit of the core is exceeded, the core deforms plastically each cycle, and because the strain in the case, which may still deform elastically, must equal that in the core at the common interface, the stress in the case is higher than the nominal stress. This is also the case when a specimen having a thin case is tested in bending, because the deflection of the specimen under a given bending moment is nearly the same as a similarly loaded uncased specimen. The fact that the softer core material is detrimental is illustrated by results [201] showing that the fatigue limit of carburized specimens having the core bored out was superior to that of unbored carburized specimens. Additionally, it has been pointed out, in relation to bending tests on case-hardened specimens, [198] that if the fatigue limit stress is estimated at the point where failure occurs, that is, at the boundary between the core and case, instead of being taken as the surface stress, the depth of case has little effect on the fatigue limit.

Notched specimens, if carburized or nitrided after machining the notch, may have their fatigue limit increased from 50 per cent to 200 per cent provided that the localized high stresses at the notch root are contained within the hardened layer. In general, the sharper the notch, the greater the increase in fatigue limit due to case-hardening. For example, the plane bending fatigue limit of steel specimens [198] containing a transverse hole was increased from ±225 MN m^{-2} to ±425 MN m^{-2} by nitriding the finally machined specimens.

6.4.4. Soft layers

In contrast to surface hardening, any process which softens the surface of a material reduces its fatigue strength. Because the weakest part of such a specimen is at the free surface, the fatigue strength decreases irrespective of whether tests are carried out in bending or direct stress. Decarburization of steel (that is, loss of carbon and production of free ferrite due to heating in an oxidizing environment), which occurs when steel is heat-treated or forged, produces a softened surface layer, as does the cladding of high-strength aluminium alloy by a layer of aluminium to improve corrosion-resistance. For example [202], the fatigue limits of decarburized specimens of a 0.6% C, 0.4% Cr, 1% Mn steel, heat-treated to various tensile strengths, were all the same (namely ±325 MN m^{-2}), thus reducing the original fatigue limits by 30 per cent, 43 per cent, and 52 per cent for tensile strengths of 1100 MN m^{-2}, 1250 MN m^{-2}, and 1850 MN m^{-2} respectively. Similar results have been reported by other investigators [203, 204]. This confirms that, once a crack has formed in the softened ferritic surface layer, its rate of growth through the steel beneath is independent of the structure and properties of the steel. Similarly, it was found [205] that the fatigue limits of steel specimens (varying in tensile strength from 460 MN m^{-2} to 2000 MN m^{-2}) having as-forged surfaces varied between ±155 MN m^{-2} and ±275 MN m^{-2}, that is, the as-forged fatigue limit remained roughly the same irrespective of the strength of the steel (the variation from ±155 MN m^{-2} to ±275 MN m^{-2} was probably a consequence of the different surface roughness created by the forged finish on the different types of steel). The fatigue strength of a decarburized steel can be increased by shot-peening or by the obvious procedure of machining away the decarburized layer.

The cladding of high-strength aluminium alloys with aluminium [206] was found to reduce their fatigue strength below that of the unclad material. For example [207], the fatigue strengths ($>10^7$ cycles) of clad $5\frac{1}{2}\%$ Zn (7075-T6) and clad $4\frac{1}{2}\%$ Cu (2024-T3) aluminium alloys were 50 per cent less in reversed bending and 33 per cent less in reversed direct stress than in the unclad condition. Other investigators [208] have found that the pulsating tension fatigue strength is halved when $4\frac{1}{2}\%$ Cu–aluminium alloy plate specimens were in the clad condition. It was also found [207] that sprayed aluminium coatings gave similar reductions in fatigue strength.

Thus, a softened surface layer, such as that produced by decarburizing steel or soft aluminium cladding on an aluminium alloy, reduces the fatigue limit of the base metal, because surface microcracks are able to form and develop at a lower stress level than if the softened layer were absent.

Provided that the softened layer is deep enough to allow a microcrack to penetrate to a depth sufficient for it to grow as a macrocrack, it will be able to grow through the harder substrate at the same stress level irrespective of its strength (see Chapters 4 and 5).

6.5. Pressurized cylinders

Components such as pressure pipes, hydraulic cylinders, gas cylinders, and gun barrels are stressed by the pressurized media contained in them. When this internal pressure fluctuates, cyclic stresses are set up in the container material and fatigue failure may occur. If the presence of the fluctuating pressurizing medium (usually a fluid or a gas) were of no consequence other than to stress the container material, the fatigue limit of the container could be predicted simply from a knowledge of the container stresses and the fatigue limit of the material. However, as was mentioned in § 3.6, difficulty arose in interpreting the results of tests on thin-walled tubes subjected to in-phase uniaxial cyclic loads and fluctuating internal oil pressures because, in some of the tests, the fatigue limit under a pure cyclic hoop stress was found to be only 60–70 per cent of that under cyclic axial loading alone. This difference was ascribed to anisotropy of the material; however, the fact that the former fatigue limit was obtained with pressurized oil in intimate contact with the tube wall, whereas the latter was not, may also have had a bearing on the observed discrepancy.

The stress system at the bore surface in a pressurized closed-ended thick-walled cylinder consists of a biaxial tension superimposed on a simple shear. It has been found [209] that the results of fluctuating internal pressure tests on cylinders of various R values (R is the ratio of external to internal diameter) can be best correlated on a basis of the maximum shear stress range at the bore surface. For example, Fig. 6.19 shows S/N curves [209] plotted on this basis for En25 steel cylinders stress-relieved after final machining, having R values in the range 1·2–3; the range of shear stress at the fatigue limit is about 0–285 MN m^{-2}. The bores of the cylinders were diamond-lapped to a surface finish of 0·1 μm CLA; the pressurizing fluid used was a non-corrosive hydraulic oil. Further tests on En25 cylinders [210] at higher pulsating pressures giving lives less than 10^5 cycles showed that the finite-life portion of the S/N curve on Fig. 6.19 continued linearly upwards until the pulsating pressure caused the cylinder to exhibit gross plastic deformation.

The fatigue limits of pressurized cylinders [209, 211] of other materials having the same bore finish are given in Table 6.16; also included are the torsional plain fatigue limit and the tensile strength of each material. It is seen that, in general, the range of shear stress in the cylinder bore at the fatigue limit of a repeatedly pressurized cylinder is only about one-half the shear stress range at the zero mean load torsional fatigue limit of conventional specimens of the same material. Although the presence of a mean shear stress

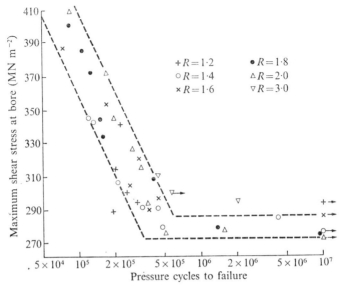

Fɪɢ. 6.19. Pulsating internal oil pressure tests on thick cylinders of En25 material. (Taken from Morrison, Crossland, and Parry [209].)

in the former case means the two fatigue limits are not directly comparable, data given in § 3.6 show that the torsional fatigue limit does not decrease appreciably when a mean stress is superimposed until the maximum shear stress in the loading cycle exceeds the yield stress. Thus, a cylinder designed on a basis of a limiting bore shear stress using material data taken from cyclic torsional tests would be unsafe. It has been suggested, as a guide to design, that the safe repeated shear stress in the bore of a pressurized closed-ended

TABLE 6.16

Cylinder material	Range of shear stress in cylinder bore at fatigue limit (MN m⁻²)	Torsional fatigue limit of plain specimens (MN m⁻²)	Tensile strength (MN m⁻²)
En25 (2½% Ni, ½% Cr, ½% Mo)	0–285	±300	860
En25	0–365	±365	1030
Hykro steel	0–285	±285	635
0·15% C steel	0–127	±135	395
18/8 stainless steel	0–210	±200	590
4½% Cu–aluminium alloy	0–140	±96	510
Titanium	0–185	±160	420
13% Cr steel	0–255	±230	710
18% Ni maraging steel	0–350	±385	1790
En31, 1% Cr steel	0–350	±510	1770
Beryllium copper	0–210	±215	1160

steel cylinder, except for the very high-strength steels, could be taken as one-third of the tensile strength of the steel [209]. It is interesting to note that a re-analysis [212] of the thin-walled tube data mentioned in § 3.6 gave reasonable correlation on a repeated bore shear stress basis, and it was suggested that the safe repeated shear stress could be taken as one-third (for steels) or one-quarter (for aluminium alloys) of the tensile strength of the tube material.

The condition of the bore of a pressurized cylinder would be expected to influence its fatigue limit; some results [211] for En25 steel cylinders are given in Table 6.17.

TABLE 6.17

Condition of bore	Surface finish (μm CLA)	Treatment	Shear stress in bore at fatigue limit (MN m^{-2})
Diamond-lapped	0·1	Stress-relieved	0–285
Diamond-lapped	0·1	Not stress-relieved	0–355
Fine-turned	0·75	Stress-relieved	0–230
Fine-turned	0·75	Not stress-relieved	0–230

Failure of a repeatedly pressurized cylinder occurs by a fatigue crack initiated in the bore growing radially through the cylinder wall in a direction normal to the hoop stress. Although there is usually no evidence that the pressurizing oil has chemically attacked the cylinder bore, preventing the pressurizing fluid from contacting the bore of a cylinder results in an increase in fatigue limit. For example, the bore shear stress at the fatigue limit of an En25 cylinder was increased [209] from 0–285 MN m^{-2} to 0–370 MN m^{-2} by the insertion of a neoprene sleeve. Processes which harden the cylinder bore and induce compressive residual stresses in the surface material also increase the fatigue limit of a cylinder; for example, nitriding the bore of a Hykro cylinder results in a marked increase in its fatigue strength [209].

It is apparent from the results quoted that fluctuating pressurized oil in intimate contact with a cylinder bore does have a detrimental effect on the fatigue strength of a material perhaps [213] by penetrating surface imperfections or discontinuities, so enabling them to develop as surface cracks at stress levels lower than would be required in the absence of the oil. Thus the cylinder fatigue limit will depend on the minimum combined cyclic bore and pressure stresses that would cause a surface imperfection to grow. An empirical expression which takes the oil effect into account, relating the fatigue limit of En25 steel cylinders to the rotating bending fatigue limit of the material, has been proposed [214], and a simple argument can be used [213] to show that the effective hoop stress (the stress controlling the growth of a crack through the cylinder wall) at the bore is twice the maximum shear stress at the bore. However, if the oil effect is caused by penetration of oil into cracks and the fatigue strength is controlled by the subsequent behaviour of such cracks, a fracture-mechanics approach is appropriate [215]. Several solutions for the stress intensity factor at a crack tip in an internally pressurized thick-walled cylinder have been summarized [216].

From a fracture-mechanics viewpoint (§ 5.2), hydrostatic stresses applied to a cracked body have no effect on the stress intensity factor at a crack tip. However, if pressure within a crack is not balanced by pressures elsewhere, this pressure produces an increase in stress intensity factor which is approximately the same as that produced by a numerically equal tensile stress applied across the crack [216]. This is the situation for cracks at the bore of an internally pressurized cylinder, and as such cracks are generally normal to the hoop stress, it is convenient to consider an effective hoop stress σ_e, which is approximately equal to the hoop stress plus the internal pressure. Haslam [217] considered that this effective stress could be written as

$$\sigma_e = \sigma_L + nP,$$

where σ_L is the Lamé hoop stress and nP describes the oil effect.

By comparison with the experimental values of the fatigue limits of repeatedly pressurized steel cylinders it was suggested that

$$\sigma_e = P\left(\frac{R^2+1}{R^2-1}+\frac{5}{R+1}\right). \tag{6.4}$$

From fracture-mechanics considerations [216], the stress intensity factor at the bore of a thick-walled cylinder is given by

$$K_I = 1 \cdot 12\sigma(\pi a)^{\frac{1}{2}} + 1 \cdot 13P(\pi a)^{\frac{1}{2}},$$

and this leads to [218]

$$\sigma_e = 1 \cdot 12P\left(\frac{R^2+1}{R^2-1}+1 \cdot 13\right).$$

For values of R up to 4 this expression does not differ greatly from eqn (6.4). The fracture-mechanics calculations assume that the internal pressure is fully effective over the entire crack depth. However, tests are usually carried out using oil as the pressuring medium and this does not necessarily penetrate to the full depth of a crack [219], particularly if the oil is viscous and a high rate of cycling is used. Thus, unless the actual pressure distribution in a crack is known, an empirical method of analysis, such as that which leads to eqn (6.4), has to be used.

To derive an expression for the fatigue limit of pressurized cylinders, Haslam used Gough's elliptic equation (see § 3.6) to combine the bore uniaxial and shear stresses and, because for internal pressure only the maximum principal stress is in the hoop direction, expressed the pressurized cylinder fatigue limit in terms of the transverse uniaxial fatigue limit of the material σ_{tr}. Expressed in terms of maximum repeated pressure P, the fatigue limit is given by

$$P = \sigma_{tr}\left\{\left(\frac{R^2+1}{R^2-1}+\frac{5}{R+1}\right)^2+1\right\}^{-1/2}. \tag{6.5}$$

Although derived from data on ductile steels, comparison with experimental results showed that this equation predicted the fatigue limits of cylinders of various materials.

Fig. 6.20 shows experimental and predicted (using eqn (6.5)) fatigue limits in terms of the maximum bore shear stress τ, where $\tau = P(R^2-1)/R^2$; the

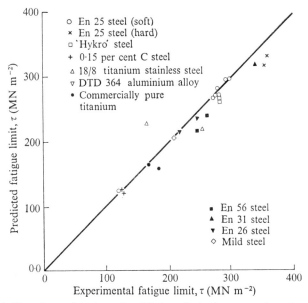

F<small>IG</small>. 6.20. Experimental and predicted fatigue limits in terms of maximum shear stress. (Taken from Haslam [215].)

predicted fatigue limits are seen to be slightly lower than the experimental results, presumably because of the value of the oil effect function used in eqn (6.4). As stated previously, this is partly empirical, and other functions have been suggested [217]. The one used here leads to an overestimate of the stress-raising effect of the oil in some cases, and therefore leads to conservative fatigue limits in such cases.

If a cylinder is subjected to fluctuating oil pressures, other than from zero to maximum pressure, it is necessary to make allowance for the effect of the mean pressure. The influence of a tensile mean stress on the fatigue limit of ductile steels may be estimated by means of the Gerber relationship (§ 3.5) which may be applied to internally pressurized cylinders by expressing the

24

stresses in terms of the local effective hoop stress. To obtain the parabola two points are required; the point where the parabola meets the mean stress axis may be obtained from a static burst test, and a second point may be obtained from an estimate of the repeated pressure fatigue limit. These two points are shown as A and B, respectively, in Fig. 6.21. At point A

$$\sigma_a = 0$$

$$\sigma_m = P_b \left(\frac{R^2+1}{R^2-1} + \frac{5}{R+1} \right),$$

where P_b is the static bursting pressure. At point B, from repeated uniaxial tension fatigue tests in the transverse direction

$$\sigma_a = \sigma_m = \frac{P}{2} \left(\frac{R^2+1}{R^2-1} + \frac{5}{R+1} \right),$$

where P is obtained from the transverse fatigue limit by using eqn (6.5). Some experimental results obtained for mild steel cylinders [215, 220] having $R = 1 \cdot 025$ are shown in Fig. 6.21.

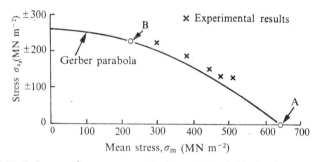

FIG. 6.21. Influence of mean pressure in terms of local effective hoop stress. (Taken from Haslam [215].)

When high mean pressures are applied, the effect of autofrettage must be considered. If the maximum internal pressure during the loading cycle is sufficient to cause the nominal hoop stress at the bore to exceed the yield stress of the material, then when this pressure is relieved the material at the cylinder bore is subjected to a compressive stress due to the elastic action of the unyielded material surrounding it. Thus, the actual mean stress at the bore of the cylinder is less than that in a fully elastic cylinder subjected to the same pulsating pressure range.

The rate of growth of a fatigue crack can conveniently be expressed (Chapter 5) by

$$\frac{da}{dN} = B(\Delta K)^m, \tag{6.6}$$

where B and m are constants and ΔK is the range of stress intensity factor during a fatigue cycle. Thus, if the initial crack size in the cylinder bore and the appropriate value of the stress intensity factor can be estimated, the life of a repeatedly pressurized cylinder can be calculated. Fatigue cracks in thick-walled cylinders are generally semi-elliptical in form; the stress intensity factor (§ 5.2) can be conveniently expressed [221] by

$$K_{\mathrm{I}} = \sigma\left(\pi a \frac{1 \cdot 21}{Q}\right)^{1/2}.$$

The flaw-shape parameter Q (given in Reference [221]) is a function of the crack geometry and the ratio of the applied stress σ to the yield stress of the material. In the case of a crack propagating from the bore of a cylinder, the crack front is semi-elliptical, but owing to the stress gradient in the cylinder wall the ratio of the major to minor axes varies as the crack grows. The final crack-shape at failure depends on the wall thickness and the internal pressure. From observation of the fracture surfaces of the cylinders after failure, Q lies within the range $1 \cdot 1$–$1 \cdot 4$, giving values of $(1 \cdot 21/Q)^{\frac{1}{2}}$ from $1 \cdot 05$ to $0 \cdot 93$. Therefore, replacing σ by σ_{e}, the stress intensity factor can be taken as

$$K_{\mathrm{I}} = \sigma_{\mathrm{e}}(\pi a)^{\frac{1}{2}}. \tag{6.7}$$

In deriving an accurate expression for the stress intensity factor around a crack in a cylinder wall, further complications arise owing to the finite wall thickness and the stress gradient in the wall: the finite wall thickness causes the value of K_{I} to increase, but the stress gradient causes a decrease in K_{I}. Since most of the fatigue crack propagation life is spent in propagating a crack over a small distance from the bore surface, the above conditions in the cylinder wall will have only a secondary effect. Therefore, in the following analysis, their combined effect has been neglected.

Using the expression for stress intensity factor given by eqn (6.7), with the stress in terms of the local effective hoop stress as given by eqn (6.4), and substituting eqn (6.7) in eqn (6.6) gives, on integration, the crack propagation life N of a pressurized cylinder (that is, the number of cycles required to propagate a fatigue crack from an initial length a_0 to a critical length a_c), namely

$$N = \frac{2}{(2-m)} \frac{1}{B\sigma_{\mathrm{e}}^m \pi^{m/2}} [a^{(2-m)/2}]_{a_0}^{a_c} \quad \text{cycles.} \tag{6.8}$$

The initial crack length a_0, is the maximum depth of flaw which, when present in the bore surface, is consistent with the known fatigue limit of the pressurized cylinder. Its value may be estimated from the fatigue crack propagation material constant C described in §§ 4.5 and 4.11. In the case of a cylinder subjected to repeated internal pressure, the alternating stress at the bore is half the effective stress. Therefore the depth of non-propagating flaw which may be present at the fatigue limit is

$$a_0 = \frac{C}{(\frac{1}{2}\sigma_e')^3},$$

where σ_e' is the value of σ_e at the fatigue limit.

The critical crack length a_c is the length of crack at which fast fracture will occur, and is therefore dependent upon the applied stress and the fracture toughness (K_{Ic}) of the cylinder material. However, for cylinders of ductile steels, a fatigue crack will propagate almost to the outer surface before fast fracture occurs and, when it does, the current rate of fatigue crack propagation is such that relatively few extra cycles would have been required to cause the crack to propagate throughout the wall thickness.

Using data for mild steel given in § 5.7 solving for B, and substituting in eqn (6.8) gives

$$N = \frac{2 \cdot 04 \times 10^6}{\sigma_e^3} \left(\frac{1}{\sqrt{a_0}} - \frac{1}{\sqrt{a_c}} \right) \times 10^6 \text{ cycles,} \tag{6.9}$$

where σ_e is in MN m^{-2} and a_0 and a_c are in millimetres. The crack-propagation lives of steel cylinders subjected to repeated internal pressure as given by eqn (6.9) are compared with experimental results from tests on En25 steel cylinders [222, 223] and with results for En26 steel cylinders [222] in Fig. 6.22. The initial and critical crack lengths for these specimens are given in Table 6.18. The fatigue limits shown in Fig. 6.22 are those predicted by eqn (6.5).

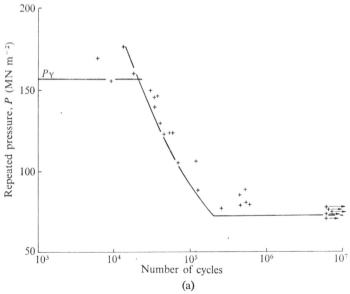

FIG. 6.22. Estimated fatigue curves for steel cylinders (a) En25, $R = 1 \cdot 8$. (b) En26, $R = 1 \cdot 2$. (Taken from Haslam [215].)

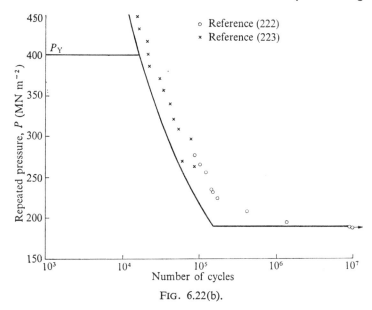

FIG. 6.22(b).

It can be seen that the experimental results give good agreement with the estimated (full-line) fatigue curves obtained from eqn (6.9); the internal pressure P_Y (given by $\sigma_Y(R^2-1)/(R^2+1)$), sufficient to cause gross yielding at the bore of the cylinders is shown. The theory is liable to predict unsafe fatigue lives when $P > P_Y$; this is because the estimated fatigue lives are obtained using linear elastic fracture mechanics theory.

The figures in Table 6.18 imply that the ratio $a_c^{-\frac{1}{2}}:a_0^{-\frac{1}{2}}$ varies from about 0·03 for cylinders of 2·5 mm wall thickness to less than 0·015 when the wall thickness exceeds 10 mm. Thus in the case of thick-walled cylinders the $a_c^{-\frac{1}{2}}$ term can be neglected in eqn (6.9), and the crack-propagation life becomes independent of wall thickness. This has been demonstrated experimentally [224] for En25 steel cylinders of $R = 2$ with wall thicknesses varying from 4·5 mm to 12 mm. For thick-walled cylinders of brittle materials, subjected to high internal pressures, the critical crack size for fast fracture may be significantly smaller than the wall thickness. However, provided $a_c^{-\frac{1}{2}}$ remains small compared to $a_0^{-\frac{1}{2}}$, it can still be neglected.

TABLE 6.18

Material	Diameter ratio R	Initial crack length a_0 (mm)	Critical crack length a_c (mm)
En25 steel	1·8	$20·4 \times 10^{-4}$	10·0
En26 steel	1·2	$28·8 \times 10^{-4}$	2·5

Various tests have been carried out to study the effect of a stress concentration on the fatigue strength of a pressurized cylinder, for example [225], on En25 cylinders having an R value of 2·25 and containing a transverse hole, either 3 mm or 5 mm diameter, drilled radially through the wall normal to the longitudinal axis of the cylinder. The hole was drilled and reamed to size, its end at the outer face of the cylinder being sealed so that a cylinder could be pressurized. The results were presented in terms of the nominal maximum shear stress in the bore of the cylinder assuming no transverse hole was present, the range of nominal bore shear stress at the fatigue limit of the holed cylinders being about 0–130 MNm $^{-2}$, that is, a reduction of fatigue strength based on the shear stress in the cylinder bore compared to a plain En25 cylinder of 2·2. To obtain the theoretical elastic stress concentration caused by the transverse hole, it was argued that the maximum hoop stress at the edge of the hole would be the sum of the stress due to the hole being a discontinuity in the bore of a pressurized cylinder and the hoop stress at the edge of the hole due to the fact that the hole contained pressurized oil. If P is the internal pressure and R the ratio of external to internal diameter of the cylinder, the former consideration gives rise to a maximum hoop stress at the edge of the hole, assuming this is small compared to the cylinder dimensions of

$$3P\left(\frac{R^2+1}{R^2-1}\right)-\frac{P}{R^2-1}.$$

The fact that the hole is pressurized gives a hoop stress in the case of a small hole in a large mass nearly equal to P. Therefore, the maximum tensile hoop stress at the edge of the hole is

$$3P\left(\frac{R^2+1}{R^2-1}\right)-\frac{P}{R^2-1}+P$$

Because the two other principal stresses are both equal to $-P$, the maximum shear stress at the edge of the hole is

$$\frac{1}{2}\left(\frac{4R^2+1}{R^2-1}P+P\right)$$

But the nominal bore shear stress is $R^2P/(R^2-1)$; therefore the elastic shear stress concentration factor is given by

$$\frac{5R^2P}{2(R^2-1)}\frac{(R^2-1)}{R^2P}$$

that is, 2·5, a value which agrees reasonably well with the experimentally determined value.

In practice, large pressure vessels contain stress raisers in the form of manholes, boiler tube fittings, and nozzles. Cyclic internal fluctuating pressure tests have been carried out on these types of vessels in order to assess the safety of any design by ensuring that fatigue cracks do not form in the region of a stress-raiser, at a given internal cyclic pressure, before some stipulated life is achieved. For example, pulsating pressure tests have been carried out [226] on model mild-steel pressure vessels, 500 mm diameter by 25 mm thick, containing pipe connection outlets having various types of reinforcement welded around the hole. Similar tests were carried out [227] using pulsating pressure on an HY-80 steel marine boiler (about 1·2 m diameter by 4 m long) having various manholes and boiler tube fittings. The boiler was cyclically pressurized between lower and upper limits of 1 MN m^{-2} and 17 MN m^{-2} (giving rise to a maximum hoop stress of 210 MN m^{-2}). The first fatigue crack was discovered at the edge of an unreinforced hole after 7800 cycles. Other pulsating pressure tests on pipes, connections, and model vessels have been carried out [226, 228, 229].

If a crack-like flaw is known to be present in a pressure vessel, then, as for the high-pressure container previously discussed, fracture-mechanics principles can be used to calculate the crack-propagation life. If the fracture toughness K_{Ic} of the material is known, a pressure test can be used to define the maximum possible flaw size in a vessel, and this information can be used to predict the subsequent fatigue life [230].

Commercial firms manufacturing gas cylinders often carry out fluctuating internal oil pressure fatigue tests in order to check either that a cylinder can withstand a stipulated number of repeated fillings or to prove some detail of the design, for example, a particular shape of end-closure. Although the mean diameter and wall thickness of a commercial gas cylinder is such that, in general, the internal pressures involved are less than those used in the thick-cylinder work described (and incidentally will be applied at a much lower frequency), unless there is abundant experimental evidence to the contrary, any assessment of the expected life of a cylinder due to repeated fillings should take into account the fact that the presence of the fluctuating pressurized medium will result in the life being less than that obtained from conventional fatigue data on the cylinder wall material.

In all the tests described above, oil was used as the pressurizing medium. Although the use of a gas instead of a fluid as the pressurizing medium would not be expected to give a significantly different fatigue limit, the fracture characteristics of a failed cylinder might well be different because, for a given maximum internal pressure, considerably more energy will be stored in a gas than in a fluid. This will tend to make a crack, once it reaches a certain size, spread in a more catastrophic manner, and can lead to the material of the cylinder wall fragmenting into small pieces. The type of fracture occurring in a cyclically stressed tubular specimen containing a static internal gas pressure has been studied [231]. Mild steel and high-strength aluminium alloy specimens (16 mm outside diameter and 0·38 mm wall thickness) were subjected to both a static internal gas (nitrogen) pressure and either reversed direct stress, alternating bending or alternating torsion cyclic loadings. A specimen was filled with gas (at pressures up to 21 MN m^{-2}), and the pressure valve closed so that, when a specimen broke, the gas released was restricted to that in the specimen and the connecting pipe between the specimen and the valve. High hoop stresses, due to the internal static pressure, did not reduce the endurance at a given cyclic stress materially in either a reversed direct stress or alternating bending test, but did so in an alternating torsion test. However, the mode and rate of crack growth was markedly affected; for example, cracks grew so fast that some of the reversed direct stress aluminium alloy specimens were blown to pieces before the gas pressure fell to zero. Explosive failure and fragmentation also occurred in the torsional tests, the crack lengths at which these fractures occurred at low shear-stress ranges being very short. Although high hoop stresses caused cracks to grow rapidly in the mild steel specimens, none were fragmented and only one failed by exploding.

6.6. Fretting

When two pieces of material, pressed together by an external static load, are subjected to a transverse cyclic loading, so that one contacting face is relatively displaced cyclically parallel to the other face, wear of the mating surfaces occurs. If the magnitude of the tangential displacement is small (that is, not more than about 0·1 mm) the wear is termed fretting. Fretting occurs by contacting asperities on the mating surfaces continually welding together and then breaking. This leads to surface pitting and the transfer of metal from one surface to another. In addition, the small fragments of metal which are broken off oxidize, forming oxide particles which, for most engineering metals, are harder than the metal itself. These become trapped between the mating surfaces and cause abrasive wear and scoring. Thus, in certain applications, fretting can lead to a loss of fit between the two mating parts. In the case of steels, the oxide debris is a brick-red colour; in the case of aluminium and magnesium alloys, it is black. Briefly, the characteristics of fretting are [232] as follows.

1. Although fretting may occur in the presence of an inert gas, it is more serious when oxygen is present and the corrosion debris consists mainly of oxide.
2. The amount of fretting is greatest under perfectly dry conditions.
3. Fretting damage increases with contact load, slip amplitude, and number of oscillations; for a given slip amplitude, increasing the contact load produces a wider distribution of damage while increasing the number of oscillations produces more localized and deeper wear markings and pits.
4. Soft materials generally exhibit a greater susceptibility to fretting than harder materials of similar type.

5. Lubricants, which reduce the frictional force between the contacting surfaces, particularly when used in conjunction with a surface treatment such as phosphating, reduce fretting damage; molybdenum disulphide is particularly effective [233].

Fretting, when considered as a wear process, is usually assessed either by visual observation of the surface damage or by measurement of the surface area and depth of the pits formed or by weight-loss measurements. General discussions of fretting, together with details of the fretting characteristics of various pairs of materials, have been given by a number of investigators [24, 212, 234, 235]. Examples of situations where fretting may occur in service are in a tapered cone and shaft assembly, in a press fit wheel and shaft assembly, in pin, bolted, or riveted joints, and between leaf springs.

Because fretting damages the surface of a material, the fatigue limit of specimens which have been damaged by fretting would be expected to be less than the plain fatigue limit of the material. For example, the fatigue limits of medium carbon and nickel–chromium molybdenum steel specimens whose surfaces had been fairly severely fretted prior to fatigue testing were 13 per cent and 18 per cent lower than the corresponding fatigue limits in the unfretted condition [236]. However, as under chemical corrosion conditions, the greatest reduction in fatigue strength occurs when the fretting process and cyclic stressing are applied simultaneously. Under such conditions, larger reductions in fatigue strength can occur. However, those fretting conditions which give a high rate of surface damage, as assessed by the quantity of debris produced (for example, large slip amplitudes and high contact pressures), are not necessarily those which produce the greatest loss of fatigue strength. That fatigue cracks can form under low nominal cyclic stresses in areas where fretting is occurring is shown, for example, by the low fatigue limit of a shaft having a pressed-on wheel or of an aluminium alloy lug loaded through a push-fit steel pin (§§ 6.9 and 6.7).

The fatigue strengths of cylindrical specimens of various materials which were clamped tightly in hardened 0·4% C steel grips and tested in rotating bending [237] are given in Table 6.19; all specimens failed in the grips, fatigue

TABLE 6.19

Material	Fretting fatigue strength, 10^7 cycles (MN m^{-2})
Annealed 0·35% C steel	±131
Cold-worked 0·35% C steel	±146
Annealed 18/8 austenitic steel	±193
Cold-worked 18/8 austenitic steel	±162
Annealed aluminium bronze	±100
Cold-worked aluminium bronze	±93
Wrought heat-treated 4½% Cu–aluminium alloy	±70
Chill-cast heat-treated aluminium alloy	±70

cracks being initiated in regions of fretting on the specimen just inside the grips. Although there was no qualitative control of the fretting conditions, it is seen that the initial condition of a material has little effect on the subsequent fretting-fatigue limit.

Reversed plane bending fatigue tests were carried out [238] on titanium alloy RC 130 B (4% Al, 4% Mn) in which pads of different materials were clamped on to a specimen under a given nominal contact pressure. At a nominal contact pressure of 100 MN m^{-2}, pads of magnesium, copper, 70/30 brass, $5\frac{1}{2}$% Zn–aluminium alloy, and titanium alloy reduced the fatigue strength (5×10^7 cycles) of the titanium alloy from ±620 MN m^{-2} to ±585 MN m^{-2}, ±495 MN m^{-2}, ±200 MN m^{-2}, ±260 MN m^{-2}, and ±250 MN m^{-2} respectively. Pads of SAE 4340 steel were used to study the effect of various clamping pressures, the results in Table 6.20 showing that, although

T ABLE 6.20

Nominal clamping pressure (MN m^{-2})	Fretting fatigue strength, 5×10^7 cycles (MN m^{-2})
Unclamped	±620
28	±193
155	±147
280	±131
420	±123

the fatigue strength (5×10^7 cycles) decreased initially with increasing clamping pressures up to 155 MN m^{-2}, further increases in clamping pressure up to 420 MN m^{-2} caused only a slight further decrease in the fretting-fatigue strength. Shot-peening a specimen increased its fretting-fatigue strength under a given clamping pressure but testing in an argon atmosphere did not cause any significant change in the fretting fatigue strength from the corresponding in-air value.

A series of controlled fretting fatigue tests were carried out by Fenner and Field [239]. Specimens, 15 mm diameter, having two diametrically opposite flats machined along their length, were tested in direct stress, flat-ended pads of circular section being held against the flats by a calibrated steel ring clamp, as shown in Fig. 6.23. Specimens of $4\frac{1}{2}$% Cu–aluminium alloy subjected to a tensile mean stress of 195 MN m^{-2} and having pads of similar material clamped against them had their fatigue strength (20×10^6 cycles) decreased from ±125 MN m^{-2} with no clamps to ±54 MN m^{-2} with a clamping pressure of 4 MN m^{-2} and to ±40 MN m^{-2} with a clamping pressure of 125 MN m^{-2}. Replacing the aluminium alloy pads by mild steel pads did not have much effect on these values. Corresponding tests at zero mean load showed a much less severe reduction in fatigue strength. Mild steel pads clamped on to mild steel specimens resulted in little change in the fatigue limit of the mild steel, but when clamped on to a nickel–chromium steel caused the fatigue limit of the alloy steel to decrease appreciably, especially when a tensile mean stress was present. In fact, under the most severe fretting test conditions, the fretting-fatigue limit of the mild steel and alloy steel were about the same. Pads of 'Aloxite', a resin-bonded aluminium oxide, were clamped on to aluminium alloy specimens in order to see whether abrasion was an important factor; although a considerable quantity of wear debris was produced, the pads caused little reduction in fatigue strength (20×10^6 cycles). Aluminium alloy specimens tested in an evacuated chamber had a higher fretting fatigue strength for the same fretting conditions than those tested in air.

To study the effect of slip amplitude on the fretting-fatigue strength of the aluminium alloy, rectangular blocks of aluminium alloy, having a narrow land across each end and spanning various lengths, were clamped against a specimen. The assessment of the slip amplitude, in a given test, was based on the assumption that the specimen deformation between the two lands was shared equally between them. The fretting-fatigue strength (20×10^6 cycles) decreased progressively as the slip amplitude increased from 0·0025 mm to 0·0075 mm, but further increase up to about 0·023 mm produced no additional reduction in fatigue strength. To determine the stage in a fretting-fatigue test at which fatigue damage, as distinct from surface fretting damage, first occurred, the fretting pads were removed from a specimen after a certain percentage of the expected life. Results obtained with aluminium alloy specimens and pads indicated that leaving the pads on a specimen, subjected to a loading cycle having a mean tensile stress of 195 MN m^{-2}, for a number of cycles equal to or greater than 20 per cent of the clamped endurance to failure at the same applied alternating stress, caused damage which, even after removal of the pads, left the total endurance unaltered. On the other hand, when the pads were removed after a smaller percentage of the clamped endurance, the total life of a specimen was of the same order as that of an unclamped specimen tested at the same stress level. Some of the results illustrating these points are shown on Fig. 6.24; they imply that there is a critical stage in a fretting test after which the damage to the specimen passes beyond the influence of the pads. This could be interpreted as saying that, once this endurance is exceeded, a crack formed as a consequence of fretting beneath the pad is able to grow under the influence of the nominal cyclic stresses and is independent of any surface effects. Metallurgical examination of the fretted areas on those specimens which remained unbroken after testing often revealed the presence of small surface cracks. It would seem therefore that, under certain fretting conditions, the fretting-fatigue limit depends on the value of the cyclic stress necessary to just cause a crack formed in the fretted area to grow, rather than on the cyclic stress necessary to initiate a surface crack.

Field [240] considered that fatigue damage due to fretting took the form of surface cracks, penetrating the fretted material for depths of up to several hundredths of a millimetre; thus the fatigue behaviour of a fretted part was largely a matter of crack propagation, the fretting fatigue limit depending on the nominal cyclic stress level necessary to cause these cracks to grow to cause complete failure. The mechanism of fretting fatigue therefore appears

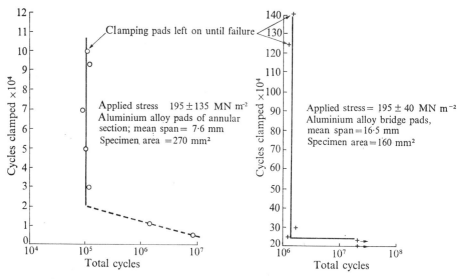

FIG. 6.24. Effect on the fretting fatigue life of removing the fretting pads after various numbers of cycles from aluminium alloy (BS L65) specimens. (Taken from Fenner and Field [239].)

to be as follows. Under normal contact load and cyclic tangential forces, the oxide film on the surface of contacting asperities breaks down and, with some metals, very strong metal–metal adhesion occurs. If the cyclic tangential slip displacements are insufficient to rip apart the microweld, the welded junction may spread over a relatively large area. The edge of this welded area is subjected to high cyclic shear stresses which, as shown by metallurgical examination, lead to the initiation of fatigue cracks in this region. Fretting leads to a reduction in fatigue strength because of this high stress concentration at the edge of the locally welded area. The microwelds are typically a few hundredths of a millimetre across, and first develop after some thousands of fretting cycles. Adjacent cracks often run together to release metal particles, leaving small pits; these, however, do not represent as serious a form of fatigue damage as the initial cracks, which often extend beyond the root of the pit at the time of its formation. Secondary effects occur in an oxidizing atmosphere, for example, the production of finely divided oxide debris and corrosion fatigue. The former, while promoting wear, tends to reduce metal–metal contact and causes abrasive removal of superficial material containing incipient cracks, thus mitigating the damage due to the basic microweld mechanism; the latter enhances the development and propagation of cracks. Anti-fretting agents such as oils and greases appear to act by reducing metal–metal contact, by absorbing the fretting movement, by spreading and reducing the local severity of the damage, and by excluding the atmosphere. Resilient dry films (for example, resin-bonded P.T.F.E.) are helpful where conditions are not too severe, because they separate the metal surfaces. Under more severe conditions, and where relative surface slip cannot be prevented, coatings containing molybdenum disulphide are the most effective although, when applied in a grease carrier, these are not markedly superior to ordinary engine oil when a film of the latter is maintained around the fretting region.

Slip can be almost completely suppressed if it is feasible to apply a contact load which bears a sufficiently high ratio to the tangential load producing the fretting movement, and this results in a marked increase in the fatigue strength of the assembly. Prevention of fretting by this means is, for example, partly responsible for the increase in fatigue strength of a pin joint when the pin is made an interference fit in the hole in the lug. The relative stiffness of the clamped parts and the coefficient of friction are important in this connection; in such a case, high friction is desirable whereas, if slip cannot be prevented, friction should be kept as low as possible.

If fretting results in small surface cracks forming at a cyclic stress less than that required in the absence of fretting, then whether or not the fretting affects the subsequent fatigue strength depends on whether the surface cracks are able to develop and grow across the specimen under the nominal applied cyclic stress. The discussion on the depth to which a surface microcrack must develop before it is able to grow as a macrocrack (given in § 4.11) implies that, for stress levels which are the same proportion of their respective fatigue limits, this changeover depth is less for high-strength aluminium alloys and alloy steels than for, say, copper and mild steel. Thus, fretting would be expected to cause a greater proportional decrease in the plain fatigue limits of the two former materials than for the latter materials. However, if at a given nominal stress level fretting produced surface cracks to the same depth in say, a mild steel and an alloy steel, then their subsequent fretting fatigue limits would be expected to be similar, for as shown in § 4.5 the cyclic stress required to cause a crack of a given length to grow is about the same for carbon and low-alloy steels. However, the value of the cyclic stress required to cause a fretting crack to grow is influenced by any residual compressive stresses introduced into the material surface during the fretting process. Both their magnitude and the depth to which they extend below the surface influence the subsequent crack growth; both depend on contact pressure, the coefficient of friction between the two contacting materials, and the amount of slip. The fact that fretting cracks may be prevented from developing by residual compressive stresses is a possible reason why the fretting-fatigue strength decreases markedly below the zero mean load value when a mean tensile stress is superimposed. In any case, if the fretting-fatigue limit is determined by the alternating stress necessary to cause a surface crack to grow, its value decreases more markedly with increasing tensile mean stress than the conventional plain fatigue limit of the material. The introduction of surface residual compressive stresses, for example, by shot-peening, alleviates the effect of fretting by keeping surface cracks closed, but to be most effective the depth of the affected zone must be greater than that at which a surface microcrack changes to a macrocrack at the stress level under consideration. Once a surface microcrack has initiated and developed from the edge of a contact area to a depth greater than the influence of the stress field set up at the edge of the contact area so that its tip is influenced only by the nominal stress in the specimen, its subsequent behaviour is independent of whether the fretting pad is kept in place or removed.

6.7. Pin, riveted, and bolted joints

6.7.1. Pin joints

A simple pin joint consists of a fork and either a tongue or lug held together by a pin passing through in-line holes in the fork and lug. The load is transmitted to the lug through the pin which may be either a clearance, a sliding, or an interference fit in the hole in the lug. The lug is usually the critical member, failure under cyclic loading being determined by the stress concentration at the edge of the loaded hole and the fretting that occurs in this region due to the relative movement between the pin and lug.

The elastic stress distribution around a hole in a lug loaded via a sliding-fit pin (that is, zero interference) has been determined photo-elastically [241, 242]. The maximum stress occurs at the edge of the hole on a transverse diameter through the minimum cross-section and may be expressed in terms of either the maximum tensile stress or the maximum shear stress; values resulting from different lug geometries are depicted graphically in the *Royal Aeronautical Society ESDU Data sheets* [243].

Heywood [244] quotes the following empirical relationships for determining the maximum value of K_t at the periphery of a hole in a rectangular shaped lug loaded by a sliding pin:

for $H/D = 1$, $K_t = 0 \cdot 6 + 0 \cdot 95\ D/d$
for $H/D = 0 \cdot 5$, $K_t = 0 \cdot 85 + 0 \cdot 95\ D/d$ } for d/D between 0·2 and 0·8,

where K_t = (maximum tensile stress in the lug at the edge of the hole)/(nominal tensile stress on the minimum cross-sectional area) D is the width of the lug, d is the diameter of the hole, and H is the distance of the hole centre from the end of the lug.

The value of K_t depends on the shape of the lug head, although when H/D is greater than unity its value is little different from that for a rectangular-shaped head; values of K_t for lugs having shapes other than rectangular have been documented [244]. If the pin bends under the applied load, the maximum stress at and near the face of the lug increases, this increase depending primarily on the ratio of the pin diameter to lug thickness. Radiusing the edge of the hole decreases this stress.

The fatigue strength of a lug loaded through a sliding pin is determined by the maximum stress range at the edge of the hole and the fretting that occurs due to the relative movement between the pin and hole material. In the case of an aluminium alloy lug and steel pin, a common practical combination, fretting can result in the joint having a very low fatigue strength at long endurances. For example [245], the fatigue strength $(20 \times 10^6$ cycles) of joints consisting of a $4\frac{1}{2}\%$ Cu–aluminium alloy lug and a sliding-fit hardened-steel pin was found to be only 39 ± 8 MN m^{-2} as against 39 ± 140 MN m^{-2} for the aluminium alloy itself; this was considered to be due to the fretting that occurred in the hole at the points of maximum stress. It was found that the joint fatigue strength could be increased by grinding diametrically opposite longitudinal parallel flats on the pins so that on assembly there was no contact between the pin and the most highly stressed material at the hole boundary. However, the origin of fracture now moved from the minimum cross-section to an area opposite one edge of the flats, showing that the onset of failure was again associated with fretting. Fatigue tests [246] on aluminium alloy (L65) lugs loaded through clearance fitting (0·075 mm) 19 mm diameter steel pins showed that a significant increase in life was obtained by grinding flats on the pins, so removing contact between the pin and lug in the region of maximum stress on the minimum cross-section of the lug. The life (at a given cyclic loading) increased as the distance across the flats on the pins was decreased, until this was equal to $\sqrt{2}$ times the pin radius. Although there was an indication that the lives increased further as the distance between the flats was reduced further, the scatter in life increased markedly and it was concluded that there was little point in decreasing the distance between the flats below $\sqrt{2}$ times the pin radius.

Heywood [244] gives S/N curves derived from fatigue tests (tensile loading cycle $T \pm S$ where $T > S$) on a variety of aluminium alloy and steel lugs loaded through sliding-fit steel pins. At 10^7 cycles, S was equal to about 4 per cent of the tensile strength of steels having tensile strengths between 900 MN m^{-2} and 1500 MN m^{-2} and to about $2\frac{1}{2}$ per cent of the tensile strength of the high-strength aluminium alloys. The value of the tensile mean stress T had little effect in the case of steel lugs, but an increase in T did result in a decrease in S for the aluminium alloy lugs. On a fatigue strength/weight ratio basis [247], SAE 4340 steel lugs were found to be superior to 2024-T4 aluminium alloy lugs when loaded through a carburized steel pin. The fatigue strength of joints of both materials decreased with increasing tensile mean stress, due partially to the increased stress concentration caused by pin bending.

The fatigue strength of a pin joint may be improved by the use of anti-fretting compounds, such as molybdenum disulphide, to minimize fretting in the hole. In the case of a steel lug, cadmium or zinc plating both the pin and the hole is beneficial. The introduction of residual compressive stresses into the material around the hole by, for example, pressing an oversized ball through the hole retards the growth of cracks formed in the fretted areas and thus results in an increased fatigue strength. The fatigue strength of an aluminium alloy lug loaded through a sliding-fit pin can be increased by from 30 per cent to 140 per cent [244] by forcing a tapered steel pin through the hole prior to fitting the sliding pin. However, the most effective method of increasing the fatigue strength of a pin joint is to make the pin an interference-fit in the hole. The radial pressure due to the interference-fit tends to eliminate the relative movement at the transverse diameter, thus minimizing fretting; relative movement, however, may still arise in regions nearer the unloaded side of the pin, and interference-fit pin joints have been reported as failing from these regions. A more important factor, however, is that the interference-fit generates a stress distribution around the hole in the lug, which is beneficial from the fatigue viewpoint in that, although the tensile mean stress in the material at the edge of the hole on either end of a transverse diameter is increased, the alternating stress to which it is subjected is reduced in comparison to that in a similar joint loaded through a sliding-fit pin. The elastic stress distribution around the hole in a lug loaded through an interference-fit pin has been determined photo-elastically [242]. The maximum stresses are most conveniently expressed in terms of the maximum shear stress at the hole boundary; data in graphical form is given for various lug geometries and interference–fits in the *Royal Aeronautical Society ESDU Data sheets* [243]. At zero pin load, the inter-ference-fit induces a high shear stress at the edge of the hole on the transverse diameter but as external load is applied to the pin, the shear stress at the edge of the hole does not increase as rapidly as when the load is applied through a sliding-fit pin. This effect is due to unloading on the free side of the pin [244]. The external pin load reduces the radial compressive stress on the free side of the pin but causes only a small increase in stress on the compressive side of the pin. Thus the applied alternating load is transmitted partially by a fluctuating radial pressure on the free side of the pin, so bypassing the mini-mum section of the lug. Consequently, the interference-fit reduces the range of maximum shear stress in the material at the edge of the hole but increases the mean shear stress; the fatigue strength of the joint tends to increase, therefore, because the beneficial effect of the former more than compensates for the detrimental effect of the latter [248]. This point is illustrated by the results [242] given in Table 6.21; they apply to a lug having $d/D = 0.375$ and cyclically loaded through a pin so that the range of nominal tensile stress on the net lug area is 0–140 MN m^{-2}. To improve the fatigue strength of lugs having interference-fit pins, the proportion of the load transmitted through the free side of the pin must be maximised and this can be accomplished by reducing the stiffness of the path around the lug and increasing the pin diameter stiffness. Such conditions follow from the use of a lug with a large hole diameter to lug width ratio.

The experimental data confirm that the use of an interference-fit pin does increase the joint fatigue strength over that of a comparable joint loaded

TABLE 6.21

Type of pin fit	Minimum shear stress at edge of hole (MN m^{-2})	Maximum shear stress at edge of hole (MN m^{-2})	Mean shear stress (MN m^{-2})	Alternating shear stress (MN m^{-2})
Sliding	0	200	100	±100
0·003 mm per mm interference	140	200	170	±30
0·006 mm per mm interference	280	310	295	±15

through a sliding-fit pin. The use of pins having interference fits greater than 0·004 and 0·003 mm per mm of pin diameter was found to increase the fatigue strengths of aluminium alloy (4$\frac{1}{2}$% Cu) and high-strength steel lugs, respectively [249]. The repeated tension fatigue strength (10^8 cycles) of 4$\frac{1}{2}$% Cu–aluminium alloy lugs loaded through a steel pin having an interference-fit of 0·004 mm per mm of pin diameter was found to be double that of similar joints loaded through a sliding-fit pin [250]. The effects of pin diameter and degree of interference-fit on the repeated tension fatigue strengths of 4$\frac{1}{2}$% Cu–aluminium alloy lugs (76 mm wide by 19 mm thick, pin centre 38 mm from end) loaded through hardened-steel pins have been investigated [251]. The results, given on Fig. 6.25, show that the maximum fatigue strength (20 × 10^6 cycles) of joints having a 25 mm diameter pin was obtained by using an interference-fit of 0·007 mm per mm of pin diameter. Keeping this degree of interference, the maximum fatigue strength of joints connected by pins ranging in diameter from 11 mm to 32 mm was obtained with 25 mm diameter pins.

A joint having an interference-fit pin cannot be dismantled and reassembled easily; if this is a necessary design requirement, it is advantageous, especially in the case of aluminium alloy lugs, to insert an interference-fit hardened-steel bush into the hole in the lug and then use a sliding-fit steel pin in the bush to make the connection. It has been shown photo-elastically [248] that the stress distribution around the hole in the lug, created by an interference-fit bush having a diametral ratio greater than 4/3, is similar to that produced by a solid pin having the same degree of interference. However, bushes of smaller diametral ratios distorted, the interference stresses consequently being less than those created by a solid pin with the same degree of interference. Fatigue

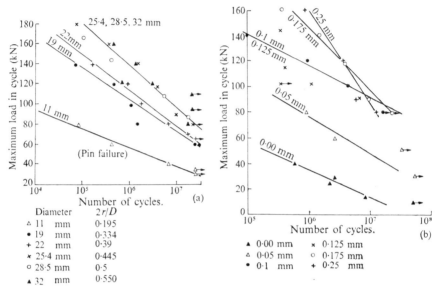

Diameter	$2r/D$
△ 11 mm	0·195
● 19 mm	0·334
+ 22 mm	0·39
✕ 25·4 mm	0·445
○ 28·5 mm	0·5
▲ 32 mm	0·550

▲ 0·00 mm	✕ 0·125 mm
△ 0·05 mm	○ 0·175 mm
● 0·1 mm	+ 0·25 mm

FIG. 6.25. Fatigue strength of aluminium alloy pin joints. (a) Effect of pin size (interference 0·007 mm per mm). (b) Effect of interference (25·4 mm diameter pin). (Taken from Low [251].)

tests [251] on aluminium alloy ($4\frac{1}{2}\%$ Cu) lugs having interference-fit hardened-steel bushes showed that the joint fatigue strength was only slightly below that of joints having a solid pin of the same interference-fit as the bush. This follows from the facts that the interference-fit due to the bush will be slightly less than that due to a corresponding solid pin and that failure of the joint is determined by cracking of the aluminium lug and not by cracking of the steel bush.

To avoid scoring during assembly and to have a closer control over the interference, tapered pins are sometimes inserted in tapered holes. Fatigue tests have been carried out [252] on $5\frac{1}{2}\%$ Zn–aluminium alloy lugs (254 mm long by 51 mm wide by 19 mm thick) containing 19 mm diameter holes into which tapered (1 in 96) steel bushes were fitted with proportional interferences of either 0 per cent, 0·2 per cent, 0·4 per cent, 0·6 per cent, 0·8 per cent, or 1·0 per cent. The life of a joint at a given stress level increased with increasing interference up to an interference of 0·6 per cent. Higher interference-fits gave no significant increase in life, presumably because yielding of the bush occurred.

In conclusion, it would seem that, to estimate the fatigue strength of a pin joint, it is necessary to know the stress distribution created around the hole by the loaded pin for the particular fit used and loading cycle applied and the fatigue strength of the lug material under conditions comparable to those occurring at the pin–lug interface.

6.7.2. Riveted and bolted joints

Although a double shear riveted or bolted joint may be thought of as simply a complex pin joint in which many through connections are made between the plates, the rivet or bolt shanks being equivalent to the push or sliding-fit pin, there are however two important differences. First, because there are several connecting pins, the load distribution will not necessarily, and indeed is most unlikely to, be shared uniformly between the bolts or rivets and, secondly, a longitudinal tensile load can be applied along the axis of a rivet or bolt, which results in some of the load being carried by frictional forces between the plates instead of being wholly transmitted through the rivet or bolt shank to the plates as in a pin joint.

Fretting can occur in a rivet or bolt hole causing fatigue failure at low alternating stresses. It can also occur between the plates themselves if these are tightly clamped together, and with high-strength aluminium alloy plates in particular it may lead to the initiation of fretting cracks and final fracture at points remote from a bolt hole. As might be expected, the fatigue strength (at long endurances) of a riveted or bolted joint is neither related to the plain fatigue limit of the plate material nor to the static strength of the joint itself. For example, it is possible for one type of bolted joint to have a static strength twice that of another type, yet both have the same fatigue strengths at lives greater than 10^6 cycles [253]. Examples of the static strength and fatigue lives at a given stress level of various types of bolted $4\frac{1}{2}\%$ Cu–aluminium alloy joints, each joint having the same net section area, are given in Table 6.22 [254]. The double shear joint is seen to have the highest static strength, yet its fatigue strength is second to the double scarf joint. Descriptions of various types of bolted joints and their behaviour under fatigue loading have been given by Spaulding [255].

Single-lap joints will always be weaker than double-lap joints because of the additional bending stresses produced by the offset loading. Failure of a riveted joint is usually through the plate, cracks being initiated and growing from rivet holes. In general, increasing the number of rows of rivets increases the fatigue strength of the joint. For example, in the case of single-lap aluminium alloy sheet riveted joints, the fatigue strength (2×10^6 cycles) of a joint containing three rows of rivets was about 1·8 times, and that of a joint containing two rows of rivets about 1·4 times, that of a comparable single row joint [244]; optimum fatigue strength was achieved by varying rivet position and spacing. On the other hand, an attempt [256] to correlate collected data on the fatigue strength of aluminium alloy single-lap riveted joints resulted in the conclusion that the large number of variables involved made any correlation impossible.

The fatigue strengths (2×10^6 cycles) of riveted double-lap joints of various steel plates [257] were found to be all between 0–123 MN m^{-2} and

TABLE 6.22

Type of joint	Static breaking load (kN)	Endurance at 110 ± 37 MN m^{-2}, (cycles)
Double shear	510	3 427 000
Uniform step	480	476 800
Plain scarf	480	210 800
Non-uniform step	450	31 300
Bolted key	380	2 457 100
Double scarf	340	26 194 600
Single shear	340	42 000
Serrated	310	77 900
Clamped keyed	250	166 400

0–139 MN m^{-2} (based on gross area), suggesting that fretting was the main cause of crack initiation. Fretting in the rivet holes of high-strength aluminium alloys can lead to very low joint fatigue strengths. For example, the fatigue strength (10^7 cycles) of riveted high-strength single-lap aluminium alloy joints (aluminium alloy rivets) was found to vary between 89 ± 12 MN m^{-2} and 89 ± 31 MN m^{-2} [258]. Various practical methods of increasing the fatigue strength of riveted joints have been suggested [259, 260].

The fatigue strength of a bolted joint may depend on the number and positioning of the bolts. Results of tests with a load ratio $R = 0.25$ on high-strength $4\frac{1}{2}\%$ Cu–aluminium bolted joints [261] are given in Table 6.23.

Heywood [244] has correlated the results of numerous fatigue tests on various aircraft structural bolted joints, in all of which the load was transferred from one high-strength aluminium plate to another via either one or more bolts in either single or double shear. He found that the fatigue strength depended principally on the detailed configuration of the joint and the mean tensile stress T in the loading cycle, the composition of the aluminium alloy being of secondary importance. In general, the alternating stress at 10^7 cycles under a wholly tensile loading cycle ($R \approx 0.5$) lay between ± 23 MN m^{-2} and ± 8 MN m^{-2} (based on net area); the former figure applied to a good design of joint, the latter to a poor design of joint.

Methods of increasing the fatigue strength of either riveted or bolted joints include using an interference-fit bolt (so gaining the advantages found with the simple pin joint, § 6.7.1), inserting anti-fretting compounds between the bolt or rivet shank and the hole wall, overloading the joint statically so inducing compressive residual stresses at the points of maximum stress which will retard the growth of cracks initiated at the bolt holes, and increasing the axial tensile stress in the rivet or bolt so enabling more of the load to be transmitted by friction at the contacting surfaces rather than by shear in the bolts.

TABLE 6.23

Bolt configuration	Fatigue strength (maximum stress in cycle) at 2×10^6 cycles based on minimum cross-section area of joint (MN m^{-2})	
	2·5 mm thick plates	9 mm thick plates
No bolts	170	170
Single central bolt	58	39
3 equi-spaced bolts across plate	54	—
2 bolts in line	85	50
3 bolts in line	89	54
2 rows of 3 equi-spaced bolts across plate	—	54
3 rows of 3 equi-spaced bolts across plate	—	70

The use of interference-fit rivets or bolts is a difficult practical proposition in a multi-holed joint; the next two procedures may give some increase but the latter procedure is by far the most effective method of increasing the fatigue strength, particularly if the axial shank tensile load is sufficient to ensure that all the load is carried by frictional forces between the plates. An advantage of the bolted joint over the riveted joint is that a more closely controlled and higher clamping force can be applied. Further benefit arises from the use of high tensile steel bolts over mild steel bolts, because a greater tightening load can be applied. In fact, the basic principle underlying the use of high tensile steel bolts is that they are sufficiently strong to enable them to be tightened to such an extent that the working loads are transmitted by frictional forces between the plates. A fluctuating external load on the joint should create very little, if any, effect on the initial bolt tightness, and a correctly tightened bolt should not come loose. Bolts should be carefully positioned over the contact area of the plates and the pitch and bolt diameter chosen to give the highest clamping force compatible with the loss in area due to the number of bolt holes.

As might be expected, many workers [262] have found that the fatigue strength of a bolted joint having properly-tightened high tensile strength steel bolts is superior to that of a joint of similar geometry fastened with either hot- or cold-driven rivets or partially tightened bolts. For example, the fatigue strengths of double-lap joints of various structural steels were found to be much higher when assembled with properly tightened high tensile steel bolts than when riveted [263, 264], while the fatigue strength (10^7 cycles) of aluminium alloy joints connected by mild steel bolts was four times higher when the bolts were tightened to an axial tensile stress equal to the yield stress of the bolt material than when the nuts were just finger tightened [265]. Provided that properly-tightened galvanized bolts are used, the fatigue strength of a galvanized plate joint is not inferior to that of an ungalvanized joint of the same geometry [266].

Summarizing, the highest joint fatigue strength is seen to occur with bolted joints in which high tensile steel bolts are tightened correctly so that the working loads are carried by the frictional forces between the plates. The low fatigue strength of riveted and bolted joints in which the tightening is insufficient to allow the alternating load to be carried by these frictional forces is due both to the unequal distribution of load between the bolts or rivets and to fretting occurring in the rivet or bolt holes. Fretting in the bolt or rivet holes of aluminium alloy joints can result in these joints having very low fatigue strengths (compared to that of the basic plate material), and even when properly tightened fitted bolts are used, cyclic slip can cause fretting between the plates, resulting in failure at places remote from a bolt hole. If failure of a bolted or riveted joint occurs as a consequence of fretting in a hole, simply substituting plates of a stronger but similar material (say a stronger alloy steel in place of a mild steel) is unlikely to have an appreciable effect on the subsequent fatigue strength at long endurances, since cracks formed in the fretted areas will be able to spread just as easily in the stronger alloy steel as in the mild steel. This is the reason why the fatigue strengths of riveted steel joints do not depend appreciably on the type of steel plates joined. Provided the bolts are properly tightened, higher joint strengths can be achieved in bolted steel joints by using higher tensile strength bolts and plates, at least up to endurances of 2×10^6 cycles [267]; at longer endurances the joint strength may again be determined by fretting of the plate material. Similarly, the fatigue strength of aluminium alloy joints (either riveted or bolted) in which failure occurs from a bolt or rivet hole is not markedly dependent on the type of aluminium alloy used. Aluminium alloy sheets are sometimes bonded or glued together as an alternative to riveting, and can have superior fatigue properties [268]; the fatigue strength of bonded joints is discussed in § 6.8.7.

It is apparent that it is not possible to predict accurately the fatigue strength of a joint, especially one having numerous bolts or rivets, from a knowledge of the fatigue strength of the material and the joint geometry. Neither does the static strength give an indication of the fatigue strength; behaviour under cyclic loading conditions can only be assessed accurately from fatigue tests on the joint itself.

6.8. Welded joints

6.8.1. Introduction

Fusion-welding of both ferrous and non-ferrous materials is an everyday procedure in the fabrication of engineering structures and machines. Various types of welding may be employed (for example, oxyacetylene, electric metallic arc, and argon arc) depending on the materials to be welded and the type and standard of joint required. The fatigue limit or strength (at long endurances) of a simple butt-welded joint of any particular design depends on the welding process, the type of filler rod, the care with which the welding is done (that is, it will depend on whether defects such as pores, blow holes, slag inclusions, shrinkage cracks, lack of fusion, and poor penetration are minimized), any post heat-treatment, and the final shape of the weld bead.

A large amount of data has been accumulated on the fatigue strength of welded joints [269–73] and built-up welded beams [274–7]. For example, Fig. 6.26 shows fatigue data for various types of welded joints in structural steels, and Table 6.24 shows some results [277] on the repeated plane bending

TABLE 6.24

Member	Fatigue strength, 2×10^6 cycles (MN m^{-2})
Plain plate	215
Rolled I-beam	210
Welded I-beam	180
Welded beam with stiffeners	160
Welded beam with splice	137
Welded beam with butt-welded flange transition	131
Welded beam with partial length cover plate	86

fatigue strength of rolled and built-up I-beams having various welded attachments.

6.8.2. Butt welds in structural steels

The effect of various variables on the fatigue strength of welded joints can conveniently be discussed in terms of the behaviour of transverse butt welds in structural steel. Some representative data, illustrating points made below, are shown in Table 6.25.

Weld type	Class as in BS 153	Fatigue strength at 2×10^6 cycles, $R=0$ (MN m^{-2})	
Plain plate as rolled	A	193	
Longitudinal fillet and butt welds made with automatic process. (No stop/start positions)	B	170	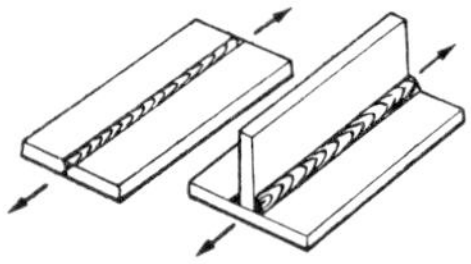
Longitudinal manual butt welds	C	147	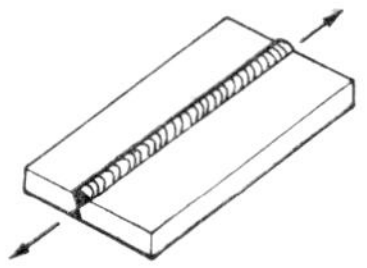
Longitudinal manual fillet welds. Transverse butt welds made in the flat position with no undercut	D	131	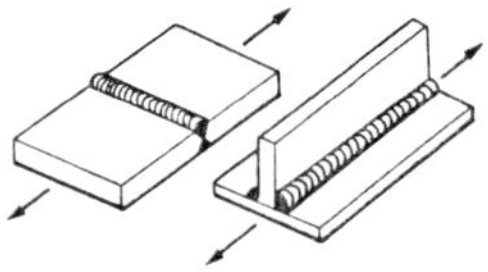
Other transverse butt welds and transverse butt welds made on backing strip. Cruciform butt welds	E	100	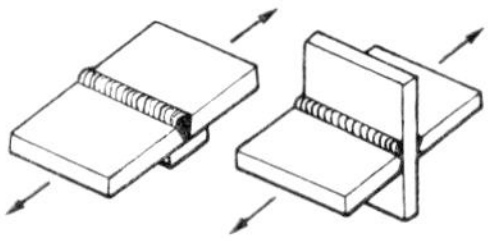
T-butt welds. Transverse non-load-carrying fillet or butt welds and weld ends. Transverse load-carrying fillet welds of type shown.	F	77	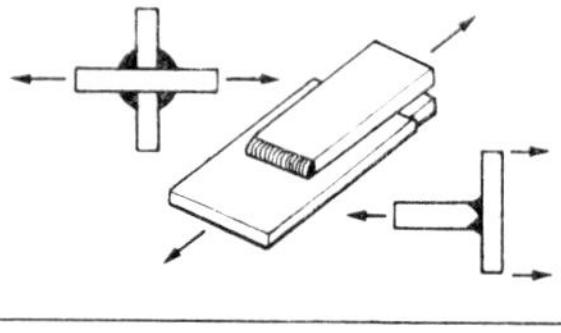
Transverse or longitudinal load-carrying fillet welds. Welds on or adjacent to plate edges	G	51	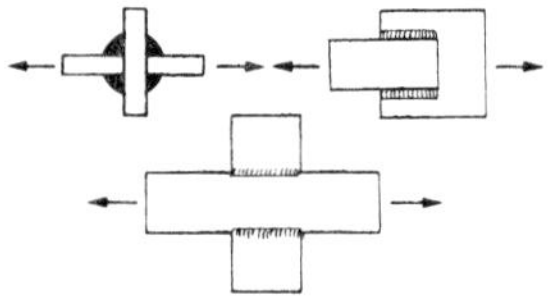

FIG. 6.26. Weld types and stresses based on BS 153 [273]. (Taken from Richards [271].)

The static tensile strength of a simple butt-welded joint is generally not less than that of the parent plate material. Fatigue failure of a good as-welded joint usually originates in the region of high local stresses at the toe of the weld bead. Photo-elastic analyses of simulated butt-welded bead geometries indicate that the elastic stress concentration at the toe of a typical unmachined weld bead is between about 1·3 and 1·9 [282, 284]. Machining away the weld bead therefore increases the fatigue limit of the joint.

Conventional welding of steel plates results in both the weld metal and the plate material in the heat-affected zone having a decarburized surface layer. Thus, unless the plate material and weld bead are machined so as to remove this decarburized layer, the fatigue limit of the joint cannot be expected to approach that of the plate material. Even if this is done and the joint is machined and polished all over, its fatigue limit can only approach that of the plate material, provided any defects in the weld do not exceed some limiting size. In general, this is not the case, and the fatigue limit of a polished welded joint is governed by the size and distribution of flaws in the weld metal. The effect of the decarburized surface layer also tends to make the fatigue limit of as-welded steel joints independent of the type of steel welded because, once surface cracks have formed in the softened surface layer the strength of the steel substrate has little effect on their subsequent propagation (see Chapters 4 and 5).

Residual tensile stresses are present around the weld-metal–parent-metal interface because the weld metal will be restrained from contracting, as it cools down, by the surrounding colder metal. Pre-heating the plates prior to welding and stress-relieving the joint after welding minimizes the magnitude of these stresses. The main purpose of such treatment is to reduce the likelihood of brittle fracture. The fatigue life under a wholly tensile loading cycle should be little affected since a tensile mean stress has little effect on crack growth rates in steels. However, if the crack is closed by compressive stresses as in zero mean load tests, the effect of tensile residual stresses will be more marked. Tensile residual stresses can affect the direction in which the major crack causing complete failure grows [285].

Although the fatigue limit of a welded joint is less than that of the parent plate material, the fatigue limit of an actual component or structural member containing stress concentrations may not be much reduced, if at all, by the presence of a weld. Obviously, if the stress concentration factor of a discontinuity is sufficient for the fatigue limit of the component to be less than that of a welded joint of the same material, the addition of a welded joint at some place in the component away from the stress concentration will have little or no effect. For example, the fatigue limit of butt-welded steel reinforcing bars for concrete, having raised external fins from which failure originated in an unwelded bar, is only 10–20 per cent lower than the unwelded bar [286].

TABLE 6.25
Fatigue strength of butt welds in structural steel

Reference	Material	Type of weld	Tensile strength of parent plate (MN m⁻²)	Fatigue strength usually 2×10^6 cycles (MN m⁻²)		Comments
				Zero mean load	Repeated tension	
278	Mild steel	Unwelded plate (mill scale)	365	±108	0–137	
	Low-alloy steel		510		0–180	
	Mild steel	Single-vee butt weld	365	±49	0–79	
	Low-alloy steel		510			
	Mild steel	Double-vee butt weld	365	±70	0–97	} Weld bead machined flush.
	Low-alloy steel		510		0–108	
	Mild steel	Double-vee butt weld	365	±88	0–108	
	Low-alloy steel		510		0–117	
					0–155 to 0–177	Stress-relief at 650 °C after welding had little effect.
279	Mild steel	13 mm thick butt weld	440		0–100	Weld bead running into plate at steep angle. Stress-relief at 650 °C after welding had little effect.
					0–247	Weld bead machined flush and polished. Stress-relief at 650 °C after welding had little effect.
280	Plain carbon steel	Butt weld	380–440		0–147 to 0–173	Shot-peening after each pass or stress relieving after welding had little effect.

No.	Material	Weld type		Remarks
281	Mild steel	Double-vee butt weld	420 / 0-140	Failure usually from toe of weld bead, occasionally from interior flaw in weld metal. Machining away weld bead increases fatigue strength, failure always from interior flaw in weld metal.
	0·2% C, 1% Mn steel		525 / 0-182	
	0·16% C, 1·2% Mn, 0·5% Si, steel		560 / 0-165	
	0·12% C, 0·8% Ni 0·6% Cr steel		710 / 0-134 to 0-252	
282	Mild steel	Butt weld	About 620 / 0-170	Weld bead dressed to about 0·25 mm proud.
	Alloy steels	Butt weld	About 620 / {0-170, 0-185}	
			0-147	Reduction compared with dressed bead in agreement with stress concentration factors obtained photo-elastically.
	Alloy steels	Butt weld	About 620 / 0-420	Weld bead ground flush, specimens polished all over. Failure always from interior flaw in weld metal.
283	Mild steel	13 mm thick butt welds, rutile welding rod	425 / 0-178	Sound weld.
			0-162	Single inclusion 2·4 mm diameter in weld metal.
			0-131	Single inclusion 4 mm diameter in weld metal.
			0-170	Multiple inclusions 1·6 mm diameter in weld metal.
			0-140	Multiple inclusions 2·4 mm diameter in weld metal.
			0-116	Multiple inclusions 8 mm diameter in weld metal.
			0-170	Single inclusion 7 mm diameter in weld metal.
			0-193	Multiple inclusions 2·4 mm diameter in weld metal.
			0-162	Multiple inclusions 6·4 mm diameter in weld metal.

If the weld bead is left unmachined, a moderate degree of porosity, slag, or lack of fusion, in general, does not reduce the fatigue strength. Defects in the surface have a higher stress intensity factor (§ 5.2) and are therefore more dangerous than those of a similar shape and size inside the weld metal; in general, the larger the projected area (on a plane normal to the loading direction) of the flaw, the sharper its ends, and the lower the modulus of elasticity of inclusions in it compared to that of the plate material, the lower will be the fatigue limit of the joint.

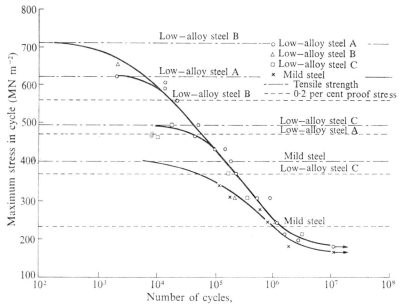

FIG. 6.27. S/N curves for butt-welded specimens having dressed weld beads (zero to maximum tensile stress). (Taken from Frost and Denton [282].)

Although the fatigue limit of an as-welded alloy steel joint is not significantly different from that of a corresponding mild steel joint, its fatigue strength at endurances less than that corresponding to the knee of the S/N curve increases progressively over that of a mild steel joint as the endurance decreases (see Fig. 6.27). Its fatigue strength at these endurances will also be superior to that of a mild steel joint if high tensile mean stresses are carried.

The fatigue strength of an as-welded joint may be increased [270] by inducing high compressive residual stresses around the edge of the weld (either by surface-rolling, spot-heating, local compression treatments, or overloading the joint in tension) because these retard the growth of cracks formed at the toe of the weld bead. The increase is greatest at long endurances and in the harder materials, that is, in those cases where the fatigue limit of the joint is low compared to the yield stress of the plate material, and the residual stresses are therefore least likely to be relaxed by the subsequent cyclic stressing.

If failure takes place from a defect, virtually the whole of the life is occupied by fatigue crack growth, so that a fracture-mechanics approach can be used to estimate the fatigue life of a joint. A fracture-mechanics approach has been successfully used [287] in the analysis of a large number of tests on steel and aluminium alloy butt welds, and the results used to construct curves (Fig. 6.28) giving maximum allowable defect sizes for various stress levels, plate thickness, and initial defect sizes. More extensive analyses have been used as the basis for a proposed method of establishing realistic standards of fabrication [271].

6.8.3. Fillet welds in structural steels

Fillet welds generally have a lower fatigue strength than butt welds because, although they form a junction between two plates, the weld bead does not penetrate right through the plate, and the change in section represented by the shape of the fillet thus gives rise to a stress concentration. For example, the fatigue strength (2×10^6 cycles) of mild steel fillet welds [273] has been quoted as about 70–80 per cent of that of corresponding butt welds, and the allowable stresses quoted in Fig. 6.26 reflect this trend. As with butt welds, the fatigue strengths (at long endurances) of alloy steel fillet welds are similar to those of corresponding mild steel joints.

Pulsating tension fatigue tests have been carried out [288] on fillet-welded mild steel specimens to determine the critical fillet sizes at which the origin of failure changed from the root of the weld to the weld toe. It was found that specimens designed to give failure at the toe had a higher fatigue strength (2×10^6 cycles) than those which failed at the root (root failures, 0–54 MN m^{-2} to 0–76 MN m^{-2}, toe failures 0–88 MN m^{-2} to 0–110 MN m^{-2}). Extensive other data on fillet welds are presented in References [212] and [270].

It is of particular interest to consider the direct stress fatigue tests carried out [289] on mild steel specimens of the type shown in Fig. 6.29, which contain transverse load-bearing partial penetration fillet welds. They were subjected to both constant amplitude and narrow-band random loading (§ 6.2.5). The test results obtained at zero mean stress are shown in Fig. 6.30 and provide a good illustration of how fracture mechanics can be applied to the analysis of test data on weldments. About equal proportions of specimens cracked at the weld root and weld toe; these two modes of failure should be considered separately when developing an extrapolation procedure for design purposes. Cracking at the weld toe is equivalent to crack initiation at a stress concentration and the stress necessary is reasonably independent of specimen size. However, cracking from the weld root is essentially a cracked specimen

(a)

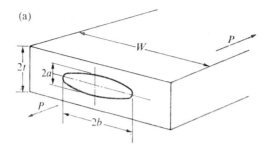

$2a$ = Defect width through thickness

$2b$ = Defect length

$2t$ = Material thickness at defect

W = Material width at defect

σ = Gross area stress $\dfrac{P}{2Wt}$

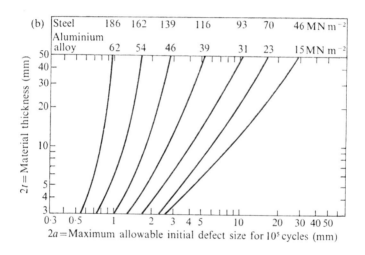

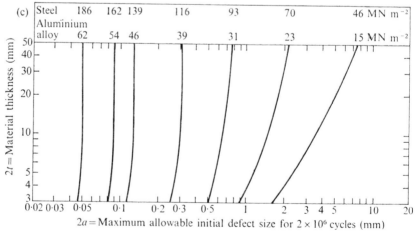

Fig. 6.28. Allowable defect sizes for repeated tension. (a) Partial penetration defect. (b) Allowable defect size for 10^5 cycles. (c) Allowable defect size for 2×10^6 cycles. (Taken from Harrison [287].)

situation, cracks growing immediately from the initial slit. In this case, a fracture mechanics analysis becomes appropriate, if meaningful extrapolations are to be made to either different specimen sizes or different endurances.

A crack at the weld root will not grow unless the range of stress intensity factor during the fatigue cycle ΔK (neglecting any compressive stresses) exceeds a critical value ΔK_o, which for mild steel in air is $6\cdot4$ MN m$^{-\frac{3}{2}}$ at zero mean stress (§ 4.5). The existence of ΔK_o is associated with a minimum possible crack growth rate of one lattice spacing per cycle, which makes it impossible (in the absence of time-dependent effects such as corrosion) to

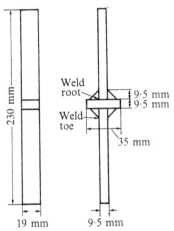

FIG. 6.29. Fillet-welded fatigue specimen. (Taken from White and Lewszuk [289].)

have fractures at greater than 10^7–10^8 cycles; the crack is either not growing or it will have grown to break the specimen before this time.

The stress intensity factor K_I for the configuration used can be written (§ 5.2)

$$K_I = S(\pi a)^{\frac{1}{2}}\alpha, \qquad (6.10)$$

where S is the gross stress, a is half the over-all crack length, and α is a geometric correction factor. The value of α may be estimated by noting that Fig. 6.30 shows a clearly defined fatigue limit at about ±62 MN m^{-2}, and assuming that this represents a ΔK of $6\cdot4$ MN m$^{-\frac{3}{2}}$. Taking a as half the plate thickness and substituting in eqn (6.10) gives $\alpha = 0\cdot84$, a value which is used in the following calculations. However, if, say, a 100 mm thick plate of the same configuration is considered, use of eqn (6.10) indicates that the fatigue limit would be only 19 MN m^{-2}, which is less than half the $9\cdot5$ mm plate result; this suggests that failure would always be from the weld root. On the other hand, for plates less than $9\cdot5$ mm thick, the estimated stress to cause crack growth would be greater than the 62 MN m^{-2} necessary to initiate

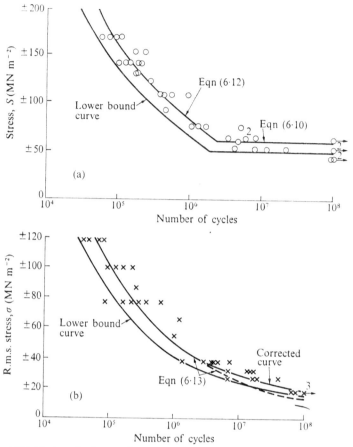

FIG. 6.30. Test results for specimens containing partial penetration fillet welds. (a) Results for constant amplitude loading at zero mean stress. (b) Results for narrow-band random loading at zero mean stress. (Data taken from White and Lewszuk [289].)

cracks at the weld toe, so that failure would now be expected to be in this region.

Truncation of peaks in fatigue testing using narrow-band random loading has been suggested [290] to have little effect on the cumulative fatigue damage caused by the various stress levels; however, whether or not a crack starts to grow will depend on the maximum stress applied, and therefore on the level at which the Rayleigh curve is truncated. The distribution appeared to be truncated at $S/\sigma = 5$ ($\sigma =$ r.m.s. stress) so that the fatigue limit, estimated as the stress necessary to cause crack growth, would be 62/5 MN m^{-2} = 12·4 MN m^{-2}. However, if truncation were at $S/\sigma = 3$, the fatigue limit would be 20·7 MN m^{-2} so that, in the estimation of fatigue limits, truncation is no longer insignificant.

In the finite-life region, endurance can be estimated from fatigue crack growth data. For mild steel, the rate of crack growth in millimetres per cycle is given by (§ 5.7)

$$\frac{da}{dN} = 2.39 \times 10^{-9} (\Delta K)^{3.3}, \qquad (6.11)$$

where ΔK is in MN m$^{-\frac{3}{2}}$. Substituting eqn (6.10) in eqn (6.11), rearranging, and integrating between the initial (a_0) and final (a_t) crack lengths, the life in a constant amplitude test is given by

$$N = \frac{2.02 \times 10^{12}}{S^{3.3}}, \qquad (6.12)$$

where S is MN m^{-2}. The value of a_t is not critical; it was taken as $2a_0$ in eqn (6.12); if it is taken as ∞, N is increased by a factor of about $2\frac{3}{4}$. Fig. 6.30(a) compares the test results with eqn (6.12): excellent agreement is obtained.

In the random-loading tests, a stress cycle did not differ greatly from its predecessor, so that crack growth rates could be predicted from constant-amplitude data assuming linear accumulation. Using the same data and units as before, the number of cycles to failure for the random loading case is given by

$$N = \frac{4.33 \times 10^{11}}{\sigma^{3.3}}. \qquad (6.13)$$

The distribution is assumed to be truncated at $S/\sigma = 5$ but the exact level is not critical for this purpose. Fig. 6.30(b) compares the test results with eqn (6.13). This equation makes no allowance for stress cycles which are below the level necessary for crack growth. If allowance is made for these cycles, the corrected line shown in Fig. 6.30(b) is obtained. The important point is that, under random loading, fractures are possible at greater than 10^7–10^8 cycles, but only because some of the stress cycles are too low to cause crack growth; the number of damaging cycles still cannot exceed 10^7–10^8.

The stress necessary for crack growth has an increasing effect as it approaches the level at which the Rayleigh distribution is truncated, and the proportion of damaging cycles drops. For example, if σ is ± 14 MN m^{-2}, which is not very much greater than the estimated fatigue limit of ± 12.4 MN m^{-2}, eqn (6.13) predicts a life of 7.3×10^7 cycles, whereas allowing for the stress necessary for crack growth gives 1.04×10^{10} cycles. Making the same allowance, the r.m.s. stress amplitude to give a life of 10^{12} cycles is ± 12.7 MN m^{-2}. This is only slightly above the fatigue limit for indefinite life: it would therefore be reasonable to base calculations for a life of, say, 10^{12} cycles on the estimated fatigue limit.

The analysis given provides curves which fit the average of the experimental data. The lower bound curves shown in Fig. 6.30 were obtained by taking a conservative value of the fatigue limit for the constant amplitude test of ± 51 MN m^{-2} and repeating the calculations; similarly, an upper bound curve can be obtained by assuming a fatigue limit of ± 77 MN m^{-2}. The excellent agreement with the experimental results demonstrates the power of fracture mechanics to provide a rational method of fitting curves to experimental data.

Perhaps the most important point arising from the analysis is the danger of the designer uncritically using fatigue data, without appreciating the mechanics of the situation. With partial-penetration weld details, it is essential to realize that a cracked test-piece situation is involved, so that the fatigue crack propagation characteristics are of paramount importance. Thus extrapolation to similar geometries in thicker plate, involving initial cracks of greater length, can have a marked effect on the fatigue strength.

6.8.4. Butt welds in light alloys

The results of tests on transverse butt welds in aluminium alloy follow the same general pattern as found for steel. Because the weld metal is in the as-cast annealed condition the fatigue strengths at long endurances of welded plates do not vary widely with plate material [291, 292]. Machining away the weld bead increases the fatigue strength; for example, reversed plane bending fatigue tests on butt-welded 5% Mg–aluminium alloy plates [293] showed (Table 6.26) that this increased the fatigue strength (10^7 cycles)

TABLE 6.26

Type of specimen	Fatigue strength 10^7 cycles (MN m^{-2})
Plate material, as-received	± 124
Plate material, annealed	± 81
Butt-welded plates	± 58
Butt-welded plates, weld bead machined flush	± 85

of the welded plate to that of the annealed plate material. The fatigue strength of aluminium alloy joints tested in reversed direct stress can be expected to be lower [269] than in reversed plane bending because, in the former case, all internal defects are subjected to the maximum stress range.

Repeated tension fatigue tests on $4\frac{1}{2}$% Mg–aluminium alloy butt-welded plates showed [291] that the geometric notch effect of the weld bead was the prime factor influencing the fatigue strength and that small differences in the fatigue strengths of welds prepared by either automatic or semi-automatic methods could be attributed primarily to differences in weld bead configurations; metallurgical changes in structure produced by the different techniques were of secondary importance. The repeated tension fatigue strength (10^7

cycles) of 9·5 mm thick, 127 mm wide butt-welded aluminium joints [294] tended to be higher (0–48 MN m^{-2} to 0–69 MN m^{-2}) when inert-gas metal arc welding was used than when conventional arc welding was used (0–34 MN m^{-2} to 0–56 MN m^{-2}). An investigation [295] into the effect of the weld bead shape on the fatigue strength of butt-welded $5\frac{1}{2}\%$ Mg–aluminium alloy plates showed that the flatter the weld bead, and the more gradually the toe radius blended into the plate, the higher the fatigue strength (2×10^6 cycles). When the bead was raised and formed a sharper angle with the plate, fatigue cracks initiated at the weld toe; with flat beads or those in which the weld bead

TABLE 6.27

Type of specimen	Fatigue strength, 5×10^7 cycles (MN m^{-2})
Plate material	0 ± 62
Butt weld, welded from one side	0 ± 25
Butt weld, welded on both sides	0 ± 25
Butt weld, weld bead machined flush	0 ± 51

was machined flush, failure originated from defects, those breaking the surface being the most dangerous.

The pattern of behaviour of magnesium alloy welded plates under cyclic stressing is similar to that of aluminium alloy welded plates. The results given in Table 6.27 (compare Table 6.26) were obtained [296] from reversed plane bending fatigue tests on butt-welded joints in a 3 mm thick structural magnesium alloy plate.

6.8.5. *Methods of improving fatigue strength*

Apart from local machining to improve the weld profile, discussed in previous sections, methods of improving the fatigue strength of welded joints are usually based on the introduction of compressive residual stresses [270]. The simplest way of inducing compressive residual stresses around a discontinuity, discussed previously in § 6.3, is to apply prior to fatigue testing, a static tension load sufficient to cause the material near to the discontinuity to deform plastically; compressive residual stresses remain on unloading. The fatigue strength (2×10^6 cycles) of a mild steel plate having a transverse gusset plate welded on can be increased from 0–112 MN m^{-2} to 0–155 MN m^{-2} by applying a static tensile overload of 250 MN m^{-2}.

In the case of plates having welded-on attachments it may be possible to induce compressive residual stresses in the neighbourhood of a weld toe by either locally compressing with a punch the material in front of the weld toe or by locally heating a small area of this material. The treatment should be applied in front of that part of the weld at which it is known fracture originated in untreated specimens. The Direct stress fatigue tests (repeated tension loading cycle) on mild steel and aluminium alloy specimens having various load-carrying [297] and non-load-carrying [298] welded-on attachments, resulted in a 100–150 per cent increase in fatigue strength (2×10^6 cycles), if either treatment was applied.

Shot-peening or surface-rolling will both work-harden and induce compressive residual stresses in the material in the region of the weld bead toe. Suitable treatment can increase the fatigue strength of longitudinal and transverse fillet welds in steel by up to 90 per cent [270].

TABLE 6.28

Type of specimen	Type of coating	Plane bending fatigue strength, 2×10^6 cycles (MN m^{-2})
Notched	None	± 29
Notched	Epoxy-resin	± 68
Notched	Epoxy-resin with 40% graphite	± 88
Notched	Polyester-resin with 40% kaolin	± 88
Butt-welded	None	± 79
Butt-welded	Epoxy-resin	± 146

The fatigue crack growth characteristics of mild steel can be improved by excluding the atmosphere from the crack tip (§ 4.10 and § 5.9.4); there is some evidence that applying air-tight plastic coatings to mild steel welded joints increases their fatigue limit. For example, coating a butt weld in a mild steel specimen with a plastic impervious to air increased its fatigue strength (2×10^6 cycles), provided the coating filled up all the weld irregularities [299]. The results given in Table 6.28 were obtained on reversed plane bending specimens from which all rust, scale, and grease had been removed mechanically before applying the coating. The type of plastic used does not appear to be important [270], provided that it is highly impermeable to oxygen and water, and does not crack under the applied loading.

6.8.6. Spot welds

Thin sheets are often joined together by spot welding. In a spot-welded joint loaded in tension, the load is transmitted from one sheet to the other through the spot welds. Fatigue failure after long endurances usually results from cracks forming in the sheet at the edge of a spot. A spot-welded joint is essentially a cracked specimen so that, like the fillet welds considered in § 6.8.4, the fatigue limit is determined by the stress necessary to cause crack growth.

The stress distribution in a spot-welded joint (which in fracture mechanics terms is a connection between two bodies) is complicated and, in general, all three modes of crack surface displacement (§ 5.2) will be present. The effect of K_{II} and K_{III} on the value of ΔK_c is not known. However, in geometrically similar situations they will be proportional to K_I, so that ΔK_c would be expected to be constant.

The stress intensity factor for a load P applied perpendicular to the centre of a circular connection, radius a, between two half spaces is [300]

$$K_I = \frac{P}{2\pi^{\frac{1}{2}}a^{\frac{3}{2}}}$$

or, in terms of the average stress σ on the connection,

$$K_I = \frac{\sigma}{2}(\pi a)^{\frac{1}{2}},$$

which is of the same form as the equations for cracks.

For inclined loads, K_{II} and K_{III} vary around the circumference and are also proportional to $P/a^{\frac{3}{2}}$. Correction factors for finite specimens are not available, but will be constant for geometrically similar situations. For spot welds made under optimum conditions, the spot-weld nugget is proportional to sheet thickness; consequently stress intensity factors are proportional to sheet thickness, and the load necessary to cause crack growth is therefore proportional to $a^{\frac{3}{2}}$. Thus, as observed experimentally [301], the fatigue strength per spot increases with increasing sheet thickness. The fatigue strength of a joint also increases as the number of spot welds in a row or the number of rows increases, but because of uneven load distribution, as in a bolted joint (§ 6.7), the fatigue strength per spot may decrease (Tables 6.29 and 6.30).

The general behaviour of spot welds in the as-welded condition follows that of butt welds in that the fatigue strength at long endurances of a high-strength steel joint is no better than that of a mild steel joint. Fatigue tests (loading cycle wholly tensile) on single-spot mild steel (1·23 mm thick sheet) simple lap joints [303] showed that mean stress had little effect on fatigue strength.

The fatigue strength of a spot weld may be increased by introducing favourable compressive residual stresses around the weld spot, either by static overloading or by applying a hydrostatic loading treatment to each spot individually. The fatigue strength (20×10^6 cycles) of simple aluminium alloy sheet (1·4 mm thick, $4\frac{1}{2}\%$ Cu) lap joints having a single central spot weld can be increased from 270 ± 135 N to 400 ± 200 N by applying a static load equal to two-thirds of the static failure load, prior to fatigue testing [304]. A hydrostatic pressure of 1035 MN m^{-2} applied to each spot weld by clamping the material around a spot weld in a steel jig to minimize lateral plastic flow, and then applying a high compressive static load by means of a hardened steel tool through a hole in the jig, noticeably increases the fatigue strength

TABLE 6.29

Repeated tension fatigue tests on steel lap joints [302]

Spot configuration (see Fig. 6.31)	Static joint strength (kN)	Fatigue strength, 10^7 cycles. Maximum load in fatigue cycle (kN) (Minimum load = 0)			
		As-welded		Hydrostatic treated (1035 MN m^{-2} to each spot)	
		per joint	per spot	per joint	per spot
Mild steel (0·95 mm thick)					
a	6·2	2·9	2·9	2·9	2·9
b	10·7	3·4	1·7	3·4	1·7
c	10·7	3·6	1·8	4·5	2·2
d	10·7	2·7	0·9	3·9	1·3
e	12	3·6	0·9	4·5	1·1
f	12	4·0	0·8	4·0	0·8
High tensile steel (1·05 mm thick)					
a	10·2	1·8	1·8	5·3	5·3
b	14·7	2·7	1·4	5·3	2·7
c	14·7	1·8	0·9	4·5	2·3
d	19·6	1·8	0·6	5·3	1·8
e	19·6	3·6	0·9	5·8	1·4
f	19·6	3·6	0·7	5·3	1·1

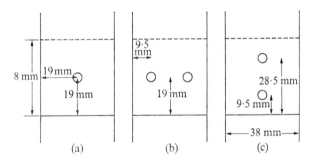

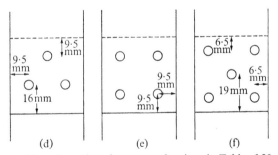

FIG. 6.31. Spot-weld configurations for test results given in Tables 6.29 and 6.30.

TABLE 6.30

Pulsating tension fatigue tests on 1·5 mm *thick* 2024 *clad aluminium alloy* $(4\frac{1}{2}\%$ Cu) *lap joints* [302]

Spot configuration (see Fig. 6.31)	Static joint strength (kN)	Fatigue strength 2×10^7 cycles. Maximum load in fatigue cycle (kN) (Minimum load $= \frac{1}{5}$ maximum load)			
		As-welded		Hydrostatic treated (1035 MN m^{-2} to each spot)	
		per joint	per spot	per joint	per spot
b	9·8	1·8	0·9	2·9	1·5
c	10·8	1·8	0·9	3·1	1·6
d	14·7	2·0	0·7	3·6	1·2
e	15·5	2·1	0·5	4·5	1·1
f	24·0	2·7	0·5	5·3	1·1

of high-strength steel and aluminium alloy joints, but has little effect on mild steel joints (Tables 6.29 and 6.30). The beneficial effect of hydrostatic pressure treatment can be improved further [305] if the load is applied to the spot in a dynamic rather than in a static manner, by dropping a weight on to the steel tool located in the clamping jig. The results given in Table 6.31, on a 17/7 stainless steel sheet 1·65 mm thick single spot lap joint, show the additional benefit resulting from this dynamic treatment, although it is difficult to see what is achieved by this method of preloading other than the induced residual stresses being higher or spread over a larger area.

Residual stress measurements taken on the material adjacent to the edge of a spot weld showed that residual tensile stresses of several hundred MN m^{-2} were present after welding, but these were converted to compressive residual stresses of roughly the same magnitude when the spot was treated by one of the preloading procedures.

6.8.7. *Glued, brazed, and pressure-welded joints*

Other common methods of joining metallic materials include glueing, brazing, and pressure welding. Glued load-carrying joints are generally

TABLE 6.31

Repeated tension fatigue tests on 17/7 *stainless steel lap joints* [305]

Condition of spot (configuration a, Fig. 6.31)	Fatigue strength, 10^7 cycles (kN)
As-welded	0–1·3
Welded and annealed	0–2·7
Hydrostatic treatment	0–3·6
Hydrodynamic treatment	0–4·5

simple single-lap joints, with the joining medium spread over the entire contacting area between the sheets. In such joints, the nominal stress in the joint is higher than that in the plate remote from the joint because of bending stresses induced by the non-axiality of the two plates inherent in a single-lap joint, and there is a local stress concentration in each plate at the point where the other plate ends. Under cyclic loading, failure of the joint at long endurances takes place by cracking of the plate in the region of the local stress concentration at the edge of the overlap, but at high stress levels giving short endurances failure may also occur by shearing of the bond. The amount of overlap must therefore be sufficient for the joint not to slide apart under the maximum load and the joining medium must be distributed uniformly over the overlap and contain no discontinuities which could act as incipient cracks. In principle, fracture mechanics can be applied to glued joints but at present only qualitative predictions of behaviour are possible (§ 5.2.2).

Thin sheets of aluminium alloy are often joined by glueing with either a phenolic-resin (Redux) or an epoxy-resin (Araldite) base glue which is cured under pressure and temperature. The repeated tension S/N curves for various aluminium alloy sheet single-lap glued joints have a knee at about 10^6 cycles. For a variety of geometries, the repeated tension fatigue strength (10^6 cycles) is about 15 per cent of the static strength [244, 306].

If the overlap is sufficient and the brazing is of a high standard, single-lap brazed steel joints can have fatigue strengths approaching that of the annealed sheet material. For example, it was found that the fatigue limit of brazed low-alloy steel strips was equal to that of the annealed unbrazed strip [307]. Even at 600 °C the fatigue limit of the joint was only 10 per cent lower than that of the strip material. The fatigue strength of any type of simple lap joint depends on the rigidity of the specimen, which controls the magnitude of the restraining moment imposed by the end-fittings holding the specimen in the testing machine. The stress concentration in one plate along the line where the adjoining plate ends can be reduced by tapering the thickness of the sheet so that it is very thin at its extremity, but this is not necessarily effective in increasing the fatigue strength of a joint [308].

The fatigue strength of brazed butt joints will obviously depend on the soundness of the brazed interface; rotating bending fatigue tests on brazed steel bars have given fatigue limits between ± 75 MN m^{-2} and ± 150 MN m^{-2}, irrespective of the type of steel and the type of brazing alloy [309].

Materials can be pressure butt-welded together at temperatures which do not lead to liquid metal being present during the joining operation. The fatigue strength of pressure butt-welded mild steel bars joined by abutting the clean faces to be joined under a moderate pressure and heating the interface in an oxyacetylene flame has been determined [310]. Rotating bending specimens were cut from the joined bars with the join in the centre of each specimen; one batch was tested as joined, another with the test-section electropolished. The fatigue strength (at a given endurance) of the electro-polished specimens was comparable to that of electropolished specimens of the bar material, provided this had been subjected to the same heating and deformation treatment as the joined specimens. The fatigue strength of the as-welded specimens was about 10 per cent less than the electropolished ones.

6.9. Shrink-fit assemblies

The shrink-fit assemblies considered in this section consist essentially of a parallel shaft having a shrunk or pressed-on collar or ring. Practical ex-amples of this type of assembly are a railway-wagon axle having a pressed on wheel, and a built-up steam turbine rotor consisting of a shaft with shrunk-on discs.

If a plain ring is shrunk on to a parallel shaft of the same material, the radial compressive contact pressure, assuming perfect elasticity, is given by $Ef(D^2-d^2)/2dD^2$, where E is Young's modulus, f is the difference between the shaft diameter and the bore of the ring before shrinking, D is the outside diameter of the ring, and d is the shaft diameter. In addition to this radial pressure, the shrunk-on ring induces longitudinal tensile stresses in the sur-face layers of the shaft outside the ring and compressive stresses in the surface layers of the shaft inside the ring. For example, for the case of a shrunk-on ring, whose width is equal to the shaft diameter, there is a longitudinal tensile stress at the surface of the shaft outside but near to the face of the ring, whose magnitude is about one-half the magnitude of the radial pressure, and a com-pressive stress of similar magnitude at the surface of the shaft just inside the ring [311]. If the shaft is loaded in bending, flexure of the shaft tends to relieve the contact pressure on the tension side of the shaft and to increase it on the compression side.

When a shaft having a shrunk-on ring is subjected to a cyclic loading (in practice such assemblies are generally subjected to rotating bending stresses), the fatigue strength of the assembly is found to be less than that of the shaft itself. This arises, first, because of the stress concentration at the edge of the ring and, secondly, because the cyclic loading results in relative cyclic move-ment between the inner surface of the ring and the shaft surface parallel to the longitudinal axis of the shaft, which gives rise to fretting. Generally fatigue cracks are found to occur on the surface of the shaft in areas of fretting just inside the ring seat. Depending on the geometry and assembly conditions, fatigue cracks may in some instances form in these fretted areas at nominal alternating stresses less than those required to cause complete failure of the shaft, that is, at stress levels less than the fatigue limit of the assembly.

Two different loading conditions are possible when a shaft and ring assembly are to be tested in fatigue, depending on whether or not the shrunk-on ring is used to react the cyclic loads carried by the shaft. In general, the bending fatigue limit of a cyclically loaded shaft merely carrying a shrunk-on ring is higher than that of a similar assembly in which the shaft loads are transmitted through the ring. For example, the rotating bending fatigue limit of a 51 mm diameter 0·45% C steel shaft having a ring shrunk-on was found to be ±104 MN m⁻² [312], but this was reduced to ±85 MN m⁻² when the shaft reactions were taken through the ring.

Photo-elastic model tests [313] have shown that the stress level on the surface of a shaft at the edge of a simple press-fit collar is about twice the nominal shaft surface stress. It was shown also that the rotating bending fatigue limit of 38 mm diameter 0·4% C steel shafts having a shrunk-on

TABLE 6.32

	Fatigue limit of shrink fit assembly (MN m⁻²)			
	As-machined		Induction hardened	
Shaft diameter (mm)	To initiate cracks	To cause complete fracture	To initiate cracks	To cause complete fracture
10	±154	±178	±300	±320
20	±125	±139	±295	±294
100	±70	±100	±178	±193

steel ring, geometrically similar to that used in the photo-elastic tests, was about one-half that of the plain fatigue limit of the shaft.

Rotating bending tests [314] on 0·4% C steel shafts having shrunk-on steel end-collars through which the shaft load was transmitted (shrink fit 0·0015 mm per mm of shaft diameter) showed that those shafts unbroken after testing at stress levels either equal to or just below the fatigue limit of the assembly contained fatigue cracks situated in fretted areas just inside the end-collar. The fatigue limits of various geometrically similar assemblies based either on the cyclic stress just required to initiate a crack in a fretted area or on that just required to cause complete fracture are given in Table 6.32; the corresponding fatigue limits of shafts, induction hardened, prior to shrinking on the collars are also given. The plain fatigue limit of the shaft material, determined on 10 mm diameter specimens, was ±310 MN m⁻².

Rotating bending fatigue tests have been carried out [315] on 240 mm diameter 0·5% C steel shafts having steel wheels shrunk on with an inter-ference-fit of 0·0025 mm per mm of shaft diameter and in which the reaction of the bending moment applied to the shaft was taken through the shrunk-on wheel. The results are shown on Fig. 6.32. It was found that fatigue cracks formed in fretted areas on the shaft surface situated just inside the wheel seat at nominal shaft surface stresses as low as ±35 MN m⁻² although complete failure of a shaft did not occur until the stress level exceeded ±85 MN m⁻². Indeed all shafts unbroken after testing for 85 × 10⁶ cycles at stress

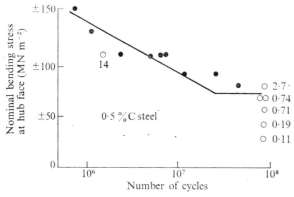

FIG. 6.32. *S/N* curve for wheel and axle assembly. Figures by open circles are depths of cracks (mm) inside wheel seats of unbroken axles. (Taken from Horger [316].)

levels between ± 35 MN m^{-2} and ± 85 MN m^{-2} were found to contain cracks. Flame-hardening the shaft in the region of the shrink-fit increased the alternating stress necessary to initiate cracks to ± 46 MN m^{-2} and that necessary to cause complete shaft fracture to ± 116 MN m^{-2}. Surface-rolling [317] resulted in a further increase in these values to ± 62 MN m^{-2} and ± 155 MN m^{-2}, respectively. Further tests [316] using 6 different shaft steels in either the normalized and tempered or quenched and tempered condition gave fatigue limits for complete fracture lying between ± 65 MN m^{-2} and ± 85 MN m^{-2}. However, inducing compressive residual stresses in the surface layers of the shafts by sub-critical quenching increased these fatigue limits to about ± 128 MN m^{-2}. In all cases, fatigue cracks were found in shafts which had been tested at stress levels either equal to or just below these fatigue limits for endurances up to 85×10^6 cycles. The results given in Table 6.33 from 51 mm diameter 0·5% C steel shafts having shrunk on collars [318] show that marked increases in both the stress to initiate cracks and to cause complete failure could result from metallizing and flame-hardening the shaft surface.

It thus seems that the fatigue limit of an interference-fit wheel and shaft assembly may be less than that expected from a knowledge of the fatigue properties of the shaft material and the stress distribution created in it by

TABLE 6.33

Surface treatment of axle	Fatigue limit (MN m^{-2})	
	To initiate cracks	To cause complete failure
Normalized and tempered	± 54	± 89
Metallized	± 147	± 147
Flame-hardened	± 170	± 310

the shrunk or pressed-on wheel, because of fretting of the shaft inside the wheel seat. Fretting can result in cracks forming at low nominal shaft stresses but, because of the longitudinal compressive stress induced in the surface of the shaft inside the wheel seat by the interference-fit, the fatigue limit of the assembly (that is, the nominal shaft stress necessary to cause such cracks to grow) can be higher than the cyclic stress necessary to initiate these fretting cracks. Hardening the shaft surface or minimizing the fretting increases the stress level required to initiate cracks. The higher the magnitude and greater the depth of penetration of the surface compressive stresses induced by the interference-fit, together with those induced by surface treatments such as case-hardening and surface-rolling, the more difficult will it be for the fretting cracks to develop and grow as macrocracks and consequently the higher will be the nominal alternating stress necessary to cause complete failure of the shaft.

Sometimes in practice a ring or wheel is shrunk on to a shaft adjacent to a filleted shoulder or circumferential groove. In such cases, failure generally occurs at the stress raiser and not from fretted areas within the wheel seat. However, the fatigue strength is less than the original notched shaft because the addition of the shrunk-on ring can cause an increase in the elastic stress concentration of the original notch, and also induce a tensile mean stress in the material at the root of the notch. Failure of a large built-up steam turbine rotor was reported [319] due to the formation of fatigue cracks at the root of a notch situated between two shrunk-on discs, at a nominal rotor bending stress of about ± 31 MN m^{-2}. To investigate the fatigue strength of a geometrically similar assembly, rotating bending fatigue tests were carried out on 100 mm diameter 3% Cr–Mo steel shafts having two discs shrunk on adjacent to a notch; these gave a fatigue limit of about ± 46 MN m^{-2}. However, it was found that an integrally machined component of the same shape as the shrunk-on disc-shaft assembly had the same fatigue limit, thus showing that the failure was due simply to the severely-notched geometry of the shrunk-on disc and shaft assembly. The behaviour of severely-notched specimens is discussed in § 4.6.

A series of rotating bending fatigue tests was carried out on steel shafts [320] containing a sharp circumferential vee-notch having either a single disc shrunk up to one edge of the notch or two discs, shrunk one on either side of the notch, using an interference of 0·002 mm per mm of shaft diameter. Tests on machined specimens of the same shape as the shrunk-on assemblies were also carried out. The results are given in Table 6.34; the 67 mm diameter shafts had a circumferential vee-notch 2·5 mm deep and 0·1 mm root radius, the 12·2 mm diameter shaft, a vee-notch 0·75 mm deep and 0·075 mm root radius. It was considered that the fatigue limit of a given assembly was governed by its geometry, the fatigue limit of the two-ring shrunk-on assembly being somewhat less than the corresponding integral construction because of the tensile mean stress induced at the notch root by the shrinking-on process. It was suggested that this latter effect would be the more significant the larger the ratio of the ring width to the shaft diameter.

Rotating bending tests were also carried out [314] on shafts containing a fillet and having a ring shrunk adjacent to the end of the fillet. The fatigue limit of the assembly was the same as that of a similarly shaped specimen machined from the solid. A similar result was obtained [321] from rotating bending tests on shafts having collars shrunk up to a shoulder; neither the

TABLE 6.34

	Fatigue limit (MN m^{-2})	
Specimen	67 mm diameter 3 % Cr–Mo steel shaft	12·2 mm diameter 2½ % Ni–Cr steel shaft
Un-notched	±370	±570
Notched	±66	±140
One ring shrunk-on	±66	±111
One ring integral	—	±113
Two rings shrunk-on	±51	±91
Two rings integral	±56	±102

hardness of the collar nor the degree of interference had any significant effect on the fatigue limit of the assembly.

Thus it appears that when failure of an interference-fit assembly occurs away from a fretted area its fatigue strength is similar to that of an integral component of the same geometry.

6.10. Screwed connections

The screwed connection, in the form of a nut and bolt or stud, is widely used in applications in which it is subjected to cyclic uniaxial loadings; various reviews of its behaviour have been given [322, 323]. A screw thread differs from a conventional cylindrical notched specimen in that, firstly, a screw thread consists of a series of adjacent notches and, secondly, the load is transmitted through the stress concentration, that is, the nut transmits the load to the bolt via the flank and root radius of the thread.

The maximum elastic stress concentration factor occurring in the vicinity of a series of adjacent notches may be less than that created by a single notch of the same geometry, the difference depending on the specimen and notch geometries and the distance between adjacent notches. The problem has been discussed theoretically by Neuber [324] and also investigated photo-elastically [325, 326]. Table 6.35 gives results [323] which show that the rotating bending fatigue limit of chromium-vanadium steel cylindrical specimens containing a screw thread cut in the test-section is higher than that of similar cylindrical specimens containing a single groove of the same geometry as the thread profile.

The fatigue limit of a bolt loaded through a nut, however, is usually much less than the fatigue limits of the threaded specimens given in Table 6.35. This is because the transmission of the load via the mating thread faces induces bending stresses at the thread roots in addition to those due to the axial bolt load. In practice, further bending stresses may be imposed if the

TABLE 6.35

Type of specimen	Thread details	Fatigue limit (MN m^{-2})
Plain	—	±355
Threaded	$\frac{1}{4}$ inch UNF	±293
Single groove		±85
Threaded	$\frac{3}{8}$ inch UNF	±255
Single groove		±147

bolt load is not axial; eccentric bolt loadings may be produced, for example, by the inclination of the contact face of the nut and the adjacent structural member or by deformation of the structure under the working loads [327].

When a bolt, loaded by a nut, is broken as a result of cyclic loading, failure is usually found to have originated at the root of the first engaged thread. (Failure may originate from the bolt-head–shank transition if this is too sharp or at the runout of the thread if this is badly machined.) This arises because the load carried by a bolt is not distributed uniformly between the mating threads, the first engaged thread carrying a higher percentage of the total bolt load than succeeding threads; the actual load distribution depends on the rigidity and accuracy of the thread forms. The problem of load distribution has been considered theoretically [328, 329]. For example, it has been shown that the maximum intensity of loading occurring at the first engaged thread can be from two to four times the mean load [328] (that is, the total load divided by the number of engaged threads), the actual factor depending on thread form, the nut and bolt geometries, and the degree of lubrication but being, for wholly elastic conditions, almost independent of the length of engaged threads. Data obtained from a photo-elastic model of a bolt and nut having six engaged threads [195] show that the percentages of the bolt load carried by the first and subsequent engaged threads were 34, 23, 16, 11, 9, and 7, respectively; this gives a value of 2·04 for the ratio of the load carried by the first engaged thread to the mean load. This load distribution is for elastic deformations; if the external load is sufficient to cause the material in the region of the thread roots to deform plastically, the distribution of load between the threads becomes more uniform.

The more uniform the load distribution between the engaged threads and the lower the stress concentration at the thread root, the higher will be the fatigue limit of a particular nut and bolt assembly. An improved load distribution may be obtained by:

(1) making the nut from a material of a lower elastic modulus than the bolt; it has been found [330] that the fatigue limit of steel bolts is increased significantly when loaded by magnesium alloy nuts rather than by mild steel nuts;

(2) making the nut of a material having a lower yield stress than the bolt;

(3) using a nut having a slightly greater pitch than the bolt;

(4) tapering the nut cross-section so as to reduce its stiffness over the first few threads.

The elastic stress concentration at the root of the first engaged thread may be decreased either by making the bolt shank diameter equal to the thread core diameter or by machining a continuous circumferential groove before the first thread. For example, it was found [331] that the fatigue strength (10^7 cycles) of a mild steel stud could be increased from 46–200 MN m^{-2} to 46–270 MN m^{-2} by machining a stress-relieving groove ahead of the first thread. Fatigue tests have been carried out [244] on various specialized thread forms designed to give both an improved load distribution and a low elastic stress concentration factor. It was found that, for a given loading cycle, a substantial increase in life was obtained by using either a nut with a slightly greater pitch than that on the bolt, a thread form having a 90° included angle instead of the usual 55° and 60° forms, or a nut which had either a convex or concave loading face.

When a bolt is subjected to a cyclic loading, fretting may occur along the band of contact around the thread helix. However, as the fretting area is remote from the region of maximum stress, fretting plays no part in crack initiation. For example, fatigue tests [332] on $\frac{3}{4}$ inch UNC bolts of 930 MN m^{-2} tensile strength steel (En16T) loaded through nuts of 540 MN m^{-2} tensile strength steel (BS 3S1) showed that fretting in tests at stresses above the fatigue limit (stress range 70–240 MN m^{-2}) was very slight. Fretting on the thread flanks of a bolt tested at the fatigue limit for 200×10^6 cycles was very heavy, but upon retesting this bolt at a higher stress level, fatigue cracks grew from the thread root and not from an area of fretting.

The fatigue strength of a bolt may be improved by rolling the thread root; this results not only in a smoother more-accurate root profile but work-hardens and induces favourable compressive residual stresses in the material at the thread root. The rolling process must be the final operation carried out on the bolt, in particular all heat-treatments must be carried out prior to rolling, otherwise they may anneal the work-hardened material, relax the residual stresses, and decarburize the material at the thread root. These points are illustrated by the results in Table 6.36; they were obtained by testing $\frac{1}{4}$ inch BSF bolts of 930 MN m^{-2} tensile strength steel in reversed plane bending (that is, not loaded through a nut) [333]. It is interesting to note that metallurgical examination of specimens unbroken after testing for 10^7 cycles showed that small non-propagating cracks were present at the roots of the threads. Many investigators [334-7] have shown that cold-rolling increases the fatigue limit of bolts loaded through nuts.

TABLE 6.36

Thread finish	Fatigue strength, 10^7 cycles (MN m^{-2})
Heat-treated, ground, and cold-rolled	± 400
Heat-treated, machine cut	± 363
Heat-treated, cold-rolled, cadmium-plated	± 317
Cold-rolled, heat-treated, cadmium-plated (no decarburization)	± 275
Cold-rolled, heat-treated, cadmium-plated (0·025 mm deep decarburization)	± 190
Cold-rolled, heat-treated, cadmium-plated (0·05 mm deep decarburization)	± 174

The fatigue strengths of various screw thread forms have been studied [338] by testing double-ended studs stressed in pulsating tension via a nut on either end. Although the threads were loaded through nuts, it was emphasized that the results obtained related mainly to the effect of thread form on fatigue strength, whereas the fatigue strength of a bolted assembly depends to a large extent on the over-all design of the fastening and is affected by the degree of tightening and the flexibility of the parts involved. In one series of tests, $\frac{3}{4}$ inch Whitworth En16T (tensile strength 960 MN m^{-2}) and En7 (tensile strength 600 MN m^{-2}) steel studs were loaded through En7 steel nuts. The threads had a symmetrical triangular form; the minor diameter, pitch, and depth of engagement were kept constant, the effect of varying the included angle from 45° to 60° and the root radius from 0·115 to 0·163 times the pitch being studied. The thread forms were either lathe-cut, ground, or cold-rolled. Some of the results are shown on Fig. 6.33; they indicate clearly that cold-rolling causes a marked increase in the fatigue strengths of both the low and high tensile strength studs, but that increasing the root radius and thread angle has little effect except in the case of the rolled high-tensile steel studs, whose fatigue strength increases markedly with increasing root radius. (This implies that non-propagating cracks must have been present at the roots of mild steel threads tested at the fatigue limit.) A second series of tests were carried out to compare the fatigue strengths of Whitworth and Unified

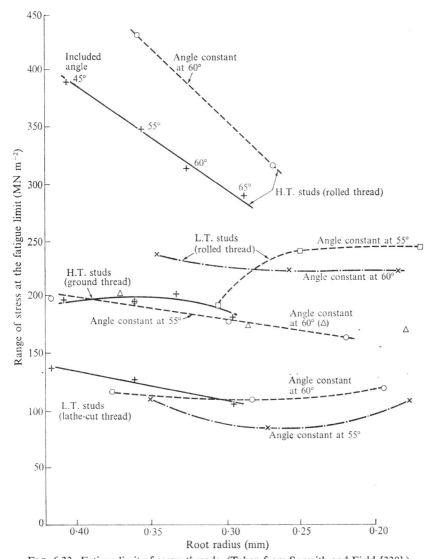

FIG. 6.33. Fatigue limit of screw threads. (Taken from Sopwith and Field [338].)

thread forms using either $\frac{3}{4}$ inch Whitworth or $\frac{3}{8}$ inch BSF studs, the thread profiles being either lathe-cut, ground, or cold-rolled. No appreciable difference was found in fatigue strengths between corresponding stud sizes, the effect of the geometrical form of the thread was not great and cold-rolling was shown to increase the fatigue strength. Tests on both ground and rolled threads showed that a reduction in the depth of engagement, even to 25 per cent of normal, caused no loss in fatigue strength, provided that the

27

truncation was either divided equally between the stud and nut or was all or nearly all in the nut. It was also found that no loss in fatigue strength resulted from 'crossing' a Unified and Whitworth thread form if low tensile steel nuts were used. Additional tests [339] on 64 mm diameter studs showed a reduction in fatigue strength of about 10–20 per cent compared to the corresponding ⅜ inch BSF and ¾ inch Whitworth studs; some results showing the effect of size on the fatigue strength of various lathe-cut and ground studs, having Unified thread forms, are given in Table 6.37. Tests were carried out in

TABLE 6.37

Size of thread	Method of forming bolt thread†	Tensile strength of bolt steel (MN m^{-2})	Tensile strength of nut steel (MN m^{-2})	Range of pulsating tensile stress at fatigue limit (MN m^{-2})
⅜ inch BSF	lathe-cut	590	570	117
⅜ inch BSF	ground	925	556	190
¾ inch Whitworth	lathe-cut	600	570	117
¾ inch Whitworth	ground	600	570	105
¾ inch Whitworth	ground	970	570	208
¾ inch Whitworth	ground	970	1010	196
64 mm, 6 mm pitch	ground	525	430	86
64 mm, 4 mm pitch	ground	525	430	77

† All nuts finished by tapping.

pulsating tension, the minimum tensile stress in the cycle being 70 MN m^{-2} except for the tests on the 64 mm diameter studs in which it was 46 MN m^{-2}.

Fatigue tests [340] on 1 inch Whitworth and 3 inch BSF, 0·16% C steel (465 MN m^{-2} tensile strength) bolts loaded through 0·12% C steel (355 MN m^{-2} tensile strength) nuts showed that the range of pulsating stress at the fatigue limit, for a tensile loading cycle in which the minimum tensile stress was 46 MN m^{-2}, was 100 MN m^{-2} and 77 MN m^{-2} respectively.

Titanium bolts are often either cadmium or zinc plated to prevent galvanic corrosion when used in contact with aluminium alloys. It has been found [341] that, although these platings reduce the bolt fatigue strength at endurances less than 10^5 cycles, they have little effect on the fatigue strength at endurances of 10^7 cycles or more.

In most practical applications a tensile load is applied to a bolt because the nut is tightened up against abutments through which the bolt passes, for example, the bolts in a connecting-rod big-end or those holding the end-cover on a hydraulic cylinder. When this is the case, the fatigue strength of the bolted assembly depends on the extent of the tightening load. If the tightening load in the bolt (or in a number of bolts) is greater than the external load applied through the abutments, most of the external load will bypass the bolt because no additional load, apart from that resulting from the elastic deformation of the abutments, will come on to the bolt until the joint faces separate. The abutments therefore should be made as stiff as possible and, conversely, the bolt should be as flexible as possible. Analyses of the load carried by a bolt (or bolts) in a pre-tightened joint, in terms of the relative stiffnesses of the component parts of the joint, have been given by various investigators [244, 342, 343]. Because a repeated external tension load insufficient to open the clamped faces results in little change in the stress in a pretightened bolt, the fatigue strength of the bolted assembly increases with increasing bolt tightness; this is illustrated by the results in Table 6.38 [344].

TABLE 6.38

Tightening load in bolt (kN)	Loading cycle (kN)	Endurance (millions of cycles)	
6·4	0–41	0·006	
26·5	0–41	0·036	
34·5	0–41	0·215	
37·5	0–41	5·0	unbroken

Other similar results have been published [345]; in practice, periodic retightening of the nut is necessary if the bolt head or nut becomes embedded in the abutments. Spring-washers inserted beneath the nut are beneficial because they provide bolt flexibility, but gaskets between the abutments are detrimental because they lower the stiffness of the abutments. The value of the load induced in a bolt by tightening the nut may be assessed either by measuring the elongation of the bolt or by tightening to a predetermined torque by means of a torque spanner. The first method is the more accurate and particularly convenient if load-indicating washers are used; the use of a torque spanner suffers from the disadvantage that variable amounts of the tightening torque are dissipated in overcoming friction at the contact surfaces.

In § 4.6 it was shown that non-propagating cracks may be present at the root of a notch in a specimen which is unbroken after testing at its conventional notched fatigue limit when the root radius is less than some limiting value. Thus, non-propagating cracks may be present at the roots of some thread profiles, especially where the thread depth or root radius is small, in bolts which remain unbroken after testing at or below their fatigue limit. When this is so, their fatigue limit depends on the cyclic stress necessary to propagate such cracks, which in turn depends on the depth of the thread form; a size-effect therefore may become apparent when testing geometrically similar bolts of different diameters because the larger the bolt diameter the greater will be the thread depth. If cold-rolling results in a marked increase in the fatigue limit of a bolt, especially one made of a stronger steel, it is highly probable that non-propagating cracks are present at the thread roots at the fatigue limit stress. This is because the stronger the steel the more probable it is that the increase in fatigue limit resulting from the cold-rolling is due to residual compressive stresses retarding the growth of cracks formed at the thread root rather than work-hardening of the material at the notch root increasing the cyclic stress necessary to initiate a crack.

6.11. Rolling contact

Fatigue under rolling contact conditions occurs when a loaded ball or roller moves over either a curved or flat surface; typical examples include two rollers in contact, a ball running round a curved track, or a wheel running along a rail. The maximum contact load and surface speed in a particular application are limited by the onset of surface pitting. This pitting is associated with the initiation and development of fatigue cracks, in either a ball or roller, due to the repeated nominal compressive load over the instantaneous contact area between the moving ball or roller and race, and is characterized by the sudden removal of surface material. The proceedings of a symposium on the subject have been published [346], and Scott [347] has reviewed factors affecting the rolling contact fatigue resistance of ball-bearing steels.

Two types of testing machine are commonly used for evaluating the fatigue characteristics of balls and rollers. One, in which an upper ball, held in a driven chuck, causes three lower balls to rotate in a race is often referred to as a four-ball machine. The other type consists of a roller or disc loaded between two rollers or cylinders of larger diameter, one of which is driven by an electric motor. A device, sensitive to vibration, is attached to both types of machine, which stops the machine automatically when pitting occurs. Contact stresses are usually expressed as elastic Hertzian stresses. In the four-ball test, both rolling and sliding motions occur in the contact area and, except for very light loads, a lubricant is necessary to prevent scuffing. On the other hand, if only pure rolling occurs in the roller rig, the presence of a lubricant may cause pitting to occur at a lower contact load than when a comparable test is carried out dry. For example, it was found that the susceptibility to pitting of both low- and high-carbon rail-steel test rollers driven by a large diameter roller was increased by the presence of a lubricant [348].

The four-ball machine is often used to compare the performance of different lubricants and ball materials; this is normally done on the basis of the times to onset of pitting of balls of different materials tested in different lubricants but at the same contact load and rotational speed. Because the scatter in the times to pitting of balls of the same material under nominally identical testing conditions is large, the 50 per cent probability life (§ 6.13) is usually estimated from 20 to 30 tests. For a given ball steel there is a trend towards longer life with increasing viscosity of mineral oils of the same type [349], but the presence of water in the oil is detrimental, although this can be countered by the addition of suitable additives [350]. Ball-bearings need to be made of high-strength steels in order to avoid gross plastic deformation in the contact areas, and their lives in a four-ball test are found to increase as their hardness increases [351]. However, as discussed in § 3.2, although a harder steel will require a higher range of resolved shear stress to initiate a surface crack, the fatigue limit of certain high-strength steels may be determined by the size, shape, and distribution of inherent defects, in which case the fatigue strength of the steel can only be increased by reducing the severity of the defects. Not unexpectedly, therefore, vacuum-melted steel balls exhibit longer lives in a four-ball test than conventionally melted steel balls. It has also been suggested [352] that manganese sulphide can reduce the severity of oxide inclusions.

Failure of a ball may result from either a surface or a sub-surface crack. The maximum Hertzian shear stress occurs just below the free surface, and sub-surface cracking is almost certainly associated with the presence of a hard non-metallic inclusion situated in this region. It has been found [353] that the propagation of surface cracks, initiated at the edges of the contact pressure area, seem to be controlled by the nature of the lubricant and the environment. These surface cracks spread into the material in two ways: they can either spread initially at an acute angle to the rolling direction and then change direction to spread parallel to the surface, detaching surface material when they intersect another surface crack, or they can spread deep into the material, so causing complete fracture. Pressurized fluid entering a crack increases its growth rate (§ 6.5), and propagation of cracks under lubricated conditions is therefore more rapid. Indeed, it has been suggested [354] that the life of a ball-bearing depends on the time to nucleate a crack, the crack propagation stage being so rapid that, if a test were stopped before pitting or flaking had occurred, no cracks would be found. However, a recent investigation [355], using specimens of both commercial electric-arc-melted and vacuum-melted steel, showed that the statistical distribution of lives in both cases fell into two distinct groups. It was suggested that, in the longer-life group, failure was governed by the initiation of microcracks at non-metallic inclusions while, in the shorter-life group, the dominant failure mechanism was the growth of cracks to final failure. As in conventional fatigue tests, whether or not failure occurs from the surface or from a sub-surface defect will depend on stress level, the strength of the material, and the size, shape, and nature of the inherent defects, with the difference that in a rolling contact test the maximum Hertzian shear stress occurs below the surface. At high load levels, it is possible that both surface and sub-surface cracking may occur, the joining together of these cracks accelerating complete failure.

The stress distribution in the contact area is somewhat simpler in the roller test than in the four-ball test because a ball tends to spin as well as roll and slide [356]. Using a roller machine [357] in which test rollers of various steels (tensile strengths ranging from 650 MN m^{-2} to 2100 MN m^{-2}) were run against an oil-lubricated case-hardened steel disc, the contact-stress–endurance curve was determined for each steel. It was found that the magnitude of the critical Hertzian contact stress, analogous to the fatigue limit in a conventional fatigue test, was roughly equal to the tensile strength of the steel. In another investigation [356], an attempt was made to correlate results of lubricated roller contact fatigue tests. The contact stress at the fatigue limit was expressed as the ratio of the maximum Hertzian stress P_0 to the shear yield stress of the material K, estimated from the hardness. It was found that the fatigue limit of each test series was close to $P_0/K = 2$. It had been shown [358] that, if $P_0/K \leqslant 4$, the deformation of an elastic–plastic material would be expected to reach elastic conditions in the contact area after the first few cycles. Thus, if no further plastic deformation occurred in the contact area, the fatigue limit value of $P_0/K = 2$ would seem unexpectedly low. However, this factor of 2 between the expected and actual fatigue limits is similar to that by which the fatigue limit of a cylinder subjected to a pulsating internal pressure is reduced below that of the cylinder material (see § 6.5). In the case of cylinders penetration of surface irregularities or incipient surface cracks by the cyclically pressurized oil causes the discrepancy; the cyclically pressurized oil film over the contact area between the rollers appears to act in an analogous manner. Similarly, some roller tests [348] gave a fatigue limit, when a lubricant was present, of $P_0/K \approx 2$, whereas rollers tested dry were able to withstand P_0/K values of about 4 for 40 million cycles without any sign of pitting. The introduction of a lubricant after this endurance caused pitting to occur in less than an additional half a million cycles.

6.12. Methods of rapidly estimating the fatigue limit of a material

Many attempts have been made to devise testing techniques which supposedly enable an estimate of the fatigue limit of a material to be made from a few tests of short endurance, although the subject attracted more attention in the early days of fatigue testing than it does at the present time. For example, just over 20 per cent of the total number of pages in Gough's [359] book on fatigue, published in 1924, were devoted to the subject; a review of later work has been made [360].

In most quick tests a specimen is subjected to a continuously increasing alternating stress, an estimation of the fatigue limit being based on either the value of the breaking stress or the measurement of some physical quantity during the progressive loading, such as the specimen deflection or temperature, which when plotted against the corresponding stress is found to deviate from linearity at some critical value of the stress.

Much of the early work was concerned with tests of the latter type. In

1910, progressive loading reversed direct stress tests were carried out [361] on various steels showing that initially there was a linear relationship between the cyclic deflection and corresponding stress level, the stress level at which this relationship departed from linearity agreeing closely with the conventional fatigue limit. Tests were also carried out at a given alternating stress but applying a progressively increasing tensile mean stress. Plotting extension of the specimen against mean stress, the graph was observed to deviate from

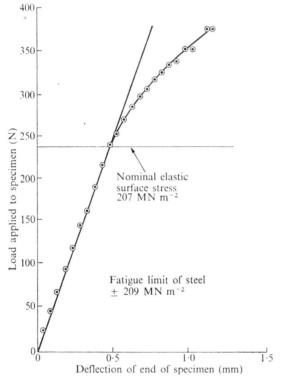

FIG. 6.34. Dynamic load–deflection curve obtained from a mild steel rotating bending test

linearity at a certain mean stress. This agreed well with the mean stress which it was necessary to apply in a series of conventional fatigue tests, in order that the resulting fatigue limit was equal to the alternating stress applied in the progressive loading test.

Many similar tests [359, 362] have since been carried out, usually in rotating bending, the deflection of the end of the specimen being measured as the bending moment is increased progressively. An example of a load–deflection curve obtained from a progressive loading rotating bending test on a mild steel specimen is shown on Fig. 6.34; the nominal elastic surface stress at the point of departure from linearity is seen to agree well with the conventional plain fatigue limit. Gough [359] compared the values of the fatigue limits of 40 materials estimated from progressively loaded rotating bending tests with the corresponding conventional values. The agreement was good for wrought ferrous materials but was less satisfactory for non-ferrous materials, especially the stronger aluminium alloys.

A calorimetric method was developed [363] for measuring the rate of heat evolution from a cylindrical bar subjected to progressively increasing completely reversed cyclic torsional stresses. A more or less well-marked discontinuity appeared when a particular stress level was reached which, for steels, agreed reasonably well with the conventional torsional fatigue limit. Other similar tests [359] also showed good agreement for steels but agreement was less satisfactory for other materials. Measurement [364] of the increase in temperature of steel specimens tested in reversed bending, in which the bending moment was progressively increased, showed that the temperature rise (measured by thermocouples) varied linearly initially with the maximum fibre stress, the maximum fibre stress at which departure from linearity occurred agreeing well with the conventional fatigue limit. In fact, for the 40 different steels tested, the average error between the two corresponding values was only about 2 per cent. Thompson and Wadsworth [365] plotted the limiting stress at departure from linearity on temperature rise versus stress diagrams against the conventional fatigue limit, for about 70 ferrous alloys, and found that there was good correlation between the two values. However, data for non-ferrous materials particularly the stronger aluminium alloys, was much less satisfactory.

It has also been found [366] that magnetic and eddy current losses in a cyclically stressed steel bar changed markedly when the fatigue limit stress was exceeded.

A technique has been used, termed the Dilastrain method [367], which consists of cyclically stressing a number of bars of a given material at different stress levels, on either side of an estimated value of the expected fatigue limit, for between 50 000 cycles and 100 000 cycles, and then measuring their coefficient of linear expansion. It was found that, on plotting the coefficient of expansion against the prior stress level, the former attained a minimum value at a particular stress level which correlated well with the conventional fatigue limit of the material. Good correlation was claimed between the estimated and conventional fatigue limits obtained for steels, brasses, and aluminium alloys.

Another suggestion [368] was that 5 or 6 specimens be cyclically stressed at stress levels on either side of a guessed fatigue limit, a test being stopped after 2×10^6 cycles and the tensile strengths of the specimens determined. The tensile strength of a fatigue specimen was then plotted against the corresponding value of the applied cyclic stress, that of any specimen breaking prior to 2×10^6 cycles being taken as zero. Based on the argument that coaxing effects

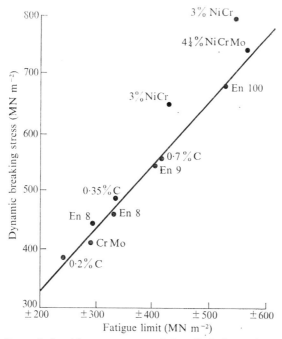

FIG. 6.35. Dynamic breaking stress versus fatigue limit for various steels. (Taken from McKeown [369].)

produced by stress levels less than the fatigue limit become more marked as the stress level approaches the fatigue limit and thus cause a progressive increase in tensile strength, whereas surface cracks initiated at stress levels above the fatigue limit cause a decrease in tensile strength, the fatigue limit of the material was taken as the stress corresponding to the maximum ordinate of the curve. Values obtained from steel specimens agreed well with the corresponding conventional fatigue limits, but the agreement was poor for the stronger aluminium alloys.

Recent work on rapid methods has generally been concerned with measurement of the breaking load. For example, progressive-loading rotating bending tests were carried out [369] in which the bending moment was increased at a constant rate until a specimen fractured, the stress at fracture being termed the dynamic breaking stress. It was found that the dynamic breaking stresses of alloys of a given base metal (that is, steels, lead alloys, copper alloys, magnesium alloys, and aluminium alloys) obtained at a constant loading rate for each group of alloys (chosen so that no specimen broke in less than half a million cycles) varied linearly with the corresponding conventional fatigue limits. The results on various steels are shown on Fig. 6.35; the corresponding data on copper alloys showed a similar correlation, but that on the other alloys exhibited a greater degree of scatter.

Prot [370] carried out progressive-loading rotating bending tests on a batch of specimens of a given material, each specimen being loaded to fracture at a different loading rate. He found that the dynamic breaking stress varied linearly with the square root of the corresponding loading rate and that, in the case of steel specimens, the stress ordinate corresponding to zero loading rate agreed well with the conventional fatigue limit. Subsequent workers have reported differing degrees of agreement between the conventional fatigue limit and that estimated from Prot tests. For example, good agreement was found for an SAE 4340 steel [371] and for 3 other steels [372]. However, there was much less satisfactory agreement in the case of an aluminium alloy [372]. Alternative methods of plotting the results of Prot tests have been suggested in an attempt to improve the degree of correlation. For example, it was found from Prot tests on mild steel, aluminium alloy, and brass [373] that the best over-all agreement between estimated and conventional fatigue limits was obtained by plotting the dynamic breaking stress against the loading rate raised to the power one quarter. Values between 0·28 and 0·40 have been suggested elsewhere [374]. However, other results [375] on steels, aluminium alloys, and titanium showed that, in general, the standard Prot plot gave estimated fatigue limits agreeing to within 10 per cent of the conventional fatigue limits. The use of modified plots employing loading rate exponents other than one-half did not give significantly better correlation.

The Prot test has been analysed [376] by assuming that the S/N curve for the material under test could be represented by the equation ($\pm$ signs omitted)

$$N = C(S - S_F)^{-m},$$

where N is the number of cycles, S is the alternating stress, S_F is the fatigue limit, and C and m are material constants. In a Prot test

$$dS/dN = R,$$

where R is the rate of stress increase and is a constant in a given test. It was assumed that the linear cumulative-damage law (§ 6.2.2) was applicable and that stresses below the fatigue limit did not contribute to failure, that is,

$$\sum \frac{dN}{N} = 1.$$

Substituting $dN = dS/R$ gives

$$\int_{S_F}^{S_B} \frac{dS}{R} \frac{(S - S_F)^m}{C} = 1,$$

where S_B is the dynamic breaking stress in the Prot test. Integrating gives

$$\left[\frac{(S-S_F)^{m+1}}{RC(m+1)}\right]_{S_F}^{S_B} = 1.$$

Therefore

$$S_B = S_F + C_1 R^{1/(1+m)},$$

where

$$C_1 = \{C(m+1)\}^{1/(1+m)}.$$

If m is put equal to unity

$$S_B = S_F + C_1 R^{\frac{1}{2}},$$

and hence if S_B varies linearly with $R^{\frac{1}{2}}$, the value of S_B at $R = 0$ will equal S_F, the plain fatigue limit. An analysis of the Prot test based on a non-linear damage law has also been made [377].

Another well-known method is that of Locati [378, 379]. Three assumed S/N curves with different fatigue limits are plotted. A single specimen is then subjected to blocks of cycles of gradually increasing stress amplitude, each block consisting of the same number of cycles and having the same stress increment, commencing from a stress amplitude slightly less than the lowest assumed fatigue limit. Results are then computed of the accumulated damage n/N for each stress level, up to failure, using each assumed S/N curve. Plotting the values of $\sum (n/N)$ against assumed fatigue limits and assuming that Miner's rule $\sum (n/N) = 1$ is valid, the 'correct' fatigue limit can be interpolated. It is immediately obvious that the method is sensitive to the choice of slopes of the assumed S/N curves; indeed, Gurney [379] has stated, in a discussion of the application of the method to welded-joint specimens, that the range of fatigue strengths produced by variations of choice of slope or variations of $\sum (n/N)$ from 0·5 to 2·0 is so great as to render the method of no practical value.

Empirical methods have been proposed for relating the plain fatigue limit to the experimentally determined stress corresponding to a given short endurance [380], or to the tensile strength, together with two experimentally determined points on the S/N curve [381]. Agreement with conventionally determined fatigue limits to within 5–8 per cent and 8–18 per cent, respectively, has been obtained [382].

There is little doubt that, irrespective of the method or technique employed to conduct a rapid fatigue limit determination, the best agreement between estimated and conventional fatigue limits occurs with mild and similar wrought steels in which the onset of plastic deformation occurs in an abrupt manner. Although the fatigue limit of a steel may be less than its static yield stress (for example, a steel of 460 MN m^{-2} tensile strength may have a static upper yield stress of 295 MN m^{-2} and a plain fatigue limit of $\pm$230 MN m^{-2}), cyclic stressing at or near the fatigue limit causes the upper yield to disappear so that, on loading statically after cyclic stressing, the elastic limit is nearer to the dynamic elastic limit or fatigue limit than to the original static yield stress. This is the reason why rapid tests involving the measurement of some physical quantity which reflects the onset of plastic deformation in a progressively loaded fatigue specimen (for example, direct measurement of specimen deflection or temperature) give stress values which agree well with the conventional fatigue limit. However, for materials in which the onset of plastic deformation in a static test is less well defined, correlations are much less satisfactory. In addition, the results of short-time tests on the high-strength precipitation and age-hardening aluminium alloys, in which the fatigue limit is well below the 0·1 per cent proof stress and whose relatively poor fatigue properties are due to the production of locally softened regions by over-ageing, can hardly be expected to correlate with the fatigue strength at long endurances. In those progressive-loading tests in which the value of the breaking stress is used to estimate the fatigue limit, the faster the loading rate the higher will be the dynamic breaking stress, and the slower the loading rate the nearer will the dynamic breaking stress approach the true fatigue limit. It is doubtful, however, in the case of steels having tensile strengths up to about 1200 MN m^{-2}, whether the correlation between the dynamic breaking stress and fatigue limit is any better than that between the tensile strength and the fatigue limit. Moreover, slight changes in surface finish and condition are known to affect the fatigue limit, especially with the harder materials, whereas it is doubtful whether these changes would be detected in a rapid test. However, in the case of stronger steels and other materials in which fatigue failure is initiated at an inherent defect, the dynamic failure stress will be a more reliable guide than tensile strength because, as in a conventional fatigue test, the failure stress will depend on the initiation of a crack at a defect.

Analysis of the Prot test in terms of the linear damage law is reasonable because, as the stress is always increasing, no compressive residual stresses are induced into the material ahead of a developing crack. In a progressive-loading test on a strain-ageing material, coaxing effects (§ 2.3.4) occurring as the stress is increased slowly tend to cause overestimation of the fatigue limit.

Rapid methods of test, in general, provide an estimate of the fatigue limit only; they give no indication of the shape of the S/N curve except in the case of the Prot test where, if the assumed equation for the S/N curve is correct, the values of the coefficients in the equation can be deduced and hence the S/N curve determined.

In conclusion, it would seem that, with the accumulation of fatigue data on a wide range of materials, the availability of large numbers of modern high-speed fatigue testing machines, and the need to have at least some indication of the shape of the S/N curve as well as the plain fatigue limit, the necessity to devise a rapid method of determining the fatigue limit of a material is not of the same importance today as it was thirty or forty years ago.

6.13. Statistical analysis of fatigue test results

6.13.1. Introduction

By its very nature, fatigue is a random process, and the consequent scatter of results, even in carefully controlled experiments, complicates both the analysis of experimental data and its subsequent application to practical problems. Thus, for example, the determination of an S/N curve involves subjective judgements when fitting the curve to the individual test points. Statistical methods provide a rational approach to this type of problem, but do not of themselves either avoid the need for subjective judgement at some stage or increase the amount of information present in a given set of data. Statistical theory also provides information on the most efficient use of a limited number of test-specimens and the number of test-specimens required to give a specified degree of confidence in the test results.

It is in the field of components and structures testing in which few actual components or structures can be fatigue tested that the estimation of a realistic service life for a given probability of failure needs to be assessed from statistical considerations. The adoption of statistical methods of testing and analysis provides, in this case, a means of making quantitative estimates of the expected service performance and of assessing the reliability of the estimates [383]. This is particularly important in the case of aircraft structures, and details of the methods used are given in the *Royal Aeronautical Society Data Sheets* [243]. The calculation of failure probabilities of a structural component, carried out rigorously, requires a large number of known quantities and relationships and a great deal of calculation; at the present time drastic simplifying assumptions have to be made [384]. Consequently, although statistical results often provide a qualitative guide, quantitative calculations have to be restricted to relatively simple situations. Calculations become particularly difficult when variable amplitude and random loadings are involved. A more rigorous treatment of the underlying statistical calculations is given in the various references cited. In any calculation, care must be taken to ensure that the statistical model used is realistic; this is often neglected in the literature, with confusing results.

It is worth reiterating at this point that the fatigue characteristics of a metallic material vary from specimen to specimen and from batch of material to batch of material, because the material itself is not a homogeneous continuum and thus, while a microcrack is developing to the macrocrack stage, variations in microstructure affect the rate of development of the microcrack. Once a microcrack has reached the stage at which it can grow as a macrocrack and, provided the material contains no gross inherent defects, a crack can be considered as growing in a homogeneous continuum, and differences between specimens and different batches of the same material become of less importance.

As mentioned in Appendix 6, experience enables a sensible estimate to be made of the number of specimens needed to determine the fatigue limit of a batch of specimens, which can be considered as effectively the fatigue limit of the batch of material from which the specimens were cut. There are few cases when the life of a plain specimen at a given cyclic stress is required for practical purposes because very few instances arise when such data can be translated directly to an actual component.

6.13.2. *Applications to S/N curves*

If a number of nominally identical fatigue specimens are tested at the same stress amplitude and the lives tabulated, a histogram may be plotted by dividing the lives into groups of a fixed interval distributed about the mean value. Of course, it is assumed that, in testing different specimens at the same stress amplitude, every care is taken to ensure that the testing conditions are as near identical as possible. Calculations of the change in life that might be expected from small variations in nominal testing conditions show [385, 386] that scatter cannot be accounted for by expected differences inherent in the experimental techniques used in testing the specimens. If a large enough number of specimens are tested, the interval width may be made sufficiently small for the histogram to be represented by a smooth curve $y = f(N)$. One function that has been found to give an adequate fit to certain data is the Gaussian or Normal distribution curve

$$p(S) = \frac{1}{\sigma(2\pi)^{\frac{1}{2}}} \exp\left(\frac{-S^2}{2\sigma^2}\right),$$

where S is the variable involved, $p(S)$ is the probability density, and σ is the root mean square value for all values of S, usually called the standard deviation; this is a measure of the width of the scatter band. Although the life distribution curve does not conform to a Gaussian distribution, it has been shown that, in many cases, the logarithm of the life distribution is a good approximation to a Gaussian distribution [387]. Large numbers of specimens are sometimes tested in attempts to find the precise form of the probability density function in given circumstances [388, 389]; some typical results are shown in Fig. 6.36.

If the log life distribution of this batch and all similar batches that could be machined from the entire population of the particular material used was indeed Normal, then the mean and standard deviation obtained from one batch would define the life distribution of the whole population. However, because the log life distribution does not conform precisely to a Normal distribution, only estimates of the probability that any specimen of the population will reach a stipulated life can be made from the mean and standard deviation determined experimentally from one batch of specimens, and this with only a certain level of confidence. The basic concept of statistics is that a group of one or more specimens is merely a sample taken from a large body or population. Such a sample is considered to be just one of a number of samples that could be tested. The results obtained from tests on a random sample from the population can be used to estimate the characteristics of the whole population or to measure the reliability of the estimates. The values of the parameters of

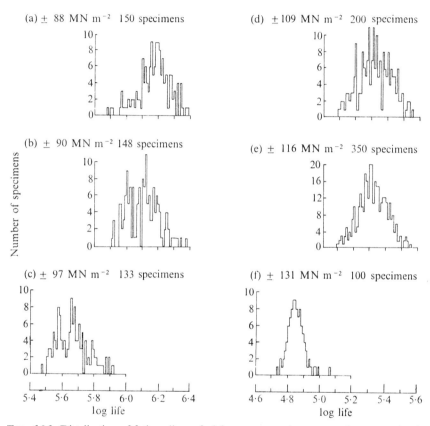

FIG. 6.36. Distribution of fatigue lives of plain copper specimens at various stress levels. (Taken from Korbacher [389].)

the population can only be estimated from tests on the sample; to obtain exact values would require the whole population to be tested. These estimates of the behaviour of the population from tests on a sample, and the confidence that can be placed in them, are the essence of statistical analysis [384, 390–2]. If batches of specimens of a particular material are tested at different stress levels, S/N curves for different probabilities of failure can be drawn; 50 per cent probability corresponds to the median, that is, the middlemost life, and is the conventional S/N curve. These curves have been referred to as P–S–N

curves [393]. These again apply only to the sample tested, and a life distribution must be assumed to estimate the probability of survival, at a given stress level, of any specimen taken from the entire population. Although these estimates may be made assuming that the logarithm of the life (at a given stress level) conforms to a Normal distribution, this may lead to errors if predictions are made at the extreme limits of the distribution, that is, at either very high or very low probabilities of failure [388].

A life distribution function, supposedly giving better correlation with experimental data than the log Normal distribution, has been proposed by Weibull [393],

$$f(N) = \frac{b}{N_a - N_0}\left(\frac{N - N_0}{N_a - N_0}\right)^{b-1} \exp\left\{-\left(\frac{N - N_0}{N_a - N_0}\right)^b\right\}$$

where N_0, N_a, and b are constants determined from the experimental data. The cumulative distribution function corresponding to the Weibull distribution function for the fraction of the batch of specimens which fail prior to N is [390, 393]

$$F(N) = 1 - \exp\left\{-\left(\frac{N - N_0}{N_a - N_0}\right)^b\right\},$$

which allows a simple graphical method to fit the distribution and hence to estimate the unknowns b, N_0, and N_a. Because this relationship has three unknowns it might be expected to give a better fit to the experimental data than the log Normal distribution which has only two, that is,

$$f(x) = \frac{1}{\sigma(2\pi)^{\frac{1}{2}}} \exp\left\{-\frac{1}{2}\left(\frac{x - \mu}{\sigma}\right)\right\}^2,$$

where $x = \log N$ and μ and σ are the log mean life and log standard deviation respectively.

Scatter in endurance increases as the fatigue limit is approached, as shown schematically in Fig. 6.37. There is a greater scatter in the lives of a batch of specimens tested at a stress level greater than their fatigue limit than in the stress levels necessary to cause failure in a given endurance. For example, although a difference of 10 to 1 in the lives of specimens tested at a given stress amplitude near the fatigue limit is not uncommon, a variation in the fatigue limits of different batches would certainly be less than 2 to 1; in fact, it would be unusual for the ratio of the highest to the lowest fatigue limits obtained from the different batches to be as high as $1\frac{1}{4}$.

Although it is a simple matter to obtain data from which it is possible to estimate the probability that the life of a specimen reaches a certain value (this merely requires the lives of a batch of specimens to be determined at the required stress level), it is not possible to obtain data in so simple a manner from which to estimate the probability that a certain stress level will give failure in a given number of cycles. This arises because it is impossible to subject each specimen of a batch to differing stress levels which will result in each specimen having the stipulated life.

Smooth S/N curves can usually be drawn without difficulty through a few test points. This is due to the high expectancy that, with a small number of test results, a large percentage will fall fairly close to the most probable values [383]. Thus for probabilities of failure between 0·25 and 0·75, appearance of continuity in results is not unexpected but, in practice, the designer is concerned with probabilities outside the band 0·05 and 0·95. For example,

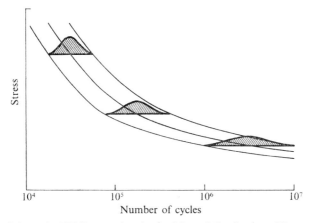

FIG. 6.37. Schematic S/N diagram showing log Normal distribution of lives at various stress levels.

if it was desirable to keep the probability of failure low, the probability of survival R should be 0·95 for easily removable parts and 0·99 or closer to unity for parts whose failure would be catastrophic. In order to predict the lives of any but simple parts which can be tested in large numbers, extrapolation from the observable central range towards the significant tails of some distribution function is the only realistic procedure. Within the central range no valid distinction can be made between the various probability functions, differences becoming significant only outside the range $0·1 < R < 0·9$.

It is often necessary to know whether some procedure has resulted in a significant improvement in fatigue life at a given stress level. If the distribution is assumed to be Normal (or log Normal), standard statistical methods [390, 392] can be applied to determine whether observed differences can reasonably be ascribed to the scatter associated with fatigue, or if a worthwhile improvement has been achieved. For example, statistical tests have shown that bevelling the ends of a particular type of glued lap joint was not worth while [308]; they have been used to show that compressive loads usually have a significant effect on fatigue crack growth rates [384].

6.13.3. Combined distributions

Scatter in the lives of specimens tested at a given stress amplitude is associated with the development of a surface microcrack to the macrocrack stage. Thus, scatter will be greater in plain specimens than in sharply notched specimens, because in plain specimens, a greater proportion of the total life is spent in developing a microcrack to the macrocrack stage. The variation in microcrack development rates is due to local changes in microstructure; thus, scatter will tend to be greater in plain specimens of complex metallic

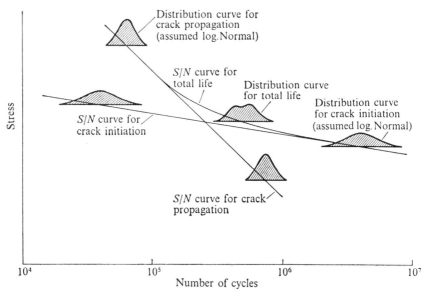

FIG. 6.38. Schematic diagram showing the S/N diagram for a combination of S/N curves for crack initiation and crack propagation.

alloys than in simple alloys or pure metals. It will also be sensitive to the condition of the surface [383].

Because the total life of a plain specimen consists of two stages, microcrack development and macrocrack propagation, the distribution of lives of plain specimens is an additive distribution made up from the distributions associated with the two stages; even if these are log Normal, the final distribution will probably not be log normal, and may be bimodal (for example, Fig. 6.36(c)). Data such as that shown in Fig. 6.36 must therefore be interpreted in this light. At high stress levels, the number of cycles to initiate a crack is negligible, so that the S/N curve shows the relatively narrow scatter in life associated with crack propagation. At low stress levels, the number of cycles to propagate the crack is negligible, so that the S/N curve shows the wide scatter in life associated with crack initiation. At intermediate stresses, crack initiation and crack propagation are of roughly equal importance, and the resultant additive distribution may show the bimodal form often associated with the presence of two different mechanisms. Thus the data can be interpreted schematically as shown in Fig. 6.38; it is not possible to separate an additive distribution into its components without prior knowledge of the components [394].

In testing structures, it is often found that one fracture mode predominates at high stresses and another at low stresses. For instance, in the testing of

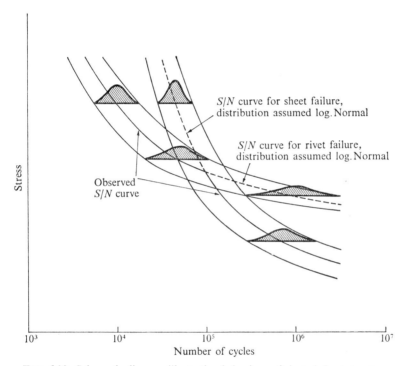

FIG. 6.39. Schematic diagram illustrating behaviour of riveted sheet structures.

riveted sheet structures, rivet failure is associated with high stresses and sheet failure with low stresses [395], as shown schematically in Fig. 6.39, where the underlying distributions are assumed log Normal. At stress levels where the scatter bands do not overlap, failure is entirely by the mode corresponding to the shorter life. In the vicinity of the crossover point where the scatter bands overlap, a proportion of the specimens will survive to fail by the mode corresponding to a longer life. As only a proportion survive to fail by the longer-life mode, the two distributions corresponding to the two modes are not statistically independent, and the longer-life mode is a conditional distribution [394]. Therefore the resulting combined distribution is skewed (Fig. 6.39) rather than being the bimodal (two-humped) distribution associated with the combination of two statistically independent processes. The over-all S/N curve has a discontinuity at the crossover point.

Similar discontinuities are sometimes observed in tests on notched specimens [396, 397]; an example is shown in Fig. 6.40. The position of the hump depends on notch severity and test frequency, and appears to be associated with metallurgical instability. At long endurances, some change takes place in the material, so that the over-all S/N curve is a combination of S/N curves for the material in two different states.

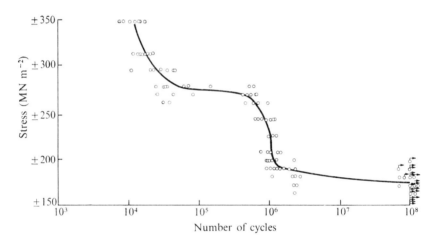

Fig. 6.40. S/N curve for 2024-T4 aluminium alloy notched specimens, $K_t = 1.5$, tested at 200 Hz. (Taken from Finney [397].)

6.13.4. Test methods based on statistical theory

It has been argued [398] that, before a fatigue test is carried out, the applied stress is known and the life unknown, whereas after the test, the life is known and thus the stress is the independent variable. This statement, although true from a statistical viewpoint, is not true physically; it is the rate at which a microcrack develops, not the stress, which is the variable. However, because tests cannot be conducted so as to permit a number of specimens to be broken at the same fixed number of cycles, it is not possible to determine directly either the mean value or the standard deviation of the stress to cause failure in a fixed number of cycles. In an attempt to determine these parameters various testing procedures have been suggested.

In the staircase method, the first specimen of a batch (the more specimens, the more reliable the estimates; in general, at least 25 specimens should be tested) is subjected to an estimated value of stress which it is hoped will result in the specimen having the stipulated life. If prior failure occurs, the stress applied to the second specimen is reduced by a particular stress increment, whereas if the life of the first specimen reaches the stipulated endurance without breaking, the stress on the second specimen is increased by the same increment. The stress applied to the third specimen is then increased or decreased by the same stress increment, depending on whether the life of the second specimen is greater or less than the stipulated life. This procedure is repeated for the complete batch of specimens. The smaller the stress increment used, the greater the reliability of the results. The results are analysed [390, 399] in terms of the less frequent event, that is, failures or runouts, because this prevents an ill-chosen starting point affecting the results. In other words, taking the number of less frequent events is equivalent to beginning the staircase at the test immediately prior to the change from a break to a non-break or vice versa. If $i = 0$ be assigned to the lowest stress level S_0 at which the less frequent event occurs, $i = 1$ be assigned to the stress level $S_0 + d$, d is the stress increment, N_i is the number of less frequent events at the corresponding stress levels S_0, S_1, etc, and N is the total number of less frequent events, then the estimated mean fatigue strength m (at the stipulated life) is given by

$$m = S_0 + d\left(\frac{\sum_i iN_i}{N} \pm \frac{1}{2}\right),$$

where the positive sign applies if the less frequent is a runout and the negative sign if it is a break. The estimated standard deviation σ is given by

$$\sigma = 1\cdot62d\left(\frac{N\sum_i i^2 N - \left(\sum_i iN_i\right)^2}{N^2}\right) + 0\cdot029.$$

In a probit method [390, 392], groups of specimens are tested at different stress levels distributed about the stress level which it is estimated will give the required life, a test being stopped if the specimen is unbroken when its endurance exceeds the required life. The percentage of failures at each stress level is plotted against stress level on normal probability paper which is scaled so that the normal probability curve plots as a straight line. The best line (usually an S-shaped curve) is then drawn through the points; the mean fatigue strength (at the stipulated life) of the sample is the stress corresponding to 50 per cent failures. To obtain significant results, about 20 specimens should be tested at at least five different stress levels. The standard deviation of the sample and statistically derived terms relating to the population at other probabilities can be estimated [400, 401]. The staircase method is actually a particular example of a probit method.

An S/N curve obtained by testing each specimen at a different stress level and then drawing the best curve through the results has a survival probability of only 50 per cent. A testing procedure which enables an S/N curve having a

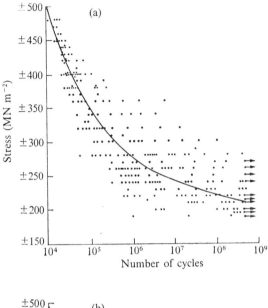

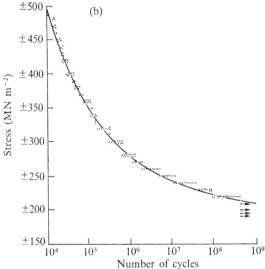

FIG. 6.41. Analysis of fatigue data by regrouping method. (a) Experimental results of fatigue tests on aluminium alloys. (b) The experimental data rearranged. For clarity all points from original diagram have not been plotted. (Taken from Gatto [403].)

higher survival probability to be drawn has been proposed [402]. The procedure is based on the fact that if a number, say 4, of nominally identical specimens are tested simultaneously at the same stress level in nominally identical machines, the weakest specimen will fail first. Groups of specimens are tested at different stress levels; as soon as one specimen in any group breaks, the rest of the tests in that group are stopped and the life corresponding to the applied stress taken as that of the broken specimen. The S/N curve obtained by plotting these points has the survival probability $p = (\frac{1}{2})^{1/n}$. Thus, if an S/N curve is obtained by testing 4 specimens at each stress level, it can be expected that 84 per cent of the material sampled will possess fatigue strengths lying above the curve compared to 50 per cent if only one specimen is tested at each stress level. At least 13 specimens would need to be tested at each stress level to estimate the 95 per cent survival curve.

A method of plotting the results of fatigue tests which enables the mean S/N curve to be drawn without any mathematical treatment has been suggested [403]. The values of applied stresses and endurances obtained from a series of fatigue tests are re-grouped into descending and ascending order, respectively, irrespective of the actual corresponding values obtained on each specimen. The two series are recombined in the order obtained to give new pairs of stress and endurance. The highest stress now corresponds to the lowest life and the lowest stress to the longest life. If these pairs are plotted as an S/N curve, the points are now more numerous in the middle of the scatter zone. An example of this re-grouping technique applied to a series of tests on aluminium alloy specimens is shown on Fig. 6.41. The efficiency of the method was stated to be proportional to the number of stress levels at which tests are carried out and to the number of specimens tested. It must be pointed out that there is no physical justification for the process described. It is based on the assumption that the mean-stress–endurance curve is a monotonically decreasing function and the fact that least scatter of stress–endurance pairs will therefore result from rearranging the stress and endurance values in descending–ascending order as described. The physical significance of individual stress and endurance values is suppressed completely.

6.14. Fabricated materials

It is not appropriate to deal extensively, in a book on metal fatigue, with the fatigue strength of fabricated non-metallic materials, particularly since it is difficult not to become involved with the fatigue strength of complete components and design considerations. Nevertheless, some general comments may be made. Glass-fibre reinforced plastics are being used increasingly in stressed applications in engineering designs because of their high strength/weight ratio, their corrosion resistance, and the relative ease with which they can be produced in complex shapes. The more recent carbon-fibre reinforced plastics additionally contribute high stiffness to weight properties.

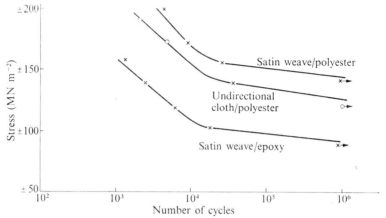

FIG. 6.42. *S/N* curves for 3 glass fibre reinforced plastics, zero mean load, 8 Hz. (Taken from Carswell [407].)

Figs. 6.42 and 6.43 show typical *S/N* curves for glass-fibre and carbon-fibre reinforced composite specimens. The fatigue properties of such materials have been discussed extensively elsewhere [244, 404–8]. Although the materials show a fatigue effect, they do not initiate a crack by cyclic slip processes as in metals; it seems probable that some sort of defect needs to be present to act as a crack starter. Indeed, in most non-metallic materials, the life under cyclic loading is merely the number of cycles required to propagate the crack from some initial defect.

The strength of a composite material is a function of the intrinsic strength of the fibres, the interfacial bond between fibres and matrix, and the shear strength of the matrix, and depends on whether the filaments are continuous or discontinuous. It was shown in § 5.9.6 that inserting strong fine

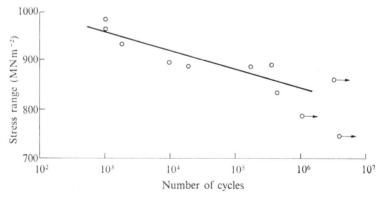

FIG. 6.43. *S/N* curve for carbon-fibre reinforced polyester-resin test-pieces, 0·70 fibre weight fraction, *R* = 0. (Taken from Owen and Morris [408].)

wire filaments into an aluminium alloy retarded the rate of growth of a fatigue crack. Therefore, the property of toughness (that is, the ability to resist the growth of a crack) can be introduced into a composite material, since the progress of a crack is known effectively to be blocked when a weak perpendicular interface is presented to its path. In fact, failure of fibre-reinforced resin composites occurs not only by the progress of a crack transverse to the principal tensile stress but also by longitudinal delamination or local crazing of the matrix. This results in a mean-stress/alternating-stress diagram which is notably more symmetric about the alternating stress axis than that of metals [407].

Other fabricated materials such as sintered metal powders [409, 410] or concrete [411–13] may also exhibit an S/N curve similar to that of wrought metals but, again, fatigue failure occurs as a result of a crack growing from an inherent flaw.

6.15. Components and structures

Unfortunately, from the designer's viewpoint, the number of variables to be considered when designing a component or structure to withstand cyclic loadings is large. The fatigue strength (at a given endurance) of all materials of engineering interest under all possible combinations of stress systems, surface finish, surface condition, heat-treatment, temperature, environment, and frequency of stress application are not and never will be available; therefore the designer must estimate the fatigue performance of his design from whatever data he has to hand. Moreover, it has been shown that the plain fatigue properties of a material provide him with only a very rough guide to the fatigue performance of a monolithic component, and have little relevance in the case of fabricated structures. Even in the case of a component of uniform cross-section, the designer can only estimate its fatigue performance if:

(1) the plain fatigue strength of the material in the required size and condition is known, with a sufficient background of information to indicate the variation in performance that is likely to occur between one component and another;

(2) the precise dynamic stresses to be withstood in service are known; this is often not the case because dynamic stresses may be induced by factors unknown to the designer, for example, vibration of nearby plant or exceptional operating conditions;

(3) the dynamic stresses involved are of constant amplitude or, if not, the designer has sufficient background data on the behaviour of the material under loading spectra similar to those to which he expects his component will be subjected in service;

(4) the effect of the operating environment on the fatigue strength of the material is known; it has been shown that small changes in environment, particularly if slightly corrosive, may have a marked effect on the fatigue behaviour.

Thus, even in the simplest design problem, difficulties arise which cannot be readily resolved. In addition, very few components are of uniform shape; most contain discontinuities of one sort or another. Indeed, of all fatigue failures which occur in practice, most result from fatigue cracks originating at some sort of discontinuity, and lack of attention to detail design in these regions is the greatest single factor responsible for the failures. The use of a general safety margin on the static strength of a material to guard against the effect of unknown high local stresses and unknown loading conditions may be a satisfactory procedure when the design has to withstand only static loads, but is quite unsuitable when cyclic loading is involved. For example, it has been stated [414] that, in ductile materials, local static stresses are usually unimportant because regions which become overstressed merely yield, with the result that the stress becomes more uniformly distributed. However, when the loading varies periodically, yield can affect only the mean value of the local stresses, and inevitably the material is called upon to sustain the full range of stress to which any local discontinuities give rise. For this reason, the merit of any design of a structure subjected to dynamic loadings depends to a great extent on the skill of the designer in avoiding unnecessary concentrations of stress. Numerous investigators with wide experience of service failures [415–18] have made the point that the fatigue failure of a large number of components could have been prevented by the application of long established and quite elementary principles and by attention to detail design, particularly the elimination of sharp corners and the avoidance of fretting. Some examples of failed components in which fatigue cracks have originated at points of stress concentration are shown in Fig. 6.44.

Most experienced designers are fully aware that violent changes in cross-section and constructional details giving rise to fretting should be avoided and, of course, many successful designs of very complicated machinery are produced. Only too often, however, it is found that, if failure does occur, the over-all functional demands have been adequately met but a whole catastrophe results from inattention to a detail not apparently of immediate concern with the functional performance of the complete unit.

However, it should be pointed out that, even when a component has been adequately designed, it may fail in service (without any reflection on the designer) because of unsatisfactory manufacturing procedures, for example, machining marks left on a highly stressed component and well-proportioned transition radii shown on the drawing not appearing on the finished article. In addition, subsequent inspection is often related only to dimensions and functionability, and therefore may allow a component to pass into service without serious consideration being given to the possibility of its fatigue strength being reduced by apparently minor discrepancies. However, it must be noted that [419], because the fatigue strengths of built-up structures or complex components are markedly less than that of plain polished specimens of comparable material, unintentional stress-raisers such as scratches or machining marks may not have such a detrimental effect on such components.

The problems of detail design become of greater importance the stronger the materials used, especially if the additional cost of the stronger material can only be justified by using the material efficiently. For example, the growth characteristics of a fatigue crack in carbon and low-alloy steels are independent of the static strength of the steel, that is, they are the same in a high-strength steel as in a common mild steel. Thus, a mild steel component may be badly designed in that it may contain very abrupt changes in cross-section (that is, no elastic stress analysis has been attempted, nominal stresses merely being restricted to some low level which from experience is known to lead to a safe design), but because the general design stress is so low, any fatigue cracks which initiate at sharp radii during the service life of the component do not grow to cause catastrophic failure. If these cracks remain undetected throughout the life of the component, the designer will justifiably consider his design a good one and could then draw the conclusion that, in mild steel at any rate, the presence of sharp corners has no serious deleterious effect. However, if the component is now to be upgraded to carry, say, twice the previous working loads and space does not permit an increase in size, simply making the same shaped component from a steel having a tensile strength (and therefore plain fatigue limit) twice that of the original mild steel will not necessarily lead to a safe design. This is because any cracks which now form at a sharp corner are subjected to a doubled nominal stress level, and they may well grow to cause catastrophic failure, since the crack propagation characteristics of the stronger steel are no better than those of mild steel. The only way to ensure that the part will not break irrespective of the number of times that the loading is applied during its service life is to carry out a complete elastic stress analysis and to ensure that the working stresses at any local discontinuity do not exceed the plain fatigue limit of the material.

Of course, in many instances, it is not feasible to carry out a complete elastic stress analysis, although the advent of the modern high-speed digital computer enables complex structural analysis problems, previously considered virtually insoluble, to be readily handled, provided that the expense can be justified. The stress analysis, however, merely translates applied loads into local stresses; this in itself will not allow for the possibility of fatigue cracks forming in regions of fretting or for the benefits deriving from the introduction of high residual compressive stresses in critical regions by surface-rolling, case-hardening, or shot-peening. Again, even with an accurate stress analysis, there still remains the problems of extrapolating the behaviour of a large fabricated structure from fatigue data obtained on small test-pieces and of predicting the behaviour of the component or structure under the varying amplitude stress conditions almost certainly met in service, using data obtained from simple constant amplitude fatigue tests. Thus, an unequivocal assessment of the likely service behaviour of a component or structure can generally only be obtained by subjecting it to a fatigue test in which the applied cyclic loads are as close a simulation as possible of the expected service loading spectrum.

Although small components can often be tested in standard fatigue machines, larger structural members can only be tested by applying loads at appropriate points through suitable loading actuators. The whole approach to simulating service fatigue loadings however, has been revolutionized in recent years by the widespread availability of sophisticated high-response servo-hydraulic loading actuators, as has been discussed in § 6.2. Thus, arguments about whether random service stress histories could be satisfactorily simulated by multi-level block programme loading have been swept away in a sense since, if necessary, virtually any service loading waveform can be simulated exactly. Similarly, the accuracy of simulation made possible by modern equipment has greatly increased the economic feasibility of laboratory testing compared to field trials. Nevertheless, full-scale testing is expensive, and its use must be justified. Where safety is a prime consideration, testing in some form is essential; in the aircraft engineering field, for example, the testing of full-scale structures is accepted as a necessity. In other situations, the decision on what full-scale testing, if any, is justifiable is largely an economic one.

Much of the early work on structural fatigue testing was in the aircraft engineering field, and indeed, the need for full-scale testing is still more readily accepted in this area than in some other areas of mechanical engineering. Many examples of aircraft structural testing have been mentioned in § 6.2, often involving gust or manoeuvre load spectra. A less obvious cause of fatigue loading is the cyclic hoop stress created in the skin of an aircraft fuselage by repeated pressurizing of the cabin; that this type of loading can be critical was illustrated by the early Comet failures, in which fatigue cracks were initiated at the corners of the cabin windows. Pressure cabins are now cyclically pressurized in order to check and prove designs [420]. Because aircraft structures must be highly stressed to overcome weight problems, it is essential that any fatigue cracks which do form do not cause immediate catastrophic failure. The design must be such that a crack which forms and is just too small to be detected at one routine inspection, will grow sufficiently slowly to avoid catastrophic failure before the next inspection. The philosophy of aircraft structural design from the viewpoint of fatigue failure has been extensively discussed elsewhere [421–4]. In addition to structural elements, the necessity for high reliability has led to extensive testing of aero-engine components such as the discs and blades of gas-turbine engines [425]. Indeed, the whole concept of full-scale testing in the aircraft field has led to extremely complex and sophisticated tests being required, such as those carried out on Concorde prototypes [426].

Although the fatigue behaviour of aircraft structures and components has been studied in probably more detail than that of any other general engineering product, nevertheless, considerable effort has been extended in fatigue testing of non-aircraft products and has often led to the development of novel testing rigs. Fatigue tests on full-size railway wagon axles [315–18, 427] and other types of railway equipment [272, 428, 429] have been described, and fatigue problems in shipbuilding have been discussed [430].

Several investigators [431, 432] have carried out fatigue tests on internal combustion engine crankshafts; Forrest [213] has collected such data. Fatigue failure of a crankshaft usually originates at either an oil-hole in a journal (due to cyclic torsional loads) or at the transition radius between a journal and its web (due to cyclic bending loads). If possible, oil-holes should be drilled normal to the journal surface and the lip radiused; the torsional fatigue strength of journals with holes breaking the surface at an inclined angle decreases as the angle deviates from the normal position [433]. When failure occurs from the fillet, the fatigue strength can be increased by cold-rolling the fillet [431]. The fatigue strength of plain journal bearings has been studied by several investigators [434–6]. Cracks can form on the surface of plain bearings due to resolved cyclic shear stresses but, because of the nature of the stressing, a crack will penetrate only a certain distance in from the surface before turning and developing parallel to the surface until it intersects another crack. Oil, under the hydrodynamic pressure created between a journal and bearing, is able to penetrate the surface cracks, causing further deterioration of the bearing surface. Failure of a steel-backed bearing is of a gradual nature because the steel backing can retain a cracked and partially disintegrated lining for a long time after the initiation of a crack [434]; because of this support from the backing the fatigue strength of a backed bearing tends to increase as the steel backing thickness increases.

Failure of ball- and roller-bearings due to rolling contact has been discussed in § 6.11. Gear teeth can also fail on the flank by a similar mechanism; failure due to fatigue cracks initiating at the root of the tooth can occur if the root radius is too small.

Both helical [437, 438] and leaf springs are subjected to alternating stresses during service and, as a consequence, may fail due to fatigue cracking. In the former, the wire is stressed in torsion and fatigue cracks usually form on the inner surface of a coil. Fretting between the end coil and the seating may also lead to failure. Leaf springs, as used in car suspensions, usually have their surfaces in the forged and decarburized condition which, together with the fact that fretting can occur due to the relative movement between adjacent leaves, means that their fatigue limit is much less than that of the material itself. However, an acceptable fatigue strength is generally obtained by shot-peening the tension surface. The fatigue limit of helical springs can also be increased by shot-peening and to a lesser extent by scragging (overloading in the same direction as that in which the spring will be loaded in service).

A common origin of failure in a loaded rotating shaft is the root of a keyway. Keyways are used in many applications yet, surprisingly, there is little information of the fatigue strength of shafts containing keyways of different geometries. Peterson [439], however, did carry out reversed bending tests on 25 mm diameter shafts containing a 3 mm deep, 6 mm wide keyway, the keyway having either a standard square end or a 19 mm radius runout; his results are given in Table 6.39.

TABLE 6.39

| | | Fatigue limit of keyed shaft (MN m^{-2}) | |
Shaft material	Plain fatigue limit (MN m^{-2})	Square-ended keyway	Radiused keyway
Carbon steel	± 255	± 162	± 193
Nickel–chromium steel	± 400	± 193	± 250

In practice, however, load is often transferred through the key and key-way, and this results in the stress concentration at the root of the keyway increasing above that due to an unloaded keyway of similar geometry. Because the load transferred through the keyway will depend on the degree of interference between the shaft and other connecting member, the fatigue strength of a keyed connection is difficult to predict. The fatigue strength is lowest when the whole of the load is transmitted through a single key. A higher fatigue strength will be obtained by using a splined or multi-key con-nection for now the load is transferred through more than one key, and the load per key is reduced [440, 441]. However, if geometric inaccuracies allow the major part of the load to be carried through only one key or spline the advantages of the multi-key connection will be lost. If possible, it is prefer-able for the torque to be transmitted from the shaft to the pulley by means of an interference fit, thus eliminating the need for a key and keyway.

Numerous investigators [272, 277, 442–8] have studied the fatigue strength of built-up beams and structures, particularly welded structures; Gurney [270] provides a good summary. Of more recent interest, in connection with off-shore structures, is the fatigue strength of tubular welded joints of various configurations such as T-joints or K-joints [449]. The fatigue strength of such joints, often characterized by the range of punching shear stress, may be very low because of high local stresses at critical regions (the 'hot spot') along the weld at the brace–chord intersection.

Unfortunately, the cost of fatigue testing structural members is high compared to that of testing standard specimens and, therefore, the number of structural members that can be tested is usually small. The results of these few tests obviously cannot be considered representative of the behaviour of the total number of similar structural members that may have been or will be manufactured. This is particularly so in the case of built-up structures containing numerous joints, because the origin of failure may vary from structure to structure, depending on slight differences in either the fit of the bolts in the case of a bolted assembly or in the type of welding in a welded structure. A further point which must be borne in mind when assessing the expected service life of certain structural members or components from laboratory fatigue tests is the difference in frequency of load application. For example, if a gas cylinder used in aqua-lung equipment is filled, on average, three times a day, it would take 50 years to accumulate 50 000 cycles. However, its condition towards the end of this 50 years would have deteriorated, compared with its initial condition, owing to corrosion and handling. Thus, an assessment of its service behaviour cannot be based simply on the results of tests on new cylinders; some factor of safety to allow for deterioration during service life must be applied. This example will apply to many structural members such as bridges and aircraft wings, where corrosion occurring over a period of time can help in the initiation of a crack and hence result in a deterioration of the fatigue characteristics compared with those of new members.

Before the experimental stress-analysis techniques of photo-elasticity and brittle lacquers were readily available, a fatigue test (at an appropriate stress level) was a useful means of revealing points of high stress in a component and thus could be used to check a theoretical elastic stress analysis. For example, the position of the maximum elastic tensile stress in a loaded ring as a function of the angle of the loading slings has been calculated [450]; observation of the positions of crack initiation in repeated tension fatigue tests on rings for different positions of the loading slings confirmed the theoretical analysis. Other examples of fatigue tests used to check theoretical elastic analyses have been given [451].

Non-destructive methods for detecting cracks or flaws in components have become highly sophisticated in recent years and include magnetic particle methods, fluid penetration techniques, radiography, surface electrical resistance methods, and ultrasonic techniques; the latter in particular have been so refined as to detect very small cracks [452, 453]. A recent development is the monitoring of acoustic emissions, outside the audible range, which are produced when a cracked component is loaded [454]. Although a structural member or component, in general, would be replaced if found to contain a surface crack, the decision whether or not to reject a casting or forging because a small internal defect has been detected is more difficult to resolve. The relationship between crack length and alternating stress discussed in § 4.5 provides some basis for assessing whether or not to reject a part containing a surface defect but, if applied directly to the case of an internal defect which is not so severe a stress raiser as a crack, may lead to the rejection of a part which, in fact, may behave satisfactorily in service. Often, the part under consideration is a large and expensive casting or forging, and consequently the decision whether or not to reject it because of the detection of some small internal flaw is one that cannot be undertaken lightly. The engineer responsible for making the decision, in general, will be able to find little information on the fatigue strength of specimens of the particular material containing flaws of the particular type under consideration, and he can only assess the likely service behaviour of the part by consideration of the working loads, the required life, the possibility of non-destructive inspection at regular intervals, and whatever data he can find on the effect of a flaw of a similar type to that found in the part on the fatigue strength of the material.

The study of failed service members to determine the cause of failure is now a well-established practice. Often careful examination of the fracture faces (both by the naked eye and with the optical and electron microscopes), termed fractography, together with a knowledge of the working loads, enables the type of fracture to be identified [455]. If this is due to fatigue, the examination generally reveals the point where a crack has initiated and the direction in which the fatigue crack has grown. Fractography of fatigue fracture surfaces has been extensively discussed in § 5.3.

References

1. MILLER, K. J. *Nature Lond.* **213**, 317 (1967).
2. SMITH, R. W., HIRSCHBERG, M. H., and MANSON, S. S. NASA Tech. Note D-1574 (1963).
3. BENHAM, P. P. *Metall. Rev.* **3**, 203 (1958).
4. YAO, J. T. P. and MUNSE, W. H. *Weld J. Easton*, **41**, 182s (1962); University of Illinois, Civil Eng. Studies, Struct. Res. Ser. No. 248 (1962).
5. LANDGRAF, R. W. *Symposium on achievement of high fatigue resistance in metals and alloys*, p. 3. American Society for Testing Materials, Special Tech. Pub. No. 467 (1970).
6. MORROW, J. *Internal friction, damping and cyclic plasticity*, p. 45 American Society for Testing Materials, Special Tech. Pub. No. 378 (1965).
7. LOW, A. C. *International Conference on fatigue, Institution of Mechanical Engineers*, p. 206 (1956).
8. STOUT, R. D. and PENSE, A. W. *Trans. Am. Soc. Mech. Engrs., J. bas. Engng.* **87**, 269 (1965).

9. MANSON, S. S. William M. Murray Lecture. *Exp. Mech.* 5, 193 (1965).
10. PETERSON, R. E. *International Conference on fatigue, Institution of Mechanical Engineers*, p. 110 (1956).
11. COFFIN, L. F. *Trans. Am. Soc. Mech. Engrs.* **78**, 527 (1956); *Internal stresses and fatigue of metals*, p. 363. Elsevier, New York (1959).
   BALDWIN, E. E., SOKOL, G. J., and COFFIN, L. F. *Proc. Am. Soc. Test. Mater.* **57**, 567 (1957).
12. JOHANSSON, A. *Colloquium on fatigue*, p. 112. Springer-Verlag, Berlin (1956).
13. COFFIN, L. F. *International Conference on fracture, Sendai, Japan* Vol. 3, p. 1543 (1965).
14. MANSON, S. S. *Mach. Des.* **32**, 139 (1960).
15. LANGER, B. F. *Weld. J. Easton*, **37**, 411s (1958).
16. TAVERNELLI, J. F. and COFFIN, L. F. *J. bas. Engng.* **84**, 533 (1962).
17. MANSON, S. S. *Mach. Des.* **33**, 165 (1961).
18. MANSON, S. S. *J. bas. Engng.* **84**, 537 (1962).
19. KAWAMOTO, M. and TANAKA, T. *Proceedings of the 10th Japanese National Congress of applied mechanics*, p. 151 (1960).
20. HALFORD, G. R. and MORROW, J. *Proc. Am. Soc. Test. Mater.* **62**, 695 (1962).
21. MARTIN, D. E. and BRINN, J. *Proc. Am. Soc. Test Mater.* **59**, 677 (1959).
22. MARTIN, D. E. *Trans. Am. Soc. mech. Engrs., J. bas. Engng.* **87**, 850 (1965).
23. SESSLER, J. G. and WEISS, V. *Trans. Am. Soc. mech. Engrs., J. bas. Engng* **85**, 539 (1963).
24. MANSON, S. S. and HIRSCHBERG, M. H. *Fatigue; an interdisciplinary approach*, p. 133. Syracuse University Press (1964).
25. SACHS, G. *Fracturing of metals*, p. 51. American Society of Metals (1948).
26. HARDRATH, H. F., LANDERS, C. B., and UTLEY, E. C. NACA Tech. Note 3017 (1953).
27. BENHAM, P. P. *J. Inst. Metals* **89**, 328 (1961); **91**, 404 (1963).
   BENHAM, P. P. and FORD, H. *J. mech. Engng. Sci.* **3**, 119 (1961).
28. BAILEY, R. W. *International Conference on fatigue, Institution of Mechanical Engineers*, p. 201 (1956).
29. SACHS, G., GERBERICH, W. W., WEISS, V., and LATORRE, J. V. *Proc. Am. Soc. Test. Mater.* **60**, 512 (1960).
30. WEISMAN, M. H. and KAPLAN, M. H. *Proc. Am. Soc. Test. Mater.* **50**, 649 (1950).
   YUKAWA, S. and McMULLIN, J. G. *Bull. Am. Soc. Test. Mater.* No. 241, 39 (1959).
   FINCH, W. G. *Proc. Am. Soc. Test. Mater.* **52**, 759 (1952).
   SACHS, G. and SCHEVEN, G. *Proc. Am. Soc. Test. Mater.* **57**, 667 (1957).
   ILLG, W. NACA Tech. Note 3866 (1956).
   HARDRATH, H. F., LANDERS, C. B., and UTLEY, E. C. NACA Tech. Note 3017 (1953).
31. WITT, F. J. *First International Conference on structural mechanics in reactor technology, Commission of the European Communities, Brussels* Vol. G, p. 325 (1971).
32. HUFF, H. W., JOYCE, J. A., and McCLINTOCK, F. A. *Second International Conference on fracture, Brighton*, p. 83. Chapman and Hall, London (1969).

33. EDMONDSON, B., FORMBY, C. L., JUREVICS, R., and STAGG, M. S. *Second International Conference on fracture, Brighton*, p. 192, Chapman and Hall, London (1969).

34. TOPPER, T. H., WETZEL, R. M., and MORROW, J. *J. Mater.* **4**, 200 (1969).

35. WETZEL, R. M. *J. Mater.* **3**, 646 (1968).

36. RAYMOND, M. H. and COFFIN, L. F. *Trans. Am. Soc. mech. Engrs, J. bas. Engng.* **85**, 548 (1963).

37. COFFIN, L. F. *Trans. Am. Soc. mech. Engrs, J. bas. Engng.* **86**, 673 (1964).

38. HOLDEN, J. Private communication (1971).

39. MAY, A. N. *Nature, Lond.* **188**, 573 (1960).

40. PRICE, A. T. and ELDER, W. J. *J. Iron Steel Inst.* **204**, 594 (1966).

41. MARTIN, D. E. *Trans. Am. Soc. mech. Engrs., J. bas. Engng.* **83**, 565 (1961).

42. PALMGREN, A. *Z. Ver. dt. Ing.* **68**, 339 (1924).

43. MINER, M. A. *J. appl. Mech.* **12**, A159 (1945).

44. WOOD, W. A. Rep. No. 24, Institute for the study of fatigue and reliability, Columbia University, New York (1965).

45. FREUDENTHAL, A. M. *Weld. World* **6**, 184 (1968).

46. SMITH, I., HOWARD, D. M., and SMITH, F. C. NACA Tech. Note 3293 (1955).

47. LEVY, J. C. *Engineering* **179**, 724 (1955).

48. BENNETT, J. A. *Proc. Am. Soc. Test. Mater.* **46**, 693 (1946); NACA Tech. Note 992 (1945).

49. MARCO, S. M. and STARKEY, W. L. *Trans. Am. Soc. mech. Engrs.* **76**, 627 (1954).

50. GUNN, K. W. Min. of Supply, S and T Memo. No. 5/56 (1956).

51. BRUEGGEMAN, W. C., MAYER, M. and SMITH, W. H. NACA Tech. Note 983 (1945).

52. ROYLANCE, T. F. Min. of Supply, S and T Memo. No. 8/57 (1957).

53. SCHIJVE, J. and JACOBS, F. A. Nat. Aero Res. Inst., Amsterdam, Rep. No. 1982 (1955); Nat. Astro. and Aero. Res. Inst., Amsterdam, Rep. No. 24 (1960).
    PLANTEMA, F. J. *Colloquium on fatigue*, p. 218. Springer-Verlag, Berlin (1956).

54. DOLAN, T. J. and BROWN, H. F. *Proc. Am. Soc. Test. Mater.* **52**, 733 (1952).

55. CORTEN, H. T., SINCLAIR, G. M., and DOLAN, T. J. *Proc. Am. Soc. Test. Mater.* **54**, 737 (1954).
    DOLAN, T. J., RICHART, F. E., and WORK, C. G. *Proc. Am. Soc. Test. Mater.* **49**, 646 (1949).

56. ENDO, K. *Bull. Fac. Engng. Hiroshima Univ.* **7**, 171 (1958).

57. LEVY, J. C. *J. R. aeronaut. Soc.* **61**, 485 (1957).

58. RUSSELL, H. W. and WELCKER, W. A. *Proc. Am. Soc. Test. Mater.* **36**, 118 (1936).
    KOMMERS, J. B. *Proc. Am. Soc. Test. Mater* **38**, 249 (1938).
    WILLIAMS, F. S. and VIGLIONE, J. *Proc. Am. Soc. Test. Mater.* **53**, 871 (1953).
    KAWAMOTO, M. and NAKAGAWA, T. *Proceedings of the 2nd Japanese Congress on testing materials, Kyoto*, p. 1 (1959).

59. HENRY, D. L. *Trans. Am. Soc. mech. Engrs.* **77**, 913 (1955).

60. MANSON, S. S., NACHTIGALL, A. J., and FRECHE, J. C. *Proc. Am. Soc. Test. Mater.* **61,** 679 (1961).

61. MANSON, S. S., NACHTIGALL, A. J., ENSIGN, C. R., and FRECHE, J. C. *Trans. Am. Soc. mech. Engrs., J. Engng. Ind.* **87,** 25 (1965).

62. BUCH, A. *Int. J. Fracture Mech.* **5,** 366 (1969).

63. KAECHELE, L. Rand Corporation Memo. RM-3650 PR (1963).

64. SWANSON, S. R. University of Toronto, Institute of Aerophysics UTIA Rep. No. 84 (1963).

65. NEWMARK, N. M. *Fatigue and brittle fracture,* p. 197. Wiley, New York (1950).
    RICHART, F. E. and NEWMARK, N. M. *Proc. Am. Soc. Test. Mater.* **48,** 767 (1948).

66. WEBBER, D. and LEVY, J. C. Min. of Supply, S and T Memo. No. 15/58 (1958).

67. WILKINS, E. W. C. *Colloquium on fatigue,* p. 321. Springer-Verlag, Berlin (1956).

68. CORTEN, H. T. and DOLAN, T. J. *International Conference on fatigue, Institution of Mechanical Engineers,* p. 235 (1956).
    LIU, H. W. and CORTEN, H. T. NASA Tech. Note D-256 (1959); NASA Tech. Note D-647 (1960).
    SPITZER, R. and CORTEN, H. T. *Proc. Am. Soc. Test. Mater.* **61,** 719 (1961).

69. ERICKSON, W. H. and WORK, E. C. *Proc. Am. Soc. Test. Mater.* **61,** 704 (1961).

70. MARSH, K. J. Min. of Technology, NEL Rep. No. 204 (1965).

71. MARSH, K. J. Min. of Technology, NEL Rep. No. 263 (1966).

72. MARSH, K. J. and MACKINNON, J. A. *J. mech. Engng. Sci.* **10,** 48 (1968).

73. MARSH, K. J. Min. of Technology NEL Rep. No. 373 (1968).

74. FREUDENTHAL, A. M. *Symposium on acoustic fatigue,* p. 26. American Society for Testing Materials Special Pub. No. 284 (1960); *International Conference on fatigue, Institution of Mechanical Engineers,* p. 257 (1956); *Colloquium on fatigue,* p. 53. Springer-Verlag, Berlin (1956).
    FREUDENTHAL, A. M. and HELLER, R. A., *Fatigue in aircraft structures,* p. 146. Academic Press, New York (1956); Wright Air Development Corporation Tech. Rep. 58–69 (1960); *J. Aero Space Sci.* **26,** 431 (1959).

75. MAY, A. N. *Nature, Lond.* **192,** 158 (1961).

76. FULLER, J. R. *Noise Control* **7,** 11 (1961).
    MUNSE, W. H., FULLER, J. R., and PETERSEN, K. S. *Bull. Am. Rly. Engng. Ass.* **544** (1958).

77. MARSH, K. J. and MACKINNON. J. A. Min. of Technology, NEL Rep. No. 234 (1966).

78. VALLURI, S. R. Aero. Research Lab. Rep. 181, Aero. Research Lab., Wright Patterson Air Force Base, Ohio (1961); Rep. RTD-TDR-63-4021, Suppl. 1, Air Force Flight Dynamics Lab., Wright Patterson Air Force Base, Ohio (1964).

79. MARSH, K. J. *J. mech. Engng. Sci.* **7,** 138 (1965).

80. HARDRATH, H. F., UTLEY, E. C., and GUTHRIE, D. E. NASA Tech. Note D-210 (1959).

81. FISHER, W. A. P. Min. of Supply, R.A.E. Tech. Note Struct. 236 (1958).
82. NAUMANN, E. C. NASA Tech. Note D-1522 (1962); NASA Tech. Note D-1584 (1964).
    LEYBOLD, H. A. and NAUMANN, E. C. Proc. Am. Soc. Test. Mater. 63, 717 (1963).
    NAUMANN, E. C., HARDRATH, H. F., and GUTHRIE, D. E. NASA Tech. Note D-212 (1959).
83. SMITH, C. R. Proc. Soc. exp. Stress Analysis 16, 9 (1958).
84. KOWALEWSKI, K. Symposium full-scale fatigue testing of aircraft Structures, p. 60. Pergamon Press, Oxford (1961).
85. SCHIJVE, J. and BROEK, D. Aircr. Engng. 34, 314 (1962).
86. Proceedings of the Symposium on fatigue of metals under service loads, Sept. 1967. Society for Materials Science, Japan (1967).
87. PATCHING, C. A. and MANN, J. Y. Fatigue design procedures, p. 395. Pergamon Press, Oxford (1969).
88. MELCON, M. A. and McCULLOCH, A. J. Current aeronautical fatigue problems, p. 347. Pergamon Press, Oxford (1965).
89. PLANTEMA, F. J. and SCHIJVE, J. Full-scale fatigue testing of aircraft structures. Pergamon Press, Oxford (1961).
90. FOSTER, L. R. and WHALEY, R. E. NASA Tech. Note D-547 (1960).
91. WINKWORTH, W. J. Min. of Aviation, R.A.E., Tech. Note No. Struct. 274 (1959).
92. PARISH, H. E. Min. of Aviation, S and T Memo. 1/65 (1965).
93. SCHIJVE, J. and JACOBS, F. A. National Aero. and Astro. Research Inst., Amsterdam Rep. No. TN M2139 (1964).
94. YEOMANS, H. Min. of Aviation, R.A.E. Tech. Note Struct. 327 (1963).
95. SCHIJVE, J. Current aeronautical fatigue problems, p. 403. Pergamon Press, Oxford (1965).
96. PAYNE, A. O. International Conference on fatigue, Institution of Mechanical Engineers, p. 641 (1956).
97. GASSNER, E. and SCHÜTZ, W. Proceedings of 9th FISITA International Automobile Technical Congress, p. 195. (1962).
98. SCHIJVE, J. 2nd Plantema Memorial Lecture. Aeronaut. J. 74, 517 (1970).
99. TAYLOR, J. International Conference on fatigue, Institution of Mechanical Engineers, p. 650 (1956).
100. COLEMAN, T. L. Fatigue design procedures, p. 161. Pergamon Press, Oxford (1969).
101. DRYDEN, H. L., RHODE, R. V., and KUHN, P. Fatigue and fracture of metals, p. 18, Wiley, New York (1952).
102. McDOUGALL, R. L. Metal fatigue, p. 247. McGraw-Hill, New York (1959).
103. HAAS, T. Materialprüfung 2, 1 (1960).
104. RAITHBY, K. D. Fatigue of aircraft structures, p. 249. Pergamon Press, Oxford (1963).
105. MATOLCSY, M. Proceedings of the 2nd Conference on dimensioning and strength calculations, Budapest, p. 383 (1965).
106. ALDER, J. F. Br. Weld. J. 43, 501 (1964).
107. WYLY, L. T. and SCOTT, M. B. Bull. Am. Rly. Engng. Ass. No. 524 (1955).

108. TANEDA, M., KOIBUCHI, K., AKATSU, T., and FUKUWATARI, I. *Hitachi Rev.* **18**, 308 (1969).

109. TANEDA, M., KOIBUCHI, K., and MATSUKAWA, Y. *Bull. J.S.M.E.*, **14**, 534 (1971).

110. SVENSON, O. and SCHWEER, W. *Stahl Eisen* **80**, 79 (1960).

111. BRAUDE, V. I. *Russ. Engng. J.* **50**, 14 (1970).

112. SCHIJVE, J. *Symposium on fatigue of aircraft structures*, p. 193. American Society for Testing Materials Special Tech. Publ. No. 338 (1962).

113. DANFORTH, C. E. and STARKEY, W. L. *Am. Soc. mech. Engrs* Paper No. 62-WA-230 (1962).

114. GASSNER, E. Min. of Supply, R.A.E. Translation 575, 1956; *International Conference on fatigue, Institution of Mechanical Engineers*, p. 304 (1956); *Proceedings of the International Conference on fatigue in aircraft structures*, p. 178. Academic Press, London (1956).
GASSNER, E. and SCHÜTZ, W. *Full scale fatigue testing of aircraft structures*, p. 14. Pergamon Press, Oxford (1960); *Fatigue design procedures*, p. 291. Pergamon Press, Oxford (1969).

115. FREUDENTHAL, A. M. and HELLER, R. A. *J. Aero Space Sci.* **26**, 431 (1959).

116. SWANSON, S. R. *Mater. Res. Stand.* **8**, 10 (1968).

117. HEAD, A. K. and HOOKE, F. H. *International Conference on fatigue, Institution of Mechanical Engineers*, p. 301 (1956).

118. FRALICH, R. W. NASA Memo. 4/12/59L (1959); NASA Tech. Note D-663 (1961).

119. LOWCOCK, M. T. and WILLIAMS, T. R. G. University of Southampton, AASU Rep. No. 225 (1962).

120. PHILLIPS, E. P. NASA Tech. Note D-3075 (1965).

121. BOOTH, R. T. and WRIGHT, D. H. MIRA Rep. No. 1966/14 (1966).

122. NINGAIAH and SUTTON, C. W. Dept. of Supply, Australian Defence Scientific Service, Aero. Research Labs., ARL/SM—Note-335 (1968).

123. KIRKBY, W. T. and EDWARDS, P. R. *AGARD/ICAF Symposium on fatigue design procedures, Munich* (1965); Min. of Aviation, R.A.E. Tech. Rep. No. 66023 (1966).

124. WHITE, D. J. and LEWSZUK, J. *J. mech. Engng. Sci.* **11**, 598 (1969).
LEWSZUK, J. and WHITE, D. J. *Proceedings of the Conference on fatigue of welded structures*, p. 296. The Welding Institute, Cambridge (1971).

125. SUHR, R. W. *Proceedings of the Conference on fatigue of welded structures*, p. 312. The Welding Institute, Cambridge (1971).

126. KOIBUCHI, K. *Hitachi Rev.* **18**, 478 (1969).

127. LAUDERT, H., JACOBY, G. H., NOWACK, H., and WEBER, H. *Fortschr.-Ber. Ver. dt. Ing. Z* **5**, 29 (1969).

128. JACOBY, G. H. Deutsche Versuchsanstalt für Luft- und Raumfahrt EV (DVL), Rep. No. I9-IB-59 (1968).

129. JACOBY, G. H. *Proceedings of the 3rd Conference on dimensioning, Budapest*, p. 81 (1968).

130. SWANSON, S. R. Society of Automotive Engineers Paper 690050 (1969).

131. MARSH, K. J. and MORRISON, A. J. Min. of Technology, NEL Rep. No. 466 (1970).

132. MADDEN, M. B. Society of Automotive Engineers, Paper 700455 (1970); LE MENSE, R. A. and FELT, D. E. Society of Automotive Engineers, Paper 700454 (1970).

133. BARROWCLIFF, B. K. and EHLERT, R. E. Society of Automotive Engineers, Paper 680148 (1968).

134. JAECKEL, H. R. Society of Automotive Engineers, Paper 700032 (1970).

135. BEAUVAIS, R. Z. and SORENSON, G. R. Society of Automotive Engineers, Paper 825C (1964).

136. GASSNER, E. and SCHÜTZ, W. *Fatigue design procedures*, p. 291. Pergamon Press, Oxford (1969).

137. GASSNER, E. *ICAF Meeting, Stockholm (1969), Proceedings of the Technical Sessions*, ICAF Doc. No. 499, 2.2/1 (1969).

138. EDWARDS, P. R. Min. of Tech., R.A.E., Tech. Rep. No. 69237 (1969).

139. ALMEN, J. O. and BLACK, P. H. *Residual stresses and fatigue in metals*. McGraw-Hill, New York (1963).

140. FROST, N. E. *Metallurgia* **57**, 279 (1958); **62**, 85 (1960).

141. ROMUALDI, J. P. and D'APPOLONIA, E. *Proc. Am. Soc. Test. Mater.* **54**, 798 (1954).
KAUFMAN, J. G. and D'APPOLONIA, E. *Proc. Am. Soc. Test. Mater.* **55**, 999 (1955).

142. TEED, P. L. *Aeroplane* **82**, 787 (1952).

143. PATTINSON, E. J. and DUGDALE, D. S. *Metallurgia* **66**, 228 (1962).

144. TEMPLIN, R. L. Contribution to discussion, Reference [148].

145. FORREST, G. *J. Inst. Metals* **72**, 1 (1946).

146. GUNN, K. W. and MCLESTER, R. Min. of Aviation, S and T Memo, 19/59 (1959).

147. HEYWOOD, R. B. *Colloquium on fatigue*, p. 92. Springer-Verlag, Berlin (1956).

148. ROSENTHAL, D. and SINES, G. *Proc. Am. Soc. Test. Mater.* **51**, 593 (1951).

149. WOOD, W. A. *J. Inst. Metals* **91**, 193 (1963).

150. DUGDALE, D. S. *Weld. J. Easton* **24**, 455 (1959).

151. SHERRATT, F. Min. of Aviation, S and T Memo. 1/66 (1966).

152. TAKEUCHI, K. and HOMMA, T. *Sci. Rep. Res. Inst., Tohoku Univ.* **10**, 426 (1958); **11**, 48 (1959).

153. BUTZ, G. A. and LYST, J. O. *Maters. Res. Stand.* **1**, 951 (1961).

154. WATKINSON, J. F. *International Conference on fatigue, Institution of Mechanical Engineers*, p. 445 (1956).

155. COOMBS, A. G. H., SHERRATT, F. and POPE, J. A. *International Conference on fatigue, Institution of Mechanical Engineers*, p. 227 (1956).

156. BROOKMAN, J. G. and KIDDLE, L. *The failure of metals by fatigue*, p. 395. Melbourne University Press (1947).

157. MATTSON, R. L. and ROBERTS, J. G. *Internal stresses and fatigue in metals*, p. 337. Elsevier, New York (1959).

158. CAMPBELL, J. E. Rep. MCIC-71-02, Metals and Ceramics Information Center, Battelle, Columbus, Ohio (1971).

159. BERRY, W. R. Min. of Aviation, S and T Memo. 1/60 (1960).

160. GUNN, N. J. F. Min. of Aviation, R.A.E., Tech. Note Met., 296 (1958).

161. MORGAN, F. G., MORGAN, J. R., and LONGSON, J. Min. of Aviation, R.A.E. Tech. Note Struct. 317 (1962).

162. REED, E. C. and VIENS, J. A. *Trans. Am. Soc. mech. Engrs.* **82**, 76 (1960).

163. TARASOV, L. P., HYLER, W. S., and LETNER, H. R. *Proc. Am. Soc. Test. Mater.* **57**, 601 (1957).

164. LOVE, R. J. *Symposium on properties of metallic surfaces, Institute of Metals*, p. 161 (1952); *International Conference on fatigue, Institution of Mechanical Engineers*, p. 570 (1956); Motor Industries Research Assoc, Rep. No. 1950/9 (1950).

165. FUCHS, H. O. *Metal fatigue*, (Eds G. Sines and J. L. Waisman) p. 197. McGraw-Hill, New York (1959).

166. ROSENTHAL, D. *Metal fatigue*, (Eds G. Sines and J. L. Waisman) p. 170. McGraw-Hill, New York (1959).

167. WRIGHT, D. H., WILLIN, J. E., and LOVE, R. J. Motor Industries Res. Assoc. Rep. 1962/5 (1962).

168. HAMMOND, R. A. F. and WILLIAMS, C. *Metall. Rev.* **5**, 165 (1960).
WILLIAMS, C. and HAMMOND, R. A. F. ARDE Materials Division Rep. (M) 6/55, (1955); *Proc. Am. Electropl. Soc*, 195 (1959).

169. LOGAN, H. L. *Proc. Am. Soc. Test. Mater.* **50**, 699 (1950).

170. KUUN, T. C. K. *S. Afr. Mech. Engrs* **9**, 139 (1960).

171. BEERWALD, A. *Sh. Metal Inds.*, Dec. 1889 (1942).

172. ALMEN, J. O. *Prod. Engng.* **22**, 109 (1951).

173. BRENNER, A. and JENNINGS, C. W. *Plating* **35**, 1228 (1948).

174. *Metals engineering design.* American Society of Mechanical Engineers Handbook, McGraw-Hill, New York (1953).

175. WEDDEN, P. R. *Trans. Inst. Metal Finish.* **38**, 175 (1961).

176. LEA, F. C. *Proc. R. Soc.* **123**, 171 (1929).

177. JACKSON, J. S. *International Conference on fatigue, Institution of Mechanical Engineers*, p. 500 (1956).

178. SWANGER, W. H. and FRANCE, R. D. *Proc. Am. Soc. Test. Mater.* **32**, 430 (1932).

179. STARECK, J. E., SEYB, E. J. and TULEMELLO, A. C. *Plating*, **41**, 1171 (1954).
STARECK, J. E. and SEYB, E. J. *Plating* **42**, 1395 (1955).

180. BURMEISTER, R. A. and DODD, R. A. *Proc. Am. Soc. Test. Mater.* **62**, 675 (1962).

181. BROWN, M. B. Mines Branch, Canada, Res. Rep. R-23 (1958).

182. BIRCHON, D. *Metallurgia* **57**, 273 (1958).

183. STICKLEY, G. W. and HOWELL, F. M. *Proc. Am. Soc. Test. Mater.* **50**, 735 (1950).

184. STICKLEY, G. W. *Proc. Am. Soc. Test. Mater.* **60**, 577 (1960).

185. SAVAGE, E. G. and SAMPSON, E. G. Min. of Supply, R.A.E. Tech. Note Met., 216 (1955).

186. BENNET, J. A. *Proc. Am. Soc. Test. Mater.* **55**, 1015 (1955).

187. FINNEY, J. M. *Metallurgia* **60**, 93 (1959).

188. HARRIS, W. J. *Metallic fatigue.* Pergamon Press, Oxford (1961).

189. ZIMMERMAN, J. H. *Iron Age* **145**, 38 (1940); *Weld. J. Easton* **19**, 104 (1940).

190. CASE, S. L., BERRY, J. M., and GROVER, H. J. *Trans. Am. Soc. Metals* **44**, 667 (1952).
191. BECKER, M. L. and PHILLIPS, C. E. *J. Iron Steel Inst.* **133**, 427 (1936).
192. BUHLER, H. and BUCHHOLTZ, H. *Stahl Eisen*, **52**, 1331 (1933).
193. ALMEN, J. O. *American Society for Metals, Symposium on surface stressing of metals* (1946).
194. BARDGETT, W. E. *Metal Treatm.* **10**, 87 (1943).
195. CAZAUD, R. *Fatigue of metals*. Chapman and Hall, London (1953).
196. SUTTON, H. *Metal Treatm.* **2**, 89 (1936).
197. MOORE, H. F. and ALLEMAN, N. J. *Trans. Am. Soc. Steel Treat.* **13**, 405 (1928).
198. FRITH, P. H. *J. Iron Steel Inst.* **159**, 385 (1948).
199. BENHAM, P. P. *Proc. Instn. mech. Engrs* **177**, 87 (1963).
200. TAUSCHER, H. *Symposium on fatigue damage in machine parts, Prague*, p. 238 (1960).
201. WOODVINE, H. *J. Iron Steel Inst.* **13**, 197 (1924).
202. SPIEGLER, B. WEISS, B. Z., and TAUB, A. *J. Iron Steel Inst.* **202**, 509 (1964).
203. JACKSON, L. R. and POCHAPSKY, T. E. *Trans. Am. Soc. Metals* **39**, 45 (1947).
204. KENNEFORD, A. S. and ELLIS, G. C. *J. Iron Steel Inst.* **164**, 265 (1950).
205. HANKINS, G. A., BECKER, M. L., and MILLS, H. R. *J. Iron Steel Inst.* **133**, 399 (1936).
     HANKINS, G. A. and BECKER, M. L. *J. Iron Steel Inst.* **126**, 205 (1932).
206. BRICK, R. M. and PHILLIPS, A. *Trans. Am. Soc. Metals* **29**, 435 (1941).
207. NORDMARK, G. E. *J. Spacecraft Rockets* **1**, 125 (1964).
208. DINSDALE, W. O. and NEWMAN, R. P. *Br. Weld. J.* **8**, 402 (1961).
209. MORRISON, J. L. M., CROSSLAND, B., and PARRY, J. S. C., *Proc. Instn. mech. Engrs.* **170**, 697 (1956); **174**, 95 (1960); *Trans. Am. Soc. mech. Engrs., J. Engng. Ind.* **82**, 143 (1960).
210. AUSTIN, B. A. and CROSSLAND, B. *Proc. Instn. mech. Engrs.* **180**, 43 (1965–6).
     DAVIDSON, T. E., EISENSTADT, R., and REINER, A. N. *Trans. Am. Soc. Mech. Engrs., J. bas. Engng.* **85**, 555 (1963).
211. PARRY, J. S. C. *International Conference on fatigue, Institution of Mechanical Engineers*, p. 132 (1956); *Proc. Inst. mech. Engrs.* **180**, 387 (1965–6).
212. FORREST, P. G. *Fatigue of metals*. Pergamon Press, Oxford, (1962).
213. FROST, N. E. *J. Mech. Phys. Solids* **9**, 143 (1961).
214. HANNON, B. M. *Trans. Am. Soc. mech. Engrs., J. bas. Engng.* **87**, 405 (1965).
215. HASLAM, G. H. *J. Engng. Ind.* **94B**, 284 (1972).
216. UNDERWOOD, J. H. *Stress analysis and growth of cracks*, p. 59. American Society for Testing and Materials, Special Tech. Pub. 513 (1972).
217. HASLAM, G. H. *High Temp., high Press.* **1**, 705 (1969).
218. HASLAM, G. H. and JOHNSTON, A. G. *Joint NEL/AIRAPT Conference on hydrostatic extrusion, Stirling* (1973). *Institution of Mechanical Engineers* (to be published).
219. ENDO, K., OKADA, T., KOMAI, K. and KIYOTA, M. *Bull. J.S.M.E.* **15**, 1316 (1972).
220. MARSH, K. J. and HASLAM, G. H. Min. of Tech., NEL Rep. No. 381 (1969).

221. TIFFANY, C. F. and MASTERS, J. N. *Fracture toughness testing and its applications*, p. 249, American Society for Testing Materials, Special Tech. Pub. 381 (1965).
222. MORRISON, J. L. M., CROSSLAND, B., and PARRY, J. S. C. *Proc. Instn. mech. Engrs.* **174,** 95 (1960).
223. AUSTIN, B. A. and CROSSLAND, B. *Proc. Instn. mech. Engrs.*, **180,** 43 (1965–6).
224. OATES, G. and PRICE, A. T. *Conference on practical application of fracture mechanics to pressure vessel technology*, p. 209. Institution of Mechanical Engineers, London (1971).
225. MORRISON, J. L. M., CROSSLAND, B., and PARRY, J. S. C. *J. mech. Engng. Sci.* **1,** 207 (1959).
226. LANE, P. H. R. *Br. Weld. J.* **5,** 327 (1958); *International Conference on fatigue, Institution of Mechanical Engineers*, p. 687 (1956).
227. BERMAN, I. and PAI, D. H. *Weld. J.*, *Easton* **29,** 24s (1964).
228. MARKL, A. R. C. *Trans. Am. Soc. mech. Engrs.* **74,** 287 (1952).
229. KOOISTRA, L. F. *Weld. J.*, *Easton* **36,** 120s (1957).
230. EGAN, G. R. and HARRISON, J. D. *Conference on practical application of fracture mechanics to pressure vessel technology*, p. 129. Institution of Mechanical Engineers, London (1971).
231. COX, H. L. and OWEN, N. B. *Aeronaut. Q.* **12,** 1 (1961).
232. WRIGHT, K. H. R. *Proc. Instn. mech. Engrs.* 1B, 556 (1952–3); *Corros. Prev. Control* **1,** 405 (1954); **1,** 465 (1954).
TEED, P. L. *Metall. Rev.* **5,** 267 (1960).
CORNELIUS, H. *Z. Metallk.* **36,** 101 (1944).
UHLIG, H. H. *J. appl. Mech.* **21,** 401 (1954).
ALLSOP, R. T. *Metallurgia* **60,** 43 (1951); **60,** 87 (1951).
233. GODFREY, D. and BISSON, E. E. NACA Tech. Note 2180 (1950).
234. TEED, P. L. *Metall. Rev.* **5,** 267 (1960).
235. WATERHOUSE, R. B. *Proc. Instn. mech. Engrs.* **169,** 1157 (1955).
236. WARLOW-DAVIES, E. J. *Proc. Instn. mech. Engrs* **146,** 32 (1946).
237. SACHS, G. and STEFAN, P. *Trans. Am. Soc. Metals* **29,** 373 (1941).
238. LIU, H. W., CORTEN, H. T., and SINCLAIR, G. M. *Proc. Am. Soc. Test. Mater.* **57,** 623 (1957).
239. FENNER, A. J. and FIELD, J. E. *Revue Métall.*, *Paris* **55,** 475 (1958); *Trans. N.E Cst Instn. Engrs. Shipbldrs* **76,** 183 (1960).
FENNER, A. J., WRIGHT, K. H. R., and MANN, J. Y. *International Conference on fatigue, Institution of Mechanical Engineers*, p. 386 (1956)
FIELD, J. E. DSIR, NEL Rep. No. 120 (1963).
240. FIELD, J. E. and WATERS, D. M. Min. of Tech. NEL Rep. No. 275 (1967); Min. of Tech. NEL Rep. No. 340 (1968).
241. FROCHT, M. M. and HILL, H. N. *J. appl. Mech.* **62,** A5 (1940).
242. JESSOP, H. T., SNELL, C., and HOLISTER, G. S. *Aeronaut. Q.* **9,** 147 (1958); **7,** 297 (1956); **6,** 230 (1955).
243. *Royal Aeronautical Society Data Sheets.* Issued by the Royal Aeronautical Society, 4 Hamilton Place, London.
244. HEYWOOD, R. B. *Designing against fatigue.* Chapman and Hall, London (1962).

245. FENNER, A. J. and Low, A. C. DSIR, NEL Rep. No. PM96 (1952).
246. CLARKE, B. C. Min. of Aviation, R.A.E., Tech. Rep. No. 66015 (1966).
247. MITTENBERGS, A. A. and BEALL, L. G. *Proc. Am. Soc. Test. Mater.* **62**, 710 (1962).
248. LAMBERT, T. H. and BRAILEY, R. J. *Aeronaut. Q.* **13**, 275 (1962).
249. FISHER, W. A. P. and WINKWORTH, W. J. Min. of Supply, R.A.E. Rep. No. Struct. 127 (1952); Aero. Res. Council, R and M 2874, H.M.S.O. (1955).
250. HARTMAN, A. and JACOBS, F. A. Nat. Aero. and Astro. Lab., Amsterdam, NLL Rep. M1946 (1954).
251. Low, A. C. *Proc. Instn. mech. Engrs.* **172**, 821 (1958).
252. MORGAN, F. G. Min. of Aviation, R.A.E. Tech. Note Struct. 316 (1962).
253. TEMPLIN, R. L. *Proc. Am. Soc. Test. Mater.* **54**, 641 (1954).
254. HARTMAN, E. C., HOLT, M. and EATON, I. D. NACA Tech. Note 2276 (1951); NACA Tech. Note 3269 (1955).
255. SPAULDING, E. H. *Metal fatigue*, (Eds G. Sines and J. L. Waisman). p. 325. McGraw-Hill, New York (1959).
256. DERRY, L. W. and HOUSE, S. R. Min. of Aviation, S and T Memo. 4/60 (1960).
257. WILSON, W. M. and THOMAS, F. P. University of Illinois, Engineering Experimental Station Bull. No. 302 (1938).
258. HARTMAN, A. and KLAASEN, W. Nat. Aero. Res. Lab., Amsterdam, Rep. M2011 (1956).
259. WALKER, P. B. *Fatigue in metals*, p. 82. Institute of Metallurgists (1955).
260. SMITH, C. R. *Aircr. Engng.* **32**, 142 (1960).
261. JACKSON, L. R., WILSON, W. M., MOORE, H. F., and GROVER, H. J. NACA Tech. Note 1030 (1946).
262. LEWITT, C. W., CHESSON, E., and MUNSE, W. H. *Proc. Am. Soc. civ. Engrs. J. Struct. Div.* **89**, 49 (1963); *New concepts in structural joint design*. Report of Research Council on Riveted and Bolted Joints of the Engineering Foundation, Chicago (1953).
HANSEN, G. N. *Proc. Am. Soc. Civ. Engrs., J. Struct. Div.* **85**, 51 (1959).
CARTER, J. W., LENZEN, K. H., and WYLY, L. T. *Trans. Am. Soc. civ. Engrs.* **120**, 1353 (1955).
263. HANSEN, G. N. *Proc. Am. Soc. civ. Engrs., J. Struct. Div.*, **85**, 51 (1959).
264. MUNSE, W. H., WRIGHT, D. T., and NEWMARK, N. M. University of Illinois, Civil Engineering Studies Struct. Res. Ser. No. 46.
265. FISHER, W. A. P. and WINKWORTH, W. J. Min. of Supply, R.A.E. Rep. Struct. 121 (1952).
266. DIVINE, J. R., CHESSON, E. and MUNSE, W. H. Department of Civil Engineering, Illinois University, Project 2M-96 (1966).
267. BIRKEMOE, P. C., MEINHEIT, D. F. and MUNSE, W. H. *Proc. Am. Soc. civ. Engrs. J. Struct. Div.* **95**, 2011 (1969).
268. KELSEY, S. and SPOONER, J. B. *Aircr. Engng.* **30**, 56 (1958).
269. TOMLINSON, J. E. and WOOD, J. L. *Br. Weld. J.* **7**, 250 (1960).
270. GURNEY, T. R. *Fatigue of welded structures*. Cambridge University Press (1968).

271. RICHARDS, K. G. *Fatigue strength of welded structures.* Welding Institute, Cambridge (1969).
272. *Fatigue of welded structures Conference, Welding Institute, London* (1971).
273. British Standards Institute. BS 153: 1958, Part 3B, *Stresses.* Part 4, *Design and Construction.*
274. GURNEY, T. R. *Br. Weld. J.* **7,** 569 (1960).
275. YEN, B. T. and MUELLER, J. A. *Bull. Weld. Res. Coun.* No. 118 (1966).
276. OKADA, M. and MORIWAKI, Y. *Report on the stress criterion for fatigue fracture of welded built-up beams under bending load.* University of Osaka, Japan (1964).
277. MUNSE, W. H. and STALLMEYER, J. E. *Br. Weld. J.* **7,** 188 (1960).
278. ERKER, A. *Weld. J., Easton* **33,** 295s (1954).
279. NEWMAN, R. P. and GURNEY, T. R. *Br. Weld. J.* **6,** 569 (1959).
280. HARRIS, L. A., NORDMARK, G. E., and NEWMARK, N. M. *Weld. J., Easton* **34,** 83s (1955).
281. STALLMEYER, J. E., NORDMARK, G. E., MUNSE, W. H., and NEWMARK, N. M. University of Illinois, Struct. Res. Ser. No. 122 (1956).
    STALLMEYER, J. E. and MUNSE, W. H. *Br. Weld. J.* **7,** 281 (1960).
282. FROST, N. E. and DENTON, K. Min. of Technology, NEL Rep. No. 196 (1965).
283. NEWMAN, R. P. and GURNEY, T. R. *Br. Weld. J.* **11,** 341 (1964).
284. KOZIARSKI, J. *Weld. J., Easton* **34,** 446s (1955).
285. SELBY, K. A., STALLMEYER, J. E., and MUNSE, W. H. University of Illinois, Civil Engineering Studies, Struct. Res. Ser. No. 297 (1965).
286. SANDERS, W. W., HOADLEY, P. G., and MUNSE, W. H. *Weld. J., Easton* **40,** 529s (1961).
287. HARRISON, J. D. *Fracture,* p. 777 Chapman and Hall, London (1969).
288. OUICHIDA, H. and NISHIOKA, A. *Hitachi Rev.* **13,** 3 (1964).
289. WHITE, D. J. and LEWSZUK, J. *Proc. Instn. mech. Engrs* **185,** 339 (1970–1).
290. WHITE, D. J. *Int. J. mech. Sci.* **11,** 667 (1969).
291. MINDLIN, H. *Weld. J., Easton* **28,** 276s (1963).
292. GUNN, K. W. and McLESTER, R. *Br. Weld. J.* **7,** 201 (1960).
293. WOOD, J. L. *Br. Weld. J.* **7,** 365 (1960).
294. HARTMANN, E. C., HOLT, M., and EATON, I. D. *Weld. J. Easton* **33,** 21s (1954).
295. DINSDALE, W. O. *Br. Weld. J.* **11,** 233 (1964).
296. BREEN, J. E. and DWYER, A. S. *Bull. Am. Soc. Test. Mater.* No. 234, 60 (1958).
297. GURNEY, T. R. *Br. Weld. J.* **9,** 609 (1962); **8,** 541 (1961); **7,** 415 (1960); **10,** 526 (1963); **10,** 530 (1963).
298. GURNEY, T. R. and TREPKA, L. N. *Br. Weld. J.* **6,** 491 (1959).
299. GILDE, W. *Br. Weld. J.* **7,** 208 (1960).
300. KASSIR, M. K. and SIH, G. C. *Int. J. Fracture Mech.* **4,** 347 (1968).
301. GROVER, H. J. *Metal fatigue,* (Eds. G. Sines and J. L. Waisman). p. 307. McGraw-Hill, New York (1959).
302. WELTER, G. and CHOQUET, J. A. *Weld. J., Easton* **27,** 286s (1948); **33,** 134s (1954); **33,** 91s (1954).
    WELTER, G. *Weld. J., Easton* **28,** 414s (1949).
    GRAF, O. *Welding J., Easton* **28,** 116s (1949).

303. YOUNGER, A., GOURD, L. M., and JUBB, J. E. M. College of Aeronautics, Cranfield, Rep. Mat. No. 1 (1966).

304. FORREST, G. *J. Inst. Metals* **72**, 1 (1946).

305. WELTER, G. and CHOQUET, J. A. *Weld. J., Easton* **24**, 145s (1959); **29**, 202s (1964).

306. JACOBS, F. A. and HARTMAN, A. Nat. Aero. and Astro. Lab., Amsterdam, Rep. No. M1969 (1954).

307. ASPDEN, R. G. and FEDUSKA, W. *Weld. J., Easton* **37**, 125s (1958).

308. HAMEL, D. R., KORBACHER, G. K., and SMITH, D. M. *J. bas. Engng.* **930**, 649 (1971).

309. HANSEL, G. *Weld. J., Easton* **35**, 211s (1956).

310. PLUMTREE, A. and HOLMES, E. *J. Iron Steel Inst.* **201**, 422 (1963).

311. HIRST, G. W. C. *Trans. Instn. Engrs. Aust.* **18**, 215 (1937); *The failure of metals by fatigue*, p. 431. Melbourne University Press (1947).

312. HORGER, O. J. and MAULBETSCH, J. L. *Trans. Am. Soc. mech. Engrs, J. appl. Mech.* **58**, A91 (1936).

313. PETERSON, R. E. and WAHL, A. M. *J. appl. Mech.* **2**, A1 (1935).

314. OUICHIDA, H. *Bull. J.S.M.E.* **5**, 587 (1962).

315. HORGER, O. J. and CANTLEY, W. I. *J. appl. Mech.* **13**, A17 (1946).

316. HORGER, O. J. *International Conference on fatigue, Institution of Mechanical Engineers*, p. 352 (1956).

317. HORGER, O. J. and NEIFERT, H. R. *Fatigue and fracture of metals*, p. 108. Wiley, New York. (1952).

318. HORGER, O. J. and BUCKWALTER, T. V. *Proc. Am. Soc. Test. Mater.* **40**, 733 (1940); **41**, 682 (1941).

319. COYLE, M. B. and WATSON, S. J. *Proc. Instn. mech. Engrs.* **178**, 147 (1963–4).

320. MCALLAN, J. D. Contribution to discussion. Reference [319].

321. NISHIOKA, K. and KOMATSU, H. *Bull. J.S.M.E.* **7**, 286 (1964).

322. ARNOLD, S. H. *Mech. Engng.* **65**, 497 (1943).

323. THURSTON, R. C. A. *Trans. Am. Soc. mech. Engrs.* **73**, 1085 (1951).

324. NEUBER, H. *Theory of notch stresses*. Edwards, London (1946).

325. DURELLI, A. J., LAKE, R. L., and PHILLIPS, E. *Proceedings of the 1st U.S. National Congress of applied mechanics*, p. 309 (1952).

326. NISHIOKA, K. and HISAMITSU, N. *Trans. Am. Soc. mech. Engrs., J. appl. Mech.* **84**, 575 (1962).

327. WALKER, P. B. *J. R. aeronaut. Soc.* **62**, 395 (1958).

328. SOPWITH, D. G. *Proc. Instn. mech. Engrs.* **159**, 373 (1948).

329. GOODIER, J. N. *J. appl. Mech.* **7**, A10 (1940).

330. KAUFMANN, F. and JANICHE, W. *Z. Ver. dt. Ing.* **85**, 504 (1941).

331. BROWN, A. F. C. and McCLIMONT, W. *Engineering* **189**, 430 (1960).

332. FIELD, J. E. *Engineer* **200**, 301 (1955).

333. ANON, Min. of Aviation, S and T Memo. 36/60 (1960).

334. GROVER, H. J., GORDON, S. A., and JACKSON, L. R. *Fatigue of metals and structures*. U.S. Government Printing Office, Washington (1954).

335. BOLLENRATH, F. and CORNELIUS, H. *Werkst. Betr., München* **80**, 217 (1947).

336. DINNER, H. and FELIX, W. *Engrs. Digest* **6**, 332 (1945).

337. SHIMAMURA, S. and KANAE, Y. *J. mech. Lab. Japan, Eur. Lang. Edn.* **5**, 96 (1959).
338. SOPWITH, D. G. and FIELD, J. E. *Engineer.* **203**, 793 (1957).
339. FIELD, J. E. *Engineer* **198**, 123 (1954).
340. TAYLOR, B. *Trans. Inst. mar. Engrs.* **64**, 233 (1952).
341. BROWN, G. T. and ALLSOP, R. T. *Aircr. Prod.* July, 245 (1962).
342. ERKER, A. *International Conference on fatigue, Institution of Mechanical Engineers*, p. 290 (1956).
343. FIELD, J. E. *Engng. Desr.* Aug., 3 (1961).
344. ALMEN, J. O. *S.A.E. Trans.* **52**, 151 (1944).
345. FISHER, W. A. P., CROSS, R. H., and NORRIS, G. M. *Aircr. Engng.* **24**, 160 (1952).
346. *Symposium on fatigue in rolling contact, Institution of Mechanical Engineers* (1964).
347. SCOTT, D. Min. of Technology, NEL Rep. No. 360 (1968).
348. OLLERTON, E. and MOREY, J. W. W. *Symposium on fatigue in rolling contact, Institution of Mechanical Engineers*, p. 11 (1964).
349. SCOTT, D. *Proceedings of Conference on Lubrication and wear, Institution of Mechanical Engineers*, p. 463 (1958).
350. GRUNBERG, L., JAMIESON, D. T., and SCOTT, D. *Phil. Mag.* **8**, 1553 (1963).
351. MOYAR, G. J. University of Illinois, Department of Theoretical and Applied Mechanics, Rep. No. 565 (1958).
     CARTER, T. L., ZARETSKY, E. V., and ANDERSON, W. J. NASA Tech. Note D-270, (1960).
     ZARETSKY, E. V. and ANDERSON, W. J. *Proc. Am. Soc. Test. Mater.* **60**, 627 (1960).
352. ENEKES, S. *J. Iron Steel Inst.* **210**, 83 (1972).
353. SCOTT, D. *Symposium on fatigue in rolling contact, Institution of Mechanical Engineers*, p. 97 (1964).
354. UCHIYAMA, I., HOSHINO, A., and UENO, M. *Trans. nat. Res. Inst. Metals, Japan* **2**, 6 (1960).
355. NAGUMO, M., SUGINO, K., AOKI, K., and OKAMOTO, K. *Second International Conference on fracture, Brighton*, p. 587. Chapman and Hall, London 1969.
356. JOHNSON, K. L. *Symposium on fatigue in rolling contact, Institution of Mechanical Engineers*, p. 155 (1964).
357. CHESTERS, W. T. *Symposium on fatigue in rolling contact, Institution of Mechanical Engineers*, p. 80 (1964).
358. MERWIN, J. E. and JOHNSON, K. L. *Symposium on fatigue in rolling contact, Institution of Mechanical Engineers*, p. 145 (1964).
359. GOUGH, H. J. *Fatigue of metals.* Scott, Greenwood, and Son, London (1924).
360. VITOVEC, F. H. and LAZAN, B. J. Wright Air Development Center, Rep. No. 52–122, (1953).
361. SMITH, J. H. *J. Iron Steel Inst.* **82**, 246 (1910).
362. LEA, F. C. *Engineering* **115**, 217 (1923).
363. STROMEYER, C. E. *Proc. R. Soc.* **90**, 411 (1914).
364. MOORE, H. F. and JASPER, T. M. University of Illinois, Engineering Experimental Station, Bull. No. 142 (1924).

365. THOMPSON, N. and WADSWORTH, N. J. *Phil. Mag. Suppl.* **7**, 72 (1958).

366. CAVANAGH, P. E. *Proc. Am. Soc. Test. Mater.* **47**, 639 (1947).

367. ROSENHOLTZ, J. L. and SMITH, D. T. *Metal Prog.* **61**, 85 (1952), *Engineer* **195**, 767 (1953).

368. MOORE, H. F. and WISHART, H. B. *Proc. Am. Soc. Test. Mater.* **33**, 334 (1933).

369. MCKEOWN, J. *Metallurgia* **54**, 151 (1956); **59**, 31 (1959).

370. PROT, E. M. *C.r. hebd. Séanc. Acad. Sci., Paris* **225**, 667 (1947); *Revue, Métall., Paris* **45**, 481 (1948); **48**, 822 (1951).

371. WARD, E. J., SCHWARTZ, R. T., and SCHWARTZ, D. C. *Proc. Am. Soc. Test. Mater* **53**, 885 (1953).

372. CORTEN, H. T., DIMOFF, T., and DOLAN, T. J. *Proc. Am. Soc. Test. Mater.* **54**, 875 (1954).

373. ENOMOTO, N. *Proc. Am. Soc. Test. Mater* **55**, 903 (1955).

374. ZHUK, E. I. *Zav. Lab.* **36**, 87 (1970).

375. VITOVEC, F. H. and LAZAN, B. J. *Proc. Am. Soc. Test. Mater.* **55**, 844 (1955).

376. HIJAB, W. A. *J. appl. Mech.* **24**, 214 (1957).

377. GATTS, R. R. *J. bas. Engng.* **84**, 403 (1962).

378. LOCATI, L. *Metallurgia ital.* **9**, 241 (1955).

379. GURNEY, T. R. and CHAPMAN, G. British Welding Research Association, Rep. D7/12/61 (1962).

380. IVANOVA, V. S. *Fatigue failure of metals* (in Russian), p. 230. Metallurgizdat, Moscow (1963).

381. MEDVEDEV, S. F. *Cyclic strength of metals* (in Russian), p. 126. Mashgiz, Moscow (1961).

382. EFIMOV, A. S. and MOROZOV, B. A. *Zav. Lab.* **35**, 840 (1969).

383. FREUDENTHAL, A. M. *J. appl. Phys.* **31**, 2196 (1960).

384. BRUSSAT, T. R. *Damage tolerance in aircraft structures*, p. 122. American Society for Testing and Materials, Special Tech. Pub. No. 486 (1971).

385. EPREMIAN, E. and MEHL, R. F. NACA Tech. Note 2719 (1952).

386. MCCLINTOCK, F. A. *Colloquium on fatigue*, p. 171. Springer-Verlag, Berlin (1956).

387. SINCLAIR, G. M. and DOLAN, T. J. *Trans. Am. Soc. mech. Engrs.* **75**, 867 (1953).

388. BLOOMER, N. T. and ROYLANCE, T. F. *Aeronaut. Q.* **16**, 307 (1965).

389. KORBACHER, G. K. *Exp. Mech.* **11**, 540 (1971).

390. *Guide to fatigue testing and statistical analysis of fatigue data.* American Society for Testing Materials, Special Tech. Publ. No. 91-A (2nd edn.) (1963).

391. PETERSON, R. E. *Bull. Am. Soc. Test. Mater.* **156**, 50 (1949).
MCCLINTOCK, F. A. *Metal fatigue*, (Eds G. Sines and J. L. Waisman). p. 112. McGraw-Hill, New York (1959).
ROELOFFS, R. and GAROFALO, F. *Proc. Am. Soc. Test. Mater.* **56**, 1081 (1956).
ARMITAGE, P. H. *Metall. Rev.* No. 60 (1961).
JOHNSON, L. G. *The statistical treatment of fatigue experiments.* Elsevier, New York (1964).

392. British Standards Institute, BS 3518: 1966, Part 5, *Guide to the application of statistics.*

393. WEIBULL, W. *Fatigue testing and analysis of results.* Pergamon Press, Oxford (1961).

394. PAPOULIS, A. *Probability, random variables and stochastic processes.* McGraw-Hill, New York (1965).

395. RYMAN, R. J. *Aircr. Engng.* **34**, 34 (1962).

396. FINNEY, J. M. *J. Aust. Inst. Metals* **13**, 16 (1968).

397. FINNEY, J. M. *J. Inst. Metals* **92**, 380 (1964).

398. GATTO, F. *Métaux- Corros. Usure*, **32**, 18 (1957).

399. DIXON, W. J. and MOOD, A. M. *J. Am. stat. Ass.*, **40**, 109 (1948).

400. FINNEY, D. J. *Probit analysis.* Cambridge University Press (1952).

401. CAZAUD, R. *Rev. Métall., Paris*, **50**, 290 (1953).

402. SCHUETTE, E. H. *Proc. Am. Soc. Test. Mater.* **54**, 853 (1954).

403. GATTO, F. *Colloquium on fatigue*, p. 66. Springer-Verlag, Berlin (1956).

404. HEYWOOD, R. B. Min. of Supply, R.A.E. Tech. Note Chem. 1337 (1958).

405. BOLLER, K. H. *Mod. Plast.* **34**, 163 (1957); U.S. Forrest Products Lab. Rep. WADC, 55–389 (1956).

406. CARSWELL, W. S. and BORWICK, G. R. *Trans. Plast. Inst., Lond.* **33**, 169 (1965).

407. CARSWELL, W. S. Ph.D. Thesis, University of Strathclyde (1970).

408. OWEN, M. J. and MORRIS, S. *International Conference on carbon fibres, their composites and applications*, p. 51/1. The Plastics Institute, London (1971); *Mod. Plast.* **47**, 158 (1970).

409. GEOTZEL, C. G. and SEELIG, R. P. *Proc. Am. Soc. Test. Mater.* **40**, 746 (1940).

410. WHEATLEY, J. M. and SMITH, G. C. *Powder Metall.* **12**, 141 (1963).

411. NORDBY, G. M. *J. Am. Concrete Inst.* **55**, 191 (1958).

412. BATE, S. C. C. *Proceedings of the Symposium on strength of concrete structures*, p. 487. Cement and Concrete Association (1958).

413. GLUCKLICH, J. *International Conference on fracture, Sendai, Japan*, Vol. 3. p. 1343 (1965).

414. COX, H. L. *International Conference on fatigue, Institution of Mechanical Engineers*, p. 212 (1956).

415. COTTELL, G. A. *International Conference on fatigue, Institution of Mechanical Engineers*, p. 563 (1956).

416. *Prevention of the failure of metals under repeated stress.* Battelle Memorial Institute, Wiley, New York (1941).

417. *Mechanical failures of metals in service.* National Bureau of Standards, U.S. Dept. of Commerce, Circular No. 550 (1954).

418. Conference on safety and failure of components, University of Sussex, 1969. *Proc. Inst. mech. Engrs.*, **184** (3B) (1969–70).

419. HARTMANN, E. C. *International Conference on fatigue, Institutions of Mechanical Engineers*, p. 195 (1956).

420. ATKINSON, R. J., WINKWORTH, W. J., and NORRIS, G. M. Min. of Aviation, Aero. Res. Council, R and M No. 3248 (1962).

421. LUNDBERG, B. Aero. Res. Inst., Sweden, FFA Rep. HE206 (1947); *J. aeronaut. Sci.* **22**, 349 (1955).

422. HARPUR, N. F. *J. R. aeronaut. Soc.* **62**, 363 (1958).
    WALKER, P. B. Min. of Supply, R.A.E. Rep. No. Struct. 242 (1948).

SPAULDING, E. H. *International Conference on fatigue, Institution of Mechanical Engineers*, p. 628 (1956).

423. FREUDENTHAL, A. M. *Conference on dimensioning and strength calculations*, p. 55. Acta Technica, Budapest (1961).

424. *5th. ICAF Symposium, Melbourne* (1967); *4th ICAF Symposium, Munich* (1965).

425. OWEN, M. J. and DUDLEY, B. R. *J. Strain Anal.* **1**, 121 (1966).

426. RIPLEY, E. L. *3rd. Plantema Memorial Lecture, 6th. ICAF Symposium, Miami Beach* (1971).

427. FENNER, A. J., TAIT, J., and MORLEY, J. D.S.I.R., NEL Rep. No. 100 (1963).

428. KELLER, W. M. and MAGEE, G. M. *International Conference on fatigue, Institution of Mechanical Engineers*, p. 677 (1956).

429. TENNIKAIT, H. G. *Closed Loop* **4(2)**, 10 (1974).

430. VEDELER, G. Det. Norske Veritas, Pub. No. 32, Oslo (1962).
POOK, L. P. *Trans. N.E. Cst Instn. Engrs. Shipbldrs* **90**, 77 (1974).

431. LOVE, R. J. *International Conference on fatigue, Institution of Mechanical Engineers*, p. 571 (1956).

432. NISHIHARA, M., NAKANO, T., YAMAMOTO, S., and SATO, E. *Proceedings of the 4th Japanese Congress on testing materials*, p. 10 (1961).

433. FIELD, J. E. Min. of Technology, NEL Rep. No. 226 (1966).

434. DUCKWORTH, W. E. and WALTER, G. H. *International Conference on fatigue, Institution of Mechanical Engineers*, p. 585 (1956).
ENDO, K. and OKADA, T. *Bull. J.S.M.E.* **9**, 457 (1966) **8**, 540 (1965).

435. FORRESTER, P. G. *Engng. Mater. Des.*, **2**, 494 (1959).

436. CUTHBERTSON, J. W. *Metal fatigue*, pp. 249 and 339. Chapman and Hall, London (1959).

437. COATES, R. C. and POPE, J. A. *International Conference on fatigue, Institution of Mechanical Engineers*, p. 604 (1956).

438. FUNKE, P. and KAYSER, K. H. *Draht* **22**, 189 (1971).

439. PETERSON, R. E. *Proc. Am. Soc. Test. Mater.* **32**, 413 (1932).

440. ALLSOPP, H. C., LOVE, R. J., and ANDREW, S. MIRA Rep. No. 1959/3 (1959).

441. YOSHITAKE, H. *7th. Japanese Congress on testing materials*, p. 10 (1964).

442. HIRT, M. A., YEN, B. T. and FISHER, J. W. *J. struct. Div. Am. Soc. civ. Engrs.* **97**, 1897 (1971).

443. MUNSE, W. H. *Weld. J., Easton* **39**, 172s (1960).

444. YEN, B. T. and COOPER, P. B. *Weld. J., Easton* **28**, 261s (1963).

445. NEWMAN, R. P., GURNEY, T. R., and COATES, G. *Br. Weld. J.*, **6**, 534 (1959).

446. WHITMAN, J. G. and ALDER, J. F. *Br. Weld. J.*, **7**, 272 (1960).

447. STREBELLE, J. *Steel.* **147**, 467 (1960).

448. WECK, R. *International Conference on fatigue, Institution of Mechanical Engineering*, p. 704 (1956).
CERARDINI, C. *Weld. J., Easton* **28**, 241s (1949).

449. TOPRAC, A. A. and LOUIS, B. G. Structures Fatigue Research Laboratory, University of Texas, Tech. Rep. P 550–13 (1970).
MARSHALL, P. W. and TOPRAC, A. A. American Society of Civil Engineers, National Structural Engineering Meeting, San Francisco. Preprint 2008 (1973).

BOUWKAMP, J. G. and STEPHEN, R. M. University of California, Department of Civil Engineering, Structures and Materials Research Rep. No. 70–4 (1970).

450. GOUGH, H. J., COX, H. L., and SOPWITH, D. G. *Proc. Instn. mech. Engrs.* **128,** 253 (1934).

451. DELEIRIS, H. *International Conference on fatigue, Institution of Mechanical Engineers*, p. 118 (1956).

452. KUSENBERGER, F. N., LEONARD, B. E., BARTON, J. R., and DONALDSON, W. L. Southwest Research Inst. Rep. No. 65-0981 (1965).

453. KLIMA, S. J., LESCO, D. J., and FRECHE, J. C. NASA Tech. Memo. TMX-52109 (1965).

454. DUNEGAN, H. L. and HARRIS, D. O. *Experimental techniques in fracture mechanics* (Ed. A. S. Kobayashi), p. 38. Iowa State University Press, Iowa (1973).

455. FIELD, J. E. and SCOTT, D. *Proc. Instn mech. Engrs.* **184** (3B), 119 (1969–70).

Appendix 1: Terms used in defining the stress–strain relationships of a material

IF A cylindrical bar of perfectly elastic material is subjected to a gradually increasing uniaxial tensile load (that is, the load is applied in a direction parallel to the longitudinal axis of the bar so that the loading over a transverse section is uniform) and the longitudinal extension of the bar measured over a fixed length (the gauge length), the load–extension diagram (Fig. A1.1(a)) is linear. A diagram of similar shape is obtained from corresponding measurements of the load and the decrease in bar diameter (that is, the lateral contraction).

Stress is defined as load/original cross-sectional area and strain as change in gauge length/original gauge length. Stress–strain diagrams are derived easily for small strains. From such diagrams, values of the material constants, Young's modulus (ratio of increment of stress to corresponding increment of longitudinal strain) and Poisson's ratio (ratio of lateral to longitudinal strain increments for a given stress increment) can be obtained. These constants enable the stress and strain distributions in a component or structure, made of a perfectly elastic material, of not too intricate shape and subjected to known loadings to be calculated [1].

Engineering materials, however, are not perfectly elastic; their stress–strain diagrams are generally of the form shown in Fig. A1.1(b). The diagram is linear initially but, as the stress is increased beyond a certain value, the ratio of strain increment to stress increment becomes progressively larger. If the load is removed before the bar breaks, only the elastic component of the strain is recovered; the irrecoverable or permanent component is termed plastic strain. The experimentally determined value of the upper stress limit of the linear portion of the stress–strain diagram depends on the sensitivity of the strain measuring equipment, and it is usual for design and specification purposes to quote the stress required to cause a given amount of plastic strain. If this, for example, is taken as 0·2 per cent plastic strain, the corresponding stress is called the 0·2 per cent proof stress (see Fig. A1.1(b)). The onset of plastic deformation is sharply defined in a few materials (mild steel is a common example), the limiting upper stress point being called the upper yield stress (see Fig. A1.1(c)). The extent of the linearity between stress and strain varies with the rate of application of the load, the upper limiting stress generally increasing as the loading rate increases.

It is obvious that the stress and strain distributions in a component or structural member made of a material having a stress–strain diagram as shown in either Fig.

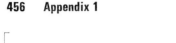

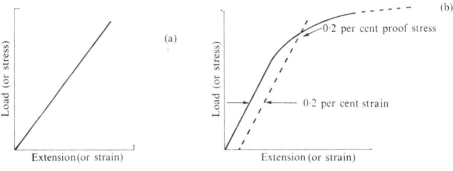

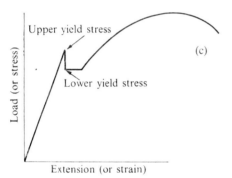

FIG. A1.1. Load–extension or stress–strain curves (diagrammatic).

A1.1(b) or Fig. A1.1(c) can only be calculated from elastic theory provided the external loads do not result in any part of the component or structure deforming plastically. In practice, a component or structure may be subjected to a loading, perhaps accidentally, such that plastic deformation does occur locally at some place. However, if the component or structure is made of a ductile material and the applied loads are of a static nature, the fact that some part of the component has deformed plastically does not necessarily mean that the component will break.

If the tensile load applied to the cylindrical bar is increased progressively until the bar breaks, an indication of the ductility of the material is given by the percentage increase in length of the original gauge length; this is termed the percentage permanent elongation. It should always be stated with reference to the original gauge length, for example, 20 per cent on a certain gauge length or, as the gauge length is normally specified as a multiple of the square root of the bar cross-sectional area A, 20 per cent on a gauge length of some factor times $\sqrt{A}$. The reason for this requirement is that bars of some materials neck down locally before fracture, and the percentage permanent elongation then varies with the original gauge length. If the cross-sectional area of the bar at fracture is calculated from the mean diameter of the fracture plane, an alternative indication of ductility is given by the reduction in cross-sectional area expressed as a percentage of the original cross-sectional area.

The tensile strength of the material is defined as the maximum load that can be applied to the bar divided by the original cross-sectional area.

References

1. See, for example, LOVE, A. E. H. *Theory of elasticity*. Cambridge University Press (1927).

   TIMOSHENKO, S. and GOODIER, J. N. *Theory of elasticity*. McGraw-Hill, New York (1951).

Appendix 2 Repeated loading and fracture

As defined in Appendix 1, the tensile strength of a material is the maximum load per unit original area that a bar of the material can support before it breaks. Now consider a bar of this material subjected to a gradually increasing tensile load, but when the stress reaches a value σ_1, where σ_1 is less than the tensile strength, let the load be reduced to zero. Let the bar be reloaded to σ_1, the load again reduced to zero and this loading sequence continued. Then, depending on the value of σ_1 and the number of times the loading cycle is repeated, the bar may eventually break.

The stress cycle 0 to σ_1 may be resolved into two components, namely a tensile mean stress $\sigma_1/2$ and an alternating stress $\pm\sigma_1/2$, that is,

$$0 \text{ to } \sigma_1 \equiv \sigma_1/2 \pm \sigma_1/2.$$

The magnitude of the stress range rather than the value of the mean stress or the maximum tensile stress in the loading cycle determines the number of times the loading cycle needs to be applied before the bar breaks or whether, indeed, it breaks at all. This is shown by the fact that a bar of the same material may eventually break if it is loaded in tension to a stress σ_2, where $\sigma_2 < \sigma_1$, the load reduced to zero, loaded in compression to a stress $-\sigma_2$, the load increased to zero, and this loading sequence continued, that is, the bar is subjected to the stress cycle $0 \pm \sigma_2$. Thus the continual application of either of the stress cycles 0 to σ_1 or $\pm\sigma_2$ may result in the bar breaking. Tests in which specimens are subjected to a continuously varying stress pattern are known as fatigue tests. The fracture of a material by the application of cyclic loadings is termed a fatigue failure.

Conditions under which fatigue failure may occur in practice vary widely. For example, a compressor blade vibrating at its natural frequency (say, 10^4–10^5 Hz), a shaft rotating at 2000 r.p.m., or a member of a railway bridge which is stressed every time a train passes or an aircraft cabin which may be pressurized only two or three times a day.

Because of the relatively simple testing techniques involved, much fatigue data has been obtained using the stress cycle having zero mean load, that is, $\pm\sigma_2$. This is the stress cycle which an element of material on the surface of a rotating cylindrical bar subjected to a constant applied bending moment undergoes.

It is possible for a smooth cylindrical metallic bar subjected to a zero mean stress loading cycle to break eventually even though the maximum tensile stress in the loading cycle is less than the yield or 0·2 per cent proof stress of the material. For example, a mild steel bar having a tensile strength of 430 MN m^{-2} and a yield stress of 280 MN m^{-2} will break eventually if subjected to a stress cycle greater than

±230 MN m^{-2}. Similarly, a solution-treated age-hardened high-strength aluminium alloy bar having a tensile strength of 500 MN m^{-2} and a 0·2 per cent proof stress of 420 MN m^{-2} will break eventually if the stress cycle applied is greater than ±185 MN m^{-2}, although in both cases it may be necessary to apply the stress cycle many millions of times.

If a cylindrical bar is loaded in tension to a stress greater than the limit of linearity on the materials stress–strain diagram (Fig. A1.1), unloaded, reloaded in compression to the same numerical stress value, the load increased to zero, and this

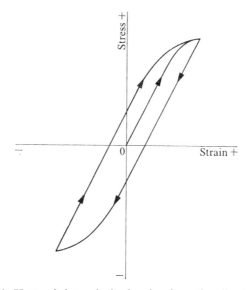

FIG. A2.1. Hysteresis loop obtained under alternating direct stress.

loading sequence continued, the diagram obtained by plotting the corresponding stress and strain values for a complete loading cycle is called a hysteresis loop. After a certain number of loading cycles, the number depending on material and the maximum stress value applied, the diagram will form a stable loop as shown in Fig. A2.1. The width of the loop is a measure of the plastic strain range occurring during the loading cycle. The limit of elasticity on the first compression loading is less than that on the initial tension loading; this phenomenon is referred to as the Bauschinger effect [1]. When hysteresis loops are plotted during the course of a fatigue test, their shape and width alters as the test proceeds (see § 6.1). Some materials may continually exhibit a hysteresis loop of finite width, indicating that the material is deforming plastically each cycle, even when subjected to alternating stresses which never result in fracture of the specimen, no matter how long the test is continued.

References

1. BAUSCHINGER, J. *Mitt. mech.-tech. Lab. Münch.* **13,** 1 (1886).

Appendix 3: Comparison of appearances of broken tensile and fatigue specimens

EVEN specimens of ductile metals broken in zero mean load fatigue tests do not generally exhibit any ductility in the region of the fracture when examined at low magnifications. The difference in over-all appearance of broken fatigue and static tensile mild steel specimens is seen in Fig. A3.1. That on the right, broken in a static tensile test, shows considerable 'necking-down' in the fracture region, whereas the fatigue specimen on the left, broken in reversed direct stress (zero mean load), shows no permanent deformation.

The appearance of the actual fracture face is also different. Fig. A3.2 shows the fracture faces of two mild steel specimens, one broken by a static tensile load and the other broken in a rotating bending fatigue test. That shown on Fig. A3.2(b) was loaded initially at a fairly high stress level, but as soon as a small crack formed the stress amplitude was reduced, so that the crack grew slowly across the specimen until the increased deflection stopped the machine. The specimen was finally broken in static bending. The outline of the initial crack is clearly visible and suggests that it originated at and grew inwards from some point on the specimen surface. The subsequent unmarked matt fracture face created by a growing fatigue crack is in complete contrast to the jagged fibrous appearance of the fracture face of the broken static tensile test specimen (Fig. A3.2(a)).

FIG. 6.44. Examples of failed components.

FIG. 6.44(a). Cracks at roots of buttress threads on large crane screw

FIG. 6.44(b). Fatigue failure of elevator winding shaft; failure from keyway terminating in inadequate fillet radius.

(c)

(d)

Fig. 6.44(c). Fatigue failure from spot weld in propeller shaft.

Fig. 6.44(d). Fatigue crack at undercut in stub axle.

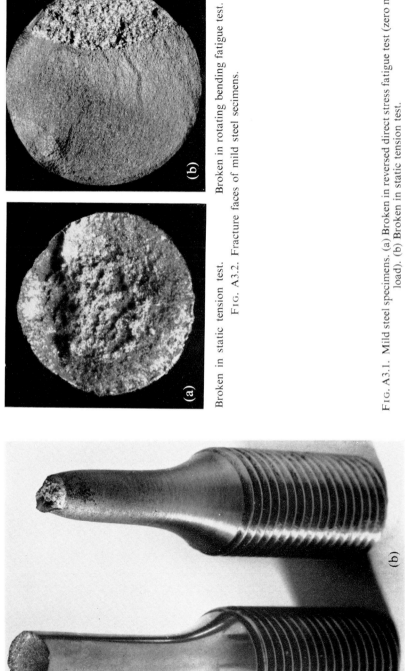

Broken in static tension test.

(a)

(b)

Broken in rotating bending fatigue test.

FIG. A3.2. Fracture faces of mild steel secimens.

FIG. A3.1. Mild steel specimens. (a) Broken in reversed direct stress fatigue test (zero mean load). (b) Broken in static tension test.

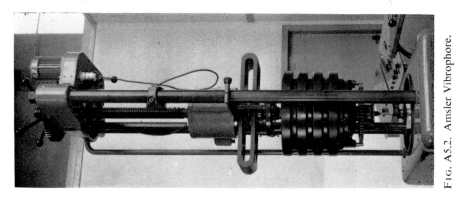

FIG. A5.2. Amsler Vibrophore.

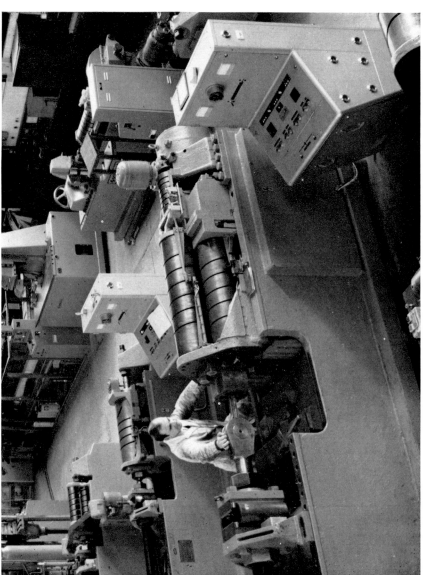

FIG. A5.1. 600 kN capacity Schenck pulser machine.

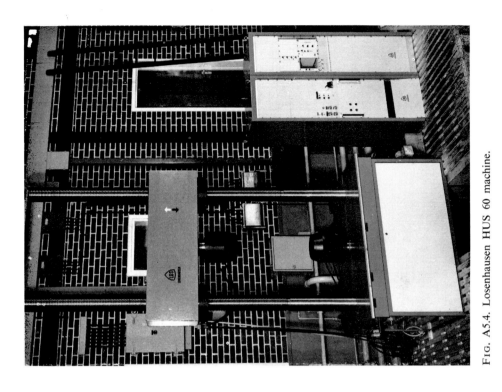

FIG. A5.4. Losenhausen HUS 60 machine.

FIG. A5.3. Losenhausen UHS 40 machine.

Fig. A5.6. Two-point loading rotating bending fatigue machine.

Fig. A5.5. MTS ±2·5 MN machine.

Appendix 4: Elementary concepts of plastic deformation in ductile metals

A METAL subjected to a stress greater than some critical value is able to deform plastically because its regular crystalline structure enables adjacent parts of a grain to glide past one another. The glide surfaces follow certain crystallographic planes, called slip planes. However, it is found that the experimental value of the stress necessary to cause slip to occur in a metallic crystal is several orders of magnitude less than the theoretical value of the stress required to slide a perfect plane of atoms over an adjacent plane. This arises because, although ideally a crystal consists of a perfectly periodic array of atoms, inherent imperfections are known to form in the crystal lattice during growth and subsequent handling. A certain type of imperfection in which a line of atoms is displaced from its position in the ideal crystal lattice is known as a dislocation. An imperfection of this type would arise if, in the slipping process, atomic planes did not slip over each other as rigid entities but, instead, slip started at one or more places in the slip plane and then spread gradually over the remainder of the plane. This is because, at any instant, there would be a boundary line on the slip plane dividing the area over which slip had already taken place from that over which it had not yet occurred [1]. This line is by definition a dislocation. There are basically two kinds of dislocation (Fig. A4.1): an edge dislocation, for which the slip direction is normal to the dislocation line, and a screw dislocation, for which the direction of slip is parallel to the dislocation line. In general, a dislocation is neither wholly edge nor screw but is of a mixed character. Because a dislocation line divides a region of the slip plane over which slip has occurred from a region in which it has not, the line must either have its ends in free surfaces or form a closed loop. Mathematical studies [2] of the resultant atomic forces of various atomic arrangements in the neighbourhood of a dislocation indicate that a stress much smaller than that required to glide one perfect plane of atoms over another is able to cause the dislocation to move through an otherwise perfect crystal. A review of the experimental evidence of dislocations has been given by Hirsch [1].

Although a metal may deform plastically at room temperature when subjected to a certain stress, the magnitude of the plastic deformation has a limiting value, and the stress must be increased to cause further plastic deformation. Because the

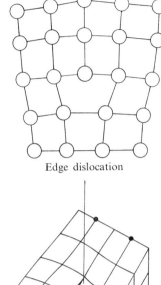

Edge dislocation

Screw dislocation

FIG. A4.1. Crystal dislocations.

stress now required to cause plastic deformation is higher than that required initi-ally, the metal is said to have strain- or work-hardened. Lucid descriptions of dislo-cation geometries and other structural imperfections such as interstitials, vacancies, stacking faults (an upset in the stacking of the planes of atoms, one on top of the other, is called a stacking fault), and twin and grain boundaries, together with discussions of how they contribute to slip processes, work-hardening, and strain-ageing (that is, strengthening due to combined strain and time effects) are given by Cottrell [2] and McLean [3].

    Grain boundaries are layers of atomic misfit, a few atoms wide, and exist as a three-dimensional network throughout a metal. Grain boundaries cause high work-hardening because slip cannot continue uninterruptedly across a grain boundary into the next grain. Individual grains in a polycrystal are stressed in an irregular way because each grain is forced to deform unevenly, owing to the fact that it is faced by different grains across each boundary and multiple slip has to take place in nearly every grain if each grain is to remain coherent with its neighbour.

Slip occurring in a plastically deformed grain having a free surface results in surface steps of varying height which, if the surface has been suitably prepared metallurgically, are visible as lines or if there are many lines close to each other as bands, when viewed under the optical microscope. It is possible to observe the gradual development of slip lines and bands on the surface of suitably prepared fatigue specimens during the course of a test.

References

1. HIRSCH, P. B. *Metall. Rev.* **4,** 101 (1959).
2. COTTRELL, A. H. *Dislocations and plastic flow in crystals.* Oxford University Press (1953); *The mechanical properties of matter.* Wiley, New York (1964).
3. McLEAN, D. *Mechanical properties of metals*, Wiley, New York (1962).

Appendix 5: Fatigue testing machines

THERE are many commercial fatigue machines available in which the fatigue properties of a material may be determined under controlled testing conditions. Their purpose is to apply repeatedly a stipulated loading cycle to a specimen and to record the number of times the loading cycle is applied before either the specimen breaks or the test is stopped.

There are two main methods of applying such a loading cycle: direct-stress tests and rotating bending tests. In the latter, the stress distribution across any cross-section of the specimen is not uniform, varying from a maximum value at the surface to zero at the neutral axis, and the mean stress is necessarily zero. Most fatigue testing is now carried out in direct-stress machines, where the stress distribution over the cross-section of the specimen is uniform, where static mean tensile or compressive loads may be applied, and where the specimen cross-section need no longer be circular.

A5.1. Conventional direct-stress machines

All such machines require control equipment to ensure that the desired stress cycle is maintained throughout a test. In some direct-stress machines the alternating stress amplitude depends on the speed of operation of the machine, and hence the testing speed cannot be varied independently of the applied load. Both mean and alternating loads must be measured by some type of dynamometer connected in series with the specimen. The dynamometer may be calibrated in terms of the alternating loads using an elastic strain-gauged weighbar; BS 3518: Part 6 lays down suitable procedures [1]. Suitable electronic equipment for recording peak-to-peak strain-gauge resistance changes has been described [2–5].

Conventional direct-stress machines fall into two classes: either the system operates at resonance or near resonance in order to reduce the power requirement, such as in the Schenck Pulser or the Amsler Vibrophore machines, or else the machine is required to provide the full power requirement directly, as in hydraulically-operated machines such as the Losenhausen UHS machine. Detailed descriptions of various types of direct-stress machine have been given by Cazaud [6] and more recently by Forrest [7] or may be obtained from the manufacturers. However, brief descriptions of the above three commonly-used machines will be given to illustrate the mode of operation.

Schenck Pulser [8]

A photograph of a 600 kN capacity machine is shown in Fig. A5.1.
Machines of various load capacities are available, those commonly used being of

20, 60, 200, 600, or 1000 kN capacity. It is possible with the 600 kN machine to apply alternating loads of up to ±300 kN, together with static tensile or compressive loads of up to 300 kN. The mean and alternating loads are applied by independent helical springs. The springs are attached at one end to the specimen holder, the other end of the alternating load springs being attached to a large mass which is excited by an out-of-balance weight driven by an electric motor via a flexible drive. The spring–mass system operates on the rising slope of the resonance curve, the load amplitude therefore depending on the speed of the driving motor (mean speed about 30 Hz). This necessitates an accurate speed control in order to maintain a constant load amplitude. The dynamometer consists of a massive elastic steel ring whose deflection is measured by a microscope. Because the machine operates at near resonance, a specimen cannot be subjected to a large cyclic deformation. However, on some models, the screw which actuates the mean load spring or springs can be driven, through a reduction gearing system, by an automatically reversing electric motor, so enabling a specimen to be subjected to large cyclic deformations, although the speed of operation is low (about 0·2–0·5 Hz).

Amsler Vibrophore [9]

Machines are available from 20 kN to 450 kN load capacity. A photograph of a 100 kN capacity Vibrophore is shown in Fig. A5.2.

The cyclic load is applied at the natural frequency of the specimen plus attachments, weights being provided which can be attached rigidly at the upper end of the specimen to vary the natural frequency of the system, so allowing tests to be carried out at different testing speeds. The speed of operation is in the range 60–300 Hz for the 100 kN capacity machine. The variable mass–specimen system is set vibrating by an electromagnet, the lower end of the specimen being connected to a much heavier mass via a dynamometer which operates a tilting mirror, giving a band of light on a transparent scale. Mean stresses are applied by a static spring arrangement.

Because of its high operating speed, the machine is particularly useful for testing specimens for long endurances, that is, 10^8 cycles or more. A 100 kN capacity machine, for example, can apply alternating loads of up to ±50 kN, the value of the mean load (either tension or compression) in any test being limited by the condition that the maximum load in the cycle must not exceed 100 kN. Care in calibration is needed when operating at very high speeds, especially if heavy specimen adapters are to be used.

Losenhausen UHS machine [10]

These Losenhausen machines are hydraulically operated, and are manufactured in sizes up to 2 MN static load capacity, the maximum permissible load range in a cyclic loading test being half the maximum static capacity. Thus a UHS 40 machine has a static load capacity of 400 kN and can apply load ranges of 0–200 kN in tension or compression or ±100 kN. (It should be noted, however, that these machines can be modified to give a cyclic load range equal to the static capacity by incorporating the more recent Losenhausen EHR control equipment.) A photograph of a UHS 40 machine is shown in Fig. A5.3.

The pulsator cylinder is connected to the working cylinder (which applies the load to the specimen) by a large bore pipe. The reciprocating movement of the pulsator piston transmits a pulsating oil pressure to the working cylinder and the force on the specimen fluctuates between two selected load limits. The speed of operation may be varied within certain limits; it is usually in the range 2–20 Hz. These machines can accommodate a larger specimen cyclic deformation than resonance and near-resonance machines.

A5.2. Servo-hydraulic machines

In recent years there has been a marked increase in the use of servo-hydraulically operated fatigue machines. In such systems the load generated by a hydraulic cylinder is measured by a strain-gauged dynamometer or load cell in series with the specimen. The signal from the load cell is amplified and compared in a differential amplifier with the desired signal obtained from the data input. The output of the differential amplifier is transmitted to a servo-valve which controls the cylinder. This system thus forms a closed-loop control circuit. The loop may also be closed from a displacement transducer or a strain gauge on the specimen instead of the load cell, if desired. The energy required is provided by a hydraulic power pack which operates at constant pressure (usually in the range 20–30 MN m^{-2}).

A major advantage of such machines is their flexibility of operation. Much larger specimen deflections are possible than can be achieved in electromechanical machines, although the operating frequencies for large strokes are necessarily low unless very large hydraulic pumping capacity is available. Thus, components involving large deflections as well as conventional stiff test-pieces can be accommodated. A more important advantage, however, is the versatility of the system regarding the input signal which can be accepted. Virtually any analogue signal, for example, from a function generator, random noise generator, magnetic tape, or punched paper tape reader, can be used as input. Thus, not only constant amplitude waveforms or simple block programmes but also random waveforms, such as service-recorded stress histories, can be accommodated. Materials specimens or components, therefore, can be subjected to much more realistic fatigue testing than is possible in conventional machines; this also applies to the use of servo-hydraulic actuators in loading-frame testing of components and structures. The major disadvantage of servo-hydraulic machines is that the power consumption is generally much higher than that of comparable conventional machines. A useful comparison of the two types of fatigue testing machine is given by Haas and Kreiskorte [11].

Machines are available in a wide range of load capacities up to ±2·5 MN from several manufacturers [8–10, 12], and are basically similar in design. Fig. A5.4 shows a Losenhausen HUS 60 machine, having a load capacity of ±500 kN, and Fig. A5.5 shows a ±2·5 MN load capacity MTS machine.

A5.3. Other machines

In the past, several machines have been designed for carrying out specialized tests; examples include the Gough–Pollard machine [13], which subjects a specimen to combined in-phase bending and torsion stresses, those which enable a tubular specimen to be subjected to both a pulsating internal oil pressure and static or alternating loads [14], the Haigh–Robertson [15] machine, which enables a rotating bending test to be carried out on a wire in the form of a collapsed strut, and plane-bending machines [16].

However, by far the most common type of machine, other than direct-stress machines, is the rotating bending machine. This provides a simple technique for determining the fatigue properties at zero mean load by applying known bending moments to rotating round bar specimens. Various types of machines which perform this function are manufactured commercially (some are described by Cazaud [6] and Forrest [7]). The load may be applied either at a single point, as in a cantilever loading machine, or by some form of two- or four-point loading. The latter methods have the advantage that they give a constant bending moment over the entire test-section of the specimen, and thus allow a specimen to have a test-section of constant diameter. The specimen used in a cantilever loading machine is usually either waisted, so that the maximum bending stress occurs at the minimum diameter, or has a tapered cross-section (which is costly to manufacture), so designed that the maximum bending stresses are constant at all cross-sections of the test-section. The stress at a point on the surface of a rotating bending specimen varies sinusoidally between numerically equal maximum tensile and compressive values (that is, assuming the specimens remain wholly elastic, $\pm \sigma = 32 \, M/\pi \, d^3$, where σ is the maximum surface stress, M is the bending moment at the cross-section under consideration, and d is the specimen diameter) once a revolution. A photograph of a two-point loading machine is shown in Fig. A5.6.

Rotating bending machines have many advantages if simple tests are required: the testing speed is varied easily, the number of stress cycles easily recorded, no additional calibration is required once no-load errors due to the weight of adapters, scale-pans, etc. have been allowed for, no control apparatus is required to keep each stress cycle identical, the specimen requires no elaborate end fittings, and the machine is easily stopped when the specimen breaks. The reliability which can be placed on the magnitude of the calculated nominal stress in a rotating bending test is governed primarily by the accuracy to which the length of the loading arm can be measured. The percentage error in stress due to all uncertainties in measurement is unlikely to exceed about $\pm 1\frac{1}{2}$ per cent.

References

1. Draft BS 3518: Part 6. *Guide to dynamic force calibration of stress testing machines* (1970).
2. BILLING, B. F. *J. R. Soc.* **58**, 508 (1954).
3. ROBERTS, M. H. *Metallurgia* **46**, 107 (1952).
4. DOWELL, T. M. *Engineering* **185**, 693 (1958).
5. HODGSON, G. Min. of Tech. NEL Rep. No. 309 (1967).
6. CAZAUD, R. *Fatigue of metals*. Chapman and Hall, London (1953).
7. FORREST, P. G. *Fatigue of metals*, Pergamon Press, Oxford (1962).
8. Agents in Britain; Carl Schenck Machinery Ltd., Acton Lane, London.
9. Agents in Britain; Hahn and Kolb (GB) Ltd., Acton, London.
10. Agents in Britain; Losenhausen (GB) Ltd., Coleshill, Birmingham.
11. HAAS, T. and KREISKORTE, H. Symposium on developments in material testing machine design, *Proc. Instn mech. Engrs.* **180** (3A) 155 (1965-6).
12. MTS Systems Corp. Agents in Britain: H. Yeomans and Co. Ltd., Gloucester.

13. Gough, H. J., Pollard, H. V., and Clenshaw, W. J. Aero. Research Council, R and M 2522 (1951).
14. Marsh, K. J. and Haslam, G. H. Min. of Tech. NEL Rep. No. 381 (1969).
15. Manufactured by Messrs. Bruntons Ltd., Musselburgh, Scotland.
16. Low, A. C. *International Conference on fatigue, Institution of Mechanical Engineers*, p. 206 (1956).

Appendix 6: Test specimens and methods for determination of plain fatigue properties

A6.1. Specimens

IT IS usual to use specimens having a circular cross-section for determining the plain fatigue properties of a material. Because fatigue failure of a homogeneous metal is always initiated at a free surface, a standard easily-reproducible surface finish, free from discontinuities in the form of machining marks and scratches, is necessary. Common practice (for example, as specified in BS 3518, *Methods of fatigue testing* (1963), which also deals with methods of machining) is to mechanically polish the finished machined specimen surface, using successively finer grades of emery papers. The polishing should be generally in a longitudinal direction, although intermediate stages may be done circumferentially in order to ensure that longitudinal scratches made by the coarser emery papers are removed. The direction of the final polishing process should always be longitudinal, using a 600 grade waterproof silicon carbide paper. This procedure enables a surface finish of from 0·05 μm to 0·1 μm centre-line average to be achieved readily (the Standard specifies 0·13 μm). Prior to polishing, the machining process should employ progressively finer cuts as the nominal size of the specimen test-section is reached. Surface work-hardening and residual stress effects due to machining, which can affect results, may be minimized by either stress-relieving in vacuum or electropolishing the finally mechanically polished specimen.

Some typical plain fatigue specimens are shown on Fig. A6.1. Direct stress specimens which are to be subjected to compressive loads must be designed to avoid buckling. The test-section must be blended into the ends of the specimen by very gradual transition radii in order to restrict failure to the test-section. The ends of the specimen and mating adapters must be designed to ensure axiality of loading and to prevent their premature failure, due, for example, to the occurrence of fretting. It is often easier to manufacture and assemble direct-stress specimens having threaded rather than button ends, but the latter provide the higher degree of axiality of loading.

In practice, few parts operate with highly polished, undamaged surfaces, and specimens of shapes other than circular cross-sections are often tested with their surfaces in a condition as near as possible to that of an actual component. When

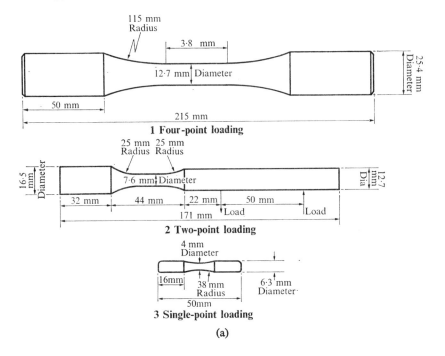

1 Four-point loading

2 Two-point loading

3 Single-point loading

(a)

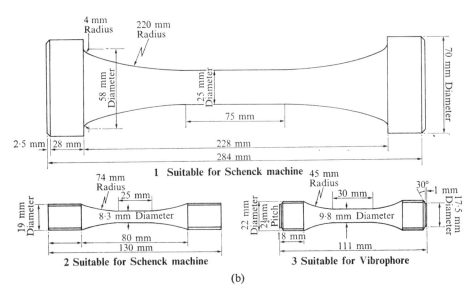

1 Suitable for Schenck machine

2 Suitable for Schenck machine

3 Suitable for Vibrophore

(b)

FIG. A6.1. Typical plain fatigue specimens. (a) Rotating bending. (b) Direct stress. Test sections of all specimens are longitudinally polished.

testing plate or strip specimens, the external corners, if left sharp, can result in a lower fatigue strength than if rounded. The specimen design will depend on whether it is supposed to simulate an actual member having a sharp external corner or whether it is required to determine the fatigue properties of a material in strip form, in which case the sharp corners should be removed.

A6.2. Testing and presentation of results

To determine the fatigue properties of a material at a given mean stress requires the production of a batch of nominally identical specimens; the number in the batch may be limited by the amount of material available, but it is usual for it to be between 6 and 12. If the fatigue properties at zero mean load are required, the specimens can be tested in either a rotating bending or a direct-stress machine; if a mean stress is to be applied, the latter type of machine is used.

An example of the setting-up procedure for a test in a rotating bending machine is as follows. The specimen should be fixed in the machine adapters so that, when the specimen is rotated, the eccentricity at any point along its length is less than about 12 μm. The testing speed is usually within the range 25–100 Hz, speeds which result in whirling obviously being avoided. After setting up correctly, the machine is started under no-load conditions, and the desired speed is attained. The required load is then applied either incrementally or continuously as quickly as possible, after which the speed is readjusted to the desired value. The bending moment required to give the stipulated nominal surface stress is calculated assuming that the specimen remains wholly elastic.

If tests are to be carried out in a direct-stress machine, the dynamometer on the machine should have been calibrated and the machine checked for alignment. The no-load reading of the dynamometer should be noted before the specimen is inserted into the machine so that a check can be kept on the magnitude of any mean loads applied to the specimen as it is being fixed into the machine. The mean load should then be adjusted to either zero or the required value, the alternating load being applied smoothly in as short a time as possible, care being taken not to overload the specimen. Recommended procedures for assembling a specimen into a machine and conducting a test are given in BS 3518 (1963).

The object of testing a batch of specimens is to determine their alternating-stress–life relationship so that the maximum alternating stress which will just not cause a specimen to break before a stipulated endurance is achieved can be estimated. If the fatigue properties at zero mean load are required, the first specimen could be tested at an alternating stress of about three-quarters of the tensile strength of the material, for example, ± 450 MN m^{-2} for a material of 600 MN m^{-2} tensile strength. The life to fracture, or endurance (that is, the number of times the stress cycle is applied), is noted and the next specimen tested at a stress, say, ± 30 MN m^{-2} lower than that applied in the previous test, and so on with subsequent specimens until a stress level is reached at which the specimen does not break after a stipulated endurance. It is usually found for steels having tensile strengths up to about 700 MN m^{-2} that, if a specimen has not broken after 10^7 cycles, it is most unlikely to break at longer endurances; tests on these materials therefore can be terminated at about 20×10^6 cycles. Tests on other materials are often continued up to about 10^8 cycles. The results are usually presented in graphical form, the stress amplitude (or its logarithm) being plotted against the logarithm of the corresponding endurance. Specimens should be tested at sufficient different stress levels to enable a line to be drawn through the experimental points. This line is referred to as an S/N curve; Fig. A6.2 shows a typical S/N curve obtained from a batch of carbon steel specimens tested in rotating bending.

The data on Fig. A6.2 show that specimens either had a life less than 5×10^6 cycles or were still unbroken when the tests were stopped at 20–40×10^6 cycles and

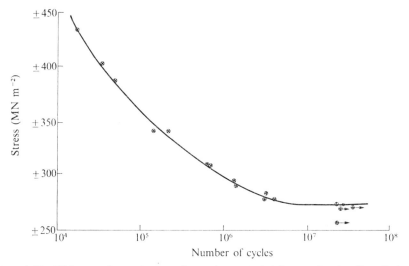

Fɪɢ. A6.2. S/N curve for carbon steel; specimens tested in rotating bending. Points having arrows attached denote specimen unbroken.

suggest that the line through the points becomes parallel to the abscissa. When this is so, the stress level corresponding to the horizontal line is called the fatigue limit; it is implied that specimens tested at stress levels less than the fatigue limit will never break no matter how many stress cycles are applied. If the finite-life portion of the S/N curve can be represented by a straight line (as, for example, the S/N curves shown in the upper diagram in Fig. A6.4) the point of intersection of this line and the horizontal line is often referred to as the 'knee'.

Not all metals give S/N curves which exhibit a definite fatigue limit, even when tests are continued to very long endurances. A typical S/N curve for a high-strength $4\frac{1}{2}\%$ Cu–aluminium alloy is shown in Fig. A6.3; failures are seen to occur at all endurances. It is usual in this case to specify the fatigue strength of the material at a given endurance, that is, specimens tested at higher stress levels will break before the stipulated life is achieved, whereas those tested at lower stress levels will be unbroken after a life of at least the stipulated value. However, the slope of an S/N curve of the form shown in Fig. A6.3 is generally small at endurances in the region of 10^8 cycles, and, provided the environment does not chemically attack the specimen surface, it is often possible to make an estimate of a stress level which, for many practical purposes, can be considered as a fatigue limit.

If a number of apparently identical specimens of the same material are tested at the same nominal stress amplitude, it is found that they do not have identical lives, the scatter in lives increasing as the stress level decreases towards the fatigue strength at long endurances. This poses the questions of what number of specimens should be tested and what method of analysing the results should be used so that the reliability of the fatigue properties can be estimated. The scatter in stress level for

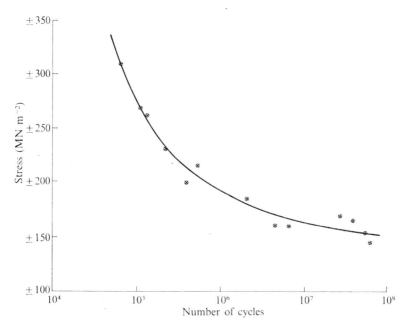

FIG. A6.3. S/N curve for high-strength aluminium alloy; specimens tested in rotating bending.

a given life, however, is much less than the scatter in life for a given stress level and, therefore, the scatter in results makes it more difficult to define the finite-life portion of an S/N curve than to define the value of the stress level at the fatigue limit or strength at long endurances. Scatter in results arises from slight variations in testing conditions (for example, exactly the same stress cannot be applied to each specimen) and slight variations in the properties of the surface layers of the material (for example, local differences in microstructure and local surface differences induced by the machining and polishing procedures).

Usually the number of specimens required to define the S/N curve for a particular material is based on previous experience of the scatter in results known to occur with materials of a similar type. For example, the results of fatigue tests on pure metals, simple alloys (for example, brass), and steels having tensile strengths up to 700 MN m^{-2} do not show a large scatter, and their S/N curves can generally be defined quite closely by testing about 10 specimens. On the other hand, the results of tests on complex alloys (for example, high-strength steel and aluminium alloys) often exhibit considerable scatter, and at least twice as many specimens may be needed to obtain a reasonably reliable S/N curve [1]. To obtain as much information as possible from a limited number of specimens, a specimen unbroken after testing is sometimes retested at a higher stress. Because of possible understressing effects, the stress increase should not be too small (say, at least 30 per cent of the initial stress),

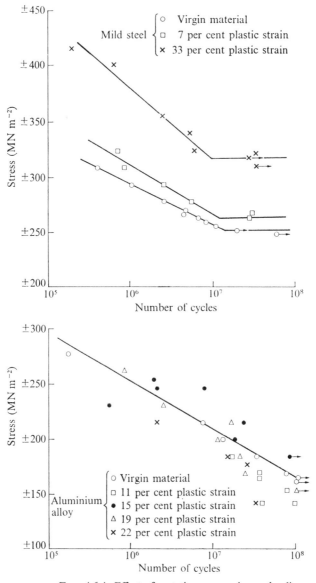

FIG. A6.4. Effect of a static compressive preloading.

and the resulting life used rather as a guide to the stress to apply to a further specimen than to define a point on the S/N curve.

If fatigue specimens are to be taken from a number of bars which have all been given supposedly similar heat-treatments then a properly planned programme, with subsequent statistical analysis of the results, may be required in order to state whether or not significant differences in fatigue properties occur from bar to bar. A similar approach would be necessary if nominally identical specimens were tested at nominally identical stress levels in different machines and it was required to determine whether the differences in lives were due to testing in different machines or were, in fact, normal for the material being tested. The application of statistical methods to the analysis of fatigue data is discussed in § 6.13, and detailed discussions are given in References [2], [3], and [4].

The results [5] shown in Fig. A6.4 are relevant to the above remarks. Mild steel and aluminium alloy blanks were subjected to compressive loads resulting in various amounts of plastic compressive deformation and 9 fatigue specimens were cut from each blank. It is seen that the S/N curves for the mild steel specimens are well defined, and there is no doubt that the fatigue limit increases with increasing prior plastic compressive strain. However, this is not the case with the aluminium alloy specimens, and more specimens would need to be tested in order to decide, with the help of a statistical analysis, whether or not the effect of the prior compressive strain was significant.

References

1. FINNEY, J. M., MANN, J. Y., and SIMPSON, R. *Metallurgia*, **81**, 11 (1970).
2. *A guide for fatigue testing and the statistical analysis of fatigue data.* American Society for Testing Materials, Special Tech. Pub. No. 91-A (1963).
3. WEIBULL, W. *Fatigue testing and analysis of results.* Pergamon Press, Oxford (1961).
4. JOHNSON, L. G. *The statistical treatment of fatigue experiments.* Elsevier, New York (1964).
5. FROST, N. E. *Metallurgia* **57**, 279 (1958).

Appendix 7: Stress concentration factors (K_t) for various configurations

THE values of K_t for a central circular hole in a sheet of finite width subjected to a uniform stress at infinity, as in Fig. A7.1, are well represented [1], by the series

$$K_t = 3\left\{1 + \left(\frac{a}{b}\right)^2 + 4\left(\frac{a}{b}\right)^4 - 4\left(\frac{a}{b}\right)^6 \ldots\right\}, \qquad 0 < \frac{a}{b} < \frac{1}{2},$$

where $2a$ and $2b$ are the hole diameter and sheet width respectively.

Inglis [2] obtained a solution for the stress distribution around an elliptical hole in an infinitely wide thin sheet, the value of the maximum longitudinal stress σ_{max} at the end of the major axis for the case where the major axis lies along AA and the loading is as shown on Fig. A7.1 being given by

$$\sigma_{max} = S\left(1 + \frac{2a}{b}\right) = S\left\{1 + 2\left(\frac{a}{\rho}\right)^{\frac{1}{2}}\right\},$$

where a and b are the lengths of the semi-major and semi-minor axes respectively, and ρ is the root radius of the ellipse. This equation is also approximately correct for a semi-elliptical notch in a semi-infinite sheet.

Plane stress or plane strain solutions for the localized stresses around holes of more complicated shape (for example, triangular, square, and rectangular holes having finite corner radii) in infinite sheets under both tensile and shear loadings have been obtained [3, 4, 5], using complex variable theory and the associated mapping of the arbitrary shaped hole into a circle.

If a hole in a material (Young's Modulus E) is filled with a perfectly-bonded second material of lower Young's Modulus E_1, K_t is less than the corresponding value for the empty hole. For example, K_t values calculated from Inglis's solution for an elliptical hole in an infinite plate are 3, 7, and 16 for a/b values of 1, 3, and 7; the corresponding values for $E_1/E = \frac{1}{4}$ are [6] 2, 2·8, and 3·3.

The external U- or V-groove configuration has been investigated extensively by Neuber [7], who derived the stress distributions around both an edge-notch in a plate and a circumferential groove in a cylindrical bar under tension, bending, and torsional end-loads. First, the stress distribution around a notch of hyperbolic profile and of infinite depth was obtained and, secondly, the stress distribution around a shallow notch in a specimen of infinite width or diameter, the profile of this notch being dictated by what was analytically feasible. This resulted in a notch profile having a rounded contour with no external corners. However, K_t at the root of this notch was in close agreement with that calculated from Inglis's solution for

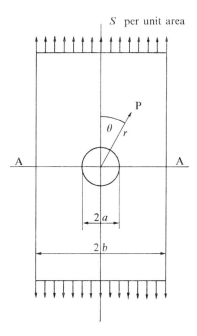

S per unit area

FIG. A7.1. Circular hole in a finite-width sheet.

the root of an external notch of the same depth and root radius but having a semi-elliptic form and sharp external corners. Solutions for both shallow notches in an infinite specimen and infinitely deep notches in specimens of finite width between the notch roots for either an applied tensile load *P* or a bending moment *M* are given below, the nomenclature used being shown on Fig. A7.2.

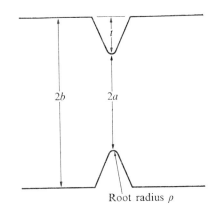

Root radius ρ

FIG. A7.2. Notch details for Neuber analysis. For plate specimens thickness = *d*. For cylindrical specimens 2*a* and 2*b* are diameters.

External notches on both edges of a plate

Infinitely deep notches
Tensile loading,

$$K_t = \frac{\sigma_{max}}{\sigma} = \frac{2\left(\frac{a}{\rho}+1\right)\left(\frac{a}{\rho}\right)^{\frac{1}{2}}}{\left\{\left(\frac{a}{\rho}+1\right)\tan^{-1}\left(\frac{a}{\rho}\right)^{\frac{1}{2}}\right\}+\left(\frac{a}{\rho}\right)^{\frac{1}{2}}} \text{ where } \sigma = \frac{P}{2ad}.$$

Bending,

$$K_t = \frac{\sigma_{max}}{\sigma} = \frac{4\frac{a}{\rho}\left(\frac{a}{\rho}\right)^{\frac{1}{2}}}{3\left\{\left(\frac{a}{\rho}\right)^{\frac{1}{2}}+\left(\frac{a}{\rho}-1\right)\tan^{-1}\left(\frac{a}{\rho}\right)^{\frac{1}{2}}\right\}}, \text{ where } \sigma = \frac{3M}{2a^2d}.$$

Shallow notches in infinite specimen
Tensile loading (rounded external corners),

$$K_t = \frac{\sigma_{max}}{\sigma} = 3\left(\frac{t}{2\rho}\right)^{\frac{1}{2}} - 1 + \frac{4}{2+t/2\rho}, \text{ where } \sigma = \frac{P}{2bd}.$$

Tensile loading (sharp external corners; Inglis' solution)

$$K_t = \frac{\sigma_{max}}{\sigma} = 1 + 2\left(\frac{t}{\rho}\right), \text{ where } \sigma = \frac{P}{2bd}.$$

Bending,

σ_{max}/σ has the same value as the corresponding tensile loading case,
where

$$\sigma = \frac{3M}{2b^2d}.$$

Cylindrical bars with circumferential grooves

Infinitely deep notches
Tensile loading

$$K_t = \frac{\sigma_{max}}{\sigma} = \frac{1}{N}\left[\frac{a}{\rho}\left(\frac{a}{\rho}+1\right)^{\frac{1}{2}} + (0.5+\nu)\frac{a}{\rho} + (1+\nu)\left\{\left(\frac{a}{\rho}+1\right)^{\frac{1}{2}}+1\right\}\right],$$

where $\quad N = \frac{a}{\rho}+2\nu\left(\frac{a}{\rho}+1\right)^{\frac{1}{2}}+2, \quad \sigma = \frac{\text{load}}{\pi a^2}, \quad \nu = \text{Poisson's ratio.}$

Bending

$$K_t = \frac{\sigma_{max}}{\sigma} = \frac{3}{4N}\left\{\left(\frac{a}{\rho}+1\right)^{\frac{1}{2}}+1\right\}\left\{3\frac{a}{\rho}-(1-2\nu)\left(\frac{a}{\rho}+1\right)^{\frac{1}{2}}+4+\nu\right\},$$

where

$$N = 3\left(\frac{a}{\rho}+1\right)+(1+4\nu)\left(\frac{a}{\rho}+1\right)^{\frac{1}{2}}+\frac{1+\nu}{1+\left(\frac{a}{\rho}+1\right)^{\frac{1}{2}}} \text{ and } \sigma = \frac{4M}{\pi a^3}.$$

Shallow notches in infinite specimen

K_t has the same value as the corresponding edge-notched plate values when σ is given its appropriate value.

To estimate K_t for a notch of finite depth in a specimen of finite width, K_{tt} and K_{tf} are calculated using the formulae for K_t for an infinitely deep notch (which neglects notch depth) and for a notch in an infinitely large specimen (which neglects the distance between the notch roots), respectively, and combined using the empirical relationship

$$\frac{1}{(K_t - 1)^2} = \frac{1}{(K_{tt} - 1)^2} + \frac{1}{(K_{tf} - 1)^2}$$

Despite the peculiarly-shaped notch profiles dictated by Neuber's analysis, the derived values of K_t are applicable to the more usual notch profiles, such as the vee-notch and parallel-sided groove, encountered in practice. For example, the values of K_t given in Table A7.1, which refer to a 0·2 m deep parallel-sided edge-

$$\text{T ABLE   A7.1}$$

| | σ_{max}/σ | | |
| | | Experimental | |
Root radius (mm)	Calculated from Neuber's analysis	Photo-elastic	Strain gauges
170	2·0	2·02	2·08
30	4·0	4·02	4·26
12·3	6·0	6·0	6·41

notch of a given root radius in a 1·2 m wide longitudinally loaded sheet, show Neuber's analysis can be applied with little error to the parallel-sided groove [8].

Agreement, however, is not always so satisfactory in the case of bending loads. For example, when values of K_t obtained from photo-elastic models of beams having straight-sided notches in the upper edge and subjected to a bending moment were compared [9] with the corresponding values computed from Neuber's analysis, there was good agreement for notches having included angles of 90° and 150°, but the agreement was not so satisfactory for the U-notch, especially when the notch depth was large compared to the beam depth.

The effect of point of application of load on the stress distribution around two opposite parallel-sided edge-notches in a flat photo-elastic model has been examined [10]. The plate was either loaded uniaxially by a uniform longitudinal load applied at edges remote from the notch or equal loads were applied to the parallel sides of the edge-notches. Although the details of the stress distribution across the minimum cross-section were somewhat different for equal total loads, the maximum longitudinal stress at the root of the notch was the same for both loading conditions.

Experimental stress-analysis techniques [11] are often resorted to in order to determine either the stress distribution or the maximum boundary stress created by those notch profile and specimen geometries which are not amenable to theoretical analysis. This applies to many notch profiles encountered in practical components and structural members because many of these are three-dimensional problems in a finite body, for which there are few theoretical solutions. Photo-elastic techniques have been extensively employed for determining the maximum boundary stresses around notches and, in general, gave the most accurate and reliable results. They consist essentially of making a model in a suitable translucent material which, when stressed, displays interference fringes when viewed in polarized light. With two-dimensional models, the maximum notch-boundary stress can be assessed directly from the number of fringes. The techniques are more involved in the case of three-dimensional models, the model needing to be loaded at an elevated temperature and the fringes 'frozen' in by a controlled cooling procedure; slices are then cut from the region in the model where the stresses are required. Other experimental techniques include the use of brittle lacquers, short gauge-length mechanical extensometers, and electrical resistance strain gauges. Strain gauges have the disadvantage that they measure deformation over a finite gauge-length and thus, unless the stress around a notch boundary remains reasonably constant over the gauge-length, the average stress value deduced from the strain-gauge reading will be less than the true maximum stress occurring at some point within the gauge-length.

Finite-element computer programs are being used increasingly in the stress analysis of structures [12], and stress concentration factors for notches and discontinuities can readily be obtained. At present, programs are largely restricted to two-dimensional and axisymmetric cases, although some programs capable of handling irregular three-dimensional shapes are available.

References

1. FROST, N. E. and DUGDALE, D. S. *J. Mechs. Phy. Solids* **6**, 92 (1958).
2. INGLIS, C. E. *Trans. Instn. nav. Archit.* **55**, 219 (1913).
3. COX, H. L. Min. of Supply, Aero. Res. Council, R and M No. 2704 (1943).
4. SAVIN, G. N. *Stress concentrations around holes*. Pergamon Press, Oxford (1961).
5. SOBEY, A. J. Min. of Aviation, R.A.E. Rep. No. Struct. 292 (1953).
6. DONNELL, L. H. *Von Karman anniversary volume*, p. 293. California Institute of Technology (1941).
7. NEUBER, H. *Theory of notch stresses*. Edwards, London (1946).
8. HARDRATH, H. F. and OHMAN, L. NACA Tech. Note 2566 (1951).
9. BANKI, I. *Proceedings of the 2nd Conference on dimensioning and strength calculations, Budapest*, p. 39 (1965).
10. WIEGAND, H. and CLAUSMEYER, H. *Proceedings of the 2nd Conference on dimensioning and strength calculations, Budapest*, p. 143 (1965).
11. HETENYI, M. *Handbook of experimental stress analysis*. Wiley, New York (1950).
    LEE, G. H. *An introduction to experimental stress analysis*. Wiley, New York (1950).
12. ZIENKIEWICZ, O. C. *The finite element method in structural and continuum mechanics*. McGraw-Hill, New York (1967).
    KHOL, R. *Mach. Des.* **40**, 136 (1968).

Author index

32

Subject index